P9-APD-687

MANAGEMENT SYSTEMS

THE WILEY SERIES IN
MANAGEMENT AND ADMINISTRATION
Elwood S. Buffa, Advisory Editor
University of California, Los Angeles

Peter P. Schoderbek
MANAGEMENT SYSTEMS

MANAGEMENT SYSTEMS

PETER P. SCHODERBEK

Assistant Professor of Management

University of Iowa

JOHN WILEY & SONS, INC.

NEW YORK · LONDON · SYDNEY

PREFACE

While teaching a course on management systems over the past years, I was made keenly aware of the lack of suitable readings texts encompassing the many and diverse fields with which this subject is concerned. Available books are generally specialized and to a great extent do not integrate the important concepts that are applicable to the business world. Topics such as information technology, cybernetics, measurement, PERT, industrial dynamics, real-time systems, and information retrieval have typically been treated in a more or less detached fashion. In this text therefore an attempt has been made to link the basic concepts employed in management systems to reveal to the reader something of their complex interrelationships.

In an effort to assemble a somewhat representative sample of the field, I have searched diligently and, at times, with some misgivings in the available literature for substantive material. Most of the selections included here have been written by individuals outstanding in their professions. An overriding principle for selection, however, was the ability of the author, as evidenced by his writing, to expound the subject matter in a clear and meaningful way. Too often articles are burdened with a jargon which, although comprehensible to specialists, needlessly deters the tyro. Since ideas, like soldiers, are best tested in actual engagement, selections describing the application of these concepts to the business world by practitioners have designedly also been included.

Although the book is intended primarily for the undergraduate and graduate student, executives may find it helpful in furthering their understanding of the total systems concept as well as in developing insight into some of the problems besetting management. The approach adopted, basically an interdisciplinary one, with material being freely drawn from the fields of engineering, accounting, data processing, business, and sociology, reflects a growing trend that best categorizes the systems viewpoint.

The introductory section of every part attempts to give the reader an overview of the subject matter, first placing it in focus and then setting the stage for what is to follow. Each of the selections is then summarized or reviewed, with emphasis being placed on salient points and on the linkage of new concepts with previous ones. The bibliography concluding each part provides additional references for those desiring further study.

In a discipline with as broad a range as management systems, it is inevitable that there should be some overlapping of content in selections garnered from so many different fields. In some instances the overlapping presents no problem since it reinforces key concepts besides placing them in another advantageous perspective. In other cases, however, the material may seem repetitious, because rather than excise entire sentences and paragraphs in a fashion that the original authors might consider capricious, I decided to forego literary surgery, leaving each of the articles intact.

Perhaps no part of an editor's task is as painful as the decision to exclude so many promising and informative selections that

v

for one reason or another do not meet the criteria for inclusion.

Many individuals have contributed both directly and indirectly to this collection of readings and to all of them I owe a debt of gratitude. I am especially grateful for the warmhearted cooperation of the authors, as well as the journals and publishing houses who made this book possible. Special thanks are due to my brother, Reverend Charles G. Schoderbek, SVD, who cheerfully undertook the task of editing the introductory material. Special appreciation is also due to the Army Management Engineering Training Agency, which provided the stimulus for the conception of this book.

PETER P. SCHODERBEK

April 1967

CONTENTS

Part X. Models and Simulation 323

Part XI. Measurement 357

Part XII. PERT-PERT/COST 379

Part XIII. Real Time Systems 413

Part XIV. Information Retrieval 451

Part XV. Prologue to the Future 481

MANAGEMENT SYSTEMS

Section A. Management and the Arts

Part I. The Systems Concept

In recent years theoretical model building has become a respectable and profitable undertaking in many a science. Not only have the mathematical and the physical sciences availed themselves of this analytical tool but particularly economics and the behavioral sciences, psychology and sociology, have increasingly turned to theoretical models for insightful analysis of data and utilitarian prognosis of trends. Past experience has too often only underscored the proposition that unless research is coupled with a theoretical framework it tends to lie fallow and produces nothing more than ephemeral results.

The general systems theory, as sketched by Kenneth Boulding in the first selection, is a skeleton of science that provides the framework or theoretical systemic structure by which the various disciplines can be oriented, integrated, and rendered mutually productive. As such, it lies midway between the highly abstract generalizations of mathematics and the lower level generalizations of specific disciplines. That the need for such a theory is acutely felt today is evidenced by the increasing difficulty in relevant communication between practitioners of related disciplines and the proliferation of interdisciplinary institutes.

Two possible approaches to the organization of general systems are proposed and illustrated. The first approach, that of general phenomena selectivity, is concerned both with the phenomena common to many disciplines and with the construction of theoretical models relevant to these phenomena. Population theory, interaction theory, growth theory, and information theory serve to illustrate this first approach.

The other approach to general systems theory is a more ambitious and difficult one. It involves the rearrangement of theoretical systems and logic constructs into an ordered hierarchy of complexity with levels of abstraction appropriate for each. Since the present state of knowledge varies considerably from science to science and within related fields of the same science, a multi-level approach, though somewhat unwieldy, seems to be the only viable avenue at present for realistic appraisal and productive research in scientific areas.

The nine levels of systematic analysis, arranged in order of increasing complexity, are summarized by Boulding as the levels of frameworks, clockworks, thermostat, cell, plant, animal, man, social organization, and transcendence. Unfortunately, adequate theoretical models have not yet advanced past the fourth level though it is only the last, the transcendental level, that will provide the framework on which basic principles of particular disciplines will be orderly and coherently organized. It is, hopefully, the general systems theory that will point the way to future scientific progress and to workable future goals.

It it is true that "nothing is so practical as a good theory," then a consideration of systemic and developmental models as key tools for diagnosis and prognosis is in order. However, such consideration necessitates the explicit formulation of concepts upon which models are built and the exposition of their underlying assumptions and limitations. Robert Chin's article takes up in sequential order an analysis of system models with their basic concepts of boundary, tension, equilibrium and feedback.

3

The concept of system utilized in this selection encompasses the components of organization, interaction, interdependency, and integration of parts.

Although open systems ("systems in contact with their environment and with input and output across system boundaries") are the type found in the extramental world, the utility of employing closed systems ("systems assumed to have little if any commerce across the boundary") must not be underestimated. Open systems are by their nature generally too complex for even simple analysis. By opening a closed system to new environmental variables, then closing it, we can observe and evaluate what really goes on.

An intersystem model consisting of two open systems joined to each other by conjunctive or disjunctive connectives is proposed by Chin as a workable tool for the agent of change since it retains all the advantages of system analysis and adds others of its own.

While systemic models have at times been associated with static analysis, developmental models designedly assume constant change and development over time. Fundamental to these models are the notions of direction or goal, states, forms of progression, forces, and potentiality, all of which are defined and illustrated in the text.

The practitioner and the social scientist generally view their fields quite differently. While the social scientist is primarily interested in learning *how* a system changes under varying conditions, the practitioner is principally set on understanding a system *in order to* change it. But to do so he must have some theory of change. Since such a theory incorporates elements from both systemic and developmental models in a framework specifically oriented to the processes facilitating change, it becomes increasingly evident that an adequate study of models is incumbent upon the practitioner.

Useful as they are, models have only limited applicability. Being abstractions of concrete events from the real world, their usefulness is in proportion to the goodness of fit between the model and the events abstracted.

Related to system theory is organizational theory. The final selection, by William Scott, presents an overview and appraisal of such a theory. To best accomplish his objectives the author has employed the historical approach, thus putting some of the concepts previously touched on in a somewhat different light, the better to relate and contrast them.

The classical theory of organization, dealing almost exclusively with the anatomy of formal organization, revolves around four pivotal concepts: the division of labor, scalar and functional processes, formal structure, and control span. Useful as these concepts are, they are of limited value for they ignore the interplay of personalities, informal groupings, interorganizational conflict, and the ever present decision-making processes.

The neoclassical theory has attempted to compensate for some of these deficiencies. Assuming as given the four basic elements of the formal organization as embedded in the classical theory, it has systematically incorporated the contributions of the behavioral sciences concerning informal organization, and it has also studied the impact of the informal group upon the formal structure. Typical of this "human relations movement" are the Hawthorne studies and many current works in industrial sociology. Like the classical theory, the neoclassical, though making use of relevant psychological and sociological findings, has also been found wanting.

Modern organizational theory is system theory. In his treatment of modern organizational theory, Scott details the various elements involved in system analysis. Although he singles out as systemic components the interdependency of parts, the linkage processes, and organizational goals, he nevertheless includes in his explanation both formal and informal organization, role theory, equilibrium and steady state, cybernetics, decision-making processes, and diverse organizational goals. Thus we see that modern organizational theory relates to the general systems theory advanced by Kenneth Boulding in the first selection in the present section, being an approximation to the level of social organization (the eighth level).

Does modern organizational theory have a future? A promising one? Scott believes that it does. Just as physics, economics, and sociology passed through an early macro stage in which schemes of broad extent were conceived, to be followed by a micro stage in which analysis dealt with parts of the organization, and then finally moved into another macro, holistic, systems period, so too will administrative science. The early classical theory of organization employed the macro approach, the neo-classical, the micro approach, whereas modern organizational theory is based on a holistic, a macro point of view. The latter's potential indeed appears great!

1. GENERAL SYSTEMS THEORY—
THE SKELETON OF SCIENCE

KENNETH E. BOULDING *

General Systems Theory [1] is a name which has come into use to describe a level of theoretical model-building which lies somewhere between the highly generalized constructions of pure mathematics and the specific theories of the specialized disciplines. Mathematics attempts to organize highly general relationships into a coherent system, a system however which does not have any necessary connections with the "real" world around us. It studies all thinkable relationships abstracted from any concrete situation or body of empirical knowledge. It is not even confined to "quantitative" relationships narrowly defined—indeed, the development of a mathematics of quality and structure is already on the way, even though it is not as far advanced as the "classical" mathematics of quantity and number. Nevertheless because in a sense mathematics contains all theories it contains none; it is the language of theory, but it does not give us the content. At the other extreme we have the separate disciplines and sciences, with their separate bodies of theory. Each discipline corresponds to a certain segment of the empirical world, and each develops theories which have particular applicability to its own empirical segment. Physics, Chemistry, Biology, Psychology, Sociology, Economics and so on all carve out for themselves certain elements of the experience of man and develop theories and patterns of activity (re-

search) which yield satisfaction in understanding, and which are appropriate to their special segments.

In recent years increasing need has been felt for a body of systematic theoretical constructs which will discuss the general relationships of the empirical world. This is the quest of General Systems Theory. It does not seek, of course, to establish a single, self-contained "general theory of practically everything" which will replace all the special theories of particular disciplines. Such a theory would be almost without content, for we always pay for generality by sacrificing content, and all we can say about practically everything is almost nothing. Somewhere however between the specific that has no meaning and the general that has no content there must be, for each purpose and at each level of abstraction, an optimum degree of generality. It is the contention of the General Systems Theorists that this optimum degree of generality in theory is not always reached by the particular sciences. The objectives of General Systems Theory then can be set out with varying degrees of ambition and confidence. At a low level of ambition but with a high degree of confidence it aims to point out similarities in the theoretical constructions of different disciplines, where these exist, and to develop theoretical models having applicability to at least two different fields of study. At a higher level of ambition, but with perhaps a lower degree of confidence it hopes to develop something like a "spectrum" of theories—a system of systems which may perform the function of a "gestalt" in theoretical construction. Such "gestalts" in special fields have been of great value in directing research towards the gaps which they reveal. Thus the periodic table of elements in chemistry directed research for many decades towards the discovery of unknown elements to fill gaps in the table until the table was com-

SOURCE: From *Management Science* (April, 1956), pp. 197–208. Reprinted by permission of the Institute of Management Science.

* Professor of Economics, University of Michigan.

[1] The name and many of the ideas are to be credited to L. von Bertalanffy, who is not, however, to be held accountable for the ideas of the present author! For a general discussion of Bertalanffy's ideas see "General System Theory: A New Approach to Unity of Science," *Human Biology*, Dec., 1951, Vol. 23, pp. 302–361.

pletely filled. Similarly a "system of systems" might be of value in directing the attention of theorists towards gaps in theoretical models, and might even be of value in pointing towards methods of filling them.

The need for general systems theory is accentuated by the present sociological situation in science. Knowledge is not something which exists and grows in the abstract. It is a function of human organisms and of social organization. Knowledge, that is to say, is always what somebody knows: the most perfect transcript of knowledge in writing is not knowledge if nobody knows it. Knowledge however grows by the receipt of meaningful information—that is, by the intake of messages by a knower which are capable of reorganizing his knowledge. We will quietly duck the question as to what reorganizations constitute "growth" of knowledge by defining "semantic growth" of knowledge as those reorganizations which can profitably be talked about, in writing or speech, by the Right People. Science, that is to say, is what can be talked about profitably by scientists in their role as scientists. The crisis of science today arises because of the increasing difficulty of such profitable talk among scientists as a whole. Specialization has outrun Trade, communication between the disciples becomes increasingly difficult, and the Republic of Learning is breaking up into isolated subcultures with only tenuous lines of communication between them—a situation which threatens intellectual civil war. The reason for this breakup in the body of knowledge is that in the course of specialization the receptors of information themselves become specialized. Hence physicists only talk to physicists, economists to economists—worse still, nuclear physicists only talk to nuclear physicists and econometricians to econometricians. One wonders sometimes if science will not grind to a stop in an assemblage of walled-in hermits, each mumbling to himself words in a private language that only he can understand. In these days the arts may have beaten the sciences to this desert of mutual unintelligibility, but that may be merely because the swift intuitions of art reach the future faster than the plodding leg work of the scientist. The more science breaks into sub-groups, and the less communication is possible among the disciplines, however, the greater chance there is that the total growth of knowledge is being slowed down by the loss of relevant communications. The spread of specialized deafness means that someone who ought to know something that someone else knows isn't able to find it out for lack of generalized ears.

It is one of the main objectives of General Systems Theory to develop these generalized ears, and by developing a framework of general theory to enable one specialist to catch relevant communications from others. Thus the economist who realizes the strong formal similarity between utility theory in economics and field theory in physics [2] is probably in a better position to learn from the physicists than one who does not. Similarly a specialist who works with the growth concept—whether the crystallographer, the virologist, the cytologist, the physiologist, the psychologist, the sociologist or the economist—will be more sensitive to the contributions of other fields if he is aware of the many similarities of the growth process in widely different empirical fields.

There is not much doubt about the demand for general systems theory under one brand name or another. It is a little more embarrassing to inquire into the supply. Does any of it exist, and if so where? What is the chance of getting more of it, and if so, how? The situation might be described as promising and in ferment, though it is not wholly clear what is being promised or brewed. Something which might be called an "interdisciplinary movement" has been abroad for some time. The first signs of this are usually the development of hybrid disciplines. Thus physical chemistry emerged in the third quarter of the nineteenth century, social psychology in the second quarter of the twentieth. In the physical and biological sciences the list of hybrid disciplines is now quite long—biophysics, biochemistry, astrophysics are all well established. In the social sciences social anthropology is fairly well established, economic psychology and economic sociology are just beginning. There are signs, even, that Political Economy, which died in infancy some hundred years ago, may have a re-birth.

In recent years there has been an additional development of great interest in the form of

[2] See A. G. Pikler, Utility Theories in Field Physics and Mathematical Economics, *British Journal for the Philosophy of Science*, 1955, Vol. 5, pp. 47 and 303.

"multisexual" interdisciplines. The hybrid disciplines, as their hyphenated names indicate, come from two respectable and honest academic parents. The newer interdisciplines have a much more varied and occasionally even obscure ancestry, and result from the reorganization of material from many different fields of study. Cybernetics, for instance, comes out of electrical engineering, neurophysiology, physics, biology, with even a dash of economics. Information theory, which originated in communications engineering, has important applications in many fields stretching from biology to the social sciences. Organization theory comes out of economics, sociology, engineering, physiology, and Management Science itself is an equally multidisciplinary product.

On the more empirical and practical side the interdisciplinary movement is reflected in the development of interdepartmental institutes of many kinds. Some of these find their basis of unity in the empirical field which they study, such as institutes of industrial relations, of public administration, of international affairs, and so on. Others are organized around the application of a common methodology to many different fields and problems, such as the Survey Research Center and the Group Dynamics Center at the University of Michigan. Even more important than these visible developments, perhaps, though harder to perceive and identify, is a growing dissatisfaction in many departments, especially at the level of graduate study, with the existing traditional theoretical backgrounds for the empirical studies which form the major part of the output of Ph.D. theses. To take but a single example from the field with which I am most familiar. It is traditional for studies of labor relations, money and banking, and foreign investment to come out of departments of economics. Many of the needed theoretical models and frameworks in these fields, however, do not come out of "economic theory" as this is usually taught, but from sociology, social psychology, and cultural anthropology. Students in the department of economics however rarely get a chance to become acquainted with these theoretical models, which may be relevant to their studies, and they become impatient with economic theory, much of which may not be relevant.

It is clear that there is a good deal of interdisciplinary excitement abroad. If this excite-ment is to be productive, however, it must operate within a certain framework of coherence. It is all too easy for the interdisciplinary to degenerate into the undisciplined. If the interdisciplinary movement, therefore, is not to lose that sense of form and structure which is the "discipline" involved in the various separate disciplines, it should develop a structure of its own. This I conceive to be the great task of general systems theory. For the rest of this paper, therefore, I propose to look at some possible ways in which general systems theory might be structured.

Two possible approaches to the organization of general systems theory suggest themselves, which are to be thought of as complementary rather than competitive, or at least as two roads each of which is worth exploring. The first approach is to look over the empirical universe and to pick out certain general *phenomena* which are found in many different disciplines, and to seek to build up general theoretical models relevant to these phenomena. The second approach is to arrange the empirical fields in a hierarchy of complexity of organization of their basic "individual" or unit of behavior, and to try to develop a level of abstraction appropriate to each.

Some examples of the first approach will serve to clarify it, without pretending to be exhaustive. In almost all disciplines, for instance, we find examples of populations—aggregates of individuals conforming to a common definition, to which individuals are added (born) and subtracted (die) and in which the age of the individual is a relevant and identifiable variable. These populations exhibit dynamic movements of their own, which can frequently be described by fairly simple systems of difference equations. The populations of different species also exhibit dynamic interactions among themselves, as in the theory of Volterra. Models of population change and interaction cut across a great many different fields—ecological systems in biology, capital theory in economics which deals with populations of "goods," social ecology, and even certain problems of statistical mechanics. In all these fields population change, both in absolute numbers and in structure, can be discussed in terms of birth and survival functions relating numbers of births and of deaths in specific age groups to various aspects of the system. In all these fields the interaction of population can be discussed in terms of competitive, complementary, or parasitic relationships among populations of different species, whether the species consist of animals, commodities, social classes or molecules.

Another phenomenon of almost universal significance for all disciplines is that of the interaction of an "individual" of some kind with its environment. Every discipline studies some kind of "individual"—electron, atom, molecule, crystal, virus, cell, plant, animal, man, family, tribe, state, church, firm, corporation, university, and so on. Each of these individuals exhibits "behavior," action, or change, and this behavior is considered to be related in some way to the environment of the individual—that is, with other individuals with which it comes into contact or into some relationship. Each individual is thought of as consisting of a structure or complex of individuals of the order immediately below it—atoms are an arrangement of protons and electrons, molecules of atoms, cells of molecules, plants, animals and men of cells, social organizations of men. The "behavior" of each individual is "explained" by the structure and arrangement of the lower individuals of which it is composed, or by certain principles of equilibrium or homeostasis according to which certain "states" of the individual are "preferred." Behavior is described in terms of the restoration of these preferred states when they are disturbed by changes in the environment.

Another phenomenon of universal significance is growth. Growth theory is in a sense a subdivision of the theory of individual "behavior," growth being one important aspect of behavior. Nevertheless there are important differences between equilibrium theory and growth theory, which perhaps warrant giving growth theory a special category. There is hardly a science in which the growth phenomenon does not have some importance, and though there is a great difference in complexity between the growth of crystals, embryos, and societies, many of the principles and concepts which are important at the lower levels are also illuminating at higher levels. Some growth phenomena can be dealt with in terms of relatively simple population models, the solution of which yields growth curves of single variables. At the more complex levels structural problems become dominant and the complex interrelationships between growth and form are the focus of interest. All growth phenomena are sufficiently alike however to

suggest that a general theory of growth is by no means an impossibility.[3]

Another aspect of the theory of the individual and also of interrelationships among individuals which might be singled out for special treatment is the theory of information and communication. The information concept as developed by Shannon has had interesting applications outside its original field of electrical engineering. It is not adequate, of course, to deal with problems involving the semantic level of communication. At the biological level however the information concept may serve to develop general notions of structuredness and abstract measures of organization which give us, as it were, a third basic dimension beyond mass and energy. Communication and information processes are found in a wide variety of empirical situations, and are unquestionably essential in the development of organization, both in the biological and the social world.

These various approaches to general systems through various aspects of the empirical world may lead ultimately to something like a general field theory of the dynamics of action and interaction. This, however, is a long way ahead.

A second possible approach to general systems theory is through the arrangement of theoretical systems and constructs in a hierarchy of complexity, roughly corresponding to the complexity of the "individuals" of the various empirical fields. This approach is more systematic than the first, leading towards a "system of systems." It may not replace the first entirely, however, as there may always be important theoretical concepts and constructs lying outside the systematic framework. I suggest below a possible arrangement of "levels" of theoretical discourse.

(i) The first level is that of the static structure. It might be called the level of *frameworks*. This is the geography and anatomy of the universe—the patterns of electrons around a nucleus, the pattern of atoms in a molecular formula, the arrangement of atoms in a crystal, the anatomy of the gene, the cell, the plant, the animal, the mapping of the earth, the solar system, the astronomical universe. The accurate description of these frameworks is the

[3] See "Towards a General Theory of Growth" by K. E. Boulding, *Canadian Journal of Economics and Political Science*, 19 Aug. 1953, 326–340.

beginning of organized theoretical knowledge in almost any field, for without accuracy in this description of static relationships no accurate functional or dynamic theory is possible. Thus the Copernican revolution was really the discovery of a new static framework for the solar system which permitted a simpler description of its dynamics.

(ii) The next level of systematic analysis is that of the simple dynamic system with predetermined, necessary motions. This might be called the level of *clockworks*. The solar system itself is of course the great clock of the universe from man's point of view, and the deliciously exact predictions of the astronomers are a testimony to the excellence of the clock which they study. Simple machines such as the lever and the pulley, even quite complicated machines like steam engines and dynamos fall mostly under this category. The greater part of the theoretical structure of physics, chemistry, and even of economics falls into this category. Two special cases might be noted. Simple equilibrium systems really fall into the dynamic category, as every equilibrium system must be considered as a limiting case of a dynamic system, and its stability cannot be determined except from the properties of its parent dynamic system. Stochastic dynamic systems leading to equilibria, for all their complexity, also fall into this group of systems; such is the modern view of the atom and even of the molecule, each position or part of the system being given with a certain degree of probability, the whole nevertheless exhibiting a determinate structure. Two types of analytical method are important here, which we may call, with the usage of the economists, comparative statics and true dynamics. In comparative statics we compare two equilibrium positions of the system under different values for the basic parameters. These equilibrium positions are usually expressed as the solution of a set of simultaneous equations. The method of comparative statics is to compare the solutions when the parameters of the equations are changed. Most simple mechanical problems are solved in this way. In true dynamics on the other hand we exhibit the system as a set of difference or differential equations, which are then solved in the form of an explicit function of each variable with time. Such a system may reach a position of stationary equilibrium, or it may not—there are plenty of examples of explosive

dynamic systems, a very simple one being the growth of a sum at compound interest! Most physical and chemical reactions and most social systems do in fact exhibit a tendency to equilibrium—otherwise the world would have exploded or imploded long ago.

(iii) The next level is that of the control mechanism or cybernetic system, which might be nicknamed the level of the *thermostat*. This differs from the simple stable equilibrium system mainly in the fact that the transmission and interpretation of information is an essential part of the system. As a result of this the equilibrium position is not merely determined by the equations of the system, but the system will move to the maintenance of any *given* equilibrium, within limits. Thus the thermostat will maintain *any* temperature at which it can be set; the equilibrium temperature of the system is not determined solely by its equations. The trick here of course is that the essential variable of the dynamic system is the *difference* between an "observed" or "recorded" value of the maintained variable and its "ideal" value. If this difference is not zero the system moves so as to diminish it; thus the furnace sends up heat when the temperature as recorded is "too cold" and is turned off when the recorded temperature is "too hot." The homeostasis model, which is of such importance in physiology, is an example of a cybernetic mechanism, and such mechanisms exist through the whole empirical world of the biologist and the social scientist.

(iv) The fourth level is that of the "open system," or self-maintaining structure. This is the level at which life begins to differentiate itself from not-life: it might be called the level of the *cell*. Something like an open system exists, of course, even in physico-chemical equilibrium systems; atomic structures maintain themselves in the midst of a throughput of electrons, molecular structures maintain themselves in the midst of a throughput of atoms. Flames and rivers likewise are essentially open systems of a very simple kind. As we pass up the scale of complexity of organization towards living systems, however, the property of self-maintenance of structure in the midst of a throughput of material becomes of dominant importance. An atom or a molecule can presumably exist without throughput: the existence of even the simplest living organism is inconceivable without ingestion, excretion and metabolic exchange.

Closely connected with the property of self-maintenance is the property of self-reproduction. It may be, indeed, that self-reproduction is a more primitive or "lower level" system than the open system, and that the gene and the virus, for instance, may be able to reproduce themselves without being open systems. It is not perhaps an important question at what point in the scale of increasing complexity "life" begins. What is clear, however, is that by the time we have got to systems which both reproduce themselves and maintain themselves in the midst of a throughput of material and energy, we have something to which it would be hard to deny the title of "life."

(v) The fifth level might be called the genetic-societal level; it is typified by the *plant,* and it dominates the empirical world of the botanist. The outstanding characteristics of these systems are first, a division of labor among cells to form a cell-society with differentiated and mutually dependent parts (roots, leaves, seeds, etc.), and second, a sharp differentiation between the genotype and the phenotype, associated with the phenomenon of equifinal or "blueprinted" growth. At this level there are no highly specialized sense organs and information receptors are diffuse and incapable of much throughput of information—it is doubtful whether a tree can distinguish much more than light from dark, long days from short days, cold from hot.

(vi) As we move upward from the plant world towards the animal kingdom we gradually pass over into a new level, the "animal" level, characterized by increased mobility, teleological behavior, and self-awareness. Here we have the development of specialized information-receptors (eyes, ears, etc.) leading to an enormous increase in the intake of information; we have also a great development of nervous systems, leading ultimately to the brain, as an organizer of the information intake into a knowledge structure or "image." Increasingly as we ascend the scale of animal life, behavior is response not to a specific stimulus but to an "image" or knowledge structure or view of the environment as a whole. This image is of course determined ultimately by information received into the organism; the relation between the receipt of information and the building up of an image however is exceedingly complex. It is not a simple piling up or accumulation of informa-

tion received, although this frequently happens, but a structuring of information into something essentially different from the information itself. After the image structure is well established most information received produces very little change in the image—it goes through the loose structure, as it were, without hitting it, much as a sub-atomic particle might go through an atom without hitting anything. Sometimes however the information is "captured" by the image and added to it, and sometimes the information hits some kind of a "nucleus" of the image and a reorganization takes place, with far reaching and radical changes in behavior in apparent response to what seems like a very small stimulus. The difficulties in the prediction of the behavior of these systems arises largely because of this intervention of the image between the stimulus and the response.

(vii) The next level is the "human" level, that is of the individual human being considered as a system. In addition to all, or nearly all, of the characteristics of animal systems man possesses self-consciousness, which is something different from mere awareness. His image, besides being much more complex than that even of the higher animals, has a self-reflexive quality—he not only knows, but knows that he knows. This property is probably bound up with the phenomenon of language and symbolism. It is the capacity for speech—the ability to produce, absorb, and interpret *symbols,* as opposed to mere signs like the warning cry of an animal—which most clearly marks man off from his humbler brethren. Man is distinguished from the animals also by a much more elaborate image of time and relationship; man is probably the only organization that knows that it dies, that contemplates in its behavior a whole life span, and more than a life span. Man exists not only in time and space but in history, and his behavior is profoundly affected by his view of the time process in which he stands.

(viii) Because of the vital importance for the individual man of symbolic images and behavior based on them it is not easy to separate clearly the level of the individual human organism from the next level, that of social organizations. In spite of the occasional stories of feral children raised by animals, man isolated from his fellows is practically unknown. So essential is the symbolic image in human behavior that one suspects that a truly isolated man would not be "human" in the usually accepted sense, though he would be potentially human. Nevertheless it is convenient for some purposes to distinguish the individual human as a system from the social systems which surround him, and in this sense social organizations may be said to constitute another level of organization. The unit of such systems is not perhaps the person—the individual human as such—but the "role"—that part of the person which is concerned with the organization or situation in question, and it is tempting to define social organizations, or almost any social system, as a set of roles tied together with channels of communication. The interrelations of the role and the person however can never be completely neglected—a square person in a round role may become a little rounder, but he also makes the role squarer, and the perception of a role is affected by the personalities of those who have occupied it in the past. At this level we must concern ourselves with the content and meaning of messages, the nature and dimensions of value systems, the transcription of images into a historical record, the subtle symbolizations of art, music, and poetry, and the complex gamut of human emotion. The empirical universe here is human life and society in all its complexity and richness.

(ix) To complete the structure of systems we should add a final turret for transcendental systems, even if we may be accused at this point of having built Babel to the clouds. There are however the ultimates and absolutes and the inescapable unknowables, and they also exhibit systematic structure and relationship. It will be a sad day for man when nobody is allowed to ask questions that do not have any answers.

One advantage of exhibiting a hierarchy of systems in this way is that it gives us some idea of the present gaps in both theoretical and empirical knowledge. Adequate theoretical models extend up to about the fourth level, and not much beyond. Empirical knowledge is deficient at practically all levels. Thus at the level of the static structure, fairly adequate descriptive models are available for geography, chemistry, geology, anatomy, and descriptive social science. Even at this simplest level, however, the problem of the adequate description of complex structures is still far from solved. The theory of indexing and cataloguing, for instance, is only in its infancy.

Librarians are fairly good at cataloguing books, chemists have begun to catalogue structural formulae, and anthropologists have begun to catalogue culture traits. The cataloguing of events, ideas, theories, statistics, and empirical data has hardly begun. The very multiplication of records however as time goes on will force us into much more adequate cataloguing and reference systems than we now have. This is perhaps the major unsolved theoretical problem at the level of the static structure. In the empirical field there are still great areas where static structures are very imperfectly known, although knowledge is advancing rapidly, thanks to new probing devices such as the electron microscope. The anatomy of that part of the empirical world which lies between the large molecule and the cell however, is still obscure at many points. It is precisely this area however—which includes, for instance, the gene and the virus—that holds the secret of life, and until its anatomy is made clear the nature of the functional systems which are involved will inevitably be obscure.

The level of the "clockwork" is the level of "classical" natural science, especially physics and astronomy, and is probably the most completely developed level in the present state of knowledge, especially if we extend the concept to include the field theory and stochastic models of modern physics. Even here however there are important gaps, especially at the higher empirical levels. There is much yet to be known about the sheer mechanics of cells and nervous systems, of brains and of societies.

Beyond the second level adequate theoretical models get scarcer. The last few years have seen great developments at the third and fourth levels. The theory of control mechanisms ("thermostats") has established itself as the new discipline of cybernetics, and the theory of self-maintaining systems or "open systems" likewise has made rapid strides. We could hardly maintain however that much more than a beginning had been made in these fields. We know very little about the cybernetics of genes and genetic systems, for instance, and still less about the control mechanisms involved in the mental and social world. Similarly the processes of self-maintenance remain essentially mysterious at many points, and although the theoretical possibility of constructing a self-maintaining machine which would be a true open system has been suggested, we seem to be a long way from the actual construction of such a mechanical similitude of life.

Beyond the fourth level it may be doubted whether we have as yet even the rudiments of theoretical systems. The intricate machinery of growth by which the genetic complex organizes the matter around it is almost a complete mystery. Up to now, whatever the future may hold, only God can make a tree. In the face of living systems we are almost helpless; we can occasionally cooperate with systems which we do not understand: we cannot even begin to reproduce them. The ambiguous status of medicine, hovering as it does uneasily between magic and science, is a testimony to the state of systematic knowledge in this area. As we move up the scale the absence of the appropriate theoretical systems becomes ever more noticeable. We can hardly conceive ourselves constructing a system which would be in any recognizable sense "aware," much less self-conscious. Nevertheless as we move towards the human and societal level a curious thing happens: the fact that we have, as it were, an inside track, and that we ourselves *are* the systems which we are studying, enables us to utilize systems which we do not really understand. It is almost inconceivable that we should make a machine that would make a poem: nevertheless, poems *are* made by fools like us by processes which are largely hidden from us. The kind of knowledge and skill that we have at the symbolic level is very different from that which we have at lower levels—it is like, shall we say, the "knowhow" of the gene as compared with the knowhow of the biologist. Nevertheless it is a real kind of knowledge and it is the source of the creative achievements of man as artist, writer, architect, and composer.

Perhaps one of the most valuable uses of the above scheme is to prevent us from accepting as final a level of theoretical analysis which is below the level of the empirical world which we are investigating. Because, in a sense, each level incorporates all those below it, much valuable information and insights can be obtained by applying low-level systems to high-level subject matter. Thus most of the theoretical schemes of the social sciences are still at level (ii), just rising now to (iii), although the subject matter clearly involves level (viii). Economics, for instance, is still largely a "me-chanics of utility and self-interest," in Jevons' masterly phrase. Its theoretical and mathematical base is drawn largely from the level of simple equilibrium theory and dynamic mechanisms. It has hardly begun to use concepts such as information which are appropriate at level (iii), and makes no use of higher level systems. Furthermore, with this crude apparatus it has achieved a modicum of success, in the sense that anybody trying to manipulate an economic system is almost certain to be better off if he knows some economics than if he doesn't. Nevertheless at some point progress in economics is going to depend on its ability to break out of these low-level systems, useful as they are as first approximations, and utilize systems which are more directly appropriate to its universe—when, of course, these systems are discovered. Many other examples could be given—the wholly inappropriate use in psychoanalytic theory, for instance, of the concept of energy, and the long inability of psychology to break loose from a sterile stimulus-response model.

Finally, the above scheme might serve as a mild word of warning even to Management Science. This new discipline represents an important breakaway from overly simple mechanical models in the theory of organization and control. Its emphasis on communication systems and organizational structure, on principles of homeostasis and growth, on decision processes under uncertainty, is carrying us far beyond the simple models of maximizing behavior of even ten years ago. This advance in the level of theoretical analysis is bound to lead to more powerful and fruitful systems. Nevertheless we must never quite forget that even these advances do not carry us much beyond the third and fourth levels, and that in dealing with human personalities and organizations we are dealing with systems in the empirical world far beyond our ability to formulate. We should not be wholly surprised, therefore, if our simpler systems, for all their importance and validity, occasionally let us down.

I chose the subtitle of my paper with some eye to its possible overtones of meaning. General Systems Theory is the skeleton of science in the sense that it aims to provide a framework or structure of systems on which to hang the flesh and blood of particular disciplines and particular subject matters in an orderly and coherent corpus of knowledge. It is also, however, something of a skeleton in a cup-board—the cupboard in this case being the unwillingness of science to admit the very low level of its successes in systematization, and its tendency to shut the door on problems and subject matters which do not fit easily into simple mechanical schemes. Science, for all its successes, still has a very long way to go. General Systems Theory may at times be an embarrassment in pointing out how very far we still have to go, and in deflating excessive philosophical claims for overly simple systems. It also may be helpful however in pointing out to some extent *where* we have to go. The skeleton must come out of the cupboard before its dry bones can live.

2. THE UTILITY OF SYSTEM MODELS AND DEVELOPMENTAL MODELS FOR PRACTITIONERS [1]

ROBERT CHIN [2]

All practitioners have ways of thinking about and figuring out situations of change. These ways are embodied in the concepts with which they apprehend the dynamics of the client-system they are working with, their relationship to it, and their processes of helping with its change. For example, the change-agent encounters resistance, defense mechanisms, readiness to change, adaptation, adjustment, maladjustment, integration, disintegration, growth, development, and maturation as well as deterioration. He uses concepts such as these to sort out the processes and mechanisms at work. And necessarily so. No practitioner can carry on thought processes without such concepts; indeed, no observations or diagnoses are ever made on "raw facts," because facts are really observations made within a set of concepts. But lurking behind concepts such as the ones stated above are assumptions about how the parts of the client-system fit together and how they change. For instance, "Let things alone, and natural laws (of economics, politics, personality, etc.) will work things out in the long run." "It is only human nature to resist change." "Every organization is always trying to improve its ways of working." Or, in more technical forms, we have assumptions such as: "The adjustment of the personality to its inner forces as well as adaptation to its environment is the sign of a healthy personality." "The coordination and integration of the departments of an organization is the task of the executive." "Conflict is

an index of malintegration, or of change." "Inhibiting forces against growth must be removed."

It is clear that each of the above concepts conceals a different assumption about how events achieve stability and change, and how anyone can or cannot help change along. Can we make these assumptions explicit? Yes, we can and we must. The behavioral scientist does exactly this by constructing a simplified *model* of human events and of his tool concepts. By simplifying he can analyze his thoughts and concepts, and see in turn where the congruities and discrepancies occur between these and actual events. He becomes at once the observer, analyzer and modifier of the system [3] of concepts he is using.

The purpose of this paper is to present concepts relevant to, and the benefits to be gained from using, a "system" model and a "developmental" model in thinking about human events. These models provide "mind-holds" to the practitioner in his diagnosis. They are, therefore, of practical significance to him. This suggests one essential meaning of the oft-quoted and rarely explained phrase that "nothing is so practical as a good theory." We will try to show how the "system" and "developmental" approaches provide key tools for a diagnosis of persons, groups, organizations, and communities for purposes of change. In doing so, we shall state succinctly the central notions of each model, probably sacrificing some technical elegance and exactness in the process. We shall not overburden the reader with citations of the voluminous

[1] SOURCE: *The Planning of Change,* by Warren G. Bennis, Kenneth D. Benne, and Robert Chin, © 1961, Holt, Rinehart and Winston, Inc., New York. Pp. 201–214. Reprinted by permission.
[2] Director of Research, Human Relations Center, Boston University.

[3] "System" is used here as any organized and coherent body of knowledge. Later we shall use the term in a more specific meaning.

set of articles from which this paper is drawn.

We postulate that the same models can be used in diagnosing different sizes of the units of human interactions—the person, the group, the organization, and the community.

One further prefatory word. We need to keep in mind the difference between an "analytic" model and a model of concrete events or cases. For our purposes, *an analytic model* is a constructed simplification of some part of reality that retains only those features regarded as essential for relating similar processes whenever and wherever they occur. A *concrete model* is based on an analytic model, but uses more of the content of actual cases, though it is still a simplification designed to reveal the essential features of some range of cases. As Hagen [4] puts it: "An explicitly defined analytic model helps the theorist to recognize what factors are being taken into account and *what relationships among them are assumed* and hence to know the basis of his conclusions. The advantages are ones of both exclusion and inclusion. A model lessens the danger of overlooking the indirect effects of a change of a relationship" (our italics). We mention this distinction since we find a dual usage that has plagued behavioral scientists, for they themselves keep getting their feet entangled. We get mixed up in analyzing "the small group as a system" (analytic) and a school committee as a small group (concrete) or a national social system (analytic) and the American social system (concrete) or an organizational system (analytic) and the organization of a glue factory (concrete). In this paper, we will move back and forth between the analytic usage of "model" and the "model" of the concrete case, hopefully with awareness of when we are involved in a semantic shift.

THE "SYSTEM" MODEL

Psychologists, sociologists, anthropologists, economists, and political scientists have been "discovering" and using the system model. In so doing, they find intimations of an exhilarating "unity" of science, because the system models used by biological and physical scientists seem to be exactly similar. Thus, the system model is regarded by some system theorists as universally applicable to physical and social events, and to human relationships in small or large units.

The terms or concepts that are a part of the system model are "boundary," "stress or tension," "equilibrium," and "feedback." All these terms are related to "open system," "closed system," and "intersystem" models. We shall first define these concepts, illustrate their meaning, and then point out how they can be used by the change-agent as aids in observing, analyzing, or diagnosing—and perhaps intervening in—concrete situations.

The Major Terms

System. Laymen sometimes say, "you can't beat the system" (economic or political), or "he is a product of the system" (juvenile delinquent or Soviet citizen). But readers of social science writings will find the term used in a rather more specific way. It is used as an abbreviated term for a longer phrase that the reader is asked to supply. The "economic system" might be read as: "we treat price indices, employment figures, etc., as if they were closely interdependent with each other and we temporarily leave out unusual or external events, such as the discovery of a new gold mine." Or in talking about juvenile delinquency in "system" terms, the sociologists choose to treat the lower-class values, lack of job opportunities, ragged parental images, as interrelated with each other, in back-and-forth cause-and-effect fashion, as determinants of delinquent behavior. Or the industrial sociologist may regard the factory as a "social system," as people working together in relative isolation from the outside, in order to examine what goes on in interactions and interdependencies of the people, their positions, and other variables. In our descriptions and analyses of a particular concrete system, we can recognize the shadowy figure of some such analytic model of "system."

The analytic model of system demands that we treat the phenomena and the concepts for organizing the phenomena as if there existed organization, interaction, interdependency, and integration of parts and elements. System analysis assumes structure and stability within some arbitrarily sliced and frozen time period.

[4] E. Hagen, chapter on "Theory of Social Change," unpublished manuscript.

It is helpful to visualize a system [5] by drawing a large circle. We place elements, parts, variables, inside the circle as the components, and draw lines among the components. The lines may be thought of as rubber bands or springs, which stretch or contract as the forces increase or decrease. Outside the circle is the environment, where we place all other factors which impinge upon the system.

Boundary. In order to specify what is inside or outside the system, we need to define its "boundary" line. The boundary of a system may exist physically: a tightly corked vacuum bottle, the skin of a person, the number of people in a group, etc. But, in addition, we may delimit the system in a less tangible way, by placing our boundary according to what variables are being focused upon. We can construct a system consisting of the multiple roles of a person, or a system composed of varied roles among members in a small work group, or a system interrelating roles in a family. The components or variables used are roles, acts, expectations, communications, influence and power relationships, and so forth, and not necessarily persons.

The operational definition of *boundary* is: the line forming a closed circle around selected variables, where there is less interchange of energy (or communication, etc.) *across* the line of the circle than *within* the delimiting circle. The multiple systems of a community may have boundaries that do or do not coincide. For example, treating the power relationships may require a boundary line different from that for the system of interpersonal likes or dislikes in a community. In small groups we tend to draw the same boundary line for the multiple systems of power, communications, leadership, and so on, a major advantage for purposes of study.

In diagnosing we tentatively assign a boundary, examine what is happening inside the system and then readjust the boundary, if necessary. We examine explicitly whether or not the "relevant" factors are accounted for within the system, an immensely practical way of deciding upon relevance. Also, we are free to limit ruthlessly, and neglect some factors

temporarily, thus reducing the number of considerations necessary to be kept in mind at one time. The variables left outside the system, in the "environment" of the system, can be introduced one or more at a time to see the effects, if any, on the interrelationship of the variables within the system.

Tension, Stress, Strain, and Conflict. Because the components within a system are different from each other, are not perfectly integrated, or are changing and reacting to change, or because outside disturbances occur, we need ways of dealing with these differences. The differences lead to varying degrees of tension within the system. *Examples:* males are not like females, foremen see things differently from workers and from executives, children in a family grow, a committee has to work with a new chairman, a change in the market condition requires a new sales response from a factory. To restate the above examples in conceptual terms: we find built-in differences, gaps of ignorance, misperceptions, or differential perceptions, internal changes in a component, reactive adjustments and defenses, and the requirements of system survival generating tensions. Tensions that are internal and arise out of the structural arrangements of the system may be called *stresses and strains* of the system. When tensions gang up and become more or less sharply opposed along the lines of two or more components, we have *conflict.*

A word of warning. The presence of tensions, stresses or strains, and conflict within the system often are reacted to by people in the system as if they were shameful and must be done away with. Tension reduction, relief of stress and strain, and conflict resolution become the working goals of practitioners but sometimes at the price of overlooking the possibility of increasing tensions and conflict in order to facilitate creativity, innovation, and social change. System analysts have been accused of being conservative and even reactionary in assuming that a social system always tends to reduce tension, resist innovation, abhor deviancy and change. It is obvious, however, that tension and conflict are "in" any system, and that no living system exists without tension. Whether these facts of life in a system are to be abhorred or welcomed is determined by attitudes or value judgments not derivable from system theory as such.

The identification of and analysis of how tensions operate in a system are by all odds

[5] A useful visual aid for "system" can be constructed by using paper clips (elements) and rubber bands (tensions) mounted on a peg board. Shifting of the position of a clip demonstrates the interdependency of all the clips' positions, and their shifting relationships.

the major utility of system analysis for practitioners of change. The dynamics of a living system are exposed for observation through utilizing the concepts of tension, stress and strain, and conflict. These tensions lead to activities of two kinds: those which do not affect the structure of the system (dynamics), and those which directly alter the structure itself (system change).

Equilibrium and "Steady State." A system is assumed to have a tendency to achieve a balance among the various forces operating within and upon it. Two terms have been used to denote two different ideas about balance. When the balance is thought of as a fixed point or level, it is called "equilibrium." "Steady state," on the other hand, is the term recently used to describe the balanced relationship of parts that is not dependent upon any fixed equilibrium point or level.

Our body temperature is the classic illustration of a fixed level (98.6° F.), while the functional relationship between work units in a factory, regardless of the level of production, represents a steady state. For the sake of simplicity, we shall henceforth stretch the term "equilibrium" to cover both types of balance, to include also the idea of "steady state."

There are many kinds of equilibria. A *stationary equilibrium* exists when there is a fixed point or level of balance to which the system returns after a disturbance. We rarely find such instances in human relationships. A *dynamic equilibrium* exists when the equilibrium shifts to a new position of balance after disturbance. Among examples of the latter, we can observe a *neutral* type of situation. *Example:* a ball on a flat plane. A small push moves it to a new position, and it again comes to rest. *Example:* a farming community. A new plow is introduced and is easily incorporated into its agricultural methods. A new level of agricultural production is placidly achieved. A *stable type of situation* exists where the forces that produced the initial equilibrium are so powerful that any new force must be extremely strong before any movement to a new position can be achieved. *Example:* a ball in the bottom of a goblet. *Example:* an organization encrusted with tradition or with clearly articulated and entrenched roles is not easily upset by minor events. An *unstable type of situation* is tense and precarious. A small disturbance produces large and rapid movements to a new position. *Example:* a ball balanced

on the rims of two goblets placed side by side. *Example:* an organization with a precarious and tense balance between two modes of leadership style. A small disturbance can cause a large swing to one direction and a new position of equilibrium. *Example:* a community's balance of power between ethnic groups may be such that a "minor" disturbance can produce an upheaval and movement to a different balance of power.

A system in equilibrium reacts to outside impingements by: (1) resisting the influence of the disturbance, refusing to acknowledge its existence, or by building a protective wall against the intrusion, and by other defensive maneuvers. *Example:* A small group refuses to talk about a troublesome problem of unequal power distribution raised by a member. (2) By resisting the disturbance through bringing into operation the homeostatic forces that restore or re-create a balance. The small group talks about the troublesome problem of a member and convinces him that it is not "really" a problem. (3) By accommodating the disturbances through achieving a new equilibrium. Talking about the problem may result in a shift in power relationships among members of the group.

The concepts of equilibrium (and steady state) lead to some questions to guide a practitioner's diagnosis.

1. What are the conditions conducive to the achievement of an equilibrium in this case? Are there internal or external factors producing these forces? What is their quality and tempo?

2. Does the case of the client-system represent one of the typical situations of equilibrium? How does judgment on this point affect intervention strategy? If the practitioner feels the situation is tense and precarious, he should be more cautious in intervention than in a situation of stable type.

3. Can the practitioner identify the parts of the system that represent greatest readiness to change, and the greatest resistance to and defense against change? Can he understand the functions of any variable in relation to all other variables? Can he derive some sense of the direction in which the client system is moving, and separate those forces attempting to restore an old equilibrium and those pushing toward a new equilibrium state?

Feedback. Concrete systems are never closed off completely. They have inputs and outputs across the boundary; they are affected by and in turn affect the environment. While affecting the environment, a process we call output, systems gather information about how they are doing. Such information is then fed back into the system as input to guide and steer its operations. This process is called feedback. The "discovery" of feedback has led to radical inventions in the physical world in designing self-guiding and self-correcting instruments. It has also become a major concept in the behavioral sciences, and a central tool in the practitioner's social technology. *Example:* In reaching for a cigarette we pick up tactile and visual cues that are used to guide our arm and finger movements. *Example:* Our interpersonal communications are guided and corrected by our picking up of effect cues from the communicatees. *Example:* Improving the feedback process of a client system will allow for self-steering or corrective action to be taken by him or it. In fact, the single most important improvement the change-agent can help a client system to achieve is to increase its diagnostic sensitivity to the effects of its own actions upon others. Programs in sensitivity training attempt to increase or unblock the feedback processes of persons; a methodological skill with wider applicability and longer-lasting significance than solving the immediate problem at hand. In diagnosing a client system, the practitioner asks: What are its feedback procedures? How adequate are they? What blocks their effective use? Is it lack of skill in gathering data, or in coding and utilizing the information?

Open and Closed Systems

All living systems are open systems—systems in contact with their environment, with input and output across system boundaries. What then is the use of talking about a closed system? What *is* a closed system? It means that the system is temporarily assumed to have a leak-tight boundary—there is relatively little, if any, commerce across the boundary. We know that no such system can be found in reality, but it is sometimes essential to analyze a system as if it were closed so as to examine the operations of the system as affected "only by the conditions previously established by the environment and not changing at the time of analysis, plus the relationships among the internal elements of the system." The analyst

then opens the system to a new impact from the environment, again closes the system, and observes and thinks out what would happen. It is, therefore, fruitless to debate the point; both open and closed system models are useful in diagnosis. Diagnosing the client as a system of variables, we have a way then of managing the complexity of "everything depends upon everything else" in an orderly way. Use of system analysis has these possibilities: (*a*) diagnosticians can avoid the error of simple cause-and-effect thinking; (*b*) they can justify what is included in observation and interpretation and what is temporarily excluded; (*c*) they can predict what will happen if no new or outside force is applied; (*d*) they are guided in categorizing what is relatively enduring and stable, or changing, in the situation; (*e*) they can distinguish between what is basic and what is merely symptomatic; (*f*) they can predict what will happen if they leave the events undisturbed and if they intervene; and (*g*) they are guided in selecting points of intervention.

Intersystem Model

We propose an extension of system analysis that looks to us to be useful for the problems confronting the change-agent. We urge the adoption of an intersystem model.

An intersystem model involves two open systems connected to each other.[6] The term we need to add here is *connectives*. Connectives represent the lines of relationships of the two systems. Connectives tie together parts (mechanics) or imbed in a web of tissue the separate organs (biology); connectives in an industrial establishment are the defined lines of communication, or the leadership hierarchy and authority for the branch plants; or they represent the social contract entered into by a therapist and patient; or mutual role expectations of consultant and client; or the affective ties between family members. These are conjunctive connectives. But we also have conflicts between labor and management, teenage gang wars, race conflicts, and negative emotional responses to strangers. These are disjunctive connectives.

[6] A visualization of an intersystem model would be two systems side by side, with separately identified links. Two rubber band-paper clip representatives can be connected with rubber bands of a different color representing the connectives.

Why elaborate the system model into an intersystem model? Cannot we get the same effect by talking about "sub-systems" of a larger system? In part we can. Labor-management conflicts, or interpersonal relations, or change-agent and client relationships can each be treated as a new system with sub-systems. But we may lose the critical fact of the autonomy of the components, or the direct interactional or transactual consequences for the separate components when we treat the sub-systems as merely parts of a larger system. The intersystem model exaggerates the virtues of autonomy and the limited nature of interdependence of the interactions between the two connected systems.

What are some of the positive advantages of using intersystem analysis? First, the external change-agent, or the change-agent built into an organization, as a helper with planned change does not completely become a part of the client-system. He must remain separate to some extent; he must create and maintain some distance between himself and the client, thus standing apart "in another system" from which he re-relates. This new system might be a referent group of fellow professionals, or a body of rational knowledge. But create one he does and must. Intersystem analysis of the change-agent's role leads to fruitful analysis of the connectives—their nature in the beginning, how they shift, and how they are cut off. Intersystem analysis also poses squarely an unexplored issue, namely the internal system of the change-agent, whether a single person, consultant group, or a nation. Helpers of change are prone at times not to see that their own systems as change-agents have boundaries, tensions, stresses and strains, equilibria, and feedback mechanisms which may be just as much parts of the problem as are similar aspects of the client-systems. Thus, relational issues are more available for diagnosis when we use an intersystem model.

More importantly, the intersystem model is applicable to problems of leadership, power, communication, and conflict in organizations, intergroup relations, and international relations. *Example:* Leadership in a work group with its liaison, negotiation, and representation functions is dependent upon connectives to another group and not solely upon the internal relationships within the work group. Negotiators, representatives, and leaders are parts of separate systems each with its own interdependence, tensions, stresses, and feedback, whether we are thinking of foreign ministers, Negro-white leaders, or student-faculty councils.

In brief, the intersystem model leads us to examine the interdependent dynamics of interaction both within and between the units. We object to the premature and unnecessary assumption that the units always form a single system. We can be misled into an utopian analysis of conflict, change-agent relations to client, and family relations if we neglect system differences. But an intersystem model provides a tool for diagnosis that retains the virtues of system analysis, adds the advantage of clarity, and furthers our diagnosis of the influence of various connectives, conjunctive and disjunctive, on the two systems. For change-agents, the essence of collaborative planning is contained in an intersystem model.

DEVELOPMENTAL MODELS

Practitioners have in general implicitly favored developmental models in thinking about human affairs, while social scientists have not paid as much attention to these as they have to system models. The "life sciences" of biology and psychology have not crystallized nor refined their common analytic model of the development of the organism, despite the heroic break-throughs of Darwin. Thus, we are forced to present only broad and rough categories of alternative positions in this paper.

Since there is no standard vocabulary for a developmental model, we shall present five categories of terms that we deem essential to such models: direction, states, forces, form of progression, and potentiality.

The Major Terms

Developmental Models. By developmental models, we mean those bodies of thought that center around growth and directional change. Developmental models assume change; they assume that there are noticeable differences between the states of a system at different times; that the succession of these states implies the system is heading somewhere; and that there are orderly processes which explain how the system gets from its present state to wherever it is going. In order to delimit the nature of change in developmental models we should perhaps add the idea of an increase in value accompanying the achievement of a new state. With this addition, developmental models focus on processes of growth and maturation. This addition might seem to rule out processes of decay, deterioration, and death from consideration. Logically, the developmental model should apply to either.

There are two kinds of "death" of concern to the practitioner. First, "death" or loss of some part or subvalue, as a constant concomitant of growth and development. Theories of life processes have used concepts such as catabolic (destructive) processes in biology, death instincts in Freud's psychology, or role loss upon promotion. On balance, the "loss" is made up by the "gains," and thus there is an increase in value. Second, "death" as planned changed for a group or organization—the dissolution of a committee or community organization that has "outlived its purpose and function," and the termination of a helping relationship with deliberateness and collaboration of participants is properly included as part of a developmental model.

Direction. Developmental models postulate that the system under scrutiny—a person, a small group, interpersonal interactions, an organization, a community or a society—is going "somewhere"; that the changes have some direction. The direction may be defined by (*a*) some *goal* or end state (developed, mature); (*b*) the *process* of becoming (developing, maturing) or (*c*) the degree of achievement *toward* some goal or end state (increased development, increase in maturity).

Change-agents find it necessary to believe that there is direction in change. *Example:* self-actualization or fulfillment is a need of the client-system. When strong directional tendencies are present, we modify our diagnosis and intervention accordingly. A rough analogy may be helpful here. A change-agent using a developmental model may be thought of as a husbandman tending a plant, watching and helping it to grow in its own natural direction of producing flowers. He feeds, waters, and weeds. Though at times he may be ruthless in pinching off excess buds, or even in using "grafts," in general he encourages the plant to reach its "goal" of producing beautiful flowers.

Identifiable State. As the system develops over time, the different states may be identified and differentiated from one another. Terms such as "stages," "levels," "phases," or "periods" are applied to these states. *Example:* psychosexual definition of oral, and anal stages, levels of evolution of species, or phases of group development.

No uniformity exists in the definition and operational identification of such successive states. But since change-agents do have to label the past, present, and future, they need some terms to describe successive states and to identify the turning points, transition areas, or critical events that characterize change. Here, system analysis is helpful in defining how parts are put together, along with the tensions and directions of the equilibrating processes. We have two polar types of the shifts of states: (*a*) small, nondiscernible steps or increments leading to a qualitative jump. (*Example:* black hair gradually turning gray, or a student evolving into a scholar); (*b*) a cataclysmic or critical event leading to a sudden change. (*Example:* a sickness resulting in gray hair overnight, or an inspirational lecture by a professor.) While the latter type seems more frequently to be externally induced, internal factors of the system can have the same consequence. In other words, the internal disequilibration of a balance may lead to a step-jump of the system to a new level. Personality stages, group stages, and societal phases are evolved and precipitated from internal and from external relations.

Form of Progression. Change-agents see in their models of development some form of progression or movement. Four such forms are typically assumed. First, it is often stated that once a stage is worked through, the client-system shows continued progression and normally never turns back. (Any recurrence of a previous state is viewed as an abnormality. Freudian stages are a good example: recurrence of a stage is viewed as regression, an abnormal event to be explained.) Teachers expect a steady growth of knowledge in students, either in a straight line (linear) or in an increasingly accelerating (curvilinear) form.

Second, it is assumed that change, growth, and development occur in a *spiral* form. *Example:* A small group might return to some previous "problem," such as its authority relations to the leader, but now might discuss the question at a "higher" level where irrational components are less dominant.

Third, another assumption more typically made is that the stages are really phases which occur and recur. There is an oscillation between various states, where no chronological priority is assigned to each state; there are cycles. *Example:* Phases of problem-solving or decision-making recur in different time periods as essential to progression. Cultures and societies go through phases of development in recurrent forms.

Fourth, still another assumption is that the form of progression is characterized by a branching out into *differentiated* forms and processes, each part increasing in its specialization, and at the same time acquiring its own autonomy and significance. *Example:* biological forms are differentiated into separate species. Organizations become more and more differentiated into special task and control structures.

Forces. First, forces or causal factors producing development and growth are most frequently seen by practitioners as "natural," as part of human nature, suggesting the role of genetics and other in-born characteristics. At best, environmental factors act as "triggers" or "releases," where the presence of some stimulus sets off the system's inherent growth forces. For example, it is sometimes thought that the teacher's job is to trigger off the natural curiosity of the child, and that growth of knowledge will ensue. Or the leadership of an organization should act to release the self-actualizing and creative forces present in its members.

Second, a smaller number of practitioners and social scientists think that the response to new situations and environmental forces is a coping response which gives rise to growth and development. Third, at this point, it may be useful to remind ourselves of the earlier discussion of the internal tensions of the system, still another cause of change. When stresses and strains of a system become too great, a disruption occurs and a set of forces is released to create new structures and achieve a new equilibrium.

Potentiality. Developmental models vary in their assumptions about potentialities of the system for development, growth, and change. That is, they vary in assumptions about the capabilities, overt or latent, that are built into the original or present state so that the necessary conditions for development may be typically present. Does the "seed"—and its genetic characteristics—represent potentialities? And are the supporting conditions of its environment available? Is the intelligence or emotional capability or skill-potential sufficient for development and change in a social and human process?

Change-agents typically assume a high degree of potentiality in the impetus toward development, and in the surrounding conditions that effectuate the potential.

Utility to Practitioners

The developmental model has tremendous advantages for the practitioner. It provides a set of expectations about the future of the client-system. By clarifying his thoughts and refining his observations about direction, states in the developmental process, forms of progression, and forces causing these events to occur over a period of time, the practitioner develops a time perspective which goes far beyond that of the mere here-and-now analysis of a system-model, which is bounded by time. By using a developmental model, he has a directional focus for his analysis and action and a temporal frame of reference. In addition, he is confronted with a number of questions to ask of himself and of his observations of the case: Do I assume an inherent end of the development? Do I impose a desired (by me) direction? How did I establish a collaboratively planned direction? What states in the development process may be expected? What form of progression do I foresee? What causes the development? His diagnoses and his interventions can become strategic rather than merely tactical.

THE CHANGE-AGENT AND MODELS

The primary concern of this paper has been to illustrate some of the major kinds of analytic models and conceptual schemes that have been devised by social scientists for the analysis of change and of changing human processes. But we need to keep in mind that the concern with diagnosis on the part of the social scientist is to achieve understanding, and to educe empirically researchable hypotheses amenable to his methods of study. The social scientist generally prefers not to change the system, but to study how it works and to predict what would happen if some new factor were introduced. So we find his attention focused on a "theory of change," of how the system achieves change. In contrast, the practitioner is concerned with diagnosis:

how to achieve understanding in order to engage in change. The practitioner, therefore, has some additional interests, he wants to know how to change the system, he needs a "theory of changing" the system.

A theory of changing requires the selection, or the construction, by theoretically minded practitioners, of thought-models appropriate to their intended purpose. This has to be done according to explicit criteria. A change-agent may demand of any model answers to certain questions. The responses he receives may not be complete or satisfactory since only piecemeal answers exist. At this period in the development of a theory of changing, we ask four questions as our guide lines for examining a conceptual model intended for the use of change-agents.

The first question is simply this: does the model account for the stability and continuity in the events studied at the same time that it accounts for changes in them? How do processes of change develop, given the interlocking factors in the situation that make for stability? Second, where does the model locate the "source" of change? What place among these sources do the deliberate and conscious efforts of the client-system and change-agent occupy? Third, what does the model assume about how goals and directions are determined? What or who sets the direction for movement of the processes of change? Fourth, does the model provide the change agent with levers or handles for affecting the direction, tempo, and quality of these processes of change?

A fifth question running through the other four is this: How does the model "place" the change-agent in the scheme of things? What is the shifting character of his relationship to the client-system, initially and at the termination of relationship, that affects his perceptions and actions? The question of relationship of change-agent to others needs to be part and parcel of the model since the existential relationships of the change-agent engaged in processes of planned change become "part of the problem" to be investigated.

The application of these five questions to the models of systems and models of development crystallizes some of the formation of ingredients for a change-agent model for changing. We can now summarize each model as follows:

"A "system" model emphasizes primarily the details of how stability is achieved, and only derivatively how change evolves out of the incompatibilities and conflicts in the system. A system model assumes that organization, interdependency, and integration exist among its parts and that change is a derived consequence of how well the parts of the system fit together, or how well the system fits in with other surounding and interacting systems. The source of change lies primarily in the structural stress and strain externally induced or internally created. The process of change is a process of tension reduction. The goals and direction are emergent from the structures or from imposed sources. Goals are often analyzed as set by "vested interests" of one part of the system. The confronting symptom of some trouble is a reflection of difficulties of adaptability (reaction to environment) or of the ability for adjustment (internal equilibration). The levers or handles available for manipulation are in the "inputs" to the system, especially the feedback mechanisms, and in the forces tending to restore a balance in the system. The change-agent is treated as separate from the client-system, the "target system."

The developmental model assumes constant change and development, and growth and decay of a system over time. Any existing stability is a snapshot of a living process—a stage that will give way to another stage. The supposition seems to be that it is "natural" that change should occur because change is rooted in the very nature of living organisms. The laws of the developmental process are not necessarily fixed, but some effects of the environment are presumably necessary to the developmental process. The direction of change is toward some goal, the fulfillment of its destiny, granting that no major blockage gets in the way. "Trouble" occurs when there is a gap between the system and its goal. Intervention is viewed as the removal of blockage by the change-agent, who then gets out of the way of the growth forces. Developmental models are not very sharply analyzed by the pure theorist nor formally stated, usually, as an analytic model. In fact, very frequently the model is used for studying the unique case rather than for deriving "laws of growth"; it is for descriptive purposes.

The third model—a model for "changing"— is a more recent creation. It incorporates some elements of analyses from system models, along with some ideas from the developmental model, in a framework, where direct attention is paid to the induced forces producing

Assumptions and Approaches of Three Analytic Models

Assumptions and Approaches to:	Models of Change		
	System Model	Developmental Model	Model for Changing
1. *Content*			
Stability	Structural integration	Phases, stages	Unfreezing parts
Change	Derived from structure	Constant and unique	Induced, controlled
2. *Causation*			
Source of change	Structural stress	Nature of organisms	Self and change-agent
Causal force	Tension reduction		Rational choice
3. *Goals*			
Direction	Emergent	Ontological	Deliberate selection
Set by	"Vested interests"		Collaborative process
4. *Intervention*			
Confronting symptoms	Stresses, strains, and tensions	Discrepancy between actuality and potentiality	Perceived need
Goal of intervening	Adjustment, adaptation	Removal of blockages	Improvement
5. *Change-Agent*			
Place	Outside the "target" system	Outside	Part of situation
Role	External diagnoser and actor	External diagnoser and actor	Participant in here and now

change. It studies stability in order to unfreeze and move some parts of the system. The direction to be taken is not fixed or "determined," but remains in large measure a matter of "choice" for the client-system. The change-agent is a specialist in the technical processes of facilitating change, a helper to the client-system. The models for changing are as yet incompletely conceptualized. The intersystem model may provide a way of examining how the change-agent's relationships, as part of the model, affect the processes of change.

We can summarize and contrast the three models with this chart. We have varying degrees of confidence in our categories, but, as the quip says, we construct these in order to achieve the laudable state of "paradigm lost." It is the readers' responsibility to help achieve this goal!

THE LIMITATIONS

It is obvious that we are proposing the use of systematically constructed and examined models of thought for the change-agent. The advantages are manifold and—we hope—apparent in our preceding discussion. Yet we must now point out some limitations and disutility of models.

Models are abstractions from the concreteness of events. Because of the high degree of selectivity of observations and focus, the "fit" between the model and the actual thought and diagnostic processes of the change-agent is not close. Furthermore, the thought and diagnostic processes of the change-agent are not fixed and rigid. And even worse, the "fit" between the diagnostic processes of the change-agent and the changing processes of the "actual" case, is not close. Abstract as the nature of a model is, as applied to the change-agent, students of the change-agent role may find the concepts of use. But change-agents' practices in diagnosing are not immediately affected by models' analyses.

Furthermore, there are modes of diagnosing by intervening, which do not fall neatly into models. The change-agent frequently tries out an activity in order to see what happens and to see what is involved in the change. If successful, he does not need to diagnose any further, but proceeds to engage in further actions with the client. If unsuccessful, however, he may need to examine what is going on in more detail.

The patch work required for a theory and model of changing requires the suspension of acceptance of such available models. For this paper has argued for some elements from both the system models and the developmental models to be included in the model for prac-

titioners, with the use of a format of the intersystem model so as to include the change-agent and his relationships as part of the problem. But can the change-agent wait for such a synthesis and emerging construction? Our personal feeling is that the planning of change cannot wait, but must proceed with the available diagnostic tools. Here is an intellectual challenge to the scientist-scholar of planned change that could affect the professions of practice.

3. ORGANIZATION THEORY: AN OVERVIEW AND AN APPRAISAL [1]

WILLIAM G. SCOTT [2]

Man is intent on drawing himself into a web of collectivized patterns. "Modern man has learned to accommodate himself to a world increasingly organized. The trend toward ever more explicit and consciously drawn relationships is profound and sweeping; it is marked by depth no less than by extension." [3] This comment by Seidenberg nicely summarizes the pervasive influence of organization in many forms of human activity.

Some of the reasons for intense organizational activity are found in the fundamental transitions which revolutionized our society, changing it from a rural culture, to a culture based on technology, industry, and the city. From these changes, a way of life emerged characterized by the *proximity* and *dependency* of people on each other. Proximity and dependency, as conditions of social life, harbor the threats of human conflict, capricious antisocial behavior, instability of human relationships, and uncertainty about the nature of the social structure with its concomitant roles.

Of course, these threats to social integrity are present to some degree in all societies, ranging from the primitive to the modern. But, these threats become dangerous when the harmonious functioning of a society rests on the maintenance of a highly intricate, delicately balanced form of human collaboration. The civilization we have created depends on the preservation of a precarious balance. Hence, disrupting forces impinging on this shaky form of collaboration must be eliminated or minimized.

Traditionally, organization is viewed as a vehicle for accomplishing goals and objectives. While this approach is useful, it tends to obscure the inner workings and internal purposes of organization itself. Another fruitful way of treating organization is as a mechanism having the ultimate purpose of offsetting those forces which undermine human collaboration. In this sense, organization tends to minimize conflict, and to lessen the significance of individual behavior which deviates from values that the organization has established as worthwhile. Further, organization increases stability in human relationships by reducing uncertainty regarding the nature of the system's structure and the human roles which are inherent to it. Corollary to this point, organization enhances the predictability of human action, because it limits the number of behavioral alternatives available to an individual. As Presthus points out:

Organization is defined as a system of structural interpersonal relations . . . individuals are differentiated in terms of authority, status, and role with the result that personal interaction is prescribed. . . . Anticipated reactions tend to occur, while ambiguity and spontaneity are decreased. [4]

In addition to all of this, organization has built-in safeguards. Besides prescribing acceptable forms of behavior for those who elect to submit to it, organization is also able to counterbalance the influence of human action which transcends its established patterns. [5]

[1] SOURCE: *Journal of the Academy of Management*, Vol. 4, No. 1 (April, 1961), pp. 7–26. Reprinted by permission of *Journal of the Academy of Management*.

[2] Associate Professor of Management, DePaul University.

[3] Roderick Seidenberg, *Posthistoric Man* (Boston: Beacon Press, 1951), p. 1.

[4] Robert V. Presthus, "Toward a Theory of Organizational Behavior," *Administrative Science Quarterly* (June, 1958), p. 50.

[5] Regulation and predictability of human behavior are matters of degree varying with different organizations on something of a continuum. At one extreme are bureaucratic type organizations with tight bonds of regulation. At the other ex-

Few segments of society have engaged in organizing more intensively than business.[6] The reason is clear. Business depends on what organization offers. Business needs a system of relationships among functions; it needs stability, continuity, and predictability in its internal activities and external contacts. Business also appears to need harmonious relationships among the people and processes which make it up. Put another way, a business organization has to be free, relatively, from destructive tendencies which may be caused by divergent interests.

As a foundation for meeting these needs rests administrative science. A major element of this science is organization theory, which provides the grounds for management activities in a number of significant areas of business endeavor. Organization theory, however, is not a homogeneous science based on generally accepted principles. Various theories of organization have been, and are being evolved. For example, something called "modern organization theory" has recently emerged, raising the wrath of some traditionalists, but also capturing the imagination of a rather elite *avant-garde*.

The thesis of this paper is that modern organization theory, when stripped of its irrelevancies, redundancies, and "speech defects," is a logical and vital evolution in management thought. In order for this thesis to be supported, the reader must endure a review and appraisal of more traditional forms of organization theory which may seem elementary to him.

In any event, three theories of organization are having considerable influence on management thought and practice. They are arbitrarily labeled in this paper as the classical, the neo-classical, and the modern. Each of these is fairly distinct; but they are not unrelated.

treme are voluntary associations and informal organizations with relatively loose bonds of regulation.

This point has an interesting sidelight. A bureaucracy with tight controls and a high degree of predictability of human action appears to be unable to distinguish between destructive and creative deviations from established values. Thus the only thing which is safeguarded is the *status quo*.

[6] The monolithic institutions of the military and government are other cases of organizational preoccupation.

Also, these theories are on-going, being actively supported by several schools of management thought.

THE CLASSICAL DOCTRINE

For lack of a better method of identification, it will be said that the classical doctrine deals almost exclusively with the *anatomy of formal organization*. This doctrine can be traced back to Frederick W. Taylor's interest in functional foremanship and planning staffs. But most students of management thought would agree that in the United States, the first systematic approach to organization, and the first comprehensive attempt to find organizational universals, is dated 1931 when Mooney and Reiley published *Onward Industry*.[7] Subsequently, numerous books, following the classical vein, have appeared. Two of the more recent are Brech's, *Organization*[8] and Allen's, *Management and Organization*.[9]

Classical organization theory is built around four key pillars. They are the division of labor, the scalar and functional processes, structure, and span of control. Given these major elements just about all of classical organization theory can be derived.

(1) *The division of labor* is without doubt the cornerstone among the four elements.[10] From it the other elements flow as corollaries. For example, *scalar* and *functional* growth requires specialization and departmentalization of functions. Organization *structure* is naturally dependent upon the direction which specialization of activities travels in company development. Finally, *span of control* problems result from the number of specialized functions under the jurisdiction of a manager.

(2) *The scalar and functional processes* deal with the vertical and horizontal growth of

[7] James D. Mooney and Alan C. Reiley, *Onward Industry* (New York: Harper and Brothers, 1931). Later published by James D. Mooney under the title *Principles of Organization*.

[8] E. F. L. Brech, *Organization* (London: Longmans, Green and Company, 1957).

[9] Louis A. Allen, *Management and Organization* (New York: McGraw-Hill Book Company, 1958).

[10] Usually the division of labor is treated under a topical heading of departmentation, see for example: Harold Koontz and Cyril O'Donnell, *Principles of Management* (New York: McGraw-Hill Book Company, 1959), Chapter 7.

the organization, respectively.[11] The scalar process refers to the growth of the chain of command, the delegation of authority and responsibility, unity of command, and the obligation to report.

The division of the organization into specialized parts and the regrouping of the parts into compatible units are matters pertaining to the functional process. This process focuses on the horizontal evolution of the line and staff in a formal organization.

(3) *Structure* is the logical relationships of functions in an organization, arranged to accomplish the objectives of the company efficiently. Structure implies system and pattern. Classical organization theory usually works with two basic structures, the line and the staff. However, such activities as committee and liaison functions fall quite readily into the purview of structural considerations. Again, structure is the vehicle for introducing logical and consistent relationships among the diverse functions which comprise the organization.[12]

(4) *The span of control* concept relates to the number of subordinates a manager can effectively supervise. Graicunas has been credited with first elaborating the point that there are numerical limitations to the subordinates one man can control.[13] In a recent statement on the subject, Brech points out, "span" refers to ". . . the number of persons, themselves carrying managerial and supervisory responsibilities, for whom the senior manager retains his overembracing responsibility of direction and planning, co-ordination, motivation, and control." [14] Regardless of interpretation, span of control has significance, in part, for the shape of the organization which evolves through growth. Wide span yields a flat structure; short span results in a tall structure. Further, the span concept directs attention to the complexity of human and functional interrelationships in an organization.

[11] These processes are discussed at length in Ralph Currier Davis, *The Fundamentals of Top Management* (New York: Harper and Brothers, 1951), Chapter 7.

[12] For a discussion of structure see: William H. Newman, *Administrative Action* (Englewood Cliffs, New Jersey: Prentice-Hall, Incorporated, 1951), Chapter 16.

[13] V. A. Graicunas, "Relationships in Organization," *Papers on the Science of Administration* (New York: Columbia University, 1937).

[14] Brech, *op. cit.*, p. 78.

It would not be fair to say that the classical school is unaware of the day-to-day administrative problems of the organization. Paramount among these problems are those stemming from human interactions. But the interplay of individual personality, informal groups, interorganizational conflict, and the decision-making processes in the formal structure appears largely to be neglected by classical organization theory. Additionally, the classical theory overlooks the contributions of the behavioral sciences by failing to incorporate them in its doctrine in any systematic way. In summary, classical organization theory has relevant insights into the nature of organization, but the value of this theory is limited by its narrow concentration on the formal anatomy of organization.

NEOCLASSICAL THEORY OF ORGANIZATION

The neoclassical theory of organization embarked on the task of compensating for some of the deficiencies in classical doctrine. The neoclassical school is commonly identified with the human relations movement. Generally, the neoclassical approach takes the postulates of the classical school, regarding the pillars of organization as givens. But these postulates are regarded as modified by people, acting independently or within the context of the informal organization.

One of the main contributions of the neoclassical school is the introduction of behavioral sciences in an integrated fashion into the theory of organization. Through the use of these sciences, the human relationists demonstrate how the pillars of the classical doctrine are affected by the impact of human actions. Further, the neoclassical approach includes a systematic treatment of the informal organization, showing its influence on the formal structure.

Thus, the neoclassical approach to organization theory gives evidence of accepting classical doctrine, but superimposing on it modifications resulting from individual behavior, and the influence of the informal group. The inspiration of the neoclassical school were the Hawthorne studies.[15] Current examples of the neoclassical approach are

[15] See: F. J. Roethlisberger and William J. Dickson, *Management and the Worker* (Cambridge: Harvard University Press, 1939).

found in human relations books like Gardner and Moore, *Human Relations in Industry*,[16] and Davis, *Human Relations in Business*.[17] To a more limited extent, work in industrial sociology also reflects a neoclassical point of view.[18]

It would be useful to look briefly at some of the contributions made to organization theory by the neoclassicists. First to be considered are modifications of the pillars of classical doctrine; second is the informal organization.

Examples of the Neoclassical Approach to the Pillars of Formal Organization Theory

(1) The *division of labor* has been a long standing subject of comment in the field of human relations. Very early in the history of industrial psychology study was made of industrial fatigue and monotony caused by the specialization of the work.[19] Later, attention shifted to the isolation of the worker, and his feeling of anonymity resulting from insignificant jobs which contributed negligibly to the final product.[20]

Also, specialization influences the work of management. As an organization expands, the need concomitantly arises for managerial motivation and coordination of the activities of others. Both motivation and coordination in turn relate to executive leadership. Thus, in part, stemming from the growth of industrial specialization, the neoclassical school has developed a large body of theory relating to motivation, coordination, and leadership. Much of this theory is derived from the social sciences.

(2) Two aspects of the *scalar and functional* processes which have been treated with

some degree of intensity by the neoclassical school are the delegation of authority and responsibility, and gaps in or overlapping of functional jurisdictions. The classical theory assumes something of perfection in the delegation and functionalization processes. The neoclassical school points out that human problems are caused by imperfections in the way these processes are handled.

For example, too much or insufficient delegation may render an executive incapable of action. The failure to delegate authority and responsibility equally may result in frustration for the delegatee. Overlapping of authorities often causes clashes in personality. Gaps in authority cause failures in getting jobs done, with one party blaming the other for shortcomings in performance.[21]

The neoclassical school says that the scalar and functional processes are theoretically valid, but tend to deteriorate in practice. The ways in which they break down are described, and some of the human causes are pointed out. In addition the neoclassicists make recommendations, suggesting various "human tools" which will facilitate the operation of these processes.

(3) *Structure* provides endless avenues of analysis for the neoclassical theory of organization. The theme is that human behavior disrupts the best laid organizational plans, and thwarts the cleanness of the logical relationships founded in the structure. The neoclassical critique of structure centers on frictions which appear internally among people performing different functions.

Line and staff relations is a problem area, much discussed, in this respect. Many companies seem to have difficulty keeping the line and staff working together harmoniously. Both Dalton[22] and Juran[23] have engaged in research to discover the causes of friction, and to suggest remedies.

Of course, line-staff relations represent only one of the many problems of structural frictions described by the neoclassicists. As often

---

[16] Burleigh B. Gardner and David G. Moore, *Human Relations in Industry* (Homewood, Illinois: Richard D. Irwin, 1955).

[17] Keith Davis, *Human Relations in Business* (New York: McGraw-Hill Book Company, 1957).

[18] For example see: Delbert C. Miller and William H. Form, *Industrial Sociology* (New York: Harper and Brothers, 1951).

[19] See: Hugo Munsterberg, *Psychology and Industrial Efficiency* (Boston: Houghton Mifflin Company, 1913).

[20] Probably the classic work is: Elton Mayo, *The Human Problems of an Industrial Civilization* (Cambridge: Harvard University, 1946, first printed 1933).

[21] For further discussion of the human relations implications of the scalar and functional processes see: Keith Davis, *op. cit.*, pp. 60–66.

[22] Melville Dalton, "Conflicts Between Staff and Line Managerial Officers," *American Sociological Review* (June, 1950), pp. 342–351.

[23] J. M. Juran, "Improving the Relationship Between Staff and Line," *Personnel* (May, 1956), pp. 515–524.

as not, the neoclassicists will offer prescriptions for the elimination of conflict in structure. Among the more important harmony-rendering formulae are participation, junior boards, bottom-up management, joint committees, recognition of human dignity, and "better" communication.

(4) An executive's *span of control* is a function of human determinants, and the reduction of span to a precise, universally applicable ratio is silly, according to the neoclassicists. Some of the determinants of span are individual differences in managerial abilities, the type of people and functions supervised, and the extent of communication effectiveness.

Coupled with the span of control question are the human implications of the type of structure which emerges. That is, is a tall structure with a short span or a flat structure with a wide span more conducive to good human relations than high morale? The answer is situational. Short span results in tight supervision; wide span requires a good deal of delegation with looser controls. Because of individual and organizational differences, sometimes one is better than the other. There is a tendency to favor the looser form of organization, however, for the reason that tall structures breed autocratic leadership, which is often pointed out as a cause of low morale.[24]

The Neoclassical View of the Informal Organization

Nothing more than the barest mention of the informal organization is given even in the most recent classical treatises on organization theory.[25] Systematic discussion of this form of organization has been left to the neoclassicists. The informal organization refers to people in group associations at work, but these associations are not specified in the "blueprint" of the formal organization. The informal organization means natural groupings of people in the work situation.

In a general way, the informal organization appears in response to the social need—the need of people to associate with others. However, for analytical purposes, this explanation is not particularly satisfying. Research has pro-

duced the following, more specific determinants underlying the appearance of informal organizations:

1. The *location* determinant simply states that in order to form into groups of any lasting nature, people have to have frequent face-to-face contact. Thus, the geography of physical location in a plant or office is an important factor in predicting who will be in what group.[26]

2. *Occupation* is a key factor determining the rise and composition of informal groups. There is a tendency for people performing similar jobs to group together.[27]

3. *Interests* are another determinant for informal group formation. Even though people might be in the same location, performing similar jobs, differences of interest among them explain why several small, instead of one large, informal organizations emerge.

4. *Special issues* often result in the formation of informal groups, but this determinant is set apart from the three previously mentioned. In this case, people who do not necessarily have similar interests, occupations, or locations may join together for a common cause. Once the issue is resolved, then the tendency is to revert to the more "natural" group forms.[28] Thus, special issues give rise to a rather impermanent informal association; groups based on the other three determinants tend to be more lasting.

When informal organizations come into being they assume certain characteristics. Since understanding these characteristics is important for management practice, they are noted below:

1. Informal organizations act as agencies of *social control*. They generate a culture based on certain norms of conduct which, in turn, demands conformity from group members. These standards may be at odds with the

[24] Gardner and Moore, *op. cit.*, pp. 237–243.

[25] For example: Brech, *op. cit.*, pp. 27–29; and Allen, *op. cit.*, pp. 61–62.

[26] See: Leon Festinger, Stanley Schachter, and Kurt Back, *Social Pressures in Informal Groups* (New York: Harper and Brothers, 1950), pp. 153–163.

[27] For example see: W. Fred Cottrell, *The Railroader* (Palo Alto: The Stanford University Press, 1940), Chapter 3.

[28] Except in cases where the existence of an organization is necessary for the continued maintenance of employee interest. Under these conditions the previously informal association may emerge as a formal group, such as a union.

values set by the formal organization. So an individual may very well find himself in a situation of conflicting demands.

2. The form of human interrelationships in the informal organization requires *techniques of analysis* different from those used to plot the relationships of people in a formal organization. The method used for determining the structure of the informal group is called sociometric analysis. Sociometry reveals the complex structure of interpersonal relations which is based on premises fundamentally unlike the logic of the formal organization.

3. Informal organizations have *status and communication* systems peculiar to themselves, not necessarily derived from the formal systems. For example, the grapevine is the subject of much neoclassical study.

4. Survival of the informal organization requires stable continuing relationships among the people in them. Thus, it has been observed that the informal organization *resists change.*[29] Considerable attention is given by the neoclassicists to overcoming informal resistance to change.

5. The last aspect of analysis which appears to be central to the neoclassical view of the informal organization is the study of the *informal leader.* Discussion revolves around who the informal leader is, how he assumes this role, what characteristics are peculiar to him, and how he can help the manager accomplish his objectives in the formal organization.[30]

This brief sketch of some of the major facets of informal organization theory has neglected, so far, one important topic treated by the neoclassical school. It is the way in which the formal and informal organizations interact.

A conventional way of looking at the interaction of the two is the "live and let live" point of view. Management should recognize that the informal organization exists, nothing can destroy it, and so the executive might just as well work with it. Working with the informal

organization involves not threatening its existence unnecessarily, listening to opinions expressed for the group by the leader, allowing group participation in decision-making situations, and controlling the grapevine by prompt release of accurate information.[31]

While this approach is management centered, it is not unreasonable to expect that informal group standards and norms could make themselves felt on formal organizational policy. An honestly conceived effort by managers to establish a working relationship with the informal organization could result in an association where both formal and informal views would be reciprocally modified. The danger which at all costs should be avoided is that "working with the informal organization" does not degenerate into a shallow disguise for human manipulation.

Some neoclassical writing in organization theory, especially that coming from the management-oriented segment of this school, gives the impression that the formal and informal organizations are distinct, and at times, quite irreconcilable factors in a company. The interaction which takes place between the two is something akin to the interaction between the company and a labor union, or a government agency, or another company.

The concept of the social system is another approach to the interactional climate. While this concept can be properly classified as neoclassical, it borders on the modern theories of organization. The phrase "social system" means that an organization is a complex of mutually interdependent, but variable, factors.

These factors include individuals and their attitudes and motives, jobs, the physical work setting, the formal organization, and the informal organizations. These factors, and many others, are woven into an overall pattern of interdependency. From this point of view, the formal and informal organizations lose their distinctiveness, but find real meaning, in terms of human behavior, in the operation of the system as a whole. Thus, the study of organization turns away from descriptions of its component parts, and is refocused on the system of interrelationships among the parts.

One of the major contributions of the Haw-

[29] Probably the classic study of resistance to change is: Lester Coch and John R. P. French, Jr., "Overcoming Resistance to Change," in Schuyler Dean Hoslett (editor), *Human Factors in Management* (New York: Harper and Brothers, 1951), pp. 242-268.

[30] For example see: Robert Saltonstall, *Human Relations in Administration* (New York: McGraw-Hill Book Company, 1959), pp. 330–331; and Keith Davis, *op. cit.,* pp. 99–101.

[31] For an example of this approach see: John T. Doutt, "Management Must Manage the Informal Group, Too," *Advanced Management* (May, 1959), pp. 26–28.

thorne studies was the integration of Pareto's idea of the social system into a meaningful method of analysis for the study of behavior in human organizations.[32] This concept is still vitally important. But unfortunately some work in the field of human relations undertaken by the neoclassicists has overlooked, or perhaps discounted, the significance of this consideration.[33]

The fundamental insight regarding the social system, developed and applied to the industrial scene by the Hawthorne researchers, did not find much extension in subsequent work in the neoclassical vein. Indeed, the neoclassical school after the Hawthorne studies generally seemed content to engage in descriptive generalizations, or particularized empirical research studies which did not have much meaning outside their own context.

The neoclassical school of organization theory has been called bankrupt. Criticisms range from, "human relations is a tool for cynical puppeteering of people," to "human relations is nothing more than a trifling body of empirical and descriptive information." There is a good deal of truth in both criticisms, but another appraisal of the neoclassical school of organization theory is offered here. The neoclassical approach has provided valuable contributions to lore of organization. But, like the classical theory, the neoclassical doctrine suffers from incompleteness, a shortsighted perspective, and lack of integration among the many facets of human behavior studied by it. Modern organization theory has made a move to cover the shortcomings of the current body of theoretical knowledge.

MODERN ORGANIZATION THEORY

The distinctive qualities of modern organization theory are its conceptual-analytical base, its reliance on empirical research data and, above all, its integrating nature. These qualities are framed in a philosophy which accepts the premise that the only meaningful way to study organization is to study it as a system. As Henderson put it, the study of a system must rely on a method of analysis, ". . . involving the simultaneous variations of mutually dependent variables." [34] Human systems, of course, contain a huge number of dependent variables which defy the most complex simultaneous equations to solve.

Nevertheless, system analysis has its own peculiar point of view which aims to study organization in the way Henderson suggests. It treats organization as a system of mutually dependent variables. As a result, modern organization theory, which accepts system analysis, shifts the conceptual level of organization study above the classical and neoclassical theories. Modern organization theory asks a range of interrelated questions which are not seriously considered by the two other theories.

Key among these questions are: (1) What are the strategic parts of the system? (2) What is the nature of their mutual dependency? (3) What are the main processes in the system which link the parts together, and facilitate their adjustments to each other? (4) What are the goals sought by systems? [35]

Modern organization theory is in no way a unified body of thought. Each writer and researcher has his special emphasis when he considers the system. Perhaps the most evident unifying thread in the study of systems is the effort to look at the organization in its totality. Representative books in this field are March and Simon, *Organizations*,[36] and Haire's anthology, *Modern Organization Theory*.[37]

Instead of attempting a review of different writers' contributions to modern organization theory, it will be more useful to discuss the various ingredients involved in system analysis. They are the parts, the interactions, the processes, and the goals of systems.

[32] See: Roethlisberger and Dickson, *op. cit.*, Chapter 24.

[33] A check of management human relations texts, the organization and human relations chapters of principles of management texts, and texts on conventional organization theory for management courses reveals little or no treatment of the concept of the social system.

[34] Lawrence J. Henderson, *Pareto's General Sociology* (Cambridge: Harvard University Press, 1935), p. 13.

[35] There is another question which cannot be treated in the scope of this paper. It asks, what research tools should be used for the study of the system?

[36] James G. March and Herbert A. Simon, *Organizations* (New York: John Wiley and Sons, 1958).

[37] Mason Haire (editor), *Modern Organization Theory* (New York: John Wiley and Sons, 1959).

The Parts of the System and Their Interdependency

The first basic part of the system is the *individual,* and the personality structure he brings to the organization. Elementary to an individual's personality are motives and attitudes which condition the range of expectancies he hopes to satisfy by participating in the system.

The second part of the system is the formal arrangement of functions, usually called the *formal organization.* The formal organization is the interrelated pattern of jobs which make up the structure of a system. Certain writers, like Argyris, see a fundamental conflict resulting from the demands made by the system, and the structure of the mature, normal personality. In any event, the individual has expectancies regarding the job he is to perform; and, conversely, the job makes demands on, or has expectancies relating to, the performance of the individual. Considerable attention has been given by writers in modern organization theory to incongruencies resulting from the interaction of organizational and individual demands.[38]

The third part in the organization system is the *informal organization.* Enough has been said already about the nature of this organization. But it must be noted that an interactional pattern exists between the individual and the informal group. This interactional arrangement can be conveniently discussed as the mutual modification of expectancies. The informal organization has demands which it makes on members in terms of anticipated forms of behavior, and the individual has expectancies of satisfaction he hopes to derive from association with people on the job. Both these sets of expectancies interact, resulting in the individual modifying his behavior to accord with the demands of the group, and the group, perhaps, modifying what it expects from an individual because of the impact of his personality on group norms.[39]

Much of what has been said about the various expectancy systems in an organization can also be treated using status and role concepts. Part of modern organization theory rests on research findings in social-psychology relative to reciprocal patterns of behavior stemming from role demands generated by both the formal and informal organizations, and role perceptions peculiar to the individual. Bakke's *fusion process* is largely concerned with the modification of role expectancies. The fusion process is a force, according to Bakke, which acts to weld divergent elements together for the preservation of organizational integrity.[40]

The fifth part of system analysis is the *physical setting* in which the job is performed. Although this element of the system may be implicit in what has been said already about the formal organization and its functions, it is well to separate it. In the physical surroundings of work, interactions are present in complex man-machine systems. The human "engineer" cannot approach the problems posed by such interrelationships in a purely technical, engineering fashion. As Haire says, these problems lie in the domain of the social theorist.[41] Attention must be centered on responses demanded from a logically ordered production function, often with the view of minimizing the error in the system. From this standpoint, work cannot be effectively organized unless the psychological, social, and physiological characteristics of people participating in the work environment are considered. Machines and processes should be designed to fit certain generally observed psychological and physiological properties of men, rather than hiring men to fit machines.

In summary, the parts of the system which appear to be of strategic importance are the individual, the formal structure, the informal organization, status and role patterns, and the physical environment of work. Again, these parts are woven into a configuration called the organizational system. The processes which link the parts are taken up next.

[38] See Chris Argyris, *Personality and Organization* (New York: Harper and Brothers, 1957), esp. Chapters 2, 3, 7.

[39] For a larger treatment of this subject see: George C. Homans, *The Human Group* (New York: Harcourt, Brace and Company, 1950), Chapter 5.

[40] E. Wight Bakke, "Concept of the Social Organization," in Mason Haire (editor), *Modern Organization Theory* (New York: John Wiley and Sons, 1959), pp. 60–61.

[41] Mason Haire, "Psychology and the Study of Business: Joint Behavioral Sciences," in *Social Science Research on Business: Product and Potential* (New York: Columbia University Press, 1959), pp. 53–59.

The Linking Processes

One can say, with a good deal of glibness, that all the parts mentioned above are interrelated. Although this observation is quite correct, it does not mean too much in terms of system theory unless some attempt is made to analyze the processes by which the interaction is achieved. Role theory is devoted to certain types of interactional processes. In addition, modern organization theorists point to three other linking activities which appear to be universal to human systems of organized behavior. These processes are communication, balance, and decision making.

(1) Communication is mentioned often in neoclassical theory, but the emphasis is on description of forms of communication activity, i.e., formal-informal, vertical-horizontal, line-staff. Communication, as a mechanism which links the segments of the system together, is overlooked by way of much considered analysis.

One aspect of modern organization theory is study of the communication network in the system. Communication is viewed as the method by which action is evoked from the parts of the system. Communication acts not only as stimuli resulting in action, but also as a control and coordination mechanism linking the decision centers in the system into a synchronized pattern. Deutsch points out that organizations are composed of parts which communicate with each other, receive messages from the outside world, and store information. Taken together, these communication functions of the parts comprise a configuration representing the total system.[42] More is to be said about communication later in the discussion of the cybernetic model.

(2) The concept of *balance* as a linking process involves a series of some rather complex ideas. Balance refers to an equilibrating mechanism whereby the various parts of the system are maintained in a harmoniously structured relationship to each other.

The necessity for the balance concept logically flows from the nature of systems themselves. It is impossible to conceive of an ordered relationship among the parts of a

system without also introducing the idea of a stabilizing or an adapting mechanism.

Balance appears in two varieties—quasi-automatic and innovative. Both forms of balance act to insure system integrity in face of changing conditions, either internal or external to the system. The first form of balance, quasi-automatic, refers to what some think are "homeostatic" properties of systems. That is, systems seem to exhibit built-in propensities to maintain steady states.

If human organizations are open, self-maintaining systems, then control and regulatory processes are necessary. The issue hinges on the degree to which stabilizing processes in systems, when adapting to change, are automatic. March and Simon have an interesting answer to this problem, which in part is based on the type of change and the adjustment necessary to adapt to the change. Systems have programs of action which are put into effect when a change is perceived. If the change is relatively minor, and if the change comes within the purview of established programs of action, then it might be fairly confidently predicted that the adaptation made by the system will be quasi-automatic.[43]

The role of innovative, creative balancing efforts now needs to be examined. The need for innovation arises when adaptation to a change is outside the scope of existing programs designed for the purpose of keeping the system in balance. New programs have to be evolved in order for the system to maintain internal harmony.

New programs are created by trial and error search for feasible action alternatives to cope with a given change. But innovation is subject to the limitations and possibilities inherent in the quantity and variety of information present in a system at a particular time. New combinations of alternatives for innovative purposes depend on:

1. The possible range of output of the system, or the capacity of the system to supply information.

2. The range of available information in the memory of the system.

3. The operating rules (program) governing the analysis and flow of information within the system.

4. The ability of the system to "forget" pre-

[42] Karl W. Deutsch, "On Communication Models in the Social Sciences," *Public Opinion Quarterly*, 16 (1952), pp. 356–380.

[43] March and Simon, *op. cit.*, pp. 139–140.

viously learned solutions to change problems.[44] A system with too good a memory might narrow its behavioral choices to such an extent as to stifle innovation. In simpler language, old learned programs might be used to adapt the change, when newly innovated programs are necessary.[45]

Much of what has been said about communication and balance brings to mind a cybernetic model in which both these processes have vital roles. Cybernetics has to do with feedback and control of all kinds of systems. Its purpose is to maintain system stability in the face of change. Cybernetics cannot be studied without considering communication networks, information flow, and some kind of balancing process aimed at preserving the integrity of the system.

Cybernetics directs attention to key questions regarding the system. These questions are: How are communication centers connected, and how are they maintained? Corollary to this question: what is the structure of the feedback system? Next, what information is stored in the organization, and at what points? And as a corollary: how accessible is this information to decision-making centers? Third, how conscious is the organization of the operation of its own parts? That is, to what extent do the policy centers receive control information with sufficient frequency and relevancy to create a real awareness of the operation of the segments of the system? Finally, what are the learning (innovating) capabilities of the system?[46]

Answers to the questions posed by cybernetics are crucial to understanding both the balancing and communication processes in systems.[47] Although cybernetics has been applied largely to technical-engineering problems of automation, the model of feedback, control, and regulation in all systems has a

good deal of generality. Cybernetics is a fruitful area which can be used to synthesize the processes of communication and balance.

(3) A wide spectrum of topics dealing with types of decisions in human systems makes up the core of analysis of another important process in organizations. Decision analysis is one of the major contributions of March and Simon in their book *Organizations*. The two major classes of decisions they discuss are decisions to produce and decisions to participate in the system.[48]

Decisions to produce are largely a result of an interaction between individual attitudes and the demands of the organization. Motivation analysis becomes central to studying the nature and results of the interaction. Individual decisions to participate in the organization reflect on such issues as the relationship between organizational rewards versus the demands made by the organization. Participation decisions also focus attention on the reasons why individuals remain in or leave organizations.

March and Simon treat decisions as internal variables in an organization which depend on jobs, individual expectations and motivations, and organizational structure. Marschak[49] looks on the decision process as an independent variable upon which the survival of the organization is based. In this case, the organization is viewed as having, inherent in its structure, the ability to maximize survival requisites through its established decision processes.

The Goals of Organization

Organization has three goals which may be either intermeshed or independent ends in themselves. They are growth, stability, and interaction. The last goal refers to organizations which exist primarily to provide a medium for association of its members with others. Interestingly enough these goals seem to apply to different forms of organization at varying levels of complexity, ranging from simple clockwork mechanisms to social systems.

[44] Mervyn L. Cadwallader, "The Cybernetic Analysis of Change in Complex Social Organization," *The American Journal of Sociology* (September, 1959), p. 156.

[45] It is conceivable for innovative behavior to be programmed into the system.

[46] These are questions adapted from Deutsch, *op. cit.*, 368–370.

[47] Answers to these questions would require a comprehensive volume. One of the best approaches currently available is Stafford Beer, *Cybernetics and Management* (New York: John Wiley and Sons, 1959).

[48] March and Simon, *op. cit.*, Chapters 3 and 4.

[49] Jacob Marschak, "Efficient and Viable Organizational Forms" in Mason Haire, editor, *Modern Organization Theory* (New York: John Wiley and Sons, 1959), pp. 307–320.

These similarities in organizational purposes have been observed by a number of people, and a field of thought and research called system theory has developed, dedicated to the task of discovering organizational universals. The dream of general system theory is to create a science of organizational universals, or if you will, a universal science using common organizational elements found in all systems as a starting point.

Modern organization theory is on the periphery of general system theory. Both general system theory and modern organization theory studies:

1. The parts (individuals) in aggregates, and the movement of individuals into and out of the system.
2. The interaction of individuals with the environment found in the system.
3. The interactions among individuals in the system.
4. General growth and stability problems of systems.[50]

Modern organization theory and general system theory are similar in that they look at organization as an integrated whole. They differ, however, in terms of their generality. General system theory is concerned with every level of system, whereas modern organizational theory focuses primarily on human organization.

The question might be asked, What can the science of administration gain by the study of system levels other than human? Before attempting an answer, note should be made of what these other levels are. Boulding presents a convenient method of classification:

1. The static structure—a level of framework, the anatomy of a system; for example, the structure of the universe.
2. The simple dynamic system—the level of clockworks, predetermined necessary motions.
3. The cybernetic system—the level of the thermostat. The system moves to maintain a given equilibrium through a process of self-regulation.
4. The open system—level of self-maintaining systems—moves toward and includes living organisms.

5. The genetic-societal system—level of cell society, characterized by a division of labor among cells.
6. Animal systems—level of mobility, evidence of goal-directed behavior.
7. Human systems—level of symbol interpretation and idea communication.
8. Social system—level of human organization.
9. Transcendental systems—level of ultimates and absolutes which exhibit systematic structure but are unknowable in essence.[51]

This approach to the study of systems by finding universals common at all levels of organization offers intriguing possibilities for administrative organization theory. A good deal of light could be thrown on social systems if structurally analogous elements could be found in the simpler types of systems. For example, cybernetic systems have characteristics which seem to be similar to feedback, regulation, and control phenomena in human organizations. Thus, certain facets of cybernetic models could be generalized to human organization. Considerable danger, however, lies in poorly founded analogies. Superficial similarities between simpler system forms and social systems are apparent everywhere. Instinctually based ant societies, for example, do not yield particularly instructive lessons for understanding rationally conceived human organizations. Thus, care should be taken that analogies used to bridge system levels are not mere devices for literary enrichment. For analogies to have usefulness and validity, they must exhibit inherent structural similarities or implicitly identical operational principles.[52]

Modern organization theory leads, as it has

---

[50] Kenneth E. Boulding, "General System Theory—The Skeleton of a Science," *Management Science* (April, 1956), pp. 200–202.

[51] *Ibid.*, pp. 202–205.

[52] Seidenberg, *op. cit.*, p. 136. The fruitful use of the type of analogies spoken of by Seidenberg is evident in the application of thermodynamic principles, particularly the entropy concept, to communication theory. See: Claude E. Shannon and Warren Weaver, *The Mathematical Theory of Communication* (Urbana: The University of Illinois Press, 1949). Further, the existence of a complete analogy between the operational behavior of thermodynamic systems, electrical communication systems, and biological systems has been noted by Y. S. Touloukian, *The Concept of Entropy in Communication, Living Organisms, and Thermodynamics*, Research Bulletin 130, Purdue Engineering Experiment Station.

been shown, almost inevitably into a discussion of general system theory. A science of organization universals has some strong advocates, particularly among biologists.[53] Organization theorists in administrative science cannot afford to overlook the contributions of general system theory. Indeed, modern organization concepts could offer a great deal to those working with general system theory. But the ideas dealt with in the general theory are exceedingly elusive.

Speaking of the concept of equilibrium as a unifying element in all systems, Easton says, "It (equilibrium) leaves the impression that we have a useful general theory when in fact, lacking measurability, it is a mere pretense for knowledge."[54] The inability to quantify and measure universal organization elements undermines the success of pragmatic tests to which general system theory might be put.

Organization Theory: Quo Vadis?

Most sciences have a vision of the universe to which they are applied, and administrative science is not an exception. This universe is composed of parts. One purpose of science is to synthesize the parts into an organized conception of its field of study. As a science matures, its theorems about the configuration of its universe change. The direction of change in three sciences, physics, economics, and sociology, is noted briefly for comparison with the development of an administrative view of human organization.

The first comprehensive and empirically verifiable outlook of the physical universe was presented by Newton in his *Principia*. Classical physics, founded on Newton's work, constitutes a grand scheme in which a wide range of physical phenomena could be organized and predicted. Newtonian physics may rightfully be regarded as "macro" in nature, because its system of organization was concerned largely with gross events of which the movement of celestial bodies, waves, energy

forms, and strain are examples. For years classical physics was supreme, being applied continuously to smaller and smaller classes of phenomena in the physical universe. Physicists at one time adopted the view that everything in their realm could be discovered by simply subdividing problems. Physics thus moved into the "micro" order.

But in the nineteenth century a revolution took place motivated largely because events were being noted which could not be explained adequately by the conceptual framework supplied by the classical school. The consequences of this revolution are brilliantly described by Eddington:

From the point of view of philosophy of science the conception associated with entropy must I think be ranked as the great contribution of the nineteenth century to scientific thought. It marked a reaction from the view that everything to which science need pay attention is discovered by microscopic dissection of objects. It provided an alternative standpoint in which the centre of interest is shifted from the entities reached by the customary analysis (atoms, electric potentials, etc.) to qualities possessed by the system as a whole, which cannot be split up and located—a little bit here, and a little bit there. . . .

We often think that when we have completed our study of *one* we know all about *two*, because "two" is "one and one." We forget that we have still to make a study of "and." Secondary physics is the study of "and"—that is to say, of organization.[55]

Although modern physics often deals in minute quantities and oscillations, the conception of the physicist is on the "macro" scale. He is concerned with the "and," or the organization of the world in which the events occur. These developments did not invalidate classical physics as to its usefulness for explaining a certain range of phenomena. But classical physics is no longer the undisputed law of the universe. It is a special case.

Early economic theory, and Adam Smith's *Wealth of Nations* comes to mind, examined economic problems in the macro order. The

[53] For example see: Ludwig von Bertalanffy, *Problem of Life* (London: Watts and Company, 1952).

[54] David Easton, "Limits of the Equilibrium Model in Social Research," in *Profits and Problems of Homeostatic Models in the Behavioral Sciences,* Publication 1, Chicago Behavioral Sciences (1953), p. 39.

[55] Sir Arthur Eddington, *The Nature of the Physical World* (Ann Arbor: The University of Michigan Press, 1958), pp. 103–104.

Wealth of Nations is mainly concerned with matters of national income and welfare. Later, the economics of the firm, micro-economics, dominated the theoretical scene in this science. And, finally, with Keynes' *The General Theory of Employment Interest and Money,* a systematic approach to the economic universe was reintroduced on the macro level.

The first era of the developing science of sociology was occupied by the great social "system builders." Comte, the so-called father of sociology, had a macro view of society in that his chief works are devoted to social re-organization. Comte was concerned with the interrelationships among social, political, religious, and educational institutions. As sociology progressed, the science of society compressed. Emphasis shifted from the macro approach of the pioneers to detailed, empirical study of small social units. The compression of sociological analysis was accompanied by study of social pathology or disorganization.

In general, physics, economics, and sociology appear to have two things in common. First, they offered a macro point of view as their initial systematic comprehension of their area of study. Second, as the science developed, attention fragmented into analysis of the parts of the organization, rather than attending to the system as a whole. This is the micro phase.

In physics and economics, discontent was evidenced by some scientists at the continual atomization of the universe. The reaction to the micro approach was a new theory or theories dealing with the total system, on the macro level again. This third phase of scientific development seems to be more evident in physics and economics than in sociology.

The reason for the "macro-micro-macro" order of scientific progress lies, perhaps, in the hypothesis that usually the things which strike man first are of great magnitude. The scientist attempts to discover order in the vastness. But after macro laws or models of systems are postulated, variations appear which demand analysis, not so much in terms of the entire system, but more in terms of the specific parts which make it up. Then, intense study of the microcosm may result in new general laws, replacing the old models of organization. Or, the old and the new models may stand together, each explaining a different class of phenomena. Or, the old and the

new concepts of organization may be welded to produce a single creative synthesis.

Now, what does all this have to do with the problem of organization in administrative science? Organization concepts seem to have gone through the same order of development in this field as in the three just mentioned. It is evident that the classical theory of organization, particularly as in the work of Mooney and Reiley, is concerned with the principles common to all organizations. It is a macro-organization view. The classical approach to organization, however, dealt with the gross anatomical parts and processes of the formal organization. Like classical physics, the classical theory of organization is a special case. Neither are especially well equipped to account for variation from their established framework.

Many variations in the classical administrative model result from human behavior. The only way these variations could be understood was by a microscopic examination of particularized, situational aspects of human behavior. The mission of the neoclassical school thus is "micro-analysis."

It was observed earlier, that somewhere along the line the concept of the social system, which is the key to understanding the Hawthorne studies, faded into the background. Maybe the idea is so obvious that it was lost to the view of researchers and writers in human relations. In any event, the press of research in the microcosmic universes of the informal organization, morale and productivity, leadership, participation, and the like forced the notion of the social system into limbo. Now, with the advent of modern organization theory, the social system has been resurrected.

Modern organization theory appears to be concerned with Eddington's "and." This school claims that its operational hypothesis is based on a macro point of view, that is, the study of organization as a whole. This nobility of purpose should not obscure, however, certain difficulties faced by this field as it is presently constituted. Modern organization theory raises two questions which should be explored further. First, would it not be more accurate to speak of modern organization theor*ies*? Second, just how much of modern organization theory is modern?

The first question can be answered with a

quick affirmative. Aside from the notion of the system, there are few, if any, other ideas of a unifying nature. Except for several important exceptions,[56] modern organization theorists tend to pursue their pet points of view,[57] suggesting they are part of system theory, but not troubling to show by what mystical means they arrive at this conclusion.

The irony of it all is that a field dealing with systems has, indeed, little system. Modern organization theory needs a framework, and it needs an integration of issues into a common conception of organization. Admittedly, this is a large order. But it is curious not to find serious analytical treatment of subjects like cybernetics or general system theory in Haire's *Modern Organizational Theory*, which claims to be a representative example of work in this field. Beer has ample evidence in his book *Cybernetics and Management* that cybernetics, if imaginatively approached, provides a valuable conceptual base for the study of systems.

The second question suggests an ambiguous answer. Modern organization theory is in part a product of the past; system analysis is not a new idea. Further, modern organization theory relies for supporting data on microcosmic research studies, generally drawn from the journals of the last ten years. The newness of modern organization theory, perhaps, is its effort to synthesize recent research contributions of many fields into a system theory characterized by a reoriented conception of organization.

One might ask, But what is the modern theorist reorienting? A clue is found in the almost snobbish disdain assumed by some authors of the neo-classical human relations school, and particularly, the classical school. Re-evaluation of the classical school of organization is overdue. However, this does not mean that its contributions to organization theory are irrelevant and should be overlooked in the rush to get on the "behavioral science bandwagon."

Haire announces that the papers appearing

in *Modern Organization Theory* constitute, "the ragged leading edge of a wave of theoretical development."[58] Ragged, yes; but leading, no! The papers appearing in this book do not represent a theoretical breakthrough in the concept of organization. Haire's collection is an interesting potpourri with several contributions of considerable significance. But readers should beware that they will not find vastly new insights into organizational behavior in this book, if they have kept up with the literature of the social sciences, and have dabbled to some extent in the esoteria of biological theories of growth, information theory, and mathematical model building. For those who have not maintained the pace, *Modern Organization Theory* serves the admirable purpose of bringing them up-to-date on a rather diversified number of subjects.

Some work in modern organization theory is pioneering, making its appraisal difficult and future uncertain. While the direction of this endeavor is unclear, one thing is patently true. Human behavior in organizations, and indeed, organization itself, cannot be adequately understood within the ground rules of classical and neo-classical doctrines. Appreciation of human organization requires a *creative* synthesis of massive amounts of empirical data, a high order of deductive reasoning, imaginative research studies, and a taste for individual and social values. Accomplishment of all these objectives, and the inclusion of them into a framework of the concept of the system, appears to be the goal of modern organization theory. The vitality of administrative science rests on the advances modern theorists make along this line.

Modern organization theory, 1960 style, is an amorphous aggregation of synthesizers and restaters, with a few extending leadership on the frontier. For the sake of these few, it is well to admonish that pouring old wine into new bottles may make the spirits cloudy. Unfortunately, modern organization theory has almost succeeded in achieving the status of a fad. Popularization and exploitation contributed to the disrepute into which human relations has fallen. It would be a great waste if

[56] For example: E. Wight Bakke, *op. cit.*, pp. 18–75.

[57] There is a large selection including decision theory, individual-organization interaction, motivation, vitality, stability, growth, and graph theory, to mention a few.

[58] Mason Haire, "General Issues," in Mason Haire (editor), *Modern Organization Theory* (New York: John Wiley and Sons, 1959), p. 2.

modern organization theory yields to the same fate, particularly since both modern organization theory and human relations draw from the same promising source of inspiration—system analysis.

Modern organization theory needs tools of analysis and a conceptual framework uniquely its own, but it must also allow for the incorporation of relevant contributions of many fields. It may be that the framework will come from general system theory. New areas of research such as decision theory, information theory, and cybernetics also offer reasonable expectations of analytical and conceptual tools. Modern organization theory represents a frontier of research which has great significance for management. The potential is great, because it offers the opportunity for uniting what is valuable in classical theory with the social and natural sciences into a systematic and integrated conception of human organization.

BIBLIOGRAPHY

1. Bertalanffy, L. von, "General System Theory: A New Approach to Unity of Science," *Human Biology,* December, 1951.
2. Boulding, Kenneth, *The Image,* University of Michigan Press, 1961.
3. Carasso, Max, "Total Systems," *Systems and Procedures,* November, 1959.
4. Eckman, Donald P., *Systems: Research and Design,* John Wiley and Sons, 1961.
5. Fisher, R. A., *The Design of Experiments,* Hafner Publishing Co., Inc., 1951.
6. Goode, Harry H., and Robert E. Machol, *System Engineering,* McGraw-Hill Book Co., Inc., 1957.
7. Hitch, Charles J., "An Appreciation of Systems Analysis," *Journal of the Operations Research Society of America,* November, 1955.
8. Hitch, Charles J., *On the Choice of Objectives in Systems Studies,* The RAND Corporation, P-1955, 1960.
9. Hoag, Malcolm, "What Is a System?", *Operations Research,* June, 1957.
10. Kuhn, Alfred, *The Study of Society; A Unified Approach,* Richard D. Irwin, Inc., 1963.
11. McMillan, Claude, and Richard F. Gonzalez, *Systems Analysis—A Computer Approach to Decision Models,* Richard D. Irwin, Inc., 1965.
12. March, James G., and Herbert A. Simon, *Organizations,* John Wiley and Sons, Inc., 1958.
13. Optner, Stanford L., *Systems Analysis for Business and Industrial Problem Solving,* Prentice-Hall, Inc., 1965.

Part II.   Information Technology

Space age technology has decidedly invaded the managerial field. Through the utilization of high speed computers with their seemingly unlimited capabilities for instantaneous processing of vast amounts of information, the operating manager has been substantially aided in his decision-making process. The simple increase, however, in the quantity of information generated does not necessarily lead to more informed decisions. In fact, the very redundancy of inputs, and in some cases of outputs also, has led many a manager down the primrose path of confusion. Some companies apparently operate under the erroneous assumption that the more information available to the manager, the better must be the decision reached. Even the continuous updating of information and the graphical and visual display of relevant data will not of themselves lead to better decisions. What is needed is an understanding of the type of information actually required by the decision-maker at his own particular organizational level. It should be fairly obvious that even now information must still be carefully filtered at the various organizational levels just as was the case a decade or so ago when computers were first coming into use in the business world.

While increasing amounts of information can considerably aid middle managers in making decisions, the top echelon must still rely on intuitive judgment. This is not to gainsay the value of computers as well as the newer mathematical and statistical techniques now available for processing the mountains of data pertinent to scientific decision making. Electronic computers do enable top management to focus more attention on the data but they have not rendered obsolete the time-honored managerial intuitive know-how. The reason, of course, is that the high level decisions are less susceptible to automation than those made at lower managerial levels. Often the type of information collected and analyzed by the computer is of little value to top management precisely because these decisions do not rely solely or even mainly on the fund of computer-generated information but rather are based on historical data in the budgetary sense, for example, long-range planning as to products, competition, customers, service areas, etc.

One can readily understand how the premise ("the more information the better the decision") may have come into vogue. Since the use of costly computers, which is currently the fad, must somehow be justified, there is a tendency to have them generate as much data as possible, irrespective of the utility or cost of the output. What underlies this faulty premise is the confusion of what constitutes information.

In the past, information was identified with data, facts, news, and similar phenomena. Ignoring for the present the valid distinction that can be drawn between data and information, we prefer to define information in a more meaningful way as being concerned with the use of selected data for the reduction of the amount or range of uncertainty. It is rather obvious that from this standpoint simply increasing the amount of data or facts does not of itself decrease the degree of uncertainty surrounding a decision, although in many instances it may do so.

The older distinction between data and

information does contain some useful insights which have been incorporated in the present operational definition of information. The distinction between data and information was predicated on this difference: *data* were materials to be used inferentially but had not been evaluated for their worth to a specified individual in a particular situation, whereas *information* was inferentially intended material evaluated for a particular problem, for a specified individual, at a specific time, and for the explicit purpose of achieving a definite goal. Thus what constitutes information for one individual in a specific instance may not do so for another or even for the same individual at a different time or for a different problem. Useful information for one manager may well turn out to be sheer nonsense for another. Not only is the particular organizational level important but also the intended functional area. A production manager, for example, is typically unconcerned with sales analysis by product, territory, customer, etc. while the one in charge of inventory control is little concerned with the conventional accounting reports that affect him only indirectly. To recapitulate, in the definition adopted above, information concerns *selected data*—data selected with respect to problem, user, time, place, and function (reduction of uncertainty).

The amount of information necessary for a particular individual in a decision-making situation will therefore be proportional to the amount of uncertainty initially surrounding the problem. The greater the uncertainty, the greater will be the amount of information necessary to reduce it. One can also view this topic from a probabilistic viewpoint. If the decision-maker is practically certain of which alternative he will decide upon, then this choice would have a probability close to unity while the other choices would approximate a zero probability. In many instances the assigning of some probability to particular choices or alternatives is necessary for the validity and utility of the information. For example,

in a simulation model in which one of the factors is sales, some weighting would definitely be necessary for ascertaining the changes in demand.

As a consequence, all information must be viewed as imbued with merely relative value. One must take into consideration not only the problem to be resolved, but also the potential user, time, situation, and function. Much of the so-called information utilized in management systems today enjoys a "sacred definiteness" which in reality is subject to wide ranges of both human and institutional errors. Valueless data has in many instances been accepted simply because of an emotional investment on the part of the practitioners who have traditionally treated such data in their routine operations. Understanding and caution are therefore called for if the computer is not to add to the confusion already compounded.

How information technology developed and how it can be applied in the managerial realm is the subject of the first selection. John Diebold points out that information technology was founded both on information theory with its origins in World War II and on the more recent advances in the physical sciences that made possible the electronic computer, the most widely understood symbol of this technology. The implications of this technology upon business are highlighted and the critical issues in the field articulated.

In the second selection, Daniel points out that one of the consequences of the information explosion made possible by the electronic computer is the impact upon organizational structure. After World War II changes in organizational structure in the United States were precipitated by the tremendous growth, diversification and international character of many corporations. However, the intimate linkage of information requirements with organizational structure has not always been acknowledged. Reorganization was not always followed up by a revamping of the information system. This failure may have been due to a basic misunderstanding of the nature of information required by managerial decision-makers.

The type of information necessary for managers must be related to their planning and control functions. This planning function is concerned with the setting up of realistic goals or objectives, with the formulation of alternative strategies for realizing the objectives, and with the determination of a particular choice of action from among the many alternatives possible. For this purpose, environmental information relating to population composition, labor force, transportation, price levels, and foreign trade is necessary; information concerning one's competitors in the field must be systematically gathered; necessary internal information of both quantitative and nonquantitative nature must be amassed. The control function of the manager is concerned with measuring performance, with isolating variances that develop, and with necessary replanning. Quite different in nature is the information suited for the control role of the manager.

The revolutionary impact of information technology on management is analyzed in the selection by Tuthill. As a consequence of computer science, managers are being forced to rethink their basic business goals, to restudy from the vantage point of the new technology their own managerial objectives and the gamut of their responsibilities, and to reappraise their customary operational procedures. It will be nigh impossible for them to survive by conservatively retreating into the snug precomputer age of management science or by failing to utilize to the full the vast potentialities of the new information technology that has drastically altered the life of nearly everyone.

Not only is the immense scope of the changes triggered by the exploding information technology assayed, but the many and varied social factors involved in the extremely rapid rate of these changes are also examined. The intensive and extensive aspects of the changes brought about by computerization will affect on the one hand an emancipation of the manager from the trivial, irrelevant, nonmanagerial tasks of today's executive and on the other his commitment to the scientific planning and control of timely information—the hallmark of the manager of the future.

4. THE APPLICATION OF INFORMATION TECHNOLOGY

JOHN DIEBOLD *

Since World War II, rapid advances in theory and hardware have given us a significant new technology of information processing with widespread applicability. Electronic computers are the most common manifestation of this new technology. Today, about 5,000 general-purpose computers are in use in the United States, but more than 7,000 computer systems are on order. Computers are coming into use in such fields as machine teaching, language translation, medical diagnosis, air and ground traffic control, and weather forecasting. Prototypes of newer information systems promise pattern-recognition devices and self-programming machines. The most obvious advantages of automatic data processing are not likely to be the most important long-run effects of the techniques. The most critical issues that arise out of the potentialities of automation of information processing are not yet generally recognized.

The automation of information processing is destined to have a far greater influence upon all of us than would be apparent from a superficial view of what appears to be primarily a change in office and manufacturing methods. The force behind this influence is a new technology of information. This new technology will produce profound change in all human activity wherever information, its communication, and its uses occur.

In one generation, the technology has produced a whole new family of machines, the electronic computer. That it will continue to spawn more new machine families—only a few of whose forms and purposes we can yet see—is inherent to the nature of the technology.

Information technology will produce changes in how we do our work and in what we do with our lives. It will raise many new problems—technical, economic, social. We know little today about the form the technology will assume. But we can be sure that it will raise great problems and produce great change.

The experience we have had thus far in application of the technology to business and industry can perhaps provide some indication of the fundamental problems and changes that

SOURCE: *Annals of the American Academy of Political and Social Science* (March, 1962), pp. 39–45. Reprinted by permission of The American Academy of Political and Social Science.
* President, The Diebold Group, Inc.

will be encountered. Management's experiences in the uses of the technology offer an interesting phenomenon for study. They provide the basis for some observations which may be useful in gauging the dimensions of some of the problems we will face as use of the technology develops throughout other areas of society.

INFORMATION TECHNOLOGY

It is to the technology itself that we must turn for a start in understanding the business, economic, and social consequences of the new developments it will create.

Underlying this technology is a body of theory which contains new insights into the nature of information, its communication and its use, and new insights into controls—control of objects such as machine tools and industrial processes, controls for the organization and performance of work in business and in government.

Information theory had its origins in World War II in the scientific research associated with development of radar and the military systems for using radar data in directing combat fire control. As the theory developed, it opened to us a new understanding of the nature of information. It would be difficult indeed to overstate the magnitude of change that is to take place in our lifetimes and in all human history as a result of this information revolution that has so unobtrusively taken place in the past twenty years.

Information technology is built on the twin foundations of theory and of physical advances in electronics, optics, and other related sciences. Together, they are yielding to mankind entirely new tools, new resources, and new capabilities. It is ironic, and it is disturbing, that the new tools, the components and techniques of automation, are so fascinating that they tend to obscure the basic importance of the underlying technology. We must learn to distinguish between the machines of automation and the basic technology which continues to make them possible, or we invite a dangerous imbalance in our ideas and attitudes.

The technology is developing at an accelerating rate. Consequently, many tasks which are impossible or uneconomic today become the casually accepted routine of tomorow. The technology manifests itself through a constant flow of new developments which have their beginning in theory and their end in the service of men.

Among the many striking developments of recent months are the laser, a new component resulting from studies in electronics and optics, which makes a totally new means of long-distance communications possible; molectronics, which substitutes the structure of the molecule itself for electronic circuitry; the film memory, consisting of magnetized metal dots which are capable of storing enormous quantities of data. These are representative of the continually emerging devices which make us feel, with the Swiss journalist, Robert Jungk, that "tomorrow is already here." It becomes even more difficult to disagree with him when we review some of the more practical aspects of automation that are already firmly established in American business.

THE COMPUTER FAMILY

The automation of information processing is part of a technology that is less than twenty years old. The electronic computer was its first physical manifestation, and the computer's record is impressive. Today, over 5,000 general-purpose computers, 1,200 magnetically controlled machines, and an even larger number of punched-card calculators and other small computing devices are at work in this country. They are in business offices and fac-tories, in universities and at research centers, in banks, oil refineries, department stores, engineering offices, and military installations. Nearly six hundred commercial data-processing service centers are serving clients from almost every classification of American enterprise, and new centers are opening for business at the rate of one per week. Yet, with all this current activity, United States manufacturers today have orders for over 7,000 more computer systems. In other words, more systems are on order today than have been built in the sixteen years since the first commercial computer was marketed! A dramatic illustration of the growth of computer use comes from American Telephone and Telegraph Company, which expects its 1970 revenue from long-distance communications between machines to exceed its revenue from city-to-city telephone calls placed by humans.

Information processing has many more applications than are found for it in business, however, and new uses for the computer family are under continual development. Their scope can be suggested in half a dozen brief examples of machine systems the technology will produce in the years ahead.

Networks of information-retrieval machines will soon be able to search vast stores of data automatically and print out their contents or display them on screens. The rapid and extensive literature searches thus made possible will offer expanded resources to industrial, scientific, and academic research and will enhance the role of our libraries.

Teaching machines and programed learning are altering some fundamental concepts of industrial training and public education. Machine systems can pace the individual student, can analyze his learning difficulties and mistakes as they occur, and can introduce remedial instruction as it is needed. They encourage a degree of personal participation by the student which is impossible in normal classroom work. Machine teaching is only in its infancy, but, with skillful programing, some professors have reduced university courses to one third and one quarter of the time formerly required. Significantly, machine-taught students exhibit a higher average retention level one or two years after completing their courses than has been achieved with conventional methods of instruction.

Language-translation machines can scan a printed page, translate its contents from one language to another, make an abstract of the translation and store both text and abstract in "memory" until they are called for by an information-retrieval network.

Medical research is hampered by insufficient, rough statistics and reporting procedures. Information technology will allow the accurate measurement and uniform recording of hundreds of variables—pulse, temperature, blood pressure, respiration, individual medical histories, and so on—to assist the medical research scientist and to aid the physician in diagnosis and therapy.

Traffic control of air and ground vehicles is urgently needed as airlanes, highways, and streets become congested and as ever higher speeds become possible. Information technology makes it possible to monitor traffic flow and to make calculations and decisions with lightninglike speed. Such effective control systems are being installed both in this country and in Europe.

Reliable long-range weather forecasting will become a reality as earth-circling systems of satellites, electronic communications networks, and recording machines are developed which are capable of assembling, processing, and evaluating prodigious quantities of data from the atmosphere and outer space. Weather intelligence is a first step toward weather control.

SOME SIGNIFICANT PROTOTYPES

These and other computers and computer systems are the existing hardware of information processing. The facts of their existence, their usefulness, and their influence on our daily lives are of paramount importance. Yet they only suggest the achievements that may be possible for us in the future, the future that we are overtaking so rapidly. It is again to the underlying technology that we must look if we are to discern the pattern of machine-information systems and the impact that new machine families will have in serving all mankind.

Some of these new families are already in prototype. One is the "cybertron," an electronic information-processing system that does not have to be programed, that is, it does not have to be given step-by-step instructions as we must give them to computers. The cybertron goes through a learning process much like a child. After it learns the correct responses to certain stimuli, it will give those responses automatically when confronted with the same circumstances again. The cybertron has already learned to distinguish between real and false target echoes in sonar operations for the military, and its performance compares quite favorably with that of human operators. Soon it will be set to learn to evaluate data from electrocardiograms. Another highly advanced system is the "perceptron," a pattern-recognition device that distinguishes between letters of the alphabet and that can recognize faces and other objects. The perceptron is made possible by advanced research in human processes. Its designer is not an electronics engineer but a psychologist who based his work on studies of human perception and conceptualization.

Basic research into the processes involved in learning and recognition, knowing and remembering, association and interpretation of ideas and facts and events is contributing new knowledge about information systems. A whole new breed of technologists is conducting studies into organizational behavior patterns, taking their data from human groups such as corporation and government units. They study management methods and a variety of business situations with the hope that, by simulating human thought processes, they will find the key to understanding how decision-making takes place. Neurophysiologists are attempting to simulate environmental influences and the adaptive behavior of the human metabolic system. Clinical and applied psychologists are studying human behavior, both normal and abnormal, and are investigating human perception, conceptualization, and memory processes. They are studying the problem-solving behavior of humans and of lower animals.

Scientific research into these and other areas makes substantial contributions to the automation of information processing by supplying new knowledge and new information to automation technologies. At the same time, it is the information technology itself whose capacity for collecting, sorting, analyzing, and projecting scientific data has created a resource without which the research would not be possible. The mutual support proffered by automation technology on the one hand and by the physical, behavioral, and biological sciences on the other offers great promise to mankind. Many of our horizons are still distant, but they seem more and more to be attainable.

COMPUTER APPLICATIONS

For a sound assessment of practical achievements in the automation of information processing, American business furnishes the central reference. Business experience and familiarity with automation in manufacturing processes, in accounting, in sales and inventory analysis, and in the maintenance of many financial, bookkeeping, and operational records offers substantial evidence of the problems and opportunities involved. Business applications of the technology are limited almost entirely to the computer family. Table 1 indicates the extent to which they have pervaded all segments of our business economy, including government, in a very brief span of years.

Table 1. Electronic Data-Processing Applications in the United States Economy as a Percentage of Total Data-Processing Market, 1960 *

Economic Sector	Small-Medium Systems	Large Systems
Agriculture	.4	—
Mining	.7	—
Contract Construction	1.0	—
Manufacturing	50.1	33.4
Food-Textile	11.6	2.2
Process Industry (including metals)	14.7	10.4
Machinery	12.4	9.5
Transportation	5.9	8.6
Other	5.5	2.7
Wholesale and Retail Trade	10.7	7.4
Finance, Insurance, and Real Estate	10.8	13.9
Transportation	9.0	8.4
Communication and Public Utilities	2.8	6.8
Services	2.8	5.5
Government	11.7	24.6
Federal	8.3	22.3
State and Local	3.4	2.3
Total	100.0	100.0

* Data developed by John Diebold and Associates, Incorporated.

When studying the figures in Table 1, it is important to keep in mind that hundreds of millions of dollars are invested every year in the technology itself, in the manufacture of computing equipment, in the development of program systems or "software" for putting the equipment to use, and in providing scores of computer services for business and industry. The technology of itself is an important element in our economy.

In considering the business applications of automation, a number of misconceptions and oversimplifications are usually encountered. Prominent among these is the popular idea of the advantages that automation brings to business. Generally, these fall into the following groups.

1. Economies through labor saving and reductions in work force, both in factory and office.

2. Performance of new clerical tasks.

3. New statistical and accounting procedures.

4. Construction of performance models which project the consequences of action prior to final decision making.

These are the standard considerations usually advanced today when computer use is discussed. Within a relatively few years, they will, in fact, be looked back upon as having been among the least important business consequences of information technology. While the businessman is only too glad to recognize their benefits, he will find his operations even more greatly affected by organizational changes brought about in order to make better use of the technology and, most important of all, by organizational changes that will inevitably occur as a result of applying the technology within his business.

IMMEDIATE QUESTIONS

These changes—which will have the most basic and far-reaching implications for our entire business structure and, therefore, for all of us—are not always perceived by businessmen or by students of the technology. When they consider the application and procedural problems that automation offers, they find many fronts of more apparent immediacy on which to focus. There are myriad pressing questions for the business executive to face. Among them:

1. In the face of rapid change, improvement, and almost daily advances in technology, when and how does he finally make the decision to go ahead with the purchase and installation of new equipment?

2. What is the optimum investment he can make without jeopardizing his ability to meet future needs and to make future adjustments? How much of his investment now, in facilities, equipment, software, and staff, will he be able to justify in the light of new developments three years, five years, ten years hence?

3. Are his cost standards and performance measures sufficiently developed to assure him of reasonable return on investment?

4. How is he to resolve conflicting recommendations from automation engineers, from his own management executives, from equipment manufacturers?

5. How far should be attempt to coordinate the activities of his separate divisions within a machine system? How much compatibility exists between the demands of his operating units?

These are undeniably realistic, substantive issues. But, just as the layman tends to associate business automation only with manpower problems and record-keeping functions, businessmen, industrialists, and engineers overlook or fail to be aware of the most fundamental issues of all. It is imperative that we all awaken to them, for their consequences are of crucial import not to business alone but to our entire economic and social structure.

FOUR CRITICAL ISSUES

These critical issues are almost never articulated, seldom recognized. Three of them are scarcely even acknowledged to be associated with the business consequences of automation; a fourth reveals a lack of appreciation for the true scope of information technology which must be corrected.

1. *An organized discipline of information systems in business must be developed to replace the piecemeal approach that exists now.* The systems function, when it exists at all within a business, is a collection of mixed techniques usually dealing with operations at a very low level—how many carbon copies to make, how to maintain usable cross-reference files, how to handle purchase requisitions, and the like.

Business is a complex information system, but we have yet to organize an effective approach to handling the flow of information within business. Our limitation is not attributable to the computer system, for the capability of machines has far outstripped our knowledge of how to use them to optimum advantage. What we lack is a fundamental understanding of the very business processes with which we have lived for many years. It is a truism that only when we attempt really to understand the functioning of a business system, in order to utilize most effectively our new technology, do we discover how little we know of our business operations and of ourselves.

Systems discipline will ultimately come from improved understanding of control concepts and control opportunities. It will spring, too, from a more perceptive appreciation of organization and organizational relationships, of the flow of information, and of how it should be used.

2. *In order to achieve an organized discipline of business-information systems fully to utilize automation technology, a new professional classification is called for in business and industry.* The problem of building systems control requires the most thorough consideration and analysis by management. Yet management's very first rule, that authority must be commensurate with responsibility, is disregarded at almost every computer installation I am familiar with. The responsibility for incorporating technological advances, and putting them to work, is almost universally placed at too low a level, usually in a financial department, sometimes in the engineering department. Further, this responsibility tends to be associated with just one functional leg of the business and is not accepted as a company-wide service. These factors make it extraordinarily difficult to attract and hold men of the caliber to make truly great and imaginative management use of the technology. It makes it difficult for those working in the area to accomplish the magnitude of change that can and should be accomplished.

A new position must emerge within business organization to fill this vacuum. A differentiation must be made between operating responsibilities—between the manufacturing, marketing, and planning functions. A planning function, charged with responsibility for analyzing a company's business and performing research in business information and information systems, is now beginning to become apparent at suitably high levels within some managements. It is urgent that this new function, this new profession, be recognized and developed rapidly if full use is to be made of information technology.

EDUCATION FOR MANAGERS

3. *The third basic issue is that of educating future managers in information disciplines.* The newly emerging planning functions call for versatile, skillful, highly trained information specialists and planning executives. The International Business Machines Corporation has initiated a professional Systems Institute, at graduate school level, which is attempting to piece together an organized discipline for education in information systems. Industry as a whole has not yet squarely faced the problem. Universities are more keenly aware of their responsibilities to prepare for the radical changes that will occur in professional standards. A number of special courses have been created in computers and information technology at undergraduate and graduate levels. It is essential, however, for the implications of the new technology to be given greater attention in finance courses, in production, marketing, and industrial engineering courses.

4. *The fourth great issue concerns the problem of business leadership in the social changes being created by automation.* The issue separates into two basic parts. Ironically, part of the difficulty we experience in comprehending them grows out of the fact that the consequences of one aspect have been overstated, those of the other understated.

Understatement applies to the degree of change that will occur in society as a result of automation technology. None of us should harbor any doubts that the change will be very great indeed. Technology is truly an explosive agent of social change. The first industrial revolution was a revolution not because of the new machines that were developed but because of the sweeping alterations they created in the social body. Society

was completely and irrevocably changed, and the role of business within society was completely changed. The same thing is happening again, it is happening more rapidly, and the effects of the technological revolution we are now living through will run even deeper. We must identify the issue and prepare to meet it, or social change will engulf us.

MANPOWER DISPLACEMENT

Overstatement applies to the question of manpower displacement. It is unfortunate that almost all public discussion of automation has turned on this single issue. We know little about it. Emotional reaction runs high. It gives credibility to inaccurate accounts of the human suffering that will be caused by automation.

Manpower displacement deserves much attention and study. In actual practice it is difficult, if not impossible, to determine authoritatively how much labor displacement has taken place due to automation alone. The central facts are simply that very rapid change is taking place and that we are going to have to adapt to it. It would be irresponsible for any of us to pretend that unemployment will not occur; it is even more irresponsible to assume that society is incapable of meeting such a challenge. The task is complex but deserves attention and action. The heart of the matter is that of adaptability; it can and will be resolved by education.

It is critically important that we develop a capacity and talent for leadership in this new era of technology. If we do not establish the momentum to lead society into tomorrow's world of automation, we will have no choice but to fight a retreating, defensive action that will ultimately cost us our political and economic freedoms.

We are demonstrating that we can lead in developing the physical aspects of a new technology. We must demonstrate that we can direct it for the enrichment of men's lives everywhere. In shaping the society of the future, we must never lose sight of the overriding responsibilities and outstanding opportunties that are posed to business leadership.

5. MANAGEMENT INFORMATION CRISIS

D. Ronald Daniel *

In late 1960 a large defense contractor became concerned over a major project that was slipping badly. After 15 months costs were running far above the estimate and the job was behind schedule. A top-level executive, assigned as program manager to salvage the project, found he had no way of pinpointing what parts of the system were causing the trouble, why costs were so high, and which subcontractors were not performing.

Recently an American electronics company revamped its organization structure. To compete more aggressively in international markets, management appointed "area managers" with operating responsibility—e.g., in Latin America, Western Europe, and the Far East. After nine months it was apparent that the new plan was not coming up to expectations. On checking with three newly created area managers, the company president heard each say, in effect:

- "In half of the countries in my area the political situation is in flux, and I can't anticipate what's going to happen next."
- "I'm still trying to find out whether our operating costs in Austria are reasonable."
- "I don't know where in South America we're making a profit."

A small but highly successful consumer products company recently followed the lead of its larger competitors by establishing product-manager positions. Although outstanding men were placed in the new jobs, an air of general confusion soon developed, and the product managers began to show signs of frustration. After much study it became apparent that an important cause of the trouble was that no one had determined what kind of information the

product managers would need in order to perform their new functions.

In retrospect it is obvious that these three companies were plagued by a common problem: inadequate management information. The data were inadequate, not in the sense of there not being enough, but in terms of relevancy for setting objectives, for shaping alternative strategies, for making decisions, and for measuring results against planned goals.

ASSESSING THE GAP

In each company the origin of the problem lay in the gap between a static information system and a changing organization structure. This difficulty is not new or uncommon. There is hardly a major company in the United States whose plan of organization has not been changed and rechanged since World War II. And with revised structures have come new jobs, new responsibilities, new decision-making authorities, and reshaped reporting relationships. All of these factors combine to create new demands for information—information that is usually missing in existing systems. As a result, many leading companies are suffering a major information crisis—often without fully realizing it.

Far-Reaching Trends

Some idea of the scope of this problem can be gained by reviewing the intensity of the three major causes of recent organization changes in American business:

Growth. Since 1945 the Gross National Product has risen 135%. In specific industries the growth rate has been even greater. Plastic production, for example, tripled between 1948 and 1958; electronics sales nearly quadrupled in the decade from 1950 to 1960. Many individual companies have shown even more startling growth. This growth, in turn, has fostered organizational change:

SOURCE: *Harvard Business Review* (September–October, 1961), pp. 111–121. Reprinted by permission of *Harvard Business Review*.

* McKinsey & Company, Inc.

• Divisions have been created and decentralization has been encouraged.

• Greater precision in defining line-staff relationships has been necessitated.

• Organization structures that were once adequate for $50-million businesses have proved unworkable for $500-million enterprises.

Diversification. Merger and acquisition have accounted for the growth of many large organizations. For these companies, the task of finding, evaluating, and consummating diversification deals—and assimilating newly acquired products and businesses—has required continuous organizational adjustment. Some corporations have diversified by developing new product lines to satisfy shifting market requirements; some have used other means. But always the effect has been the same: different organization structures for parts of or perhaps for the entire enterprise.

International Operations. There has been a threefold increase in the value of United States investments abroad since World War II. Major companies that once regarded foreign markets as minor sources of incremental profits, or as markets for surplus production, now look overseas for the bulk of their future profits and growth. They are setting up manufacturing and research as well as marketing organizations in foreign countries. Consequently, we are growing used to seeing a company's "export department" evolve into the "international division," and national companies grow into world-wide enterprises.[1] All this calls for extensive modifications of organization structure.

The impact of any one of the above factors alone would be sufficient to create great change in an enterprise, but consider that in many cases at least two, and sometimes all three, have been at work. It is easy to see why so many company organization structures do become unstable and how this creates a management information problem large enough to hamper some firms and nearly paralyze others.

Linking Systems and Needs

Organization structure and information requirements are inextricably linked. In order to

[1] See Gilbert H. Clee and Alfred di Scipio, "Creating a *World* Enterprise," *HBR*, November–December 1959, p. 77.

translate a statement of his duties into action, an executive must receive and use information. Information in this case is not just the accounting system and the forms and reports it produces. It includes *all* the data and intelligence —financial and nonfinancial—that are really needed to plan, operate, and control a particular enterprise. This embraces external information such as economic and political factors and data on competitive activity.

When viewed in this light, the impact of organization structure on needs for management information becomes apparent. The trouble is that in most companies it is virtually taken for granted that the information necessary for performance of a manager's duties flows naturally to the job. To a certain extent this is so. For example, internally generated information— especially accounting information—does tend to flow easily to the job or can be made to do so. Also, in companies doing business in only one industry and having a small, closely knit management group much vital interdepartmental and general information is conveyed by frequent face-to-face contact and coordination among executives. Economic and competitive information from outside is similarly transmitted, the bulk of it coming into the concern informally. Further, through trade contacts, general reading, and occasional special studies, executives toss bits of information into the common pool and draw from it as well.

The point is, however, that while such an informal system can work well for small and medium-size companies in simple and relatively static industries, it becomes inadequate when companies grow larger and especially when they spread over several industries, areas, and countries. At this point, most large companies have found that information has to be conveyed in a formal manner and less and less through direct observation.

Unfortunately, management often loses sight of the seemingly obvious and simple relationship between organization structure and information needs. Companies very seldom follow up on reorganizations with penetrating reappraisals of their information systems, and managers given new responsibilities and decision-making authority often do not receive all the information they require.

Causes of Confusion

The cornerstone for building a compact, useful management information system is the determination of each executive's information needs. This requires a clear grasp of the individual's role in the organization—his responsibilities, his authorities, and his relationships with other executives. The task is then to—

• Design a network of procedures that will process raw data in such a way as to generate the information required for management use.

• Implement such procedures in actual practice.

Such action steps, while demanding and time-consuming, have proved to be far less difficult than the creative and conceptual first step of defining information requirements. Seldom is the open approach of asking an executive what information he requires successful. For one thing, he may find it difficult to be articulate because the organization structure of his company is not clearly defined.

Further, and more important, there is a widespread tendency among operating executives to think of information exclusively in terms of their companies' accounting systems and the reports thus generated. This way of thinking can be a serious deterrent because:

1. Many conventional accounting reports cause confusion in the minds of nonfinancially trained executives. Take, for example, the profit-and-loss statement, with its arbitrary treatment of inventories, depreciation, allocated overhead expenses, and the like, or the statistical sales report, which is often a 40-page, untitled, machine-prepared tabulation of sales to individual customers. Such reports have made an indelible impression on managers' thinking, coloring their understanding and expectations of reports in general.

2. By its very nature traditional accounting fails to highlight many important aspects of business operations. Accounting systems often are designed primarily to meet SEC, Internal Revenue, and other statutory requirements— requirements that, more often than not, fail to correspond to management's information needs. Accounting describes the past in dollars, usually without discriminating between the critical and noncritical elements of a business—the elements that control competitive success in a particular industry and the elements that do not.

3. Accounting reports generally describe what has happened inside a company. Just consider what this approach omits:

• Information about the future.

• Data expressed in nonfinancial terms— e.g., share of market, productivity, quality levels, adequacy of customer service, and so on.

• Information dealing with external conditions as they might bear on a particular company's operations.

Yet all of these items are essential to the intelligent managing of a business.

PLANNING NEEDS DEFINED

The key to the development of a dynamic and usable system of management information is to move beyond the limits of classical accounting reports and to conceive of information as it relates to two vital elements of the management process—planning and control. In the pages to follow I shall focus largely on the planning aspect.

We hear more and more these days about new techniques for inventory, cost, and other types of control, but information systems for business planning still represent a relatively unexplored horizon.

Planning, as used in this article, means: setting objectives, formulating strategy, and deciding among alternative investments or courses of action. This definition can be applied to an entire company, an integrated division, or a single operating department.

As Exhibit I shows, the information required to do planning of this kind is of three basic types:

1. *Environmental information.* Describes the social, political, and economic aspects of the climate in which a business operates or may operate in the future.

2. *Competitive information.* Explains the past performance, programs, and plans of competing companies.

3. *Internal information.* Indicates a company's own strengths and weaknesses.

Now let us consider each of these categories in some detail.

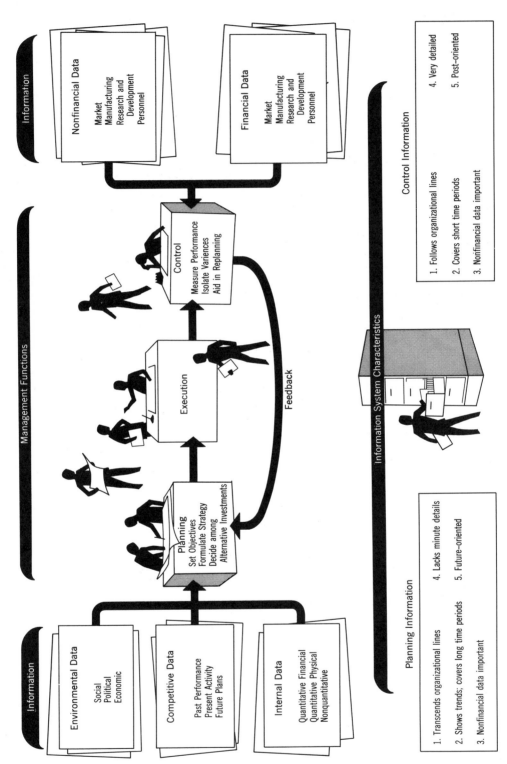

EXHIBIT I. Anatomy of Management Information.

Information

Nonfinancial Data

Market
Manufacturing
Research and
Development
Personnel

Financial Data

Market
Manufacturing
Research and
Development
Personnel

Management Functions

Control

Measure Performance
Isolate Variances
Aid in Replanning

Execution

Feedback

Planning

Set Objectives
Formulate Strategy
Decide among
Alternative Investments

Information

Environmental Data

Social
Political
Economic

Competitive Data

Past Performance
Present Activity
Future Plans

Internal Data

Quantitative Financial
Quantitative Physical
Nonquantitative

Information System Characteristics

Planning Information

1. Transcends organizational lines
2. Shows trends; covers long time periods
3. Nonfinancial data important
4. Lacks minute details
5. Future-oriented

Control Information

1. Follows organizational lines
2. Covers short time periods
3. Nonfinancial data important
4. Very detailed
5. Post-oriented

Environmental Information

The environmental data category is one of the least formalized and hence least used parts of a management information system in most companies. Specific examples of the data included in this category are:

- Population—current levels, growth trends, age distribution, geographical distribution, effect on unemployment.
- Price levels—retail, wholesale, commodities, government regulation.
- Transportation—availability, costs, competition, regulation.
- Foreign trade—balance of payments, exchange rates, convertibility.
- Labor force—skills, availability, wages, turnover, unions.

To this list a company operating internationally would add another item—systematic collection and interpretation, on a country-by-country basis, of information on political and economic conditions in the foreign areas where business is being done. Here is an example of what can be accomplished:

A well-established international corporation with a highly sophisticated management makes a three-pronged effort to get data on local political and economic conditions. (a) There is a small but highly competent and well-paid four-man staff at corporate headquarters which travels extensively and publishes, using its own observations plus a variety of other sources, a weekly commentary on world events as they relate to the company. (b) This corporation has trained all its country managers to be keen observers of their local scene and to report their interpretive comments to headquarters regularly. (c) There is a little-talked-about group of "intelligence agents" who are not on the company's official payroll but are nevertheless paid for the information they pass along.

Certainly, not every organization has to go to these ends to keep itself informed of the situation in which it operates. However, those organizations that ignore environmental data or that leave its collection to the informal devices of individual executives are inviting trouble. Those companies that are knowledgeable concerning their environment are almost always in tune with the times and ahead of their competition. To illustrate:

1. Good intelligence on the sociological changes taking place in the United States led several heavy manufacturing companies to enter the "leisure time" field with a great deal of success.

2. Insight into the possible impact of foreign labor costs on parts of the electronics industry caused some U.S. corporations to acquire their own manufacturing facilities abroad. As a result, the firms were able not only to protect their domestic markets but also to open up profitable operations overseas.

3. Knowledge of trends in age distribution in the United States added to an awareness of the rate of change of scientific learning provides ample proof for some firms of the desirability of being in the educational publishing field for the next decade.

To be of real use, environmental data must indicate trends; population figures, balance-of-payment data, or political shifts are of little significance when shown for one period because they don't help management make *analytical* interpretations.

The collection and transmission of good environmental data are often problematical. Even in the United States some kinds of information are not readily available and must be pieced together from several sources or acquired *sub rosa* from officially inaccessible sources. Transmitting environmental data, particularly political information, is so awkward that sometimes the data collector must sit down personally with those who need to know the information.

In sum, environmental data are an aspect of planning information that requires more attention and warrants formalization, especially in large geographically dispersed companies. The emergence of the corporate economics department [2] is one development that could lead to better results in this area, but it is my impression that so far the progress of these units has been uneven.

Competitive Information

Data on competition comprise the second category of planning information. There are three important types to consider:

[2] Clark S. Teitsworth, "Growing Role of the Company Economist," *HBR*, January–February 1959, p. 97; and the article by Henry B. Arthur in this issue, p. 80.

1. *Past performance*. This includes information on the profitability, return on investment, share of market, and so forth of competing companies. Such information is primarily useful in identifying one's competitors. It also is one benchmark when setting company objectives.

2. *Present activity*. This category covers new product introductions, management changes, price strategy, and so on—all current developments. Good intelligence on such matters can materially influence a company's planning; for example, it may lead to accelerating research programs, modifying advertising strategy, or switching distribution channels. The implication here is not that a company's plans should always be defensive and prompted by a competitor's moves but simply that anything important a competitor does should be recognized and factored into the planning process.

3. *Future plans*. This includes information on acquisition intentions, facility plans, and research and development efforts.

Competitive information, like environmental data, is an infrequently formalized part of a company's total information system. And so there seldom is a concerted effort to collect this kind of material, to process it, and to report it to management regularly. But some interesting exceptions to this general lack of concern exist:

Oil companies have long employed "scouts" in their land departments. These men report on acreage purchases, drilling results, and other competitive activity that may be pertinent to the future actions of their own company.

Business machine companies have "competitive equipment evaluation personnel" who continually assess the technical features of competitors' hardware.

Retail organizations employ "comparison shoppers" who appraise the prices and quality of merchandise in competitive stores.

Commercial intelligence departments are appearing more and more on corporate organization charts. An excerpt from the charter of one such group states its basic responsibility thus:

To seek out, collect, evaluate, and report information covering the past performance

and future plans of competitors in such a manner that the information will have potential utility in strategic and operational planning of the corporation. This means that in addition to reporting factual information, emphasis should be on determining the implications of such information for the corporation.

Internal Information

The third and final basic category of planning information is made up of internal data. As they relate to the total planning process, internal data are aimed at identifying a company's strengths and weaknesses—the characteristics that, when viewed in the perspective of the general business environment and in the light of competitive activity, should help management to shape its future plans. It is useful to think of internal data as being of three types:

1. *Quantitative-financial*—e.g., sales, costs, and cost behavior relative to volume changes.

2. *Quantitative-physical*—e.g., share of market, productivity, delivery performance, and manpower resources.

3. *Nonquantitative*—e.g., community standing and labor relations.

In reporting internal data, a company's information system must be discriminating and selective. It should focus on "success factors." In most industries there are usually three to six factors that determine success; these key jobs must be done exceedingly well for a company to be successful. Here are some examples from several major industries:

• In the automobile industry, styling, an efficient dealer organization, and tight control of manufacturing costs are paramount.

• In food processing, new product development, good distribution, and effective advertising are the major success factors.

• In life insurance, the development of agency management personnel, effective control of clerical personnel, and innovation in creating new types of policies spell the difference.

The companies which have achieved the greatest advances in information analysis have consistently been those which have developed systems that have (a) been selective and (b) focused on the company's strengths and weaknesses with respect to its acknowledged success factors. By doing this, the managements have generated the kind of information that is most useful in capitalizing on strengths and correcting weaknesses. To illustrate:

An oil company devised a system of regularly reporting its "finding" costs—those costs incurred in exploring for new reserves of oil divided by the number of barrels of oil found. When this ratio trended upward beyond an established point, it was a signal to the company's management to consider the acquisition of other oil companies (together with their proved reserves) as a less expensive alternative to finding oil through its own exploratory efforts.

In the minds of most executives the accounting system exists primarily to meet the company's internal data needs; yet this is often an unreasonable and unfulfilled expectation. Accounting reports rarely focus on success factors that are nonfinancial in nature. Moreover, accounting practices with respect to allocation of expenses, transfer prices, and the like, often tend to obscure rather than clarify the underlying strengths and weaknesses of a company. This inadequacy should not be surprising since the *raison d'être* of many accounting systems is not to facilitate planning but rather to ensure the fulfillment of management's responsibility to the stockholders, the government, and other groups.

TAILORING THE REQUIREMENTS

If a company is to have a comprehensive, integrated system of information to support its planning process, it will need a set of management reports that regularly covers the three basic categories of planning data—i.e., environmental, competitive, and internal. The amount of data required in each area will naturally vary from company to company and will depend on such factors as the nature of the industry, the size and operating territory of the company, and the acceptance by management of planning as an essential function. However, it is important in every case for management to *formalize* and *regularize* the collection, transmission, processing, the presentation of planning information; the data are too vital to be ignored or taken care of by occasional "special studies." It is no accident that many of the most successful companies in

this country are characterized by well-developed planning information systems.

What is gained if such an approach is taken? What difference does it make in operations? We do not need to conjecture to answer these questions; we can turn to concrete company experience. For instance, Exhibit II illustrates how the information used by the marketing department of an oil company changed as a result of a thorough study of the information needed to formulate effective plans. In this instance, the study indicated an increase in the data required by the vice president and his staff. (However, this result is not inevitable; it holds only for this particular situation. In other circumstances reviews of this kind have led to significant *cutbacks* in information.)

Several points should be noted in examining Exhibit II:

1. The information shown is not all for the *personal* use of the vice president, although much of it is generated and used in his field.

2. For simplicity, most of the information listed in the exhibit was presented to company executives in graphic form.

3. The exhibit highlights only the reports used for retail gasoline marketing; omitted are fuel oil marketing, commercial and industrial marketing, and other topics which the new reporting system also covered.

Many companies have found that the most effective approach to determining requirements for planning information, whether it be for one executive or an entire company, is to relate the three types of planning data described earlier to the steps in the planning process—i.e., setting objectives, developing strategy, and deciding among alternative investments. Thus, one asks himself questions like these:

• What political data are needed to set reasonable objectives for this company?

• What sociological and economic data about the areas in which this company operates are needed to formulate new product strategy?

• What competitive intelligence is necessary to develop share-of-market objectives?

• What internal cost information is needed to choose between alternative facility locations?

Reports Formerly Used for Planning

Reports Used After the Management Information Study

Defects

Division and District Expenses

Sales Volume by Product for Divisions and Districts

Marketing Department Profit and Loss

Capital Budgets by Division for Five Years

- No information on the total market for gasoline and other automotive products—its size, its location, its rate of growth, etc.
- No information on competitors—what they are doing, where, and how well
- Marketing "profit and loss" concept encouraged faulty planning because of arbitrary transfer prices
- No information that discloses the company's marketing strengths and weaknesses by class of trade, e.g., company-owned stations, independent dealers, distributors, etc.
- Marketing expense information misleading because of allocations of headquarters' overhead
- Inadequate data on size "mix" of stations, e.g., number and percentage of stations selling different volumes of gasoline
- Inadequate data on the sales performance of newly built or aquired stations

Environment

- 10-year industry sales by product, by marketing division, and where possible, by trading area
- 10-year car registration records by state and trading area (where possible)
- 10-year population records by trading area
- 10-year record of new road-mile construction by state and trading area (where possible)
- 5-year projection of 100 fastest growing trading areas in country—by percentage and absolute numbers
- 5-year projection of car registration by state and trading area (where possible)
- Report on federal road-building program
- 5-year report (and 5-year projection) on composition of country's automobile population by size, weight, horsepower, etc., for each division

Purpose: to provide an over-all picture of the market, its composition, its size, its location, significant trends affecting any of these factors, etc.

Competition

- 10-year share-of-market reports by product, by division, and where possible, by trading area
- Special price reports intended to show (a) competitor's price strategy and (b) areas of the country classified by the nature of price conditions—stable, volatile, strong, weak, etc.
- 5-year record of new station construction by competition, by division and trading area
- 5-year summary of new refinery, terminal, and bulk plant construction by competition
- Analysis of 100 largest and 100 fastest growing markets (trading areas) showing leading competitors in terms of volume, market share, laid-down costs, facilities, construction or acquisition activity, etc.
- Special reports on key market developments, e.g., rebrander activity, additional quantities of gasoline, multiple octane pumps, etc.

Purpose: to identify who competitors are, how well they've been doing, and the likely direction of their future efforts

Internal

- 5-year sales and realizations per gallon, by product, by division, by class of trade
- Division and district expenses per gallon (without allocations of headquarters' expenses)
- Marketing "net back" statements by product, by district, and by bulk plant (realizations less expenses)
- "Laid down" costs by product, by terminal and bulk plant
- Frequency distribution studies of gasoline sales by size of retail stations, by division and district
- Share of company's total sales by product for each state
- 5-year report of number of stations, by type (owned, leased, etc.) by division and district
- 5-year report of capital budgets by division and district (amounts authorized and spent)

Purpose: to assess the company strengths and weaknesses, thus permitting a correlation between the company's capabilities and the opportunities of the market place

EXHIBIT II. Comparative Analysis of Marketing Planning Information.

Contrast with Control

In Exhibit I I have listed the five principal characteristics of planning data compared with the characteristics of control data. Note that in all but one case (nonfinancial information) they are different. It is most important to keep these differences in mind, lest the "fuel" for the planning system be confused with the "fuel" for the control system, and vice versa. Hence, I should like to emphasize the contrasts here:

1. *Coverage.* Good planning information is not compartmentalized by functions. Indeed, it seeks to transcend the divisions that exist in a company and to provide the basis on which *integrated* plans can be made. In contrast, control information hews closely to organizational lines so that it can be used to measure performance and help in holding specific managers more accountable.

2. *Length of time.* Planning information covers fairly long periods of time—months and years rather than days and weeks—and deals with trends. Thus, although it should be regularly prepared, it is not developed as frequently as control information.

3. *Degree of detail.* Excessive detail is the quicksand of intelligent planning. Unlike control, where precision and minute care do have a place, planning (and particularly long-range planning) focuses on the major outlines of the situation ahead. In the words of two authorities, L. Eugene Root and George A. Steiner, "The further out in time the planning, the less certain one can be about the precision of numbers. As a basic principle in planning it is understood that, in the longer range, details merge into trends and patterns." [3]

4. *Orientation.* Planning information should provide insights into the future. Control information shows past results and the reasons for them.

FUTURE DEVELOPMENTS

The heightened interest of management in its information crisis is already unmistakable. Dean Stanley F. Teele of the Harvard Business School, writing on the process of change in the years ahead, states, "I think the capacity to manage knowledge will be still more important to the manager. . . . The manager will need to increase his skill in deciding what knowledge he needs." [4]

Ralph Cordiner of General Electric Company in his book, *New Frontiers for Professional Managers,* writes:

It is an immense problem to organize and communicate the information required to operate a large, decentralized organization. . . .

What is required . . . is a . . . penetrating and orderly study of the business in its entirety to discover what specific information is needed at each particular position in view of the decisions to be made there. . . . [5]

Invariably, increasing attention of leaders in education and industry precedes and prepares the way for frontal attacks on business problems. In many organizations the initial reaction to the management information problem is first evidenced by a concern over "the flood of paper work." Eventually, the problem itself is recognized—i.e., the need to define concisely the information required for intelligent planning and control of a business.

Following this awakening interest in business information problems, we are likely to see the acceleration of two developments already in view: (a) improved techniques relating to the creation and operation of total information systems, and (b) new organizational approaches to resolving information problems.

Improved Techniques

While the crisis in management information has been growing, tools that may be useful in its solution have been under development. For example, the evolution of electronic data-processing systems, the development of supporting communications networks, and the formulation of rigorous mathematical solutions to business problems have provided potentially valuable tools to help management attack its information problems. Specifically, progress on three fronts is an encouraging indication that this kind of approach will prove increasingly fruitful:

[3] "The Lockheed Aircraft Corporation Master Plan," in *Long-Range Planning for Management,* edited by David W. Ewing (New York, Harper & Brothers, 1958), p. 151.

[4] "Your Job and Mine," *The Harvard Business School Bulletin,* August 1960, p. 8.

[5] New York, McGraw-Hill Book Company, Inc., 1956, p. 102.

1. Managements of most companies are far more conversant with both the capabilities and the limitations of computer systems than they were five years ago. This growing understanding has done much to separate fact from fancy. One key result should be the increasing application of electronic data-processing concepts to the more critical, less routine problems of business.

2. Computer manufacturers and communications companies are learning the worth of their products. They show signs of recognizing that it is not hardware but an information system which is extremely valuable in helping to solve management's problems.

3. Significant improvements have been made in the techniques of harnessing computers. Advances in automatic programing and developments in creating a common business language are gratifying evidence that the gap is being narrowed between the technical potential of the hardware and management's ability to exploit it.

Organizational Moves

The development of new organizational approaches is less obvious. Earlier in this article I noted that: (a) progress in the systematic collection and reporting of information dealing with a company's environment or with its competitive situation has been slow, and (b) traditional accounting reports are often inadequate in providing the data needed for business planning. These conditions may result from a very basic cause; namely, that most organization structures do not pin down the responsibility for management information systems and tie it to specific executive positions. Controllers and other financial officers usually have been assigned responsibility for *accounting* information—but this, of course, does not meet the total need.

Nowhere has the absence of one person having specific and *total* responsibility for management information systems had a more telling effect than in defense contractor companies. In such organizations the usual information problems have been compounded by the rapid rate of technological advance and its attendant effect upon product obsolescence, and also by the requirement for "concurrency," which means that a single product or product complex is developed, tested, produced, and installed simultaneously. Under these condi-

tions, some companies have been nearly paralyzed by too much of the wrong information.

Having recognized this problem, several corporations have attacked it by creating full-time management information departments. These groups are responsible for:

1. Identifying the information needs for all levels of management for both planning and control purposes. As prerequisites to this responsibility it is necessary to (a) define the authority and duties of each manager and (b) determine the factors that really contribute to competitive success in the particular business in question.

2. Developing the necessary systems to fulfill these information needs.

3. Operating the data-processing equipment necessary to generate the information which is required.

To some extent these departments, reporting high in the corporate structure, have impinged on responsibilities traditionally assigned to the accounting organization since they are concerned with financial as well as nonfinancial information. But to me this overlapping is inevitable, particularly in companies where the financial function operates under a narrow perspective and a preoccupation with accountancy. The age of the information specialist is nearing, and its arrival is inextricably tied in with the emergence of some of the newer tools of our management sciences. This notion is not far removed from the concept of Harold J. Leavitt and Thomas L. Whisler, who foresee the evolution of information technology and the creation of a "programing elite." [6]

CONCLUSION

The day when management information departments are as common as controller's departments is still years away. But this should not rule out concerted efforts to improve a company's information system. In fact, I would expect many broad-gauged controller's organizations to assume the initiative in their companies for such programs.

To this end, the nine questions listed in Exhibit III are for the executive to ask himself as a guide to assessing the improvement potential

[6] "Management in the 1980's," *HBR*, November–December 1958, p. 41.

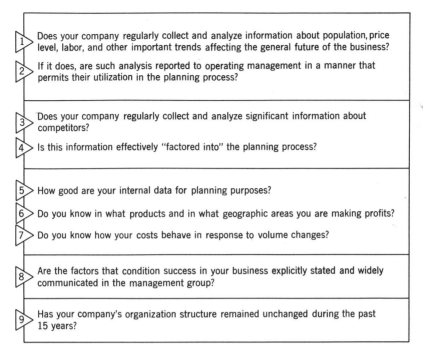

1. Does your company regularly collect and analyze information about population, price level, labor, and other important trends affecting the general future of the business?

2. If it does, are such analysis reported to operating management in a manner that permits their utilization in the planning process?

3. Does your company regularly collect and analyze significant information about competitors?

4. Is this information effectively "factored into" the planning process?

5. How good are your internal data for planning purposes?

6. Do you know in what products and in what geographic areas you are making profits?

7. Do you know how your costs behave in response to volume changes?

8. Are the factors that condition success in your business explicitly stated and widely communicated in the management group?

9. Has your company's organization structure remained unchanged during the past 15 years?

EXHIBIT III. How Good Is Your Planning Information?

in his organization's planning information. If the answers to these questions tend to be negative, the chances are strong that changes are in order.

The impact of the information crisis on the executive will be significant. To an increasing extent, a manager's effectiveness will hinge on the quality and completeness of the facts that flow to him and on his skill in using them. With technology changing at a rapid rate, with the time dimension becoming increasingly critical, and with organizations becoming larger, more diversified in product lines, and more dispersed geographically, it is inevitable that executives will rely more and more on formally presented information in managing their businesses.

What is more, some organizations are concluding that the easiest and most effective way to influence executive action is to control the flow of information into managerial positions. This notion holds that the discipline of information can be a potent factor in determining just what an executive can and cannot do

—what decisions he can make, what plans he can draw up, what corrective steps he can take.

To the extent that this is true, information systems may be increasingly used to mold and shape executive behavior. Better data handling might well become a substitute for much of the laborious shuffling and reshuffling of positions and lines of authority that now goes on. Most reorganizations seek to alter the way certain managers or groups of managers operate. But simply drawing new organization charts and rewriting job descriptions seldom ensure the implementation of new concepts and relationships. The timing, content, and format of the information provided to management, however, *can* be a strong influence in bringing about such purposeful change.

Thus, developments in management information systems will affect the executive in two ways. Not only will the new concepts influence what he is able to do, but they will to a great extent control how well he is able to do it.

6. THE THRUST OF INFORMATION
TECHNOLOGY ON MANAGEMENT

OLIVER W. TUTHILL *

Today management is confronted by the explosive development of business data systems with resultant prolific and complex problems; but they portend an era of unparalleled progress in management efficiency, in productivity gains, in over-all economic growth, and—as an end result—in the general welfare of mankind.

To survive and thrive in this competitive era, management must master and make *full* use of the new information technology. That term, as I use it, means the marriage of computer science to the communications art; and all the varied techniques of information control, storage, retrieval, and transmission which are evolving from that wedlock. Even now this relatively young science, or art, is having a profound effect on our life and times, due to developments in factory automation, in data processing and communications, and in computer design.

The most significant message for managers concerning the impact of information technology upon our society is *not* that it provides new methods for managing, but that our enterprises are undergoing vast and radical change.

CHANGE CHALLENGES

But the initiative still belongs to management. Management can adapt to this change and flourish on the new facts of business life. Our situation is something like that of the old cavalry sergeant who was demonstrating the use of a saber to new recruits:

"Can anyone tell me," he asked, "why the saber is curved from point to hilt?"

One recruit—probably an MIT grad—

SOURCE: *Financial Executive* (January, 1966), pp. 18–27. Reprinted by permission of *Financial Executive*.

* Vice President and Comptroller, Illinois Bell Telephone Co.

thoughtfully answered that he suspected the blade was curved to concentrate the striking force on a relatively small area.

To which the sergeant replied—rather colorfully—that only a raw recruit in the army would be stupid enough to try to sound intelligent.

"Remember this," he barked, "in case you're ever asked again. *The saber is curved so it will fit the scabbard!*"

And this is the essence of management's problem in adapting to the demands of modern business. Managers must fit into a scabbard that is changing shape, and they must bend or break—or design a new scabbard!

INFORMATION TECHNOLOGY TOUCHES EVERYONE

Only a handful of years have passed since computer science hammered its first crack in the structure of the business world. That crack —which began at the base of the organizational structure as firms started using computers to automate various clerical and production routines—now has spider-webbed the entire edifice.

No person, no company, no country can be either immune or aloof to the impact of information technology on human society. In America we have an edge—but no corner—on this new technology. More and more it will bring increasing competitive pressure from all parts of the world. We have no monopoly on education or technical know-how. Our major advantage lies in our diverse resources for education and research; and staying out in front demands that such leadership continue, under the stimulus of both private and public policy.

The invention of the steam engine by James Watt triggered a revolution that gave us mass production and a series of continuing social changes which have altered the life of everyone. During the two centuries since steam was first put to work, technology has developed at a tempo which permitted management to adjust—in its own good time—to slowly changing economic and social conditions as they occurred.

FASTER PACE OF PROGRESS

Information technology today—spawned by the union of computers and communications—is creating every bit as great a revolution as that started by Watt. And the tempo of change has accelerated. It is rushing headlong at management, giving precious little time to adjust. The hazards of coping with change are greater as the margin for error narrows. Management is driving a faster car today, and reaction time must shorten.

It is primarily this fantastic *rate of change* which sets current technological progress apart from the old industrial revolution and its conflict between *laissez-faire* business and the general welfare of society. Today the pressures of competition or political concern for the public interest will force laggard managers into line or into limbo if they put off learning how to grow with the changing environment. In short, a more sophisticated management is essential as the momentum of socio-economic change continues to increase.

That is why my observations will focus on what information technology means to managers. But before I wade into *that* pool, I might mention briefly some of the factors involved in the rising rate of change—in addition to information technology. All of these factors are so interrelated with the advance of scientific research that they are fundamentally managerial in nature.

FACTORS PUSHING RATE OF CHANGE

Our bulging population, with 250 million in sight for America at the end of this century, is stimulating the economy even as it tends to overload the declining market for low-skilled labor. And with the population boom comes a corresponding increase in innovation, in the quantity and level of imaginative thought being applied to the myriad problems of sprawling cities, food production, and education.

Mass education is both a factor in some of the problems posed and the ultimate solution of others. It is, in fact, the final answer to the social burden of change in the years ahead. Better education will be a requisite for almost any occupation as emphasis shifts from manual skills to the ability to absorb, organize, and interpret information. At the same time, mass education refines desires, expands markets, and, in itself, contributes to social change.

Our generally more highly educated population is mobile. It has wheels, it travels, it communicates. And it reflects changes in the social mix which urgently affect business planning. For instance:

• There is a tremendous and continuing increase in the over-all standard of living. The middle class continues to spread, as wealth is created and redistributed, with a resulting demand for more and better goods and services.

• There is a marked increase in the number of old people and young people. Because of these growing extremes in our population, products are being redesigned and new industries created.

• Suburbia, sired by the automobile, has in turn created the shopping center and the supermarket, requiring revolutionary methods of product distribution.

• The increase in leisure time has given birth to new industries and revitalized old ones. And culture follows where education and leisure lead. Today we spend more money on classical records than on baseball, our national sport. (I suspect that TV also has had a hand in this statistical rebalancing of interests!)

SOCIAL CHANGE AFFECTS BUSINESS

These changes indicate the plasticity of modern society and how extensively it is being reshaped by some of the major forces working within it. Managers must recognize and understand the influence of the same forces—and the changes they create—on the future of their businesses.

Even though we are all aware of the human impact of such social changes, it is useful to note several of the ideas about these changes which are floating in the public mind. These ideas, whether they are true or not, will have real influence on policy, because people act on belief and opinion.

Automation of factory operations is substantially reducing the number of people employed in production. The hard fact of automation is that it now requires only 9 per cent of our total population to produce all the food and manufactured goods we use. While this does not take into account all of the "backup" people involved—the white collar workers, distribution people, and retail employees—it nevertheless is a significantly small number of people *directly* engaged in farming and factory work. Some economists estimate that 20 years from now, only *two per cent* of our total population will work in direct production of food and goods.

NEED FOR RETRAINING

The decreased need for people in production jobs will have a major impact on the goals and scope of union activity—and bring increased pressure for government controls on the rate of change to automation. The fade-out of traditional job fields will stimulate pressure on business, unions, and government to re-educate and find new jobs for people displaced.

Re-education and re-employment are always considered serious problems by many influential people. Some estimate that each week 30,000 or more workers in the United States lose or change their jobs because of the advance of automation. There are other thousands who, except for automation, would have been hired for such jobs. This has been called the "silent firings." On the other side of the automation coin, we find that many thousands of new jobs—in fact, new industries—are being created by the computer. Also, automation—by permitting a reduction in the real price of products—increases demand, thus generating countless jobs in sales, distribution, and service.

The shortened work week appears to many to be a solution. In fact, we may someday find that man's central activity is related to his leisure rather than to income-producing work. In turn, this trend should further accelerate recreational and service activities as well as make a decided impact on how and where we live.

INTERNATIONAL GROWTH OF BUSINESS

World-wide corporations should accordingly grow in number and size. With necessary information readily at management fingertips, it will be possible to take the pulse of diverse and critical business activities, no matter where in the world they may be. This growth of multi-national business, coupled with the ability of computers to translate from one tongue to another, will contribute to a further breakdown in language barriers. And such widespread expansion of business activities beyond national borders should exert stronger pressure for the growth of larger political combinations.

Competition should intensify as wider use of information technology emphasizes the human differential in company capabilities. This stiffening competition is certain to bring an even greater surge in business research and development aimed at better service, improved quality, and lower costs. The intensified international nature of business competition also will impose a mandate on government to help maintain America's position through research in human and technical problem areas.

The growing emphasis on science and research, and the increasing expansion of leisure activities, imply that greatest vocational opportunity will come in professional and service areas. Specialized education—often at remarkably high levels—will be required for many important jobs, and men of truly outstanding capability will be sought after more than ever.

MANAGING IN THE MIDST OF CHANGE

That is a brief look at some of the ideas springing from information technology, as it and other factors in the spectrum of social change color our managerial outlook. Let's concentrate our attention on specific challenges which the new science throws down to us.

Back in the 1950s, with business booming, the Bell System decided to computerize high-volume repetitive clerical jobs, believing that this would provide an effective solution to the massive paperwork problem. Today, some ten years later, most routine clerical activities in the telephone business have been mechanized to some degree.

Yet it has been found that clerical jobs—not including telephone operators—have *grown* from a level of 90,000 a decade ago to about 115,000 today. Without mechanization, our clerical force requirement would be a factor severely limiting progress.

These past ten years of experience with data-processing systems have been educational for us. And I believe the lessons hold true outside the telephone business.

First—substitution of computers for clerical effort has *not* caused wholesale job displacement, although mechanization has slowed down the rate of expansion in clerical positions. Obviously, a major factor in this experience has been the healthy condition of the general economy, permitting steady growth in our business.

Second—we must develop an organized discipline of business information systems to replace the piecemeal approach that now prevails. The big benefit will come when we learn to use computers for their unique ability to give management meaningful information, when and where it is needed.

Third—the magnitude of problems posed by the introduction of sophisticated computer techniques is only now beginning to be recognized by our managers. A piecemeal approach merely involves the application of computers to automate clerical jobs, as has been done in many other businesses. For instance, the automation of billing procedures is often simply an elaboration of the way the job was done without buttons to push. This is a far cry from the provision of a complete information system.

MANAGERS ARE FLOODED WITH DATA

The information which pours onto management desks has been compared to a daily newspaper printed without headlines, capital letters, or spacing between lines and words—in effect, an incomprehensible *mess* and not a message! The vital news may be there, but it lies buried almost beyond human retrieval.

All effective action in business is based on pertinent, *timely* information. Computers, linked with networks of information retrieval devices, have almost unlimited capacity to record, store, and move information. In the future—one might even say from *now* on—the effective interplay of people, information and machines will be an important factor in determining whether management succeeds or fails, whether a business prospers or perishes.

But management—at the highest levels—has tended to be slow in coming to grips with the full implications of information technology. Despite a demonstrated willingness to buy the necessary machinery, management often seems reluctant to devote its personal interest and talent to an area where the stakes are potentially so great.

Too often management's attitude toward the new science seems like that of an amnesia victim trying to piece together his missing personality from the contents of his wallet; there's a lot of poking around and headshaking at the odd bits of information, but little recognition.

CHANGE AND THE ORGANIZATION

A natural sense of insecurity keeps us from facing up to this new and unfamiliar development. It is so fraught with significance that we instinctively try to dodge the destiny of radical change which it implies. After all, as Professor Tom Whisler at the University of Chicago has said:

"Organizations are methods which men have arrived at to maintain the *status quo.*"

And that observation elaborates the idea discussed by William McNeill, chairman of the History Department of the University of Chicago—that the fundamental nature of man has not changed very much through all the centuries. Our increasing store of knowledge usually tends to complicate and strengthen the defenses against danger which threatens the tribal compound. Maintaining the pleasant present environment can require a lot of energy!

What we really want, when we must face change, may be called *"a new idea that has stood the test of time."* And that kind is a little hard to come by! Management is always torn by opposing tensions: the "survival pull" of holding on to gains already made, and the "growth pull" of being creative and innovative in building enterprises.

CREATIVITY VERSUS CONFORMITY

If organization structure and routines are very rigid—and they can be, when management fails to readjust rapidly to changing conditions—then creative intellect in the lower echelons may be a handicap to efficient operations. When "don't question the rules" performance is demanded, a bright man will only foul it up.

How can we consciously set up an organization to produce the kind of innovation needed under the demands of drastic environmental change? How can we regroup people to make a more rational response to the new conditions of business life?

We must relinquish a certain amount of order in an organization if we want to provide a creative atmosphere, just as top-flight advertising agencies give up formality and order to stimulate their creative people.

Fortunately, successful management has had long experience in resolving the paradoxical tensions which strain any organization. The answer, of course, lies in *careful planning to meet external change by producing internal change*. In order to discipline the use of computer technology in handling information flow, top management must first of all set up a planning structure and environment to analyze company operations and objectives. Ideally, such a planning group should embody all the virtues of disciplined thoroughness and creative brilliance, with intelligent control, support, and direction coming from the top of the organization.

A HARD LOOK AT BASIC AIMS

This analyzing requirement is the greatest initial impact of computer science on business. It forces managers to rethink their basic business goals, to restudy their own aims and responsibilities. It forces original thinking, and questioning of traditional patterns of operation. Such demands on management cannot be delegated.

Automation in any phase of a business is a critical area where managers cannot shirk the job of managing. Instead of acting on this crucial fact, management can become so intimidated by the complexity of its new hardware that it allows technicians not only to operate the gadgetry, but actually to make decisions about its purpose and use!

The problem-solvers, the new professionals who are charged with the care and feeding of computers, can too easily become top management's *alter ego* in reality if management does not fulfill its planning responsibility.

MANAGERS MUST MANAGE

The basic problems of information systems are: defining objectives, markets, methods, organization, attitudes. They demand *managerial* skill, imagination, and experience—rather than that of the technical experts whose responsi-

bility it is to implement decisions, not to make them. Symphony orchestras, staffed by virtuosi, still need conductors!

Because information technology widens the horizons perceptibly for almost any company, a broad view of basic business aims will be best for the long pull. For instance, the motion picture industry proclaims that it is in the *entertainment* business. I am in the *communications* business. This is not just a matter of semantics but of basic philosophy. Economic history is littered with the wreckage of firms which took too narrow a view of their business.

Let me make a few more suggestions about management's initial planning responsibilities, prior to installation of information systems. Computers are important because they make it possible, for the first time, to organize many kinds of business operations into systems, and to control these systems far more precisely than ever before. But these new control techniques place extraordinary demands on people at all levels in an organization.

EXPANDING OPPORTUNITIES

At the bottom of the company hierarchy, people fear—and face—the risks of possible job displacement, of learning new skills, of breaking up comfortable routines.

The same is true higher up in the organization structure; and the higher the fears go, the more influence and effect people will have in resisting changes which top management has decided must be the means to long-term goals of the organization.

These changes are much more far-reaching than simply another step in the familiar routine of industrial progress. Because of this, any kind of automation program must include provision to cushion the shock of change on employees. When we disrupt routines which have become habits, people whose lives are shaped to those habits will be squeezed through a psychological wringer. This wringer can be very painful to the human beings in any organization if management fails to plan to alleviate it. The first step—and perhaps the most important—is to give employees the *full story* of what will happen to them and their jobs to the extent that it is known.

They also need to know what specialized training and retraining will be necessary. They must be encouraged to adjust to change and make a place for themselves in the new order of business life. Certainly there is no lack of opportunity. For example, capable computer programmers are now in very short supply. Some 40,000 are employed in the entire United States. It's estimated that 200,000 will be needed by 1970.

But this area of retraining involves specifics with which most managers are already familiar in automating clerical routines.

INFORMATION FOR CONTROL AND PLANNING

Intelligent planning will generally reveal two basic streams of information flowing through an organization. The first may be called *control* information, because it fulfills most of the decision-making needs of middle and lower management. It is usually historical in nature and deals with money, material, people, and their performance. Segments of this *control* information flow were among the first candidates for computer applications, but on a piece-part basis. Combining all elements in this flow into a total computer and communications system will produce either one or a series of *operating control information systems*. This provides a constant check on day-to-day results in a business.

The second information stream may be called *planning* information. This is the strategic information about critical business problems, and it flows at higher levels in the organization. It is the crucial stuff—sometimes intuitive and vague—out of which executive decisions often are carved.

Let us consider first the *operating* information system. It is the usual starting point in business data automation, and some of its effects on the organization can be severe.

MANAGEMENT BY EXCEPTION

Installation of operating information systems with feedback techniques will introduce the principle of *management by exception*—that is, directing management attention only to performance which is off-target according to established criteria. This principle is clearly stated in Exodus XVIII as proposed by Jethro to Moses, ". . . every great matter they shall bring to you but any small matter they shall decide themselves."

With exception reporting, the volume of data flowing to operating managers will be greatly reduced because on-target performance can proceed without help. This principle will thus relieve middle and lower management of much data gathering and evaluation. Computers also will take over a considerable amount of the scheduling of manpower and allocation of resources, which now requires much of operating management's time and judgment. One major result is a flattening of the decision-making process—while at the same time managers are freed to do creative work.

At Illinois Bell computer logic has been applied to scheduling and allocation problems in the area of billing. Our system uses critical path analysis to determine the best scheduling of personnel and machines for maximum efficiency on our many overlapping, repetitive monthly work operations. Critical path analysis means determining those operations which can be completed with time to spare, and those which have no slack time at all. The latter are "critical" operations, around which the rest of the job is built. Without computers, because of the tremendous number of computations required, it is not feasible to use this operations research technique. One great benefit of this system is that the manager is now freed to handle truly *managerial* problems, those which require his highest skills.

He can spend more time on the complex questions involving organization philosophy, planning, personnel evaluation, and other management areas where his human abilities are paramount. But this is not to say that he will be eager for the change.

REACTION TO CHANGE

David G. Scott, president of the Continental Assurance Company, recently expressed some very pertinent thoughts on freeing of managers from the clerical work they are often required to do:

"Much of the manager's time is now spent in comfortable routines which are basically unproductive, but since they are part of the landscape with which he has been long familiar, he will hesitate to eliminate them. To do so would be to abandon the easy part of his job. It is going to take a lot of convincing to compel acceptance of the thought that much of what the manager has been doing can be done as well by a machine. Much of the information that flows over the manager's desk reaches him only because he is expected to sort the useful items out of the mass. Many of his decisions, which seem to be the result of judgment and thought, are really automatic!"

Mr. Scott's comments point up the kind of management resistance to change which will be a phenomenon of our growing switch to modern techniques in management, and which managers must be ready to meet.

A NEED FOR REAPPRAISAL

For twenty-five years or so, companies have steadily decentralized, and the reason is clear. As they grew more complex or diversified, direct control by one man or a small headquarters group was no longer possible. Decentralization progressed as companies expanded, because the science of gathering and passing on information was not far enough advanced.

But times have most certainly changed. Now the problem is not how to *get* information to the top in a hurry, but how to keep *useless* information from hampering top management in its job. And, along with that problem, there is the question of how management is to decide on the exception information it needs to act effectively.

The result, as John Diebold states in his book, *Beyond Automation,* is that management has a capacity never known before in large organizations to centralize certain decision functions. The advances made in communications between machines as well as people now permit direct, cheap, and instant flow and feedback of information between any geographic points.

Whereas the organizational decision once fell automatically on decentralization, it now could as easily fall on centralization.

This also means that traditional concepts of departmental responsibility will change. The new technology provides ways to build information systems which transcend the need for a compartmentalized structure based on functional specializations. Organization shifts are bound to occur as businesses turn to new concepts of functional *integration* in place of the old "pigeon-hole" approach. A new breed of multi-functional managers must be found for business—whether from the ranks through retraining or from the raw as young trainees.

THE FUTURE MANAGER

Certainly emphasis will be placed upon expertise in sophisticated management techniques and on the development of professional attitudes toward the job of managing. In a sense, these "managers of the future" will be management scientists, oriented to the systems approach which deliberately *expands* a business problem until all the significant, interacting components of it can be appraised as a system. This is quite different from much of current management practice which tries to reduce a complex problem to its known critical factors, in order to get it to manageable proportions. Applying computers to management problems requires that we accumulate and program complete information on the whole spectrum of company operations where this is pertinent.

The new management scientists may tend to be less company-oriented, from a loyalty standpoint, than our present-day managers. They may reflect the attitude which a professor in the Graduate School at the University of Chicago reports observing in his students. He calls them "more skilled and more insolent." They will surely be more impersonal in their future relationship with employers, and quite probably more independent. Regardless of this attitude, a much tighter discipline in the years ahead is certain to descend on every business organization in the wake of computerization of information channels.

CRUCIAL ROLE OF PLANNING

Let me return to *planning* systems, which involve the data we need to make the more crucial, long-range decisions in our businesses.

Knowledge—provided it is timely and to the point—offers power and control. A manager can quickly suit his actions to his aims when he knows what is going on in his business almost as soon as events occur. But he must also understand—with comparable speed—what is happening in the market place in order to make really sound decisions.

Traditionally, much of the information at the top manager's disposal has been too inaccurate, incomplete and untimely for fully organized and analytical reasoning. Partly because of this, he has needed a high talent for intuitive judgment—for assaying variables and unknowns by rules of thumb, shrewd guesses, and sensitive mental antennae. Working with the computer both enables and forces him to think more explicitly and analytically.

USING THE COMPUTER CREATIVELY

The top man can now control his business and assess its environment with incomparable effectiveness, in two ways. First, he will have relevant facts as they arise; and he will get those facts promptly and abundantly enough to control the circumstances they describe while those circumstances are still developing.

But ample supply of timely facts alone will not suffice. Unless the executive understands how they are related to each other—and particularly how the relationships may be changing—he will find little value in the variety or timeliness of the information. He will know very little more than he does now about the interplay of variables.

He must therefore rely on the machine in another way. Through creative use of information processing, he can employ one or more of the management science techniques—such as critical path analysis, simulation, or game theory—to help him understand the changing relationships of business variables.

Simulation, which is the technique of imitating potential experience by hypothesizing model business situations on the computer, holds great promise for clearing away much of the uncertainty an executive faces. Many ill-defined problems can be converted into well-structured and soluble ones. The machine's unmatched capacity to compare facts lets it choose from limitless alternatives, to assess consequences and provide probable conclusions based on the logic furnished by managers beforehand.

Let me warn, however, that while use of the computer techniques may diminish the mechanical chores of decision making, it does not eliminate any of the inherent risks. It merely defines—more clearly and explicitly than ever before possible—the risks and penalties associated with each choice.

DECISION MAKING STILL TOUGH

As Gilbert Burck suggests in his book, *The Computer Age,* management *planning systems* based on information technology will make the job of the top manager at once easier and harder. He will be faced with less uncertainty

in the sense that he will know more about what is going on that affects his business. But he will have to think harder and more precisely to make good use of his knowledge. He will gain extra time to practice creative interrogation and long-range strategy, but the actual process will not be any easier than it is now. In the end, the top manager will be more analytical in his judgments, but his intuition will be more valuable than ever.

In summary, let me briefly restate some of the major effects information systems are likely to have on business organizations.

—The hierarchy of management will flatten, and much stratification will disappear. In effect, this will streamline and lighten the organization.
—A concomitant of this change is that the decision area is broadened as top management moves closer to its field operations. Managers in the field, conversely, will be much closer to the top.
—Departmental boundaries will be arranged as emphasis shifts to functional integration rather than the separation necessary under present decentralized organization.
—Discipline will be tightened as operating methods and results come under the almost instantaneous observation of top management. This makes it imperative that human as well as economic rules are applied in judging performance.
—Traditional managerial career lines will change to fit the new pattern of the organization, and managers must master new skills to succeed.
—Finally, the ability of computers to sort out options, test profit potentials, and evaluate alternate approaches means that information needed in decision making should appear *where* and *when* needed. Competition will intensify because the size and complexity of an organization will no longer be an excuse for clumsiness in getting vital information to the point of decision.

MEETING THE CHALLENGE

Management cannot neglect the implications or challenge of such change. We are moving into the midst of it, and we are—to some extent —managers of it. The Bell System has taken a step toward preparing its top managers for the challenges ahead by setting up a seminar on information technology and its effects. Each week, using the facilities of our data communications school in Cooperstown, New York, we blanket small groups of top Bell System executives with the best and most up-to-date briefing possible in five days.

I am convinced that the new awareness this kind of exposure to information technology produces is going to brighten the future of my own organization. I hope that my remarks have stimulated your own sensitivity to the new problems we all face as business managers.

BIBLIOGRAPHY

1. Burlingame, John F., "Information Technology and Decentralization," *Harvard Business Review,* November–December, 1961.
2. Churchman, C. West, Russell L. Ackoff, and E. Leonard Arnoff, *Introduction to Operations Research,* John Wiley and Sons, 1957.
3. Diebold, J., "What's Ahead in Information Technology," *Harvard Business Review,* September, 1965.
4. Evans, Marshall K., and Lou R. Hague, "Master Plan for Information Systems," *Harvard Business Review,* January–February, 1962.
5. Gallagher, James D., *Management Information Systems and the Computer,* American Management Association, Inc., 1961.
6. Green, J. C., "Information Explosion, Real or Imaginary," *Science,* May, 1964.
7. Haller, G. L., "Information Revolution," *Science Digest,* May, 1964.
8. Hattery, Lowell H., and Edward M. McCormick (eds.), *Information Retrieval Management,* American Data Processing, Inc., 1962.
9. Hockman, John, "Specification for an Integrated Management Information System," *Systems and Procedures Journal,* January–February, 1963.
10. Limberg, Herman, "Blueprint for a Management Information System," *Data Processing for Management,* March, 1964.
11. McDonough, Adrian M., and Leonard J. Garrett, *Management Systems, Working Concepts and Practices,* Richard D. Irwin, Inc., 1965.
12. Optner, Stanford L., *Systems Analysis for Business and Industrial Problem Solving,* Prentice-Hall, Inc., 1965.
13. Reitzfeld, Milton, "Effective Reports: The Poor Man's Management Information System," *Records Management Journal,* Winter, 1964.
14. Stoller, David S., and Richard L. Van Horn, *Design of a Management Information System,* The RAND Corporation, P-1362, 1958.
15. Tou, J. T., "Information Systems: Learning, Adaptation and Control; Report of Computer and Information Science Symposium," *Science,* September, 1963.
16. Wooster, H., "Post-Mortems Can Be Fun; the Cost Analysis of Information Systems," *Library Journal,* July, 1965.

Part III.   Information Technology
and the Organization

The cumulative and permanent effects of the new technology on middle management still remain to be seen. Some seers, staring steadily into their crystal balls, have already prophesied the eventual elimination of middle management as such, or, hedging a bit, they predict a significant reduction of functions to the extent that existing organizational roles will no longer be meaningful. At any rate, since more and more of the work customarily assigned to the middle management level can readily be programmed and covered by somewhat standardized procedures, the overall job structure will be noticeably altered.

Along with this change, the trend toward bigger and bigger middle management will likewise cease. At the present time middle managers are but small cogs in a gigantic bureaucratic system. Like other middle echelon specialists, they operate along rather narrow functional lines. Regardless of their qualifications, their role is segmented, specialized, and impersonal. These swollen middle layers of management, sometimes unfavorably referred to as "management by bureaucracy" or "management by bureaucratic specialists," are destined to shrink appreciably within the very near future.

Leavitt and Whisler, in the first selection, are of the opinion that centralization of management will be made easier by the new technology. The line of demarcation between top management and middle management will be more sharply drawn as time goes on and on the whole middle managers will be downgraded since more and more of their routine functions will be programmable. However, not all middle management jobs will be affected in the same way by the new technological explosion. At least two classes of middle jobs will move upwards, toward a state of deprogramedness. One of these will be the programmers, who are themselves the high priests of the new information technology. The other will be the research and development engineers whose innovative abilities will become increasingly important to top management.

As for top management, the newer and more efficient information-processing techniques will free them from the more mundane executive details so that they can extend their abilities to encompass newer and broader tasks. They will not only be more free to think but now they will be forced to do so. Since change will be the ethos of the times, we can expect a heavy turnover in top managers who quickly burn themselves out as far as innovative ideas are concerned.

With the advent of management systems departments in numerous organizations, many of the predictions of Leavitt and Whisler have already taken shape. Production problems have become increasingly routinized; simulation has proved an invaluable managerial device; tools such as PERT and similar planning and control techniques have been developed; programmers and operation researchers have been assigned important top-level roles; innovation and creativity have become increasingly vital, and the modern trend of employing more and more mathematicians has shown no signs of letting up.

To date, many companies have reorganized in an attempt to meet the changing and challenging technology of the twentieth century. One large company created a management systems department, one section of which employs 54 mathematical and programming technicians, seventeen of whom are Ph.D's.

Although some organizations have created new systems departments, not all writers concur with the view that middle management is adversely affected by the new information technology. Burlingame, in the second selection, contends that "all managers are deeply involved in problems where judgment and human values are the important elements." And, more specifically, "they are concerned with situations where the decisions cannot be anticipated, the information needs predicted, or the decision elements quantified." Far from eliminating middle management, the new technology, in Burlingame's view, will provide middle management with the tools it needs to do a better job. Instead of rendering managerial ability obsolescent, it will put a high premium on native ability for exercising initiative and for shouldering judgment responsibilities. "This effect," he believes, "should far outweigh in importance any tendency of computers to eliminate jobs where the nature of decisions is mechanical, especially when it is remembered that the growth in the complexity of business is increasing the need for effective managers."

To be realistic, both of the above positions seem valid. While information technology on the one hand has revolutionized some managerial functions, on the other hand, it has not depersonalized the functions of the middle managers. Progressive management is not so naive as to assume that all personal needs will be adequately satisfied off the job. On the contrary, if anything, organizations have increased their efforts to cater to the personal and social needs of their managers as well as those of their rank-and-file. This practice, however, is in no way at variance with the demands of the new technology. Experienced managers are still the backbone of the organization and will conceivably continue to be so in the future. Doubtlessly, managers have been upgraded; more information has been placed at their disposal to aid them in their decision-making function. But even so, a gradual and perceptible shift is taking place and a new breed of manager is emerging.

The effect of information technology on planning is discussed by James Emery in the third selection. He is of the opinion that high-level planning essentially involves a search for a satisfactory plan among available alternatives. The new information technology permits high-level planners to use more detailed and more formalized models than before to do precisely this. Several advantages accrue from this. One, the restraints imposed upon lower management in regard to planning are both more realistic and consistent and in need of less flexibility since top management now possesses more of the requisite information previously supplied by middle managers. Also, the detailed plans generated by top management are more comprehensive in scope, making it possible for them to consider more of the interactions occurring among lower-level subunits, thus reducing the disadvantages associated with fragmentation.

The effect of information technology on lower level managers is not clear-cut in any situation. On the one hand, the greater constraints imposed may seemingly tend to stifle personal initiative and to arrest sustained interest, whereas on the other hand, because these constraints, though greater, are founded on a more realistic basis, they allow for greater certainty and, strangely enough, for even greater freedom of choice since the alternatives available to lower-level managers are not merely potential but actual in the main.

In the final selection, Blumenthal examines the role of advanced business systems from a pragmatic standpoint. He is not so much interested in the computer-manager displacement aspect of the problem as in computer-manager symbiosis. Computers are definitely here to stay but so are the managers. As a result of the interaction process middle management is on the decline, not so much functionally but simply in terms of numbers. The immediate effect of the impact of the new information system on the structure is the diminution of the clerical staff and consequently of their managers. In addition, a return to centralization is fostered by the concentration at the top of the limited pool of executives and technicians capable of dealing with the new technology.

Departmentalization is also coming to an end because more and more dimensions of an organization can effectively be coordinated into one integrated data stream based on common sources of raw data. More and more of the top management positions are being filled with professionals who can wed the realities and subtleties of management planning and control to information systems.

7. MANAGEMENT IN THE 1980's

Harold J. Leavitt * and Thomas L. Whisler †

Over the last decade a new technology has begun to take hold in American business, one so new that its significance is still difficult to evaluate. While many aspects of this technology are uncertain, it seems clear that it will move into the managerial scene rapidly, with definite and far-reaching impact on managerial organization. In this article we would like to speculate about these effects, especially as they apply to medium-size and large business firms of the future.

The new technology does not yet have a single established name. We shall call it *information technology*. It is composed of several related parts. One includes techniques for processing large amounts of information rapidly, and it is epitomized by the high-speed computer. A second part centers around the application of statistical and mathematical methods to decision-making problems; it is represented by techniques like mathematical programing, and by methodologies like operations research. A third part is in the offing, though its applications have not yet emerged very clearly; it consists of the simulation of higher-order thinking through computer programs.

Information technology is likely to have its greatest impact on middle and top management. In many instances it will lead to opposite conclusions from those dictated by the currently popular philosophy of "participative" management. Broadly, our prognostications are along the following lines:

1. Information technology should move the boundary between planning and performance upward. Just as planning was taken from the

SOURCE: *Harvard Business Review* (November–December, 1958), pp. 41–48. Reprinted by permission of the *Harvard Business Review*.

* Professor of Industrial Administration and Psychology, Carnegie Institute of Technology.

† Professor of Industrial Relations, The University of Chicago.

hourly worker and given to the industrial engineer, we now expect it to be taken from a number of middle managers and given to as yet largely nonexistent specialists: "operations researchers," perhaps, or "organizational analysts." Jobs at today's middle-management level will become highly structured. Much more of the work will be programed, i.e., covered by sets of operating rules governing the day-to-day decisions that are made.

2. Correlatively, we predict that large industrial organizations will recentralize, that top managers will take on an even larger proportion of the innovating, planning, and other "creative" functions than they have now.

3. A radical reorganization of middle-management levels should occur, with *certain classes* of middle-management jobs moving downward in status and compensation (because they will require less autonomy and skill), while other classes move upward into the top-management group.

4. We suggest, too, that the line separating the top from the middle of the organization will be drawn more clearly and impenetrably than ever, much like the line drawn in the last few decades between hourly workers and first-line supervisors.

THE NEW TECHNOLOGY

Information technology has diverse roots—with contributions from such disparate groups as sociologists and electrical engineers. Working independently, people from many disciplines have been worrying about problems that have turned out to be closely related and cross-fertilizing. Cases in point are the engineers' development of servomechanisms and the related developments of general cybernetics and information theory. These ideas from the "hard" sciences all had a direct bearing on problems of processing information—in particular, the development of techniques for conceptualizing and measuring information.

Related ideas have also emerged from other disciplines. The mathematical economist came along with game theory, a means of ordering and permitting analysis of strategies and tactics in purely competitive "think-" type games. Operations research fits in here, too; OR people made use of evolving mathematical concepts, or devised their own, for solving multivariate problems without necessarily worrying about the particular context of the variables. And from social psychology ideas about communication structures in groups began to emerge, followed by ideas about thinking and general problem-solving processes.

All of these developments, and many others from even more diverse sources, have in common a concern about the systematic manipulation of information in individuals, groups, or machines. The relationships among the ideas are not yet clear, nor has the wheat been adequately separated from the chaff. It is hard to tell who started what, what preceded what, and which is method and which theory. But, characteristically, application has not, and probably will not in the future, wait on completion of basic research.

Distinctive Features

We call information technology "new" because one did not see much use of it until World War II, and it did not become clearly visible in industry until a decade later. It is new, also in that it can be differentiated from at least two earlier industrial technologies:

1. In the first two decades of this century, Frederick W. Taylor's *scientific management* constituted a new and influential technology—one that took a large part in shaping the design of industrial organizations.

2. Largely after World War II a second distinct technology, *participative management,* seriously overtook—and even partially displaced—scientific management. Notions about decentralization, morale, and human relations modified and sometimes reversed earlier applications of scientific management. Individual incentives, for example, were treated first as simple applications of Taylorism, but they have more recently been revised in the light of "participative" ideas.

The scientific and participative varieties both survived. One reason is that scientific management concentrated on the hourly worker, while participative management has generally aimed one level higher, at middle managers, so they have not conflicted. But what will happen now? The new information technology has direct implications for middle management as well as top management.

Current Picture

The inroads made by this technology are already apparent, so that our predictions are more extrapolations than derivations.[1] But the significance of the new trends has been obscured by the wave of interest in participative management and decentralization. Information technology seems now to show itself mostly in the periphery of management. Its applications appear to be independent of central organizational issues like communication and creativity. We have tended until now to use little pieces of the new technology to generate information, or to lay down limits for subtasks that can then be used within the old structural framework.

Some of this sparing use of information technology may be due to the fact that those of us with a large commitment to participative management have cause to resist the central implications of the new techniques. But the implications are becoming harder to deny. Many business decisions once made judgmentally now can be made better by following some simple routines devised by a staff man whose company experience is slight, whose position on the organization chart is still unclear, and whose skill (if any) in human relations was picked up on the playground. For example:

We have heard recently of an electric utility which is considering a move to take away from generating-station managers virtually all responsibility for deciding when to use standby generating capacity. A typical decision facing such managers develops on hot summer afternoons. In anticipation of heavy home air-conditioning demand at the close of working hours, the manager may put on extra capacity in late afternoon. This results in additional costs, such as overtime premiums. In this

[1] Two examples of current developments are discussed in "Putting Arma Back on Its Feet," *Business Week,* February 1, 1958, p. 84; and "Two-Way Overhaul Rebuilds Raytheon," *Business Week,* February 22, 1958, p. 91.

particular geographical area, rapidly moving cold fronts are frequent. Should such a front arrive after the commitment to added capacity is made, losses are substantial. If the front fails to arrive and capacity has not been added, power must be purchased from an adjacent system at penalty rates—again resulting in losses.

Such decisions may soon be made centrally by individuals whose technical skills are in mathematics and computer programing, with absolutely no experience in generating stations.

Rapid Spread

We believe that information technology will spread rapidly. One important reason for expecting fast changes in current practices is that information technology will make centralization much easier. By permitting more information to be organized more simply and processed more rapidly it will, in effect, extend the thinking range of individuals. It will allow the top level of management intelligently to categorize, digest, and act on a wider range of problems. Moreover, by quantifying more information it will extend top management's control over the decision processes of subordinates.

If centralization becomes easier to implement, managers will probably revert to it. Decentralization has, after all, been largely negatively motivated. Top managers have backed into it because they have been unable to keep up with size and technology. They could not design and maintain the huge and complex communication systems that their large, centralized organizations needed. Information technology should make recentralization possible. It may also obviate other major reasons for decentralization. For example, speed and flexibility will be possible despite large size, and top executives will be less dependent on subordinates because there will be fewer "experience" and "judgment" areas in which the junior men have more working knowledge. In addition, more efficient information-processing techniques can be expected to shorten radically the feedback loop that tests the accuracy of original observations and decisions.

Some of the psychological reasons for decentralization may remain as compelling as ever. For instance, decentralized organizations probably provide a good training ground for

the top manager. They make better use of the whole man; they encourage more active co-operation. But though interest in these advantages should be very great indeed, it will be counterbalanced by interest in the possibilities of effective top-management control over the work done by the middle echelons. Here an analogy to Taylorism seems appropriate:

In perspective, and discounting the countertrends instigated by participative management, the upshot of Taylorism seems to have been the separating of the hourly worker from the rest of the organization, and the acceptance by both management and the worker of the idea that the worker need not plan and create. Whether it is psychologically or socially justifiable or not, his creativity and ingenuity are left largely to be acted out off the job in his home or his community. One reason, then, that we expect top acceptance of information technology is its implicit promise to allow the top to control the middle just as Taylorism allowed the middle to control the bottom.

There are other reasons for expecting fast changes. Information technology promises to allow fewer people to do more work. The more it can reduce the number of middle managers, the more top managers will be willing to try it.

We have not yet mentioned what may well be the most compelling reason of all: the pressure on management to cope with increasingly complicated engineering, logistics, and marketing problems. The temporal distance between the discovery of new knowledge and its practical application has been shrinking rapidly, perhaps at a geometric rate. The pressure to reorganize in order to deal with the complicating, speeding world should become very great in the next decade. Improvisations and "adjustments" within present organizational frameworks are likely to prove quite inadequate; radical rethinking of organizational ideas is to be expected.

Revolutionary Effects

Speculating a little more, one can imagine some radical effects of an accelerating development of information technology—effects warranting the adjective "revolutionary."

Within the organization, for example, many middle-management jobs may change in a manner reminiscent of (but faster than) the transition from shoemaker to stitcher, from old-time craftsman to today's hourly worker. As we have drawn an organizational class line between the hourly worker and the foreman, we may expect a new line to be drawn heavily, though jaggedly, between "top management" and "middle management," with some vice presidents and many ambitious suburban junior executives falling on the lower side.

In one respect, the picture we might paint for the 1980's bears a strong resemblance to the organizations of certain other societies— e.g., to the family-dominated organizations of Italy and other parts of Europe, and even to a small number of such firms in our own country. There will be many fewer middle managers, and most of those who remain are likely to be routine technicians rather than thinkers. This similarity will be superficial, of course, for the changes we forecast here will be generated from quite different origins.

What organizational and social problems are likely to come up as by-products of such changes? One can imagine major psychological problems arising from the depersonalization of relationships within management and the greater distance between people at different levels. Major resistances should be expected in the process of converting relatively autonomous and unprogramed middle-management jobs to highly routinized programs.

These problems may be of the same order as some of those that were influential in the development of American unions and in focusing middle management's interest on techniques for overcoming the hourly workers' resistance to change. This time it will be the top executive who is directly concerned, and the problems of resistance to change will occur among those middle managers who are programed out of their autonomy, perhaps out of their current status in the company, and possibly even out of their jobs.

On a broader social scale one can conceive of large problems outside the firm, that affect many institutions ancillary to industry. Thus:

- What about education for management? How do we educate people for routinized middle-management jobs, especially if the path from those jobs up to top management gets much rockier?
- To what extent do business schools stop training specialists and start training generalists to move directly into top management?
- To what extent do schools start training new kinds of specialists?
- What happens to the traditional apprentice system of training within managerial ranks?
- What will happen to American class structure? Do we end up with a new kind of managerial elite? Will technical knowledge be the major criterion for membership?
- Will technical knowledge become obsolete so fast that managers themselves will become obsolete within the time span of their industrial careers?

MIDDLE-MANAGEMENT CHANGES

Some jobs in industrial organizations are more programed than others. The job that has been subjected to micromotion analysis, for instance, has been highly programed; rules about what is to be done, in what order, and by what processes, are all specified.

Characteristically, the jobs of today's hourly workers tend to be highly programed—an effect of Taylorism. Conversely, the jobs shown at the tops of organization charts are often largely unprogramed. They are "think" jobs— hard to define and describe operationally. Jobs that appear in the big middle area of the organization chart tend to be programed in part, with some specific rules to be followed, but with varying amounts of room for judgment and autonomy.[2] One major effect of information technology is likely to be intensive programing of many jobs now held by middle managers and the concomitant "deprograming" of others.

As organizations have proliferated in size and specialization, the problem of control and integration of supervisory and staff levels has become increasingly worrisome. The best answer until now has been participative management. But information technology promises better answers. It promises to eliminate the risk of less than adequate decisions arising from garbled communications, from misconceptions of goals, and from unsatisfactory measurement of partial contributions on the part of dozens of line and staff specialists.

Good illustrations of this programing process are not common in middle management, but they do exist, mostly on the production side

[2] See Robert N. McMurry, "The Case for Benevolent Autocracy," *HBR*, January–February 1958, p. 82.

of the business. For example, the programmers have had some successes in displacing the judgment and experience of production schedulers (although the scheduler is still likely to be there to act out the routines) and in displacing the weekly scheduling meetings of production, sales, and supply people. Programs are also being worked out in increasing numbers to yield decisions about product mixes, warehousing, capital budgeting, and so forth.[3]

Predicting the Impact

We have noted that not all middle-management jobs will be affected alike by the new technology. What kinds of jobs will become more routinized, and what kinds less? What factors will make the difference?

The impact of change is likely to be determined by three criteria:

1. *Ease of measurement*—It is easier, at this stage, to apply the new techniques to jobs in and around production than in, say, labor relations, one reason being that quantitative measurement is easier in the former realms.

2. *Economic pressure*—Jobs that call for big money decisions will tend to get earlier investments in exploratory programing than others.

3. *The acceptability of programing by the present jobholder*—For some classes of jobs and of people, the advent of impersonal rules may offer protection or relief from frustration. We recently heard, for example, of efforts to program a maintenance foreman's decisions by providing rules for allocating priorities in maintenance and emergency repairs. The foreman supported this fully. He was a harried and much blamed man, and programing promised relief.

Such factors should accelerate the use of programing in certain areas. So should the great interest and activity in the new techniques now apparent in academic and research settings. New journals are appearing, and new societies are springing up, like the Operations Research Society of America (established in 1946), and the Institute of Management Sciences (established in 1954), both of which publish journals.

The number of mathematicians and eco-nomic analysts who are being taken into industry is impressive, as is the development within industry, often on the personal staffs of top management, of individuals or groups with new labels like "operations researchers," "organization analysts," or simply "special assistants for planning." These new people are a cue to the emergence of information technology. Just as programing the operations of hourly workers created the industrial engineer, so should information technology, as planning is withdrawn from middle levels, create new planners with new names at the top level.

So much for work becoming more routinized. At least two classes of middle jobs should move *upward* toward *de*programedness:

1. The programmers themselves, the new information engineers, should move up. They should appear increasingly in staff roles close to the top.

2. We would also expect jobs in research and development to go in that direction, for innovation and creativity will become increasingly important to top management as the rate of obsolescence of things and of information increases. Application of new techniques to scanning and analyzing the business environment is bound to increase the range and number of possibilities for profitable production. Competition between firms should center more and more around their capacities to innovate.

Thus, in effect, we think that the horizontal slice of the current organization chart that we call middle management will break in two, with the larger portion shrinking and sinking into a more highly programed state and the smaller portion proliferating and rising to a level where more creative thinking is needed. There seem to be signs that such a split is already occurring. The growth of literature on the organization of research activities in industry is one indication.[4] Many social scientists and industrial research managers, as well as some general managers, are worrying more and more about problems of creativity and

---

[3] See the journals, *Operations Research* and *Management Science*.

[4] Much of the work in this area is still unpublished. However, for some examples, see Herbert A. Shepard, "Superiors and Subordinates in Research," *Journal of Business of the University of Chicago*, October 1956, p. 261; and also Donald C. Pelz, "Some Social Factors Related to Performance in a Research Organization," *Administrative Science Quarterly*, December 1956, p. 310.

authority in industrial research organizations. Even some highly conservative company presidents have been forced to break time-honored policies (such as the one relating salary and status to organizational rank) in dealing with their researchers.

Individual Problems

As the programing idea grows, some old human relations problems may be redefined. Redefinition will not necessarily solve the problems, but it may obviate some and give new priorities to others.

Thus, the issue of morale versus productivity that now worries us may pale as programing moves in. The morale of programed personnel may be of less central concern because less (or at least a different sort of) productivity will be demanded of them. The execution of controllable routine acts does not require great enthusiasm by the actors.

Another current issue may also take a new form: the debate about the social advantages or disadvantages of "conformity." The stereotype of the conforming junior executive, more interested in being well liked than in working, should become far less significant in a highly depersonalized, highly programed, and more machine-like middle-management world. Of course, the pressures to conform will in one sense become more intense, for the individual will be required to stay within the limits of the routines that are set for him. But the constant behavioral pressure to be a "good guy," to get along, will have less reason for existence.

As for individualism, our suspicion is that the average middle manager will have to satisfy his personal needs and aspirations off the job, largely as we have forced the hourly worker to do. In this case, the Park Forest of the future may be an even more interesting phenomenon than it is now.

CHANGES AT THE TOP

If the new technology tends to split middle management—thin it, simplify it, program it, and separate a large part of it more rigorously from the top—what compensatory changes might one expect within the top group?

This is a much harder question to answer. We can guess that the top will focus even more intensively on "horizon" problems, on problems of innovation and change. We can

forecast, too, that in dealing with such problems the top will continue for a while to fly by the seat of its pants, that it will remain largely unprogramed.

But even this is quite uncertain. Current research on the machine simulation of higher mental processes suggests that we will be able to program much of the top job before too many decades have passed. There is good authority for the prediction that within ten years a digital computer will be the world's chess champion, and that another will discover and prove an important new mathematical theorem; and that in the somewhat more distant future "the way is open to deal scientifically with ill-structured problems—to make the computer coextensive with the human mind." [5]

Meanwhile, we expect top management to become more abstract, more search-and-research-oriented and correspondingly less directly involved in the making of routine decisions. Allen Newell recently suggested to one of the authors that the wave of top-management game playing may be one manifestation of such change. Top management of the 1980's may indeed spend a good deal of money and time playing games, trying to simulate its own behavior in hypothetical future environments.

Room for Innovators

As the work of the middle manager is programed, the top manager should be freed more than ever from internal detail. But the top will not only be released to think; it will be *forced* to think. We doubt that many large companies in the 1980's will be able to survive for even a decade without major changes in products, methods, or internal organization. The rate of obsolescence and the atmosphere of continuous change which now characterize industries like chemicals and pharmaceuticals should spread rapidly to other industries, pressuring them toward rapid technical and organizational change.

These ideas lead one to expect that researchers, or people like researchers, will sit closer to the top floor of American companies in larger numbers; and that highly creative people will

[5] See Herbert A. Simon and Allen Newell, "Heuristic Problem Solving: The Next Advance in Operations Research," *Operations Research,* January–February, 1958, p. 9.

be more sought after and more highly valued than at present. But since researchers may be as interested in technical problems and professional affiliations as in progress up the organizational ladder, we might expect more impersonal, problem-oriented behavior at the top, with less emphasis on loyalty to the firm and more on relatively rational concern with solving difficult problems.

Again, top staff people may follow their problems from firm to firm much more closely than they do now, so that ideas about executive turnover and compensation may change along with ideas about tying people down with pension plans. Higher turnover at this level may prove advantageous to companies, for innovators can burn out fast. We may see more brain picking of the kind which is now supposedly characteristic of Madison Avenue. At this creating and innovating level, all the current work on organization and communication in research groups may find its payoff.

Besides innovators and creators, new top-management bodies will need programmers who will focus on the internal organization itself. These will be the operations researchers, mathematical programmers, computer experts, and the like. It is not clear where these kinds of people are being located on organization charts today, but our guess is that the programmer will find a place close to the top. He will probably remain relatively free to innovate and to carry out his own applied research on what and how to program (although he may eventually settle into using some stable repertory of techniques as has the industrial engineer).

Innovators and programmers will need to be supplemented by "committors." Committors are people who take on the role of approving or vetoing decisions. They will commit the organization's resources to a particular course of action—the course chosen from some alternatives provided by innovators and programmers. The current notion that managers ought to be "coordinators" should flower in the 1980's, but at the top rather than the middle; and the people to be coordinated will be top staff groups.

Tight Little Oligarchy

We surmise that the "groupthink" which is frightening some people today will be a commonplace in top management of the future. For while the innovators and the programmers may maintain or even increase their autonomy, and while the committor may be more independent than ever of lower-line levels, the interdependence of the top-staff oligarchy should increase with the increasing complexity of their tasks. The committor may be forced increasingly to have the top men operate as a committee, which would mean that the precise individual locus of decision may become even more obscure than it is today. The small-group psychologists, the researchers on creativity, the clinicians—all should find a surfeit of work at that level.

Our references to a small oligarchy at the top may be misleading. There is no reason to believe that the absolute numbers of creative research people or programmers will shrink; if anything, the reverse will be true. It is the *head men* in these areas who will probably operate as a little oligarchy, with subgroups and sub-subgroups of researchers and programmers reporting to them. But the optimal structural shape of these unprogramed groups will not necessarily be pyramidal. It is more likely to be shifting and somewhat amorphous, while the operating, programed portions of the structure ought to be more clearly pyramidal than ever.

The organization chart of the future may look something like a football balanced upon the point of a church bell. Within the football (the top staff organization), problems of coordination, individual autonomy, group decision making, and so on should arise more intensely than ever. We expect they will be dealt with quite independently of the bell portion of the company, with distinctly different methods of remuneration, control, and communication.

CHANGES IN PRACTICES

With the emergence of information technology, radical changes in certain administrative practices may also be expected. Without attempting to present the logic for the statements, we list a few changes that we foresee:

With the organization of management into corps (supervisors, programmers, creators, committors), multiple entry points into the organization will become increasingly common.

Multiple sources of potential managers will develop, with training institutions outside the firm specializing along the lines of the new organizational structure.

Apprenticeship as a basis for training managers will be used less and less since movement up through the line will become increasingly unlikely.

Top-management training will be taken over increasingly by universities, with on-the-job training done through jobs like that of assistant to a senior executive.

Appraisal of higher management performance will be handled through some devices little used at present, such as evaluation by peers.

Appraisal of the new middle managers will become much more precise than present rating techniques make possible, with the development of new methods attaching specific values to input-output parameters.

Individual compensation for top staff groups will be more strongly influenced by market forces than ever before, given the increased mobility of all kinds of managers.

With the new organizational structure new kinds of compensation practices—such as team bonuses—will appear.

Immediate Measures

If the probability seems high that some of our predictions are correct, what can businessmen do to prepare for them? A number of steps are inexpensive and relatively easy. Managers can, for example, explore these areas:

1. They can locate and work up closer liaison with appropriate research organizations, academic and otherwise, just as many companies have profited from similar relationships in connection with the physical sciences.

2. They can re-examine their own organizations for lost information technologists. Many companies undoubtedly have such people, but not all of the top executives seem to know it.

3. They can make an early study and reassessment of some of the organizationally fuzzy groups in their own companies. Operations research departments, departments of organization, statistical analysis sections, perhaps even personnel departments, and other "odd-ball" staff groups often contain people whose knowledge and ideas in this realm have not been recognized. Such people provide a potential nucleus for serious major efforts to plan for the inroads of information technology.

Perhaps the biggest step managers need to take is an internal, psychological one. In view of the fact that information technology will challenge many long-established practices and doctrines, we will need to rethink some of the attitudes and values which we have taken for granted. In particular, we may have to reappraise our traditional notions about the worth of the individual as opposed to the organization, and about the mobility rights of young men on the make. This kind of inquiry may be painfully difficult, but will be increasingly necessary.

8. INFORMATION TECHNOLOGY AND DECENTRALIZATION

JOHN F. BURLINGAME *

Are the middle manager and the decentralized organization doomed to extinction as the result of advances in information technology—or destined to take an even greater role in business?

What kinds of management problems are most likely to lend themselves to solution by the new data-handling techniques?

In what ways can data technology be used to simplify business complexities and distribute decision-making responsibility more widely?

What must the manager do to ensure that the new techniques are used to further the ends of the company and society?

Recent progress in information technology has been so rapid that various observers have predicted the elimination of middle managers and the reversal of the trend of the last decade toward decentralization in business. Computers and the associated technologies, the argument runs, will make better decisions of the type now made by middle managers and will make them faster. Companies will find it possible to process and structure relevant information in such a comprehensive fashion and so quickly that decentralized responsibilities will be withdrawn and noncomputer decision making limited to a top-level elite in the organization. Apparently the manager's work in the future will be depersonalized and personal satisfaction will have to be found in activities pursued outside working hours.

If so, technological progress will have resolved some of business's most vexing problems. No longer will there be any need to sort out and evaluate the many human, social, and economic considerations hitherto important in operating and organizing a business. Rather, all there will be left to do is to climb on and ride the one band wagon harmonious with previously determined future events.

SOURCE: *Harvard Business Review* (November–December, 1961), pp. 121–126. Reprinted by permission of the *Harvard Business Review.*
* General Electric Co.

I believe it can be shown, however, that these conclusions are both dubious in themselves and unreliable as a basis for organizational action. Indeed, if we couple our experience in decentralized organizations with a realistic evaluation of the nature and extent of the future impact of information technology in such organizations, we can establish a very reasonable basis for concluding that decentralization and the middle manager are much more likely to *grow* and *flourish* than to wither and die in the decades ahead.

TYPES OF DECISIONS

For the purposes of our discussion, the concept of decentralization can be simply stated. Decision-making responsibility is assigned at the lowest point in the organization where the needed skills and competence, on the one hand, and the needed information, on the other hand, can reasonably be brought together. A great improvement is believed to result in any firm when the creative talents of responsible individuals are encouraged to develop in a climate of individual responsibility, authority, and dignity—a climate that is made possible by the decentralization of decision making.

This view of decentralization is fundamentally different from the mere application of traditional centralized managerial control concepts to smaller and more dispersed units of people. Confusion over this difference may well be a fundamental factor responsible for the earlier mentioned viewpoints predicting future trends away from decentralized organizations.

In assessing the future impact of information technology on decentralized business, some attention must be paid to the subject of decision making. The philosophy within which decisions are made distinguishes the organization which is centralized from the one which is not. The aspects of decision making that are important are (a) the way decisions are classified and (b) the way responsibility for them is assigned:

In any decision system we can identify two classes of decisions—those which can be predetermined by a rigorously defined selection process and those which cannot. The former are generally decisions concerning measurable and objective physical phenomena. The latter involve human beings and intangible, subjective human values; the balancing of social, moral, and economic values; and the assessment of situations in which information needs cannot be adequately anticipated or adequately filled.

In a centralized organization, the attempt is made to retain in as small a group as possible the responsibility for the latter type decisions and to delegate only the former. But in a decentralized organization, no attempt is made to separate the types of decisions in assigning responsibility; instead, the attempt is to relate all decisions to work purpose. Responsibility is assigned where the skills and competences, on the one hand, and the needed information, on the other, can reasonably be brought together.

Thus, in a centralized organization, the decision structure tends to be one where the decisions at the top are original and sensitive to human and social considerations; decisions at the bottom are more likely to be routine and insensitive to such considerations. By contrast, in a decentralized organization, no such division exists. Rather, all types of decisions are made throughout the organization at all levels. Only the breadth and complexity of impact tends to decrease from top to lower echelons in the organization.

Sources of Confusion

It should be noted that the use of the word *decision* to describe both of these classes of action is unfortunate and has caused much confusion in assessing the contribution of information technology to decision making. Trouble has also been caused by the term *computer decision making*, which has been applied in a glamorizing fashion to describe the application of computers to the more routine tasks. Although the terminology is new, the concept and its application substantially predate the high-speed electronic computer. For instance, the clock thermostat which turns on the furnace at 6:30 A.M. because the house temperature is below that preset for daytime operations is a mechanical "decision maker" in the same sense as the computer is when it computes and prints a bill for a customer. So is the regulating system for traffic lights which modifies the signal sequencing depending on volume of traffic, time of day, and day of week (and sometimes it factors in holidays, as well).

We now have many mechanical devices that carry out predetermined processes and actions. The additional advantage the high-speed electronic computer brings is its ability to handle a large number of variables in a complex process at high speed. Calling the action *computer decision making*, however, implies that a computer decides a man's salary because it prints out his monthly check. Such a description is, at the very least, misleading.

POTENTIAL AND LIMITATIONS

Information technology embraces the various techniques and disciplines (applied mathematics, simulation, electronic data processing, and so on) which can be and have been applied to the development of data in business. This technology has mushroomed in the past ten years with most of the practical application confined thus far to electronic data processing. However, enough theoretical and first-stage application work has been done in such areas as business simulation and computer duplication of human logical processes to envision that, ultimately, information technology will have a major impact on business. Yet, while the future impact will be great, there are factors in the growth of the technology and the evolution of business which will limit the nature and extent of the impact.

Effect of Industry Changes

One such factor is the expected increase in the complexity of business in the next few decades. When information technology was in its early development stage, a $1 billion sales volume point was a commonly accepted dividing line between the really large business and the "all-other" category. But when the technology eventually reaches a point of reasonable maturity, $10 billion or more in sales should represent such a dividing line.

In association with such a growth in sales we can expect an increase in complexity arising from such factors as increased product variety, additional manufacturing locations, foreign expansions, and the need for additional and diversified labor, which usually attend a significant volume increase. Simultaneously, the complexities arising from the changing role of industry in society—its relations with government, labor, and other segments of the economy—will undoubtedly also increase as they have during the past decade, and will require a host of new, different, difficult decisions.

When we view the impact of the advancing information technology on business, therefore, it would be naive to predict the outcome without taking into account the increased size and more diverse nature of the industrial world. Will the simplifications possible from applications of the new science outpace, keep abreast of, or fall behind trends making business more complicated? At the same time we need to be specific about the impact of data technology. To what extent do the kinds of situations to which it is amenable represent the total range of situations that must be handled in industry?

Most Likely Applications

The status of some current work in the computer application field might help in making an assessment. The prediction has been made, on the basis of this work, that a computer will be the world's chess champion within the next decade. What is significant here, as far as impact on business is concerned, is that it will take roughly a decade for enough progress to be made to handle a problem which has no unknowns—even where the rules of play are completely defined, where the scope of action is limited, where the relationships between the elements are explicit, where there is but a single, defined objective, where the value system is determined and unambiguous, and where the problem is precisely the same now as it was 100 years ago and as it will be 100 years from now.

Suppose that we look at chess as a complicated variation of ticktacktoe—the complication arising from increases in the number and kinds of relationships, but with no reduction in definition. Then we have a reasonable basis for speculating that, during the next two decades, data technology will have the greatest impact on those facets of business where the complication is due primarily to the number and kinds of explicitly known relationships. It is highly likely, for example, that an electronic computer program will be the basis for scheduling production, ordering material, and allocating output in the case of some products which historically have had highly predictable patterns of demand.

The Human Element

Such programs, however, will contain as one of their elements the limits within which scheduling, ordering, and allocating are to be computer-determined. When these limits are exceeded, as happens when the data inputs indicate environmental changes, the expansion of established patterns, or factors requiring human value consideration, then the program will shut the computer down awaiting human instruction. For example:

A large industrial company is developing an automated information system designed to permit its salesmen (located throughout the United States) to determine immediately the availability of thousands of products and, if an order is placed, when and from where an item will be shipped. This system, using the latest techniques and equipment, will keep continuous records of all products and update them each time an order is placed, a shipment made, or a product manufactured. When an order is placed, the system—in accordance with the rules of its design—will automatically process it, selecting the warehouses best able to fill it.

The first step in the automatic processing of an order in this system is to check the credit status of the customer. If the order, together with the unpaid balance, is less than the customer's credit limit, the complete order process is carried out and the proper warehouse is automatically instructed when and how to make the shipment. But if the credit limit is exceeded, this information is printed out and the system holds up processing of the order until it receives further instruction.

This company considers the decision involved in selecting a course of action when a customer's order exceeds his credit limit to have enough important intangible considerations so that human judgment should be exercised in each case and so that the disposition should be made humanly, not mechanically.

Similarly, when the business situation is one where the market is being developed, the product is new, and the distribution channels include perhaps a variety of foreign markets (all with volatile characteristics), then the information-handling techniques, while providing a factual base, will still fall very short of the requirements for taking action. The final assessment of the risk and the decision to act must be made by a manager integrating the factual information with the less well-defined elements in the situation.

Since in a great number of businesses this last kind of situation predominates, and since the number of such situations increases with the growth in complexity, we can anticipate that the major long-term impact of the new technology will be to improve the basis of human decision making rather than to make decision making routine and mechanical.

Now let us proceed to the next part of our problem. If we couple experience with decentralization and the application of information technology with likely trends in business and data technology, what conclusions can be drawn about the probable results of their interaction over the next few decades?

GREATER DECENTRALIZATION

Counter to many arguments, the anticipated advances in information technology, in my opinion, can *strengthen* decentralization in those businesses that have adopted it and will encourage *more* managements to experiment and to operate in accordance with the decentralization philosophy.

A great many businessmen are repelled by the idea that most people in industry can be used only to execute, within narrowly defined limits, the orders of an elite group who alone can exercise judgment, imagination, creativity, and intuition. They feel that this concept shuts the door on a major resource—the creative and imaginative talents and the growth potential of large numbers of people. On the other hand, these same businessmen recognize the need to guide the use of creativity and imagination so that the sum total will not be dissipated inefficiently, but will be applied in a disciplined fashion to achieve the selected goals of the organization.

This is where information becomes vital. Employees have to have the pertinent facts if they are to see clearly the interrelationships between their contribution and the contribution of others, and to act, on their own initiative, in a manner which will serve the best interests of all. The advancing data technology can make remarkable contributions to meeting this need. *This, in fact, may be its most significant feature.*

But to succeed in this way, information technology needs constantly to be guided away from its Babel-like preoccupation with designing superhuman intellects to make superhuman decisions, and brought back to its primary business purpose: contributing to the simplification of business complexities. Because this is a more difficult purpose to achieve, and because it means more focus on steady, day-by-day accomplishment and less on intoxicating expectations, shifting the emphasis to simplification will not be an easy task.

Pattern Identification

Today advanced techniques and large computers are coupled in a great assault on complex systems. Systems are analyzed microscopically and synthesized; over-all performance is predicted by considering the behavior of each element. This approach is fine as far as it goes, but often just does not go far enough.

What is needed, and what information technology *can* produce, if properly guided by the businessman, is the next step: simplification through pattern identification. This step can provide the kind of information which permits individuals to act responsibly on their own initiative. It also can make it possible to sort out those things which can best be done humanly from those best done mechanically, in order to obtain most effective use of both human and machine resources. Thus:

One of the products of a manufacturing business was an instrument device. Some 85,-000 units of 400 different models were manufactured annually with no apparent stable patterns of market preference for any particular model. Each model was manufactured to order, and shipment averaged about six weeks from the date the order was placed. All of the paper work involved in processing the order was originally handled manually, but, with the advent of electronic computing equipment, it was no trick to convert to machines.

However, those responsible for the conversion in this instance were not satisfied simply to mechanize an existing complex human routine. They felt that before a major investment was made in mechanizing the paper flow, an effort should be made to determine whether or not there were fundamental patterns in this operation which ought to be taken into account.

Although there was no apparent stable pattern of demand on a model basis, they found from an analysis of the major components (which, when assembled, made up the models) that there were significantly greater requirements for some components than for others, and that a high degree of stability existed in this pattern. They determined, by a process of regrouping and redefining components, that of the 1,800,000 components of 280 different varieties required annually, some 99% could be classed under only 84 types.

With this new understanding, they were able to change the basic concept of the business from one where each model was fabricated to order to one where 84 types of components were manufactured in more or less continuous production, 196 being stocked in inventory. Final assembly alone was accomplished subsequent to the receipt of an order. The average delivery cycle went from six weeks to four days. More important, from the point of view of this discussion, an information structure was developed showing how families of models were related through the identical components in their composition. The resulting simplification made possible better and

faster decisions and permitted further delegation of decision making to lower organizational echelons.

Prior to the work described, realistic forecasting on a model-by-model basis was just about impossible with or without a computer. Decisions on advance ordering were difficult to make and, because of the lack of pertinent information, were made relatively high in the organization. Subsequent to the simplification work, and with the business process organized around component types rather than end-product models, forecasts by family were all that were needed. Not only were these forecasts much easier to make and inherently much more accurate, but they permitted the responsibility for advance ordering to be placed at a lower organizational echelon, one nearer the level of actual manufacture since the information could now be made available for decisions at this level.

The contribution of information technology was increased manifold in this case by a recognition of the responsibility, not only to find a way to carry out complex operations more quickly, but also to find a way to simplify an operation so that a more efficient total system could be developed, one in which both the human and the machine resources could be most effectively utilized.

Dispelling Illusions

Insisting on simplification as the desirable end result is a task which must fall to businessmen. The danger of a parochial viewpoint is great, and one detects a strong tendency on the part of some to consider the complicated model as itself the "goal" and a kind of monument to their technical skills. In some instances the lack of widespread knowledge about the technology and its associated jargon is even used as a sort of witch doctor's cloak behind which to hide a growing empire, supposedly capable, ultimately, of making many of the businessman's decisions.

Businessmen, along with the technical experts, have a responsibility to ensure the technology's being used in a manner to further the ends of the company. Defining the business purposes to which the technology should be applied is essential to discharging this responsibility and cannot be left to the technologist alone.

Help for Middle Managers

How will information technology fortify the role of the middle manager in a decentralized business? As stated earlier, a characteristic of such a firm is a decision structure where the breadth of impact of the decision, rather than the judgment content, varies in the organization. Both upper-level managers and managers at the first level are deeply involved in problems where judgment and human values are the important elements. They are concerned with situations where the decisions cannot be anticipated, the information needs predicted, or the decision elements quantified. And this is equally true of many functional specialists reporting to these managers.

The stock in trade of these managers is their ability, as leaders, to obtain balanced results through the work of other people. To perform adequately here requires the ability to synthesize information, intuition, judgment, and values into courses of action and decisions which will produce the balanced results. It is reasonable to anticipate that the new technology will, over the next few decades, make a major contribution by providing such men with powerful tools to accomplish their work better. Their ability to exercise initiative and judgment responsibly should be strengthened. This effect should far outweigh in importance any tendency of computers to eliminate jobs where the nature of decisions is mechanical, especially when it is remembered that the growth in the complexity of business is increasing the need for effective managers.

IMPACT IN CENTRALIZED FIRM

I have been discussing the situation of the company with a philosophy of decentralization. But what about the firm with the opposite concept of operations?

There are two paths along which centralized businesses are likely to move as a result of the impact of information technology. Thus:

If the managers are committed to their philosophy and if the purpose for which the technology is employed is limited to the mechanization and improved efficiency of the operation as it exists, then the likely evolution

will be along those lines predicted by a number of writers. Under these conditions, organizational reconsolidations will be encouraged and the ability of the few who have nonroutine, decision-making responsibility to make better decisions will be enhanced. Many currently in middle management will be replaced. Because men in this group were needed for their knowledge of complex but now obsolete routines, relocation will be difficult for them.

On the other hand, some businesses have adopted the centralized decision-making philosophy because of the difficulties involved in achieving a harmonious unifying of individual creativity and initiative. Here the technology can be used as a tool for simplification rather than simply mechanization, and will provide a basis for the adoption of a decentralized approach as a more desirable and more effective way.

CONCLUSION

It seems hardly conceivable that the social forces which are present today and which will be important in the future could permit the separation of society into two classes—one, an elite corps of thinkers (top managers, technologists, or some combination of the two), and the second, all other human beings.

It is a simple matter to conclude, as some writers have, that information technology has the potential to force the entire organization —from the middle manager on down—to satisfy personal needs and aspirations off the job. However, with a rapidly increasing percentage of our population acquiring advanced education, it is difficult to believe that the members of this group who go into business will be satisfied with spending their daily working hours, comprising a great part of their lifetime, in pursuits devoid of intellectual satisfaction. It is more than likely that they will attempt to curtail the freedom to act of businessmen or any other group that tries to force such a condition on them.

Since at least one sound, well-conceived concept—decentralization—provides an economically and socially acceptable alternative, it appears that the nub of the situation is not in the technology but in the wisdom with which managers apply it. Businessmen should have had enough experience with the Technocrats, on the one hand, and the self-seeking, public-be-damned Robber Barons, on the other, to realize that continued progress and growth lie in the best match of economic efficiency and social responsibility. This need is met by decentralization, coupled with an advancing information technology.

If, during the next decade or two, we do not see a continued trend in the direction of business decentralization, we must look for the failure, not in any unalterable laws of technological advance, but in the decisions of businessmen.

9. THE IMPACT OF INFORMATION TECHNOLOGY ON ORGANIZATION

JAMES C. EMERY [*]

INTRODUCTION

A discussion of the impact of information technology on organization is largely a matter of speculation, since we are just now beginning to perceive its effects. Speculation, though often interesting and occasionally useful, presents some obvious hazards.

One hazard, of course, is that predictions may prove wrong. This is not as great a danger as one might suppose, however, since the dramatic developments in the field of information technology make it likely that any prediction, if it is sufficiently imaginative and glamorous, will eventually prove correct. In any event, suitable hedging can minimize the probability of error, and faulty memories will reduce the penalty of an error if the prognosticator is indiscreet enough to make it obvious.

A more serious and immediate pitfall is that the speculation may be trite and commonplace. This hazard is particularly treacherous when discussing information technology and organization, since we already have been presented with such a rich abundance of speculation on the subject.[1] I do not claim that I have avoided this hazard altogether, but I have tried to reduce the risk by confining my discussion to some of the less explored issues involved.

As I view the topic, information technology will affect organizational structure primarily through the improvements it brings in the planning process.

SOURCE: *Proceedings of the 24th Annual Meeting,* Academy of Management, Chicago, Illinois, December 28–30, 1964, pp. 69–78. Reprinted by permission of *Journal of the Academy of Management.*

[*] Assistant Professor of Management, Massachusetts Institute of Technology.

[1] Among the earliest and most perceptive, I think, is the work of Leavitt and Whisler (1958).

THE ROLE OF PLANNING WITHIN THE ORGANIZATION [2]

An organization consists of a hierarchy of subunits pursuing a common set of objectives. Consistent, purposeful behavior on the part of all subunits is achieved through planning. The results of the planning are expressed in such forms as goals, plans, budgets, schedules, policies, and procedures.

Planning, like the organization itself, has a hierarchical structure. The total process is "factored" into a hierarchy of subsidiary processes. Planning at one level has as its purpose the achievement of plans formulated at the next higher level. Conversely, high-level planning aims at imposing constraints that lead to "good" lower-level planning that, in turn, eventually results in "good" organizational behavior. Higher-level planning thus affects behavior only indirectly through lower-level planning.

High-level planning generally deals with aggregate variables extending over relatively long time spans. Lower-level planning progressively adds greater detail within the constraints provided by the more aggregate plans. For example, a quarterly plant-wide schedule might be amplified by lower-level planning into weekly departmental schedules.

Planning at a given organizational level is constrained not only by current operating plans, but also by less ephemeral forms of higher-level planning. The goal structure of the organization, for example, serves this purpose. Thus, basic long-range "objectives" restrict the choice of medium-range "goals" that limit the choice of short-term "plans." Simi-

[2] I have discussed the role of planning in a previous paper (1964) and so the remarks here provide only a sketch of that more detailed article.

larly, policies and procedures defined at one level in the organization provide constraints on lower-level planning (Granger, 1964). All of these forms of planning are, of course, designed to constrain lower-level planning in a way that will bring about satisfactory organizational behavior.

All lowest-level plans taken together describe the desired behavior. In order to do this with sufficient precision to make the description unambiguous (within "reasonable" tolerances), the composite lowest-level plan must ultimately contain a great deal of information. This information is expressed in the form of such high-resolution variables as scheduled daily production of each unit, number of employees of each skill classification, and detailed delivery schedules.

On the other hand, the aggregate, low-resolution variables used in high-level planning provide very much less information than the composite lowest-level plan. The information added in amplifying high-level plans into low-level plans must come from somewhere. It comes from the hierarchical planning process.

The design of this planning process represents a fundamental issue in managing an organization. The choice of the various constraints that impinge on planning involves a problem-solving process of the most complex sort. In order to break up the overall problem into manageable subproblems, the global objectives of the organization are factored into subobjectives. This is done through a "means-ends" analysis that relates desired end results to the means of accomplishing them. The subproblems thus generated are, in turn, factored into still less comprehensive problems. This process continues until the subproblems become manageable without further factoring (March and Simon, 1958, pp. 190–193).

The behavior of the organization depends largely on the way in which the hierarchical factoring is accomplished. Unfortunately, there exists no known method for doing this in any "optimal" fashion. The structure of the factoring basically rests on the notion of what constitutes a "manageable" subactivity. If the global objectives of the organization were themselves economically manageable without fragmentation, then it would be optimal to perform no factoring. That organizations universally resort to hierarchical planning merely reflects their inability to cope with monolithic global objectives.

Thus, the factoring of global objectives into a hierarchy of subactivities is absolutely essential. However, in order to reap the benefit of the simplifications introduced by this fragmentation, each subactivity must be largely isolated from the rest. Otherwise, each manager would need access to information about all other activities with which his activity interacts, and in effect he would have to handle the global problem.

Independence among organizational units can be increased in several ways. The organizational structure itself plays an important role in this. Communication across hierarchical lines can be reduced—and hence independence increased—by grouping together within the same subunit those activities that have a high degree of interaction (as is done, for example, in a "project" organizational structure). Interactions caused by the flow of physical inputs and outputs among subunits can be reduced through various means of "decoupling," such as standardization of specifications, use of buffer inventories, and maintaining excess resources within each subunit. Finally, apparent independence is achieved to a considerable extent by simply ignoring the less significant interactions.

These devices for achieving greater independence carry a price. The price is paid in the form of forgone opportunities for greater specialization (achieved, for example, in a "functional" organizational structure); in the higher manufacturing costs associated with closer tolerances; in the cost of acquiring and maintaining buffer inventories; in lower resource utilization; and in the penalties of suboptimization that result from ignoring interactions (Hitch, 1953; Hitch and McKean, pp. 125–133 and 158–181).

A partial trade-off exists between these costs and the costs of coordination. With closer coordination, activities can be coupled more directly, and therefore the costs of achieving greater independence can be correspondingly reduced. But coordination, too, exacts a price. It costs money in the form of data collection, data transmission, computation, and—often the most important cost—the effort required to design the information system that achieves closer coordination. Organizational structure implicitly reflects a choice of the economic balance between greater independence and greater coordination.

Coordination is achieved primarily through

the planning process. Planning necessarily relies on an abstract model of the real world whose activities are being planned.[3] The plans that emerge describe coordinated actions to the extent that the model recognizes significant interactions and has access to sufficient information about the predicted behavior of other subunits.

THE EFFECT OF INFORMATION TECHNOLOGY ON PLANNING

This brings me to the central issue of this paper. Factoring of the global objectives of the organization depends heavily on the current state of information technology.[4] Information technology affects organizational structure by permitting an increase in the scope of the activities falling within a given subunit. As the organization gains enhanced ability to manipulate information, the permitted size of a "manageable" task expands. Global objectives therefore need not be fragmented as finely as before, and the number of organizational subunits can be correspondingly reduced.

Increasing each subunit's "span of control" mitigates the problem of coordination among the subunits. Activities that formerly involved strong interactions among different units may now be included within a single comprehensive unit. Such consolidation obviously reduces the interactions among subunits and permits closer coupling of previously decoupled activities. This phenomenon has already manifested itself to a considerable extent—particularly in the field of production and inventory control—and will doubtlessly become all the more evident in the future.

The trend toward increasingly comprehensive activities will certainly not eliminate the need to parcel out the organization's global activities among different subunits. The interactions that inevitably result from such fragmentation will still call for various measures to increase the real or apparent independence among the subunits. However, the advances made in information technology move the eco-

nomic balance between independence and coordination sharply toward the latter. Like any other factor of production, a manager should employ more information handling as its cost declines.

Advances in information technology permit greater formalization of planning. Analytical or simulation models can often take the place of intuitive models. Analytical models typically permit manipulation aimed at finding the "optimum" of an objective (or criterion) function. This is obviously useful when an available model captures the essential character of the real world and when the model can be optimized by a computationally feasible algorithm. Very often, however, these conditions do not obtain, and one must resort to brute force simulation techniques.

In either case, the models provide a prediction of outcomes stemming from planned actions. The planner can continue to examine alternative plans until he judges that the cost of further search exceeds the expected improvements that would result. Even when he has available an "optimizing" model, the planner may wish to explore for improved plans that recognize factors not considered in the formal model.

MAN-MACHINE PLANNING SYSTEMS

Man-machine systems offer exciting possibilities for improving decision processes. The meager evidence that we have suggests that a symbiosis between the man and the machine will prove especially powerful and fruitful in coping with the enormously complex problems encountered in organizational planning. To the human component in such a system is relegated the responsibility for proposing alternative plans and judging the suitability of their consequences. The machine is assigned the computational task of transforming proposed actions into their consequences by means of a formal model.

The great advantage of man-machine systems is that they do not require the complete formalization of the decision process. Those decisions that are well understood and capable of being described formally can be incorporated into the computer model. Decisions that cannot be so formalized are simply reserved for the human decision maker.

A planner armed with a man-machine system can use it to explore in depth for improved

[3] The "models" may be formalized mathematical or computer models or—more often—a simplified, abstract mental image of the world that the planner necessarily resorts to in exercising his judgment and intuition.

[4] Subsumed under the broad term of information technology are the more restricted fields of operations research and the computation sciences.

plans. A sequential, hierarchical search appears particularly efficient (Dalkey, 1962; Emery, 1964). Using an aggregate model, the planner can search for a superior high-level plan. Each probe in the "space" of alternatives provides information useful to him in proposing further probes. He continues his search until a satisfactory high-level plan is found.

The aggregate plan emerging from such a process is then amplified by more detailed models. A search at a lower level is similar to the high-level search except that it is constrained by higher-level plans previously selected.[5] These constraints explicitly recognize interactions among the detailed models, and hence they can reduce the penalties of suboptimization. Furthermore, the constraints confine the range of alternatives that need to be examined at the more detailed level, thereby enormously increasing the efficiency of the search process (at the possible risk, however, of overlooking attractive detailed plans that do not meet the imposed constraints).

The sequential, hierarchical search process continues until the most detailed plan contains sufficient information for its execution. Execution, as far as a high-level manager is concerned, normally involves passing the high-level plan to the next lower level of management. The planner at the lower level may go through a similar man-machine search as part of the planning required at his level.

From this description it should be apparent that man-machine planning is completely analogous to the conventional planning process. The chief difference is that a man-machine planning system employs a hierarchy of formal models under the direct control of the planner, rather than using the organization itself as a hierarchy of informal models. Such a system allows the high-level planner to obtain consistent, detailed, rapid, and relatively inexpensive evaluations of proposed alternatives.

Because of its speed and reduced cost, man-machine planning can be performed frequently and many alternatives can be considered during each planning cycle. Improved plans will presumably emerge from an expanded search. Furthermore, an unrealistic high-level plan can be explicitly identified

during the detailed amplification by lower-level models. As a result, the high-level planner can immediately make appropriate modifications to his plan. In conventional systems, such modification may not be made until long afterwards, during attempted execution of the unrealistic plan.

CENTRALIZATION VERSUS DECENTRALIZATION

A great deal has been written about the effect of information technology on the issue of centralization versus decentralization. Unfortunately, different authors come to diametrically opposite conclusions, and so it is difficult to judge where the consensus lies.

At least part of the difference of opinion stems from the lack of a precise definition of "centralization."[6] Such a definition should, I think, recognize the sources of the information gained during the hierarchical planning process. Let me propose a tentative definition that does take this factor into account.

In amplifying higher-level plans into lower-level plans, each organizational unit adds information. In a "centralized" organization, most of the information comes from the higher levels; in a "decentralized" organization, the lower levels tend to supply a relatively greater proportion of the information.

Information content is a function of the selectivity of the information. If a given manager in the organization has only a few options open to him, then the specific plan he chooses has a relatively low information content. This is so because the plan selects one course of action from the small number of alternatives available. In the extreme case where a manager can pursue only a single course of action, the planning process at his level adds no in-

---

[5] Higher-level plans may, however, require iterative modification as a result of the detailed analysis performed by lower-level models.

[6] For example, one reads arguments to the effect that computers will lead to decentralization because they will allow top management to monitor more closely the operations of lower-level management. If close surveillance serves any purpose at all, this means that top management will be in a position to judge the detailed actions of subordinates. Presumably, a lower-level manager can exercise freedom of action as long as he takes the "right" actions as judged by his superiors. It seems to me that any reasonable definition would have to include such Orwellian surveillance as an aspect of centralization.

formation at all.[7] If, on the other hand, there exists a large number of alternative ways of amplifying higher-level constraints into lower-level plans, then planning at this level adds a great deal of information because it has the power to select one plan out of many options.

Some specific examples might make this concept clearer. Consider a plant scheduler. If his activities are severely constrained by policies, standard operating procedures, and higher-level schedules, then he has relatively little opportunity to exert much freedom of choice. At least as far as he is concerned, he lives within a centralized organization.

A different organization might leave the scheduler much greater discretion. He might, for example, be given a monthly schedule by major product line, without further specification as to how the detailed scheduling is to be performed. With such loose central direction, he could choose any of a vast number of possible detailed schedules, all of which are perfectly consistent with high-level constraints. His choice of a specific schedule therefore has a high power of selection and hence a high information content. Accordingly, the organization to him appears decentralized.

My definition of centralization obviously lacks vigor. It also has several other possible drawbacks. The most glaring one is that it does not provide an operationally measurable criterion of centralization. In most cases it would be impossible—or, at best, extraordinarily difficult—to determine the number of low-level plans that are consistent with a given high-level plan. Nevertheless, the fact that the definition is not operational need not rule out its use.[8]

Perhaps a more serious deficiency in the definition is that it fails to take into account the relative importance of information added at different levels in the organization. For example, centralization might be defined in terms of the range in value of alternative plans available at a given organizational level. However, such a definition requires a means of assessing the "value" or "utility" of alternatives. This obviously raises some very formidable conceptual problems, to say nothing of the practical ones.[9] If, in fact, the ordinal utility of alternative plans were known, then the choice among alternatives would be straightforward and could just as well be made by a centralized agency. That this is not the case provides the chief justification for decentralization.

Furthermore, the advantage of introducing utility into the definition of centralization is not at all clear. A manager presented with a simple choice between two alternatives having widely differing (but unknown) utilities might feel much more a victim of centralization than a manager faced with a choice from among a large number of alternatives differing only insignificantly in utility.

Despite its shortcomings, the proposed definition has, I think, several desirable properties that make it suitable for the purpose at hand. For instance, it recognizes the relative nature of centralization and makes explicit the fact that centralization occurs to some extent throughout the entire organization. An organization may be highly "decentralized" at the highest levels and "centralized" at the lower levels. Thus, a given division may be autonomous and decentralized within the organization as a whole, but relatively centralized within itself. Some of the well-known "decentralized" firms seem to fall within this class. Notwithstanding the often expressed opinion to the contrary, the Defense Department manifests this same tendency.[10]

The proposed definition of centralization also appears to be qualitatively reasonable. If a higher-level manager imposes additional constraints that reduce the number of lower-level alternatives, this would normally be considered a move toward greater centralization. Conversely, changes that are generally recog-

---

[7] A certain amount of amplification of a higher-level plan might take place, but if the amplification is completely determined by procedures specified by higher-level managers, then no real alternatives exist. The amplification thus does not add any information not already implicit in the higher-level planning.

[8] In any case, I have not seen any other definitions of centralization that eliminate this problem.

[9] The definition of centralization in terms of the selectivity of a plan instead of the range of its values is analogous to Shannon's definition of information in terms of its selectivity rather than its semantic content.

[10] Professor Billy Goetz of M.I.T. has observed (not altogether in jest) that most managers prefer an organization that is decentralized from the top down to them, and centralized thereafter.

nized as leading toward centralization typically result from higher-level constraints that reduce the number of alternatives available at lower levels. The polar case of complete centralization, where the highest level in the organization generates all planning information and leaves no options for lower-level managers, would surely be considered complete centralization by any definition.

After this somewhat lengthy digression to define terms, I am now in a position to discuss the effect of information technology on centralization. It seems to me that the available evidence clearly supports the view that advances in information technology will lead toward greater centralization. These advances certainly permit the organization to store, retrieve, and manipulate greater quantities of data than ever before. There is no reason to suppose that high-level managers will not exploit this capability. Nor is there a clear case to suggest that they should not.

As Leavitt and Whisler pointed out (1958, p. 43), decentralization has been largely negatively motivated. In conventional systems, high-level management has no choice but to leave considerable freedom for lower-level management. The establishment of realistic detailed constraints requires access to a great deal of information, and until recently such information was hopelessly beyond the data handling capacity of high-level management.

High-level planning, like planning at any level, involves a search for a satisfactory plan among the alternatives available. Using conventional methods, high-level planners must conduct this search based on grossly simplified and aggregated models of the real world. Under these circumstances, a high degree of centralization is usually quite rightly regarded as mischievous meddling in detailed matters well beyond the low-resolution information available at the higher levels in the organization.

Advances in information technology blunt the force of this argument against more centralized planning. An increased data handling capability permits high-level planners to develop and manipulate much more detailed and comprehensive formalized models than can be handled by conventional planning techniques. This offers two advantages.

First, detailed plans can be made more realistic and consistent. Comprehensive models submerge relatively little important information from the view of the high-level planner. As a result, he is less likely to impose infeasible constraints on lower-level planners. Consequently, the lower-level planners need less flexibility in order to compensate for the high-level planner's lack of information about their operations.

Second, detailed plans generated through complex analytic or simulation models can lead to improved organizational performance. The increased comprehensiveness of such formalized planning models makes it possible to consider more of the interactions that occur among lower-level subunits, thus reducing the penalties associated with suboptimization.

THE EFFECT OF GREATER CENTRALIZATION ON MIDDLE MANAGERS

To be sure, persuasive counterarguments can be mustered against greater centralization. Many persons may agree that there exists a clear trend toward centralization, but find the prospect both dreary and frightening. With Dr. Malik, they view such a world as having "perfect hierarchy, perfect organization, total efficiency; but no spirit, no freedom, no joy, no humor, and therefore no man." (Malik, 1963.)

It is, of course, exceedingly difficult to assess the effect of greater centralization on the human beings composing an organization (and I certainly claim no special competence to do this myself). Nevertheless, a case can be made against the more gloomy predictions about man's role in a centralized organization. In trying to do this, I will focus attention on middle managers, since they are the ones that appear most vulnerable and have the most to lose from centralization.

A manager working in the middle of a large bureaucratic organization faces several possible perils. One of these is that severe constraints might be imposed on him, stifling his initiative and robbing his job of all challenge and interest. This is the risk that probably weighs most heavily in the minds of those that decry centralization.

But the world of a manager at any level is enormously complex, and there seems little possibility that it need ever lose its zest. Most managers confront a set of multidimensional goals and a probabilistic environment that can never be fully captured by "optimizing" models. As we gain competence in dealing with various aspects of this world, our ignorance may diminish but still remains everlastingly vast. There probably exists a Parkinsonian law to the effect that the complexity of a manager's job expands to meet his ability to cope with complexity.

Under the definition that I have adopted, it is certainly true that greater centralization imposes additional constraints on a lower-level manager. On the other hand, information technology permits him to explore in greater detail the reduced space of alternatives left available to him. As a result, the number of *discernible* alternatives open to him may be very much greater than in a conventional planning system. The number of perceived alternatives, rather than the potential ones, may well represent the important psychological criterion that a manager uses in judging the scope and challenge of his job. Thus, information technology may lead to the paradoxical situation of giving managers at all levels greater effective freedom of action.

In any case, lack of alternatives is not the only problem facing the middle manager. Probably at least as great a peril is an overabundance of alternatives without a suitable means of selecting among them. Such excessive freedom of choice often breeds nothing but chaos, and one need not envy a manager placed in this position. Indeed, he might well greet a few judicious higher-level constraints with unalloyed relief.

More than one manager of production scheduling, for example, has welcomed the constraints on his job represented by a computer scheduling program. Instead of continual *ad hoc* "fire-fighting," these managers can, for the first time, focus attention on improving the planning process itself (perhaps by helping to incorporate improved algorithms in a computer program). Many of them also find more time for the non-planning and human relations aspects of their job.

Still another problem facing a middle manager is the risk of being assigned unreasonable and unrealistic plans. As discussed earlier, the quality of these plans is largely a function of the data handling capacity available to his higher-level managers. One of the most serious indictments against many of the current cen-

tralized planning schemes is that the constraints they impose are not based on a sufficiently realistic model of the world, nor on adequate information about the current state of that world. A lower-level manager naturally finds it difficult to work under such conditions. Advances in information technology eliminate much of this problem. As a result, lower-level managers may have less justification to mistrust the centralization induced by these advances.

CONCLUSIONS

There seems to be little doubt that the rapid strides made in information technology will improve high-level planning. A more accurate, timely, and accessible data base will provide a better analogue of the current state of the environment with which to predict planning data. Formalized analytic and simulation models will permit more realistic predictions of the consequences of alternative actions. The increased speed of evaluating proposed alternatives will allow a wider search for improved plans.

The plans that emerge from such high-level planning will be more comprehensive, realistic, and detailed than can be generated by conventional means. Because of their greater information content, they will impose additional constraints on lower-level planners. By definition, this results in greater centralization.

The effect of these developments on a lower-level manager is not at all clear. It is by no means certain that his job will diminish in interest or challenge. It is at least possible that it will be made more attractive through a reduction of some of its uncertainty and many of its unrealistic demands.

REFERENCES

Dalkey, N. C. 1962. Command and control—a glance at the future. *Proceedings of the First Congress on the Information System Sciences.* Hot Springs, Va., November 1962.

Emery, James C. 1964. Planning as an iterative hierarchical process and its formalization in computer models. *Proceedings of the Second Congress on the Information System Sciences.* Hot Springs, Va., November 22–25, 1964.

Granger, Charles H. 1964. The hierarchy of objectives. *Harvard Business Review.* **42**, 3, 63–74 (May–June 1964).

Hitch, Charles J. 1953. Suboptimization in operations problems. *Journal of the Operations Research Society of America.* **1**, 3, 87–99 (May 1953).

Hitch, Charles J., and McKean, R. N. 1960. *The Economics of Defense in the Nuclear Age.* Cambridge: Harvard University Press.

Leavitt, Harold J., and Whisler, Thomas L. 1958. Management in the 1980's. *Harvard Business Review.* **36**, 6, 41–48 (Nov.–Dec. 1958).

Malik, Charles H. 1963. Speech before the 13th International Management Congress. Reported in the *New York Times,* September 20, 1963, p. 43.

March, James G., and Simon, Herbert A. 1958. *Organizations.* New York: John Wiley & Sons.

10.   BREAKING THE CHAIN OF COMMAND

S. C. BLUMENTHAL *

The role of computers in large commercial enterprises is changing and expanding. A perceptible change in organizational structure is accompanying this evolution from traditional computer applications into more advanced business systems. This article describes such a trend in terms of its developing impact on large business organizations.

The first decade of the widespread application of stored program, electronic digital computer systems in commercial enterprise has been characterized by their use as adjuncts to the operational and clerical processes within the organization. Computers were swallowed within the existing organizational framework to perform such mundane functions as payroll, inventory recording, accounts payable and receivable, and so forth.

In more recent years, however, we have seen the increasing use of computer systems in communications, manufacturing control, scheduling, retailing, passenger reservations, information retrieval and the like. In areas like these it is interesting to note that computers are performing not as more efficient surrogates for clerks and calculators, but in a new role that was not generally served by their more primitive forebears. Today one enterprise after another has already, is in process, or plans to integrate all their disparate uses of computers into new "total" data collection, processing, retrieval, display and control complexes that cross over traditional functional and departmental boundaries in an organization.

Such advanced business systems are made possible by the welding together of capacious random access stores, multi-channel communications interfaces, remote on-line input and output, advanced software organization and time-sharing hardware. These systems are characteristically on-line real time in operation. One observer has said that on-line real time systems allow management to operate a business, not just account for it.

Management in its planning and decision-making capacity operates in an ambiguous and uncertain environment. The relative desirability of alternative actions is never clearly demonstrable in those areas where management most significantly fulfills its special responsibilities. Progressive management has shown a ceaseless interest in accuracy, comprehensiveness and clarity of the information available to it in its tactical and strategic decision-making.

AS CORPORATIONS GROW . . .

In recent times this interest has been especially stimulated by several factors. The first of these is corporate growth: growth in size, in product lines, in productivity, in employes, in capital investment and in geographical dispersion of the enterprise. Secondly are found two related factors, those of competition and the profit squeeze. The third stimulus has been an upsurge in research and development leading to new products and markets. Related to this is diversification through acquisitions and the drying up of old markets. Next is the rapidly burgeoning technology of automation and communications making possible the implementation of advanced business systems and the use of scientific management principles. Finally, the paper flood is inundating all levels of management. The problem here is not so much how to get information to the top, but how to keep useless information from reaching the top.

Today these influences are combining in some degree in many major industries, with manifest effects on their traditional ways of doing business. What are some of these effects, both direct and indirect?

SOURCE: *Business Automation* (November, 1963), pp. 20–27. Reprinted by permission of *Business Automation*. Copyright Business Publications International, Division of OA Business Publications, Inc.

* Touche, Ross, Bailey & Smart.

The introduction of computer systems has already created a completely new level of management in some industries, which is made up of personnel responsible for the direction and control of data processing installations and systems. This has come about in an interesting and wholly natural way.

Throughout the major part of the 1950's in the United States, decisions affecting computer acquisition, systems design, programing and operations were made largely on a departmental basis. Top management was involved only because of the size of the expenditures involved in such installations. But these business systems were typically seen performing prosaic accounting tasks in the finance or controller's departments. Later, the operating, manufacturing or engineering departments used time on these machines for their own applications, or acquired their own computers under separate authority and control.

One thing became evident pretty quickly in the course of these experiences. The accustomed ways of managing systems and methods were not adequate to deal with these new devices. Organizational arrangements and staffing, which dealt with the problems of managing traditional punched card tabulating installations, lead to no inevitable success in coping with the special needs of computer systems operations. They sometimes precipitated disasters by quickly exhausting budgeted resources and time schedules.

These inadequacies were compounded by parallel technological developments that, over the course of the first decade of widespread commercial application of computers, resulted in orders of magnitude upgrading in speed, storage capacity, reliability and economy of scale. For one thing, more and more data and programs had to be prepared for the seemingly inexhaustible appetite of the new computing monoliths in an attempt to break even on the investments made.

During this period it was common to find that every time a large scale application was commenced much experience was recapitulated from job to job, department to department, and from company to company within an industry.

More to the point, however, was the growing need within a company to concentrate the limited and scattered talent available about its several installations, and to standardize policy and procedures so that the recapitulation of

painfully acquired experience could be avoided. Today, in company after company, one finds central systems staffs reporting through a vice president or director of data systems to top management. This is true even where computer operations themselves may still be partially or wholly decentralized.

At one large appliance manufacturer, for example, the director of methods planning, reports to top management through an administrative vice president, staff. On the operations side, a vice president of EDP reports to the same top management individual through a counterpart administrative vice president, line. The data processing centers at the company's various divisions are under the control of the vice president, EDP, even though the divisions themselves are decentralized and operate on a profit center basis.

In a large eastern railroad there is now a director of data systems responsible for all information systems planning, operations and control through the company.

Endless examples could be cited, but the import is already clear. With the centralized management of these new systems, these companies have achieved a rational means of control over the equipment procurement, standards and procedures, systems design, programing, operations and maintenance.

. . . MIDDLE MANAGEMENT SHRINKS

Another significant direct effect is the decline in the role of middle management. When computer systems are introduced in the control and information loops in an organization, two things happen. First there is an immediate effect on the clerical staff previously engaged in the ingestion, transformation, summarization and production of information. Its role is reduced, changed or eliminated. Managers involved with the direction of these clerical task forces are eliminated. Even the day-to-day tactical decisions incident to these mainly clerical functions are programed into the computer.

Secondly, with fewer layers of authority, top management is achieving a broader span of control, and is enabled to run larger and more diverse units. Large and costly staffs, necessary in pre-computer operations to sift the voluminous bulk of raw data, generalizations and approximations from which top management would make decisions and establish policy are shrinking in size and responsibility. Unlike the impact of "batch processing" computers which affect job functions in one horizontal segment of the organization, the new on-line real time systems are beginning to influence working relationships of subordinates and superiors up and down the corporate ladder.

The number of middle management jobs relative to output seems to be declining. In the decade from 1950 to 1960 the growth in middle management has declined from 2.8 to 1 percent annually. One firm reduced the number of middle management positions 30 percent in two years, accompanied by recombinations of parts of former jobs into new bundles of responsibilities.

The limited pool of executive and technical talent is by necessity being concentrated at corporate headquarters, thus encouraging a swing back to centralization. A most recent and dramatic example of this is United States Steel Corp., previously a model of decentralized operation and control. This trend is aided by the advances made in EDP technology, and in turn further advances will accelerate the trend. In this and similar cases technology is minimizing both time and distance as continued justification for decentralization of planning and decision-making.

WALLS ARE TUMBLING DOWN

When the rationale of installing computer systems is no longer merely clerical cost reduction, but is aimed at satisfying the information requirements of management, a company finds itself behaving more and more in a centralized fashion. With the informational resources at hand, management is no longer happy with sub-optimization at a product line or divisional level, but begins to look meaningfully at what is best from a total company point of view.

As the role of EDP expands, it tends to break down departmental walls. Management is realizing that it can achieve a lower unit cost for each element in the corporate data processing job by their integration into one data stream based on common sources of raw data. Orders are introduced to an integrated system once and affect accounts receivable, raw material orders, crew scheduling, production scheduling, finished inventory, shipping orders, sales commissions, market forecasts,

et cetera. All these effects are correlated, consistent and accurate because they are produced on an integrated basis.

If one were simply mechanizing each of these functions separately, this would tend to produce masses of uncorrelated data faster and perhaps more expensively. This would be no more meaningful or useful to top management than what was previously available. High speed groping should not be confused with genuine problem solving.

The inherent capabilities of management information systems that include computers, communications, source data automation and information display have given mathematicians and engineers an opportunity to contribute to the development of business management as a profession. But, systems and techniques that have been imposed on an organization by outside management scientists have not been as successful as when existing management is educated and trained in their use.

Without this background, management may be coerced into believing that their responsibilities are made more explicable by being made more calculable. In computer systems, the tactics of the situation are just as important as the strategy. Otherwise, in achieving a stated goal one may get unpleasant tactical by-products. In one simulation, for example, a completion time slippage of 242 percent of schedule was incurred in a crash project because the system (PERT) did not incorporate a full understanding of the distinction between real versus perceived progress; nor did it provide for delays in reporting progress, nor the fact that the motivations of the reporting engineers might not coincide with the institutional objectives expressed in the simulation model.

Management by crisis results in wide swings in sales, inventories, employment, order backlog and profitability. For example, changes in a company's delay in delivery will influence the customer release date for new orders, which in turn may affect the company's delivery delay because the company's management, lacking full understanding of the reasons for change in order backlog, may lay off personnel, et cetera. This loop amplifies slight variations into sustained oscillations in inventory, backlog, employment and profits. All because the system, though mathematically elegant as far as it may go, fails to provide for the effects of slight fluctuations of response delays on customer behavior.

INCLUDE THE INTANGIBLE . . .

The proper design of management information systems requires the inclusion of the effects of intangibles, in particular the roles of decision makers who are part of the total system of control. Trained management must consider and treat such problems carefully, especially when the system is supra-functional or multi-departmental in its domain.

Systems planning affecting the very top layers of management is becoming more and more the business of professionals, not merely theoreticians, but people who profoundly understand the realities and subtleties of business operation and the technical intricacies of management control and information systems.

Thus the corporate high command might become less a military hierarchy and more a partnership. Operations may be centered in the computer, and creative managerial functions distributed among professional specialists.

Rarely does the computer create a structural revolution in the organization. When it is introduced, the changes which it favors usually evolve naturally. They result from the realistic, balanced understanding that the computer is only a tool which operates most effectively in an interfunctional complex. The information channels necessary to service clients, handle the needs of the business, control costs, meet management's needs in decision-making and planning, and so on, do not necessarily follow functional lines, even in a non-computerized environment. The new factor in the situation is the growing awareness that computer systems now make possible and practicable the establishment and maintenance of a vast data base that truly reflects the interplay of functions within large organizations.

Thus, situations are frequently found where the formal structure is essentially unchanged by automation, except perhaps for a centralized information systems department, but where the communications channels are vastly changed. This information tree, rather than the formal organization structure, is beginning to play a dominant role in defining the way in which an enterprise does in fact operate.

. . . AND EXPAND THE BASE

As operations are increasingly centered on the computer, one typically finds the expanding data base handling orders, inventory, production scheduling, forecasting, purchasing and accounts payable and receivable as parts of one integral whole. Thus, important elements of the functions of sales, manufacturing, accounting, customer relations and even market analysis and forecasting are centralized within a new systems synthesis. As this trend reaches its culmination, it is not too difficult to foresee the reduction and elimination in large measure of the human intermediary between the information base and direct management interaction with it through appropriate inquiry and display mechanisms.

The evidence indicates that, while formal structural compartments within an organization may be retained for some time yet, the management and staff of the "Information Systems Department," reporting directly to the top of the corporate hierarchy, is assuming responsibility for more and more of the operations, tactical decision-making, planning, and finally participation in strategic decisions. Information no longer will flow upward to the top through traditional middle management echelons, since appropriately processed data will be simultaneously available throughout the organizations. Better informed and more timely decisions, however, will continue to flow downward through the new man-machine hierarchy. This emerging pattern has not usually come about through deliberate design, but through a "Brownian" movement within the organization over a period of years. The pattern is unlikely to be successfully imposed by management fiat.

However arrived at, this new pattern has certain dangers. If the attitude of top management, consciously or otherwise, consists of finding arguments to justify what it already knows it is going to do, then there may well be a tendency on the part of the information systems designers to clothe managerial prejudices in the garb of mathematical reality.

Machines will give management what it asks for, not what it should have asked for. Thomas Whisler of the University of Chicago predicts that, "the corporate planning technique will become one of creative interrogation (of the new systems)." This means that the requirements for management training, judgment, and experience will increase rather than diminish with the advent of advanced business systems.

NEW MEN FOR NEW JOBS

In the above discussion we have attempted to describe some of the dimensions of the man-machine symbiosis in large organizations. This problem is concerned with how men and computers best complement one another, and not how computers shall replace management. Computers are part and parcel of the explosive trend that is changing management's job and, if anything, making it more demanding than ever before.

Management must learn the management of computers as well as men and organizations of men, for the emerging organizations combine men and machines in an intimate and intricate way. To cope with these new and serious prob-lems, a new breed is emerging, and taking its place at the highest levels in a corporation.

The new "Vice-President of Management Information Systems," if we may call him that, should be highly professional in his approach to the responsibilities of his job, but no narrow specialist. Too, there is some doubt that he can learn his trade while harassed with the routine of a large, multi-level organization. The extent to which such men can be developed and play their proper role in an organization will in large measure determine the success of advanced business systems in a company.

The new corporate function is tied closely to the emergence of on-line real time as opposed to batch processing systems. In the former case, the possibility of interfunctional integration of information processes is the wellspring of the organizational changes now taking place.

BIBLIOGRAPHY

1. Anshen, Melvin, and G. L. Bach, *Management and Corporations: 1985,* McGraw-Hill Book Co., 1960.
2. Burck, Gilbert, "The Boundless Age of The Computer," *Fortune,* March, 1964.
3. "Computer, Promise or Threat?" *Credit and Financial Management,* November, 1962.
4. Dunlop, John T. (ed.), *Automation and Technological Change,* The American Assembly, Columbia University, Prentice-Hall, Inc., 1962.
5. Fransica, J. R., "Electronic Data Processing and Its Significant Impact on Management," *National Underwriter,* January, 1962.
6. Johnson, Richard A., *Employees—Automation—Management,* University of Washington, Bureau of Business Research, 1961.
7. Krout, A. J., "How EDP Is Affecting Workers and Organizations," *Personnel,* July, 1962.
8. Kushner, Albert, "People and Computers," *Personnel,* January–February, 1963.
9. Mann, Floyd C., and K. Williams, "Observations on the Dynamics of a Change to Electronic Data Processing Equipment," *Administrative Science Quarterly,* September, 1960.
10. Melitz, P. W., "Impact of Electronic Data Processing on Managers," *Advanced Management,* April, 1961.
11. Michael, Donald M., *Cybernation: The Silent Conquest,* Center for the Study of Democratic Institutions, 1962.
12. "Middle Management and Technological Change," *Management Review,* October, 1963.
13. Schwitter, Joseph P., "Computer Effect Upon Managerial Jobs," *Academy of Management Journal,* September, 1965.
14. Stilian, G. M., "Impact of Automation on the Manufacturing Executive's Job," *Management Review,* March, 1958.
15. Weber, Edward, "Change in Managerial Manpower with Mechanization of Data Processing," *The Journal of Business,* April, 1959.
16. Whisler, Thomas L., *Executives and Their Jobs: The Changing Organizational Structure,* Graduate School of Business, University of Chicago, Selected Papers, Number 9.
17. Witty, M. D., "Obsolete at Age 29," *Computers and Automation,* December, 1958.

Part IV.   Design of Management Systems

Recently many articles have appeared dealing with the design of total systems, a master plan for information systems,[1] and integrated system design,[2] all purporting to establish a structure by means of which the totality of business's information needs can be categorically processed. Granted that any workable program must be tailored to the particular type and size of business under consideration, the fact still remains that there are no standard specifications which one can follow to be assured of success. Typically, all systems designers start with the proposition that one must first establish long-range objectives, then analyze the existing system, develop immediate goals and target dates, and then begin to implement the plan. Such an approach appears highly superficial, being merely a reiteration of the traditional planning function which disregards current technological developments. What is needed is the application of common criteria in light of current equipment development. In this way, information needs will be ascertained more realistically and less idealistically.

In designing an information system it is desirable however to plan for a total systems approach even though such a procedure appears to be a highly ambitious project and to approximate utopian proportions. Unless this approach is pursued there will be much duplication of inputs at diverse hierarchical levels and in functional areas as well.

Unfortunately, industry has in many cases approached systems design from a piecemeal standpoint, first wading into the automating of the payroll function, to be followed by customer billings, and then proceeding to the area of inventory control and scheduling. Perhaps this historical development was inevitable in view of the prevalent ignorance of computer potential. However, day-to-day observation of business procedures casts serious doubts on the sufficiency of this account. But no matter what the explanation, since business activities are increasing in both scope and complexity, the problems of integration and coordination are also on the increase, and the need for an integrated total systems approach is likely to assume greater urgency in the future.

When considering total systems design it is imperative that one keep in mind just what is and is not implied in such a holistic approach. There is definitely no *one* total information system which can indiscriminately serve all the needs of all of management. This conclusion can be logically derived as a corollary from the very concept of information as selected data for reducing the amount or range of uncertainty in decision-making. Because of the varying range of uncertainly, what may prove to be

---

[1] Marshall K. Evans and Lou R. Hague, "Master Plan for Information Systems," *Harvard Business Review*, January–February, 1962.

[2] Herman Limberg, "Blueprint for a Management Information System," *Data Processing for Management*, March, 1964.

useful information at one level may turn out to be useless at another.

The selection by Johnson, Kast, and Rosenzweig places stress on the fact that the systems concept is essentially a frame of mind, that unless management responds to the systems approach by developing its own integrative philosophy, the total systems design will collapse under its own weight. To be successful, any systems engineering plan must include these three elements: identification of materials, of energy, and information flow. Raw materials are the wherewithal to be acquired, processed, and distributed. Energy includes not only physical energy in terms of electricity, gas, petroleum, etc., but also human energy in its physical and mental aspects. Information flow for routing of orders, production, accounting, and decision-making is often the primary focus of attention for most systems engineers. But because it is people who can successfully resist the structural alignments called for in designing information-decision systems, the human factors may at times be the crucial ones demanding special consideration.

The human factors involved in developing a system's design are treated *in extenso* by Bower and Sefert.[3] These factors must first be isolated if the systems analyst is to devise effective ways to minimize the human problems encountered in his role of bringing about change. For convenience in analyzing the effect of human factors on systems change three operational levels are examined in detail: top management (executives participating in companywide policy determination), middle management (middle and junior executives, operating supervisors, and foremen), and nonsupervisory employees (rank-and-file). Each of these three groups presents specific problems with their specialized fears, particular outlooks, appropriate motivation, etc. Also the techniques suitable for preliminary study, for implementation and

[3] James B. Bower and J. Bruce Sefert, "Human Factors in Systems Design," *Management Services*, November–December, 1965.

follow-up are interestingly outlined and illustrated.

Modernization in the past has too often been almost exclusively identified with the installation of new facilities and the introduction of modern machinery, and not with innovation in the management function itself. The design and installation of total management systems, devices for forestalling the development of an unprofitable business situation within a corporation, involves a considerable number of technical problems. These problems are pinpointed in the second selection by R. L. Martino. Since these problems are quite formidable, involving a good deal of work, critical analysis, and far-reaching consequences for all concerned, it would be a sheer waste of time and of resources to undertake the installation of such a system unless the willingness to do the arduous work, to make the necessary decisions, and to commit the needed funds to the project were a foregone conclusion.

The functions of a total management system can be broken down for purposes of analysis into predictive, comparative, and ameliorative. It aims to predict the effect of choosing one or a set of alternatives from among many possible ones. This it does by a computer simulation process. The comparative function consists of relating the prediction to the actual results obtained, whereas the ameliorative function aims at reducing the deviations between the predicted and the actual results. However, to actually realize these functions the various stages of system development (definition of the problem, design of system, and evaluation and modification of the system) must be thoroughly understood and successfully implemented.

Perhaps the total management system is not the solution being sought for the complex problems plaguing management. In the third selection, Moravec expresses the belief that present-day data processing systems are grinding out more data than any manager can possibly assimilate. Our ability to comprehend what we already have lags far behind the computer's ability to amass data. What is needed is not a total management system that integrates all existing information subsystems at a central location but a fundamental information system that integrates only the data considered essential to the operation of the company. Other data, secondary in nature, which one or the other subsystem requires are recorded and processed outside the fundamental information system.

This proposal is worthy of serious consideration. Systems designers have been far too long concerned with the speedy accumulation and processing of all available data rather than with the development of analytical and evaluative tools that can translate data into more meaningful and hence more usable forms. Even with our most sophisticated computer systems relatively little progress has been made in integrating the various functions of management into one which really is the "nervous" system of the organization, a "nervous" system that can discriminate between incoming stimuli (input data) of prime importance and those of only secondary import.

On the other hand, some critics believe that while a central data bank can exist for maintaining central information systems such as those dealing with financial data, etc., there should exist side-by-side subinformation systems that may or may not use the data bank but which are nevertheless tied into the central system. Thus some parts of the system (as the marketing system to a great extent) would be centralized and other parts (as the inventory and production control systems) would be decentralized. It would be the function of the central systems department to assume responsibility for coordinating the various subsystems with the central system wherever and whenever appropriate.

Stanley Young feels that a useful classification of systems can be set up on the basis of the constituent elements. In his view there would be three such systems: (1) machine to machine, (2) man to machine, and finally (3) man to man. The professional engineer has traditionally been responsible for the designing of machine to machine systems; the responsibility for the man to machine system is shared by both the engineer and the operating manager. Most of these latter systems, by ignoring the behavioristic elements, leave much to be desired. The man to man systems lie in the domain of the social scientists.

Regardless of the type of system under study, the essential aspect of all systems design are input, operations, control, output, and communications. The only variation necessary in these components is that they must be translated into behavioral terms for a system which is concerned with human endeavors.

Young believes that the engineer has utilized all the available tools at his disposal in the domain of the physical sciences, including operations research, model building, etc., for the design of machine to machine systems; on the other hand, the manager has put forth far too little effort in the development of man to machine systems. In fact, the progress which has been made in the social sciences has largely been ignored in the design of such systems.

In the design of a system wherein all of the components are concerned with human hardware (man to man system), a knowledge of the behavioral sciences is crucial.

In an era where much thought and resources are being expended upon the improvement of our educational, economic, and political systems and where the systems approach shows promise of becoming an indispensable tool for accomplishing this, more effort must be devoted to the improvement of man to man systems.

11. DESIGNING MANAGEMENT SYSTEMS

RICHARD A. JOHNSON,* FREMONT E. KAST,† AND
JAMES E. ROSENZWEIG ‡

The vast growth in size, complexity, and diversity of operations of the modern business organization has made the managerial function exceedingly difficult, but even more essential to the success of the enterprise.

During the past few years there have been many new concepts advanced for improving management; e.g., organization theory, decision theory, planning theory, and the behavioral theory of the firm. Each of these philosophies has helped to sharpen management skills; however, there is still a need for an operative theory of management—a theory which provides a conceptual framework of better business design and operation. It is our contention that today's large-scale business enterprise could apply the systems concepts to meet the growing complexities and proliferation of operations, for systems theory provides a conceptual framework within which the manager can integrate his operations effectively.

We are concerned here with design—the key activity in implementing the systems concept. This function is the means for establishing subsystems and larger systems into a composite, integrated whole. However, for completeness of presentation we will review general systems concepts briefly. Specifically, we will:

• Show the relationship between the systems concept and managing,

SOURCE: *The Business Quarterly* (Summer, 1964), pp. 59–65. Reprinted by permission of *The Business Quarterly.*
* Professor of Policy and Administration, University of Washington.
† Professor of Policy and Administration, University of Washington.
‡ Professor of Policy and Administration, University of Washington.

• Set forth a practical model using the systems concept,
• Discuss the scope of the design function,
• Introduce flow concepts in systems design,
• Discuss systems design as the implementation of the systems concept and
• Appraise some of the constraints on the design function.

SYSTEMS CONCEPTS AND MANAGEMENT

A system is "an organized or complex whole; an assemblage or combination of things or parts forming a complex or unitary whole." The term system covers an extremely broad spectrum of concepts. For example, we have mountain systems, river systems, and the solar system as part of our physical surroundings. The body itself is a complex organism including the skeletal system, the circulatory system, and the nervous system. We come into daily contact with such phenomena as transportation systems, communication systems (telephone, telegraph, etc.), and economic systems.

The systems concept is a useful way of thinking about the job of managing. It provides a framework for visualizing internal and external environmental factors as an integrated whole. It allows recognition of the proper place and function of subsystems. The systems within which businessmen must operate are necessarily complex. However, management via systems concepts fosters a way of thinking which, on the one hand, helps to dissolve some of the complexity and, on the other hand, helps the manager recognize the nature of the complex problems and thereby operate within the perceived environment. It

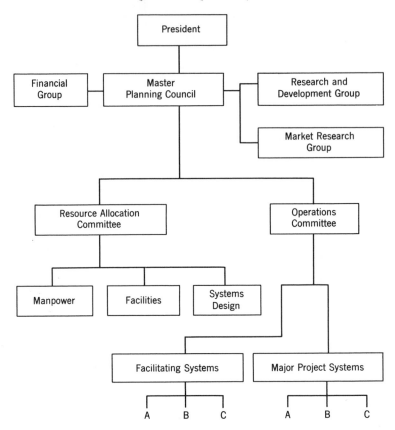

EXHIBIT 1. A Systems Model: Top Management.

is important to recognize the integrated nature of specific systems, including the fact that each system has both inputs and outputs and can be viewed as a self-contained unit. But it is also important to recognize that business systems are a part of larger systems—possibly industry-wide, or including several, perhaps many, companies and/or industries, or even society as a whole.[1]

The theory of systems is not new, for much of it has been developed and used in the natural sciences for many years. Further, it is being used to some degree in business. For example, systems theory is used in administering certain military programs where specification and time requirements are critical, and in some single-venture programs, e.g., construction projects. There is no reason, however,

[1] For a more comprehensive discussion of these concepts see R. A. Johnson, F. E. Kast, and J. E. Rosenzweig, *The Theory and Management of Systems,* McGraw-Hill Book Company, Inc., New York, 1963.

why this concept is not equally applicable to appliance manufacturing, retailing, or banking.

A MODEL OF THE SYSTEMS CONCEPT

Traditionally, business firms have not been structured to utilize the systems concept. In adjusting the typical business structure to fit within the framework of management by systems, certain organizational changes will be required. The following Model illustrates *one* arrangement which would implement the systems concept. We do not imply that this Model is the most effective arrangement, only that it illustrates the use of "systems thinking" in managing a business.

Referring to Exhibit 1, a master planning council engages in high-level design activity and establishes guidelines for the entire organization. This council would make decisions relative to the products or services the company supplied. Further, it would establish the limits of an operating program, decide on general policy matters relative to the design of operating systems and select the director for each new product. New-project decisions would be made with the assistance and advice of the product research and development, market research, and financial groups.

Within that framework, design activity is carried on by the resource-allocation planning group—a group which combines manpower and facilities to form working systems designed to accomplish given objectives. In both facilitating systems [2] and major project systems, additional design activity—systems review—is necessary to maintain working systems on a current basis.

The master planning council must have a definite approach to developing premises which serve as the basis for systems design. Meaningful information must be translated from environmental data on such questions as economic activity, political developments, and social trends. It is important that top management develop clear-cut systems of such information flow which will provide inputs for planning and decision making. In most companies such systems are left to chance, or at best, periodic review.

SCOPE OF THE DESIGN FUNCTION

Design means to "mark-out, designate, or indicate." It includes combining features or details and often calls for preparation of preliminary sketches or plans. The design function is important in establishing a relationship between the various stages or phases of a system, linking them together, and outlining the composite whole. For business systems the design function includes the arrangement of physical facilities for production and auxiliary activities. It also covers the arrangement of people and communication networks established to provide information concerning the process.

When establishing a new business operation, the design function seems fairly straightforward. However, the scope of systems design also covers the function of "redesign," assessing existing systems with an eye toward change. This activity has received consider-

[2] Facilitating systems are those designed to serve major project systems, e.g., a computer center.

able attention over the years under headings such as systems and procedures, work simplification, systems analysis, or systems engineering. Of these terms, *work simplification* seems to have the narrowest connotation in that it applies primarily to simple man-machine operations or clerical activity. However, as with most tools and techniques, its practitioners have proclaimed its applicability to a wide range of problems. In any case, it applies to existing systems rather than to the establishment of new systems.

Systems and procedures work has been pointed up as an all-encompassing activity, covering many facets of the business operation. However, implicitly it seems limited to the office, the flow of paper work, and the design of forms. Since the advent of electromechanical equipment, systems and procedures activity has included the designing and programming of data-processing systems. Unfortunately, EDP has been overemphasized in recent years to the exclusion of broader concepts of systems design. The specific aspects of programming, form design, and routing of paper work—as a part of the information-decision system—should be fitted into the overall systems design.

Another term used in describing this general sphere of activity is systems analysis. It also is focused on existing systems rather than on the design of new systems. Systems analysis often has a connotation of application primarily to information flow in the office and does not seem as applicable to a production or processing environment. This is not to say that it is not feasible; rather, most of the literature on the subject deals with information-processing problems.

Systems engineering implies the creation of systems as well as the analysis of existing systems. Systems engineering sometimes is assumed to deal only with physical components; that is, it deals with the integration of components and subcomponents into a total product such as a computer or missile. Using the definition of engineering as "the art and science by which the properties of matter and the sources of power in nature are made useful to man in structures, machines, and manufactured products," there is systems implication. Moreover, systems engineering can be defined as "making useful an array of components designed to accomplish a particular objective according to plan." This approach implies the interaction of more than equipment. It suggests the development of a man-machine system which could function as a task-oriented assemblage. Systems engineering comes closest to implying design activity. In many cases the systems-engineering function involves "starting from scratch" to develop subsystems, larger systems, and a composite whole.

FLOW CONCEPTS IN DESIGN

One general approach to systems design involves identification of material, energy, and information flow. These three elements are part of every system and subsystem. Consideration of them plus the use of flow concepts facilitates thinking about systems of systems.

Material

The material aspects of any system include both the facilities involved and the raw material, if any, which flows through the process. A system must be designed to ensure the *acquisition* of raw materials and/or components necessary for processing into finished products. The systems design would include identification or transportation means required to move the raw material to the processing location.

The processing operation needs to be designed in terms of constructing new facilities or realigning existing facilities. Questions of plant layout and materials-handling equipment would be a vital part of the systems-design function for in-plant processing and in-plant material flows. Industrial engineers have considered problems of this nature for many years and have developed detailed methods and techniques for optimizing layout and material handling. The trend toward automation has been evident in many material-processing operations.

Much attention also has been focused on distribution of finished goods. Where items become raw material or components in additional processing operations, the distribution problem is often straightforward. In such cases the material flow would be considered part of the flow of raw materials for a subsequent processing operation. Physical-distribution management, for items moving from producer to ultimate consumer, can be a much more difficult problem. In this case, channels of distribution vary from direct producer to consumer to a myriad of combinations of middlemen. Inventory management, at various points along the distribution channel, must be considered, as well as modes of transportation. In many cases transportation costs have been isolated for analysis without reference to the impact of such decisions on stocks of material in the pipeline. Systems design, in this sphere, would concern itself with identifying the flow of materials and with the development of an explicit network of distribution, recognizing *all* the costs involved—handling, inventory, and transportation costs. Increased effort is being devoted to the design of explicit material-flow systems from a raw-material stage through the production process and to the final consumer.[3]

Whenever the operation in question involves the flow and processing of material, appropriate systems can be designed. For business operations such as insurance companies or other commercial institutions, there may be no flow of material per se. Rather, the material in these systems is represented by the facilities and equipment involved. Regardless of whether there is any material flow, all business operations, whether processing a product or service, contain elements of energy and information.

Energy

Some source of energy is present in any operating system. It may be electricity obtained from available sources or generated by a firm's own power plant. The process may require natural gas, petroleum, coal or other fuel for production. A business usually requires electrical energy for operating facilitating systems, if not for the main processing operation itself.

Another obvious source of energy is people. Both physical and mental energy are required to operate business systems. People represent a renewable source of energy, at least for the short run. As an energy source, people are quite variable as individuals. However, *in toto*, the group represents a reasonably stable source of energy for the system.

Electricity, natural gas, or petroleum can be

[3] See Stanley H. Brewer and J. Rosenzweig, "Rhochrematics and Organizational Adjustments," *California Management Review*, Spring, 1961, pp. 52–71.

described in terms of flow concepts. Energy flows are under continual inspection by systems designers. However, they are concerned primarily with the energy or power system itself, not the integration of the energy system with other subsystems and the whole. It is somewhat more difficult to visualize people, or the work force, in terms of flow concepts. However, in a very real sense, this is entirely appropriate. There may be a continual flow of workers in terms of shifts where 24-hour, 7-day weeks are scheduled. Even for 5-day, 40-hour weeks there is a systematic flow of worker energy into the operation. In a larger sense, a business operation maintains a flow of worker energy throughout its life—from the recruiting, hiring, and orientation stages, all the way to retirement. Thus all energy can be considered as a flow process both in and of itself and as a part of other systems.

Information

Another basic element in any system is information. It facilitates interrelationships among subsystems and provides the linkage necessary to develop systems of systems. Information flow may be developed to flow along with the routing of material. Requisitions, orders, bills of lading, packing slips, receiving information, inspection reports, accounts payable, and cheques might represent the information flow connected with the acquisition of raw material. The information flow appropriate to production control is another example. In this case production instructions, material requirements, processing information, inspection requirements, routing, and scheduling would be developed from engineering drawings and/or other specifications. The information would flow through the system along with the material necessary to accomplish the planned objectives.

The accounting system requires a flow of information toward the development of income statements and balance sheets for tax purposes or stockholder reports or both. While many data-processing systems have developed on the basis of periodic batch processing, more and more systems are being developed which call for flow concepts approximating real-time activity; that is, the action or activity to be considered is recorded at the time it happens and action is taken at that time.

Information flow is the primary focus of attention for systems designers in many cases. If manufacturing facilities are fixed and if layout requirements are rigid, then the only variables remaining are raw materials (which may be uniform), energy (in the form of power and/or people), and information (in the form of plans and instructions). Systems design in such cases must concentrate on the arrangement of people and the use of information flow to optimize decision making within the system under observation. For many other systems where manufacturing and material flow are not present—service, commercial, and many governmental organizations—the flow of information is the critical element. Information must flow to key decision points where action is taken with regard to a service to be performed by the organization in question. In such cases the system can be defined primarily on the basis of the flow of information to appropriate decision points. Subsystems can be identified on this basis, and they in turn can be interrelated to define the total system.

Unfortunately, most present-day systems of this nature have been established on the basis of people relationships and organization charts without regard for project systems or task-oriented groups. In many cases these organizations function primarily on the basis of informal relationships and informal communications systems. One of the main points in systems design is the necessity of recognizing the natural relationships of informal subsystems in developing a total system. It is by means of these flow concepts that the total system can be conceptualized as a system of systems. Particular emphasis will be placed on the design of information-decision systems. Such systems are integral parts of any operating system, whether it is designed to yield a product or service.

INTEGRATING FLOW CONCEPTS

Basic to the theory of systems is the premise that given certain inputs, the processor will give certain outputs or operate within established limits. However, the business firm, as a whole, is not a structured or predictable system. Its equilibrium cannot be determined by equation, and it will change, within limits, as the components of the system are rearranged or as the inputs are reallocated.

In more advanced form, a system will include some means of control, i.e., a sensor for measuring output or related characteristics, a means of comparing the measurement with a standard, and an activating group to adjust inputs to correct the indicated deficiencies. The objective is to control variables so the system will tend to stabilize near the ideal equilibrium point. This objective is possible only if the ideal standard can be determined and if the operating values can be measured. A complete system, including control, is illustrated in Exhibit 2.

It shows the flow of planning information as it releases resources of materials, energy, and processing information. A record of the plan is stored where it can be used as a standard for control purposes. The resources are released by an activating group. For example, detailed schedules are planned (processing information), workers are assigned to specific tasks (energy), and the necessary raw materials or purchased parts are provided (materials). The combination of these inputs into the system results in the performance of a task (processing), and output is produced.

Sensory devices are placed at strategic points in the system flow to measure performance or output. These measurements are fed back to a control group, and this information is compared with the standard. As significant deviations from plan are recognized, information to correct the situation is released to the activating group, which in turn will change the release of resources or information, energy, or materials.

DESIGNING OPERATING SYSTEMS

Operating systems have one thing in common: they should all use a common language for communicating among themselves and with higher levels. In addition, of course, each

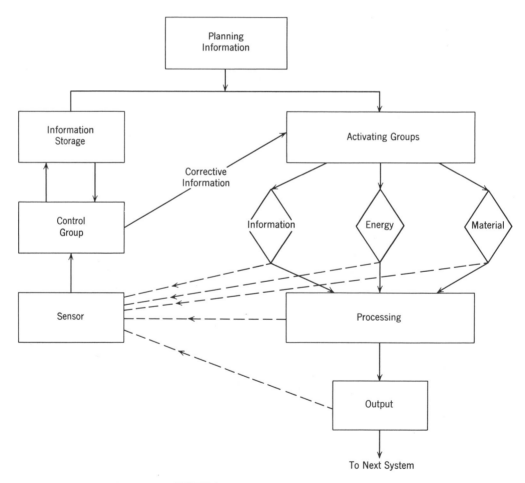

EXHIBIT 2. An Operating System.

system designed should be structured in consideration of company-wide policies. Other than these limits, each operating system can be created to meet the specific requirements of its own product or service.

The operating system is structured to (1) direct its own inputs, (2) control its own operation, and (3) review and revise its own system design as required. Input is furnished by three different groups: technical information is generated as input into the processing system, and in addition, technical information is the basis for originating processing information. Both technical and processing information are used by the material input system to determine and supply materials for processing. The operating system has its own control unit, which measures the inputs and outputs of system. However, corrective action, when necessary, would be activated by input allocation.

This model of an operating system can be related to any business situation. For example, if it represents a system to produce television sets, the technical information would refer to the design of the product, processing information would include the plan of manufacture and schedule, and the material input would pertain to the raw materials and purchased parts used in the processing. These inputs of information and material would be processed and become output. Process control would measure the output in comparison with the standard (information storage) obtained from input allocation and issue corrective information whenever the system failed to function according to plan. The design of the system would be reviewed continually, and the components rearranged or replaced when these changes would improve operating efficiency.

A systems-review function is an integral part of each project system. The system as a whole should be reviewed periodically by means of a thoroughgoing analysis and synthesis of the system and its components. The system should be broken down into its individual subsystems, and each of these should be evaluated in terms of the likelihood of continuing efficiency. Adjustments can be made on the basis of the results of such analysis. Then a process of synthesis must take place in order to restructure an integrated whole.

Why is it that subsystems and/or project systems must be reviewed and adjusted continually? One obvious reason was mentioned above; system requirements change over a period of time, and hence the system must be redesigned in the light of evolutionary trends. Static systems design goes out of date almost immediately. In fact, the battle cry of some systems analysts and designers is, "If it works, it must be obsolete!" As a particular project progresses through its life cycle, the product mission may change, as may other environmental or competitive conditions. Organizational adjustments may be required, or technological advancements may allow improvements in handling of either material or information flow.

Some systems are built around individuals within an organization. If identification of decision points is based on strong or dominant personalities, the information-decision system may be disrupted completely whenever key-personnel changes are made. Hence systems must be redesigned in order to accommodate the changes in managerial personnel.

The original allocation of resources may have been temporary in the sense of availability of necessary elements either internally or externally. Make-shift systems have a way of perpetuating themselves regardless of inefficiencies. It is important to reappraise the situation often enough to make sure that such temporary arrangements are revised when conditions allow.

Another typical problem is the tendency toward empire building, the accumulation of more than enough material, manpower, and facilities to accomplish given objectives. The project manager must resist the tendency towards bigness for the sake of prestige or status. A semi-detached, hopefully objective systems-review group can help nurture such a point of view.

Continuing attention must be devoted to systems review and the implementation of proposed changes. Follow-up is necessary because of the seemingly inherent resistance to change on the part of people involved in the system. Unless such resistance can be overcome, poor systems may be prolonged. Once the atmosphere is established for continual analysis and review, implementation of change becomes progressively easier.

CONSTRAINTS ON THE DESIGN FUNCTION

In order to place the systems-design function in proper perspective it is important to consider the various constraints on this activity. Policy decisions on the part of the master planning council not only provide guidelines for systems design at lower levels, they also provide boundaries. If top management does not embrace the systems concept as a managerial philosophy, systems design cannot be implemented. The proper atmosphere must be created at all levels in order for this approach to be utilized.

Other limiting factors include the amounts and kinds of facilities available as well as the work force and its skill mix. Elaborate and sophisticated systems designs might be forthcoming which could not be implemented because of lack of facilities and/or manpower. However, we suggest that the systems-design group start with designs for systems that are needed rather than those which obviously can be implemented. The organization will progress if it is forced to strain toward goals and objectives. If the design proves too much of a "cloud nine" approach, the system can always be scaled back to meet existing resources.

The resource-allocation council places constraints on the system-review function in terms of policy decisions with regard to allocation of the resources between major projects systems and facilitating systems. It may be that systems analysts within major project systems have designed optimal arrangements for their own operation without regard to other project systems. The resource-allocation planning group may decide that certain facilitating systems common to several or all project systems should be set up to serve the entire group. Thus policy decisions throughout the total system provide constraints within which systems designers must operate.

Along with policy decisions and equipment and facility limitations, another constraint which must be taken into consideration by systems designers is people. The remark "It would be a great system if it weren't for the people involved" is appropriate here. Problems of resistance to change or of out-and-out antagonism are evident throughout the literature describing impacts of automation and electronic data processing. Similar reaction is often evident when designing information decision systems which call for realignment of people and equipment according to the systems concept. These human factors are important variables in systems design and must be given consideration.

CONCLUSION

Systems design is the key activity in implementing the systems concept. This function provides an over-all framework by establishing subsystems, larger systems, and a composite, integrated whole.

We cannot overemphasize the fact that, first and foremost, the systems concept is a frame of mind. Management must be receptive to this approach and develop a philosophy in which planning, organizing, controlling, and communication are accomplished in terms of subsystems integrated into a composite whole. Once there is acceptance of the systems concept and the feasibility of organizing on the basis of a master planning council, a resource-allocation planning group, and an operations planning group (with facilitating and project systems reporting to it), the systems-design function can be carried out in a progressive atmosphere. The atmosphere created is all-important; it fosters creativity and innovation on the part of systems designers.

12. THE DEVELOPMENT AND INSTALLATION OF A TOTAL MANAGEMENT SYSTEM

Dr. R. L. Martino *

Modern business management is faced with a dilemma. At a time when profit margins are shrinking and both foreign and domestic competition are intensifying, heavy expenditures are required for modernization. Such expenditures are considered essential if a business is to remain competitive and if its profit margins are to improve.

In considering modernization, management usually thinks first in terms of facilities and machinery. Too often, however, that is as far as the improvements are carried. The need exists, and has long existed, for modernization of the management function itself. The need is especially acute today because of the great and growing complexity of both products and procedures. Management science has developed many new tools to modernize the management function; it is up to management to take full advantage of these developments.

Management systems in the past have been concerned mainly with the preparation and analysis of historical reports. While this kind of reporting is valuable, rarely is it timely enough to be truly useful. Production figures for January, for example, might not be available until mid-February (or later) when their usefulness will have diminished considerably.

OBJECTIVES

There is an urgent need in business to be able to look ahead as well as behind and to anticipate changes in markets and profit situa-

SOURCE: *Data Processing for Management* (April, 1963), pp. 31–37. Reprinted by permission of Data Processing Magazine, The Publication of Computers and Information Technology.

* Special Editor, *Total Systems Letter*.

tions. Basically, *a system is required that will forestall the development of an unprofitable business situation.*

Therefore, the primary objective in developing a total management system should be the production of detailed, up-to-the-minute summaries of the past and the use of these summaries to project future activity. In essence, the functions of a total management system are:

1. To predict
2. To compare the prediction with actual results, and
3. To produce the deviations between the predicted and the actual.

Thereafter, the system should use these deviations to prepare a new, updated set of predictions which can be used as the basis for management decision. This concept is known as *management by exception*. While this term has been bandied about a good deal during the past few years, there are few instances where the concept has been applied in its fullest sense.

The predictive function, it should be understood, includes the determination and consideration of alternatives, and for each alternative, the effects of a decision. The method used in this process is called *simulation,* a technique wherein the various factors involved in a given situation are assembled into a model, usually of a mathematical nature. By varying the factors systematically, it is possible to weigh each alternative and its effects. Such information can be of great value to management in making decisions.

A total management system, then, produces basically two kinds of information for all levels of management:

1. Predictions based on historical data and simulation.

2. Suggested changes of present procedures to make the selected predictions possible.

As indicated previously, the predictions are continually compared with actual results to determine deviations. These, in turn, are used to refine or revise the initial set of predictions and strategies. Then, the whole system recycles, producing new predictions, and so on.

The cycle of a total management system is summarized in the illustration in Figure 1. The upper portion of the cycle diagram, if followed in a counterclockwise manner, represents the regular path. That is, data are used to produce a model which in turn develops predictions for use by management. When decisions are reached by management as to the course of action to be followed, the program is implemented. Then, data obtained from operation of the program are used to produce required statements and reports, and are also used as updated history for the next cycle of the system. The lower half of the diagram represents management action required to analyze and correct deviations from the predicted results. The result of such action also becomes a factor in the next cycle of the system.

The value of exception reports drawn from these predictions and historical summaries will vary from function to function in the management system. For example, a daily comparison of predicted and actual sales might be quite useful to an order department, but a daily comparison of predicted with actual profits would not. Decisions as to the type and frequency of reports would be based on the function and on the degree of managed cost control involved.

SCIENTIFIC METHODS

In the development and installation of a total management system, scientific methods have played an increasingly important role. Management science involves the application of mathematics to management problems with the aid of the computer to prepare possible alternatives for management decisions. The computer is particularly valuable to management science because it can reduce vast quantities of data to meaningful trends.

When businesses were small and operations were relatively uncomplicated, management decision was often the responsibility of one man—the entrepreneur. Sufficient information was available so that the owner-operator could determine the best course of action by weighing all the alternatives and selecting the best. Whether he knew it or not, the entrepreneur simulated the operation of his business in his mind and, after weighing the various alternatives, made decisions based on the information available to him. And, because the operation was small and uncomplicated, the entrepreneur was in a position to know the consequences of his decisions.

As business volume increased and the organizational structures grew more complex, the lines of communication gradually became less direct and immediate. Without access to the most timely information, management could not know of every alternative course of action, let alone the result of each alternative.

The first attempt to ease the situation was mechanization of the accounting function. Unfortunately, the equipment available could not fully cope with the problem. While it is true that information became more readily available than previously, the voluminous reports in tabulating form were unwieldy and, by the time they reached operating management, they were often too dated to be of real value. To decision making top management, the reports were even less useful.

With the advent of the electronic computer and the introduction of mathematical techniques, management came a step nearer a solution. These new tools make it possible to simulate *all* the operations of an organization and thereby to reduce the overgrown and overly complex problems of business management to a workable form. The electronic computer can be introduced into any present corporate structure with little modification to the line and staff concept so that it is possible to simulate the function of the single entrepreneur without a return to that unrealistic organizational structure.

The emphasis upon computers, mathematics, and the scientific method does not diminish in the least the importance of common sense in distinguishing between what is wanted, what is possible, and what is currently being done. While it is true that methods and machines exist which will produce almost any desired report, economics and common sense must be applied to determine what

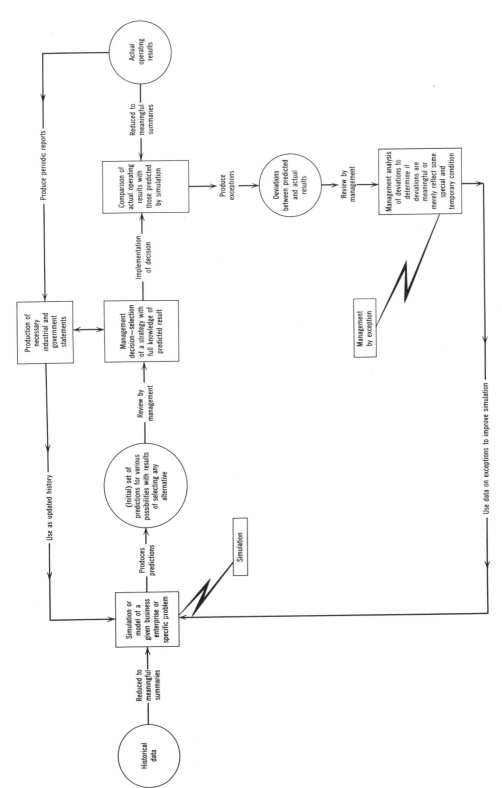

FIG. 1. Total management system cycle.

is realistic. In the development of any management system, too high an emphasis cannot be placed on basic, down-to-earth realism.

STAGES OF SYSTEM DEVELOPMENT

The development and installation of a total management system may be broken down into three major stages. These are:

1. Definition of the problem.
2. Design of the total management system.
3. Programming, cutover to the new system, and system evaluation and modification.

Within each of these areas there are a number of separate operations and activities which must be performed, many of which overlap one another. An arrow diagram [1] has been prepared which illustrates the interrelationship of these activities (see Figure 2). This diagram specifies the various tasks necessary to develop and install a total management system. Whereas the diagram is somewhat abbreviated, the exclusions would be of minor consequence to the overall logic of the plan.

PROBLEM DEFINITION

The first stage, problem definition, requires developing a realistic statement indicating the kind of system necessary to produce the reports needed for effective management. This phase must include establishing objectives of a total management system, personnel selection to develop and design such a system, and determining all requisite elements of the system.

Flow charting techniques have generally been used in the problem definition stage, but these charts are cumbersome, difficult to prepare, and difficult to read. Moreover, they of-

[1] *How to read an arrow diagram.* Each job or activity in a project is represented by an arrow. Work flows from the tail of an arrow to the head, but the length of the arrow and the direction in which it points are immaterial. Dotted arrows do not represent real activities but are used to maintain logical relationships. The junction points of arrows are called events; they are numbered so that the tail of an arrow has a number smaller than the head. Events represent points in time as opposed to arrows which represent activities that consume time. The event also indicates the point in time when all preceding activities have been completed and succeeding activities can start.

ten direct management's attention toward simply a mechanization of the old system rather than any bold new approach.

Problem definition for a total management system is based upon data handling procedures. The structure of any operating data system is based upon *data elements* (stock numbers, employee numbers, employee names) which are collected into *data files* (payroll register, stock inventory). Certain rules govern the use of data elements to produce new, or updated, data files. These new files are the *output* reports. The original data elements form the *input* reports to the system.

The rules governing the updating of information fall into three categories. These are:

1. Data movement—the transfer of an element of data from the old document to the new.
2. Arithmetic—the performance of some arithmetic operation upon one or more elements of data during the data transfer.
3. Logical decision—the examination of a data element in the input report to determine a course of action in preparing the output report. For example, the size of gross pay determines the income tax rate.

These three operations form the basis of any electronic computer program since all of the functions that any computer can perform may be reduced to data movement, arithmetic, and logical decision.

In his analysis of a data handling system, the systems engineer will isolate each type of data element and give it a name and number. Then he will determine the interrelationship of the various data elements, such as the format and type of documents in which the data will appear. At the same time, it is necessary to determine the logical selection rules to be used and the arithmetic calculations to be performed on the input data.

The steps in the analysis of a data handling system follow:

1. Determination of data elements.
2. Determination of the interrelationships of data elements and the location of data elements in the file.
3. Determination of rules governing the handling of data elements and data files.
4. Formulation of decision tables where logical choice would govern the selection of one of many possible paths.

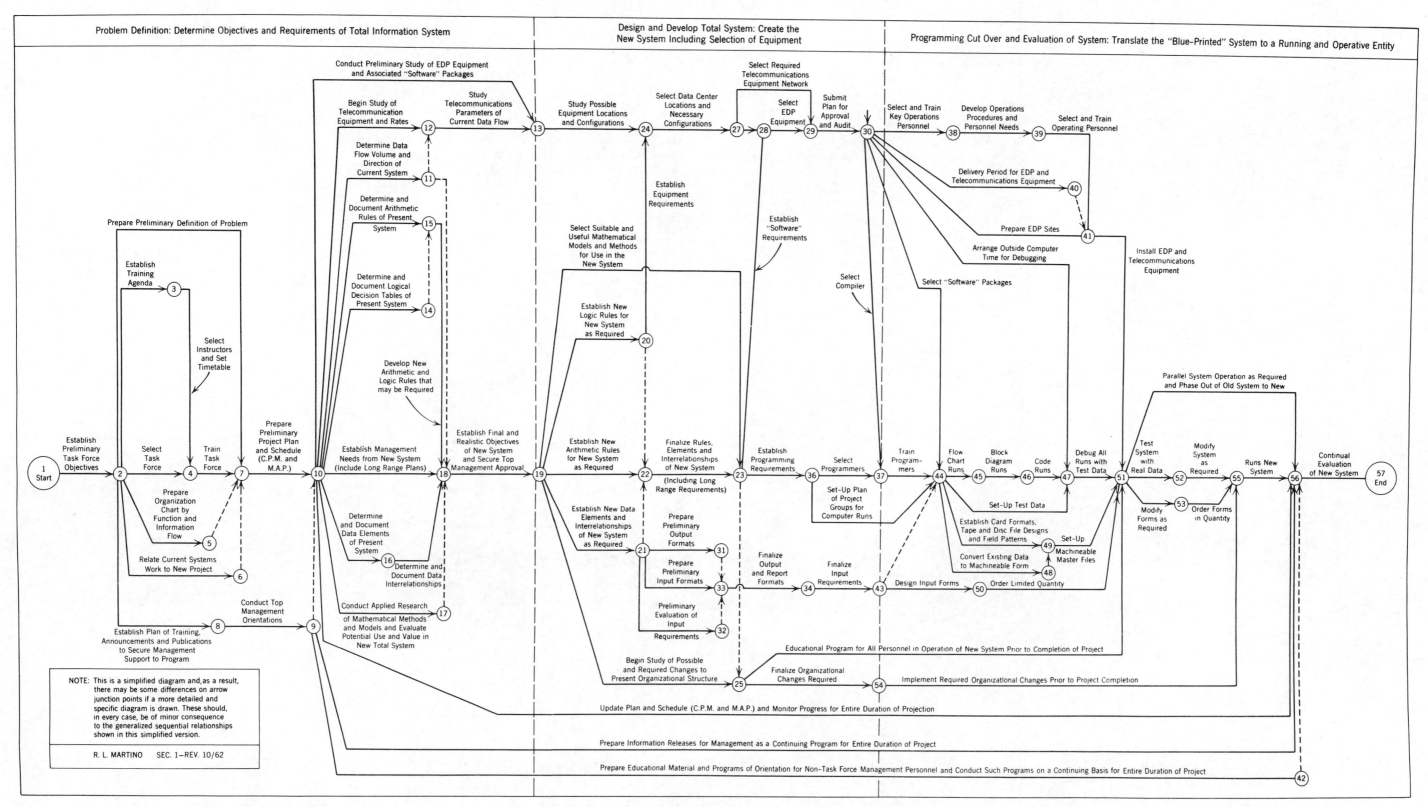

FIG. 2. A generalized plan for developing and installing a total management system.

5. Formulation of rules governing the production of specific reports required for specific management action.

Various techniques have been devised to assist in the collection of information required for problem definition. The best features of these techniques have been combined in a new system called START (systematic tabulation and analysis of requirements technique).

With this technique, the first step is to define the areas of decision (planning, controlling and operating) necessary to manage the enterprise. These areas of decision are determined from a study of the existing organization, operations and policies.

The problem definition phase, to this point, includes:

1. The establishment of operating objectives.

2. The selection and training of personnel to study the problem.

3. The use of START to analyze the present system and document the required system.

To complete the problem definition phase, management must establish the ultimate objectives of a new system so that parameters and response speeds can be determined. This procedure may lead to additions, deletions or revisions in the reports being produced which may, in turn, lead to the introduction of new data elements and the elimination of others.

Throughout problem definition and succeeding stages of the development and installation of a total management system, control should be maintained with the critical path method (CPM) and the multiple allocation procedure (MAP).

The critical path method is a management technique devised for the planning, scheduling and monitoring of large projects. The planning phase consists of drawing an arrow diagram of a project by assembling all of the project activities according to logical sequence and relationships. When time estimates are applied to each of the activities, it is possible to determine the longest (and therefore critical) path of activities. The arrow diagram thus provides easy visual assimilation of the plan and it functions as a working model which can be used to simulate project operations.

The multiple allocation procedure is used to allocate resources to the project and thereby place the plan on a calendar timetable. Resources are levelled to obtain the most economical schedule possible. MAP is applied after the logic of the arrow diagram has been thoroughly analyzed and refined. The allocation of resources automatically produces a schedule for the project. Then, when the project is in operation, data are collected and analyzed on a regular basis to be used in rescheduling or replanning when necessary.

Experience has shown that CPM and MAP used in combination enable management to determine the proper sequencing of activities and to allocate resources needed to perform these tasks in a coordinated fashion.

SYSTEM DESIGN

After the problem has been defined, the next step is to design the new system. This phase should include:

1. The continued examination of various scientific techniques, such as transportation models, simulation, and inventory models, and the final selection of those to be used in the new system.

2. The development of consolidated reports and report formats for historical record keeping to satisfy business and governmental requirements.

3. The testing of selected mathematical techniques which use recent and past experience as the basis for predictions. This would include the generation of management reports that compare the predicted with the actual and offer management various alternatives and the results of each alternative.

4. The selection of a judicious (economic) combination of telecommunications equipment to transmit data over large distances and the establishment of electronic data processing centers to meet present and projected (future) needs.

5. The development of an organization which will program and install the total management system, operate the equipment, and make full and effective use of the results of such a system.

The underlying objective in these considerations should be the most economical combination of equipment and people in an industrial complex in order to provide effective management.

While it is easy to speak of using equipment, especially electronic data processing equipment, one should never become so sophisticated as to overlook the use of pencil and paper. A real distinction between an expert and an amateur in the field of management systems and in the application of electronic data processing equipment and techniques is the ability to distinguish between the proper and improper use of machinery to solve a problem. Quite often the best and most adequate solution involves a simple technique applied with pencil and paper (and sometimes an eraser).

PROGRAMMING, CUTOVER, EVALUATION, AND MODIFICATION

Programming, which begins the third phase in formulating a total management system, has been greatly simplified by the great strides made with program compilers, especially COBOL (common business oriented language). With this automatic programming technique a single English language statement can be used to generate many computer instructions—fully checked and integrated in a running program. And looking ahead, it is conceivable that START will lead to the development of a system-type compiler that will eliminate even the block diagramming required with COBOL.

The cutover operation is so interrelated with programming and system design that it is best illustrated by the arrow diagram (Figure 2). Cutover entails such things as the design of forms, conversion of data, installation of new equipment, and the like.

No equipment should be ordered until the system design phase is virtually complete. Delivery should be specified for an appropriate time during the cutover phase. All too often equipment is ordered before the system is designed and then delivered before it is needed.

Considering that rentals range between $10,000 and $50,000 per month, a poor decision or an ill-timed delivery can be extremely expensive. In addition, the cost of programming, which often exceeds equipment rental fees, can cause total costs to skyrocket if the programming effort is not phased in properly with the installation of the new system.

Once the new system is in operation, *system evaluation and modification* begin. This phase should be a continuing effort which seeks to take advantage of new developments as they occur. The ultimate evaluation of the system's effectiveness is, of course, the financial statement.

Throughout the period of development and installation of a total management system, a planned program of training must be conducted to ensure the support of middle management for the program. If this is not done, even the best engineered system may never be completely effective.

SUMMARY

This report is an outline of the basic steps, and an introduction to some of the problems, involved in creating a total management system. The task is not an easy one. It requires a great deal of work (particularly on the part of line personnel), considerable and searching analysis, and some far reaching decisions. The installation of such a system will have tremendous impact. Properly implemented, it will undoubtedly result in increased profits. Moreover, the total management system is designed to put managing back into the hands of management by producing the information needed to "really manage." The opportunity and challenge are here. But if there is any hesitancy—to do the work, to make the decisions, to commit the necessary funds—then there is no point in even starting.

13. BASIC CONCEPTS FOR DESIGNING
A FUNDAMENTAL INFORMATION SYSTEM

A. F. Moravec *

Analyzing a corporate data system is still a primitive process. Although the computer has revolutionized data systems in the past decade, there has been no corresponding revolution in the procedures for installing and operating them. The rationale for determining what data to analyze and how to go about it and the basic techniques for interviewing, documenting, flow charting, and analyzing have changed little since the advent of the computer. Indeed, they have not changed greatly since the nineteenth century.

The large size, complexity, and variety of modern data systems cause continuing difficulties for the systems analyst. Two to eight years, depending on the scope of the application, can elapse from the initiation of a data systems study to its implementation. During this period the systems analyst is beset by continual pressures to get the system operating. Meanwhile, policy changes and personnel rotation are playing havoc with the systems planning.

In general, four major problems handicap present-day systems analysis: (1) a large workload, (2) a long span of elapsed time, (3) a lack of explicit directions both for conducting the study and for using the results, and (4) the lack of a technique to control changes in the data system throughout its life.

These problems are far from being solved. Some new techniques, however, offer promise of alleviating some of them. Data network analysis, which incorporates a method of using the electronic data processor to prepare many of the systems analyses automatically, reduces the total workload and the time span from inception of a study through the preliminary phase. Source input/output analysis facilitates

SOURCE: *Management Services* (July–August, 1965), pp. 37–45. Reprinted by permission of *Management Services*.

* Booze, Allen Applied Research, Inc.

development of the essential information that each functional group within the company needs to operate efficiently. Simulation permits study of the operation of the information system in the form of a model.

This article describes these techniques and explains how they can be applied to the design of an information system, specifically a so-called fundamental information system based on the "single information flow" concept of data processing.

Information Systems

An information system may be defined as the procedures, methodologies, organization, software, and hardware elements needed to insert and retrieve selected data as required for operating and managing a company. In this article no distinction is made between so-called management information systems and other kinds of information systems. The term is used to include all specific data required to conduct the business of the company regardless of whether the data are classified as operating, management, accounting, or any other kind of data.

In many companies the information systems are systems by courtesy only. In the early days of computer technology the components or subsystems approach prevailed. An integrated business system was thought to exist when pieces of information were introduced into the information flow and perpetuated there with a minimum of manual intervention. Mechanization of existing operations—or of data for specific random jobs—resulted in a multiplicity of relatively static systems put together on a piecemeal basis.

Now there is a growing recognition that the interactions and interdependencies among components of a system are more important than the components themselves. Managements are beginning to realize that the information system must be integrated lest data processing become a giant papermill so complex in structure that it is impossible to control.

As Richard E. Sprague has pointed out,[1] fundamental economic and system pressures are fostering a management desire for clean and uncomplicated information systems. Economic pressures include the need for functional and geographic integration of data and the pressure for sharing of computer equipment by users. System pressures, based on the desirability of carrying the processing of data to the user and in other ways making service to him more rapid and more meaningful, include the desire to mechanize data at the source; the need to solve the problems of sharing time on computers that operate on a batch processing basis; and the attractiveness of incorporating on-line real time data processing with current feedback of information to assist management in its decision making function.

These pressures do not operate on every company with equal force, of course. The organization that is considering the design of a new information system should first consider the following questions:

1. How satisfied are people throughout the organization with the existing input and output of information?

2. Have the most recent important changes in data processing operations—manual or computer—been fully "digested" as yet?

3. Have major new technical improvements in systems hardware and software recently become available?

4. Are operating management personnel receptive to new and important changes in the future?

5. Does the organization have designers with the skill and experience needed to develop a new information system?

6. Are the probable time schedules for such a project satisfactory?

7. Are financial budgets adequate?

8. Does the potential payoff justify the effort? Cost and benefit elements of both the present and the proposed system should be analyzed and compared. Exhibit 1 lists the payoff elements normally considered.

[1] Richard E. Sprague, *Electronic Business Systems,* The Ronald Press Company, New York, 1962.

SYSTEM COSTS

Hardware:
  Basic processor
  Storage devices
  Peripheral equipment
  Communication equipment
  Facilities
  Input/output devices
  Equipment maintenance
    Total

Operating Expenses:
  Program maintenance
  Equipment operators
  Media preparers (key punchers)
  Data collectors
  Data control and correction
  Utilities
  Cards, paper, etc.
    Total

Development Costs:
  Hiring and training of programers and
    analysts
  Salaries
  Disruption of normal operations
  Retraining displaced personnel
    Total

SYSTEM BENEFITS

Decreased Operating Costs:
  Fewer people
  Less inventory
  Fewer penalties for late payment or delivery
  Lower transportation or purchasing costs
  Fewer shortages to interrupt production
  Better scheduling of production
  Better service (internal-external)

EXHIBIT 1. System Payoff.

If the design of a new information system seems worthwhile, the next question is, "What kind of information system?" As an earlier article in this magazine pointed out,[2] two alternative concepts are being proposed by data processing specialists today. They are the "total" information system, based on the "total systems" approach, and the "fundamental" information system, based on the "single information flow" philosophy.

The total information system, a logical ex-

[2] A. F. Moravec, "Basic Concepts for Planning Advanced EDP Systems," *Management Services,* May–June, 1965, p. 52.

tension of the present subsystems approach, is an attempt to unite all existing information subsystems in the company into a single integrated system. The intent is to include all data for all the needs of all levels of management and operations. Each piece of data is entered in each information subsystem that may need it, with multiple records of similar data as a result.

The fundamental information system, on the other hand, is limited to data considered absolutely essential to the operation of the company. Other data needed for one reason or another by specific user groups are recorded and processed outside the fundamental information system. The fundamental data themselves are recorded only once and stored in a central location.

These two systems are compared in Exhibit 2. Since the author considers the single

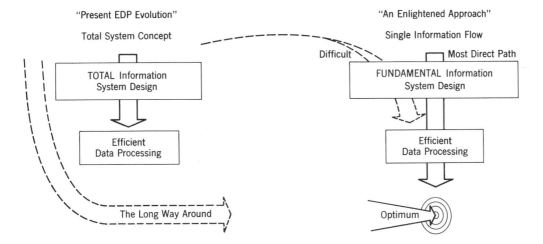

FOUNDATION FOR:
"Total" Information System
1. Includes all basic interacting and interrelating data in attainable subsystems.
2. It attempts to satisfy all data requirements for all levels of management and for all operating needs.
3. All required or desired data will be included in the information data reservoir.
4. It is envisioned that this data reservoir or data bank will certainly be the larger of the two.
5. Record lengths will be smaller but the system will include multiple records of similar data.
6. Because of tradition and the desire to use what one already has developed, this kind of an information system will be difficult to construct. Many obstacles including complex data integration and handling will have to be hurdled.

FOUNDATION FOR:
"Fundamental" Information System
1. Includes only "essential" or "fundamental" data required to effectively operate the firm as a complete entity.
2. It satisfies only the basic data needs of the firm to accomplish its mission and provides the "selective" feedback information necessary for management decisions at its proper level and station.
3. "Nonessential" or "secondary" classed data desired by some operation or by some level of management will be processed off line by peripheral equipment and will not be included in the primary information data reservoir. (Until full conversion, most "secondary" type data will be processed in their present fashion as subsystems.)
4. It is envisioned that this data reservoir or data bank will be the smaller of the two.
5. Record lengths will be long and many, but only single records will prevail.
6. Since this system involves a completely new development approach, ties with the previous EDP environment are severed making this the most direct and hence the shortest path to the target of optimum data processing.

EXHIBIT 2. Concept Comparison Between "Total" and "Fundamental" Information Systems.

information flow concept the most promising route to simple and efficient data processing, the remainder of this article will be concerned with the design of a fundamental information system.

Design Principles

The following generalizations represent principles [3] that should be kept in mind when designing the information system:

• An information system is a system for supplying information to users who must take coordinated action. If effective communication is to take place, the language used must be such that response will be identified by all members of the organization. If action is to be coordinated, the information system cannot be treated as a group of independent subsystems.

• The information system must remove all doubt about data, that is, the system must be so reliable that the user will depend upon it rather than upon his own observations. For example, information will fail to evoke response (decisions) relevant to the pursuit of its ends if it is found by receivers to be inconsistent with their own direct observations. In this case the system which produces the information will serve to increase rather than to reduce doubt; it will cloud rather than clarify issues confronting decision makers.

• There is a point at which the marginal cost of differentiation of information and comprehensiveness of information exceeds the marginal utility of information to the receiver, i.e., an individual's capacity for making sound judgments about a complex situation may be seriously impaired by supplying him with a lot of information which he believes would be relevant but whose influence on the situation is not clear to him.

• Thus, the information system is an abstracting system. Its justification lies in the reduction of the information available to the information that is relevant to action. But abstraction should not be carried to the point where differences in the significance of data are obscured.

• An information system is a device for continually bringing under notice new facts

[3] R. J. Chambers, "The Role of Information Systems in Decision Making," *Management Technology*, Vol. 4, No. 1, June, 1964.

and new knowledge. It must provide not only the premises of decisions but also a feedback so that decisions may be reaffirmed or abandoned in favor of others. The development of an organization and the development of the judgment of its agents alike depend on this feedback.

• Since both the capacity and the time available for observation are limited, an information system must provide a formal record to guard against misinterpretation of past experiences. The records of an organization are its memory. Therefore, all records and communications at any time serve not only their immediate function but also the function of memory.

• The information system must be regarded as a continuously developing instrument, in much the same way as an organization is constantly developing.

• It is a matter of experience that information processing is done according to habitual modes far more commonly than according to deliberate assessment of the user's requirements.

Requirements

For the fundamental information system to do its job properly, it must meet these requirements:

1. It must provide all the data essential to the operation of the company. These data should include both planning data and performance data. Performance data must measure both planned and present status and must indicate the probable future impact. Cost and financial data should be compared with budget or target dollars; operational schedules should be compared with planned completions; technical quality assurance data should be compared with established standards.

2. The system must be responsive to management needs. This responsiveness can be obtained by "designing in" the flexibility and adaptability needed to re-allocate resources as required. By means of computer simulations of management decision making requirements, for example, the type and frequency of changes in programs and resource allocations can be tested, and likely condition boundaries can be established.

3. It should be capable of "dynamic self-

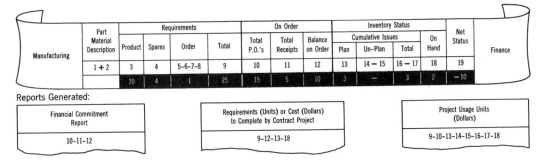

Manufacturing	Part Material Description	Requirements				On Order			Inventory Status					Net Status	Finance
		Product	Spares	Order	Total	Total P.O.'s	Total Receipts	Balance on Order	Cumulative Issues			On Hand			
									Plan	Un–Plan	Total				
	1 + 2	3	4	5–6–7–8	9	10	11	12	13	14 – 15	16 – 17	18	19		
		20	4	1	25	15	5	10	3	—	3	2	— 10		

Reports Generated:

Financial Commitment Report	Requirements (Units) or Cost (Dollars) to Complete by Contract Project	Project Usage Units (Dollars)
10–11–12	9–12–13–18	9–10–13–14–15–16–17–18

EXHIBIT 3. Essential Data Single Record Layout—Example (A Portion of Single Record).

reprograming," i.e., able to reprogram itself to meet the ever changing demands of the company. (This is a part of the single information flow concept and its design.)

Systems Analysis

To analyze the interaction of functions and departments using today's methods of operation and then to design the optimum system for mechanization using tomorrow's methods is a complex task involving complex human factors.

A completely new method of analyzing systems and describing information requirements is needed. Such a method should fulfill two requirements:

1. For understandability and workability, the method should present the system in the form of a network in order to permit visual display of data dependencies and interactions, in order to pinpoint communication requirements (volumes, load, frequencies, stations, and the like), and in order to facilitate mathematical treatment (network theory, traffic or queueing theory, linear programing, PERT/Time/Cost, and the like).

2. The principle of data feedback must be incorporated in order to ensure the availability of those data required for management decision making and also to provide a basic structure for decision making simulation programs.

Data Network Analysis

Two new systems analysis techniques are available that meet these requirements. They are data network analysis—for the synthesis phase of the systems study—and source input/output analysis—for the information-gathering phase.

Data network analysis [4] is illustrated in Exhibit 3, Exhibit 4, and Exhibit 5. With this technique, data storage points in the system are analyzed and converted to single records as indicated in Exhibit 3; each record's characteristics, the activity in and out, and the data elements it contains are detailed.

With this method of analysis, the analyst prepares a flow chart of "event chains" and activities rather than of documents. In this way he can trace the flow of data and actions throughout a data network as they are created and as they respond to events instead of trying to categorize them into arbitrary segments of an information system under such nebulous labels as "applications." Exhibit 4 shows a simple data network; Exhibit 5 shows the same data network in conjunction with a computer communication network. One advantage of this technique is that the computer can be programed to prepare much of the initial systems analysis and documentation automatically. [5]

This data network methodology provides a visual representation of data and action dependency and interdependency, time sequencing of both data and action, load and volume analysis for communication and equipment purposes, and, as a by-product, automation of analysis and documentation. Using the computer to prepare systems analyses automatically—although it does not relieve the systems

[4] Arthur D. Hall, A Methodology for Systems Engineering, D. Van Nostrand Company, Inc., Princeton, New Jersey, 1962.

[5] With some modifications, this technique is similar to Autosate, an automated data systems analysis technique developed by the Rand Corporation.

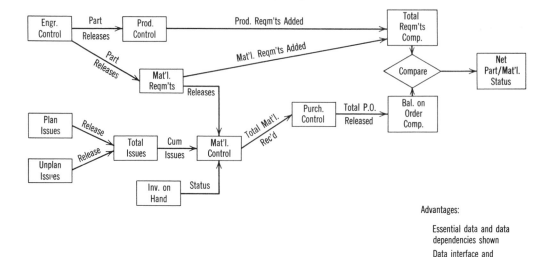

EXHIBIT 4. Data Network—Example (Part/Material Number—Description—Specifications—Price).

analyst of any of his usual analysis and design responsibilities—speeds up the preliminary analysis phase of the study and at the same time makes possible a more thorough analysis than can be prepared with present methods.

Determining records and data characteristics, volumes, relationships, and data storage needs gives the analyst a sound basis for design of a new data system. In addition, the data network analysis technique permits the tracing of data and their highly intricate chain reactions throughout the structure of the organization; in the process, user demand and users' effects on each other can be measured.

Because of the complexity of the task of defining a fundamental information system that crosses department lines and includes many functions, data network analysis should be preceded by source input/output analysis.[6] Assuming the systems designer has postulated that all information to be inserted into or withdrawn from the system by each point of origin (source) will be stored centrally and will be available on a real time basis as needed, the procedure for conducting input/output analysis is as follows:

[6] Gregory and Van Horn, *Automated Data Processing Systems—Principles and Procedures,* 2d ed., Wadsworth Publishing Company, Inc., Belmont, California, 1963.

Source Input/Output

• The characteristics (functions, departmental mission) of each point of origin are identified. The true source of information generated at each point of origin (station) and the information required by each are described in detail.

• The information that must be held in central storage to satisfy all operating and management requirements is specified in detail. For management-type information a set of decision rules based on the objectives, policies, and procedures of the organization is inserted into central storage.

• For communication purposes, the message formats and lengths for transmission to and from each point-of-origin central point are defined. In addition, the information volumes, i.e., the number of messages per hour for each hour and for each point of origin, are estimated.

• The sum total of all information generated, stored, and processed for each point of origin and each communication channel and for the central computer location is computed.

These data are then placed on a network for the synthesis phase of the systems study.

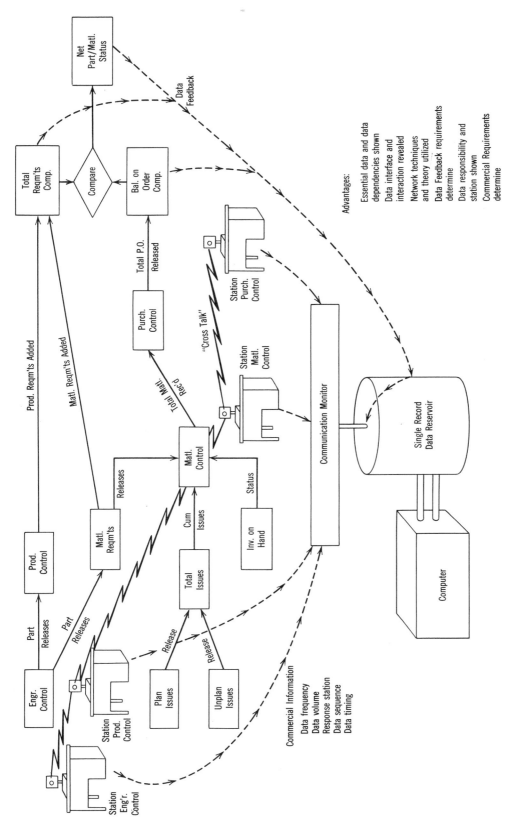

EXHIBIT 5. Communication and Data Network—Example (Part/Material Number—Description—Specifications—Price).

133

The basic steps in designing the information system may be summarized as follows:

1. Determine management's needs to monitor the enterprise as a whole.
2. Design the fundamental information flow, indicating the relationships among the major functions and data, for example, engineering, manufacturing, procurement, marketing, and finance.
3. Develop in detail the "essential" information that each function requires to operate efficiently.
4. Determine each function's data and action requirements and each function's dependence upon other functions' actions and/or information.

Administratively, the plan for conducting the systems study breaks down into three time phases. The first phase, investigation, consists of construction and testing of a simulation model of the system and of source input/output analysis. The second phase, that of preliminary design, includes merging and synthesis of the information gathered in the first phase, preparation of a composite data network analysis, complete initial design of the overall system, and design and testing of a workable automated system. The final phase, final design, consists of complete initial design of system details, selection of equipment configuration, and preparation of a plan for implementation of the information system.

Investigation Phase

The initial investigation—the first phase—calls for a simultaneous two-pronged attack. One group, composed of operations analysts, is responsible for preparing an information system model with a resultant computer simulation model. This process is illustrated in Exhibit 6.

Simulation is a technique whereby a system and its associated sequence of events are reproduced in the computer, that is, the computer is made to act like the system being studied. These simulation programs are usually referred to as "models" since they are representations of the real system.

At the same time another group, composed of systems analysts, is responsible for preparing an information system based upon review and analysis of present operations, subsystems, and data flows. Using the source input/output systems analysis approach, they determine and define "essential" data and secondary data, review present subsystem applications, prepare a network indicating data dependencies and interactions, design a single-record layout and data flow processing scheme, prepare preliminary conversion specifications, prepare a data and communication network flow, and prepare and assemble documentation.

Both groups must operate under the same systems objectives, goals, and criteria. These are established early in the study and revised as required. Examples follow:

Objectives

• Determine management's needs to monitor the whole enterprise.
• Provide for single-transaction and complete processing of "essential" data and complete single records and data storage.

Capabilities

• Include planning and performance data within single records of essential data.
• Provide for timely responsiveness to dynamic management needs, including self-reprograming abilities.

Criteria

• Does the system automatically provide for dependency tests of needed data by the user? That is, how long will these data be required?

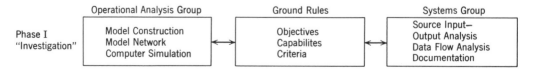

EXHIBIT 6. Plan for Designing an Information System (Operational Analysis Effort).

• Do outputs result in the required coordinated action?

• Does the cost difference for data exceed the marginal utility of the information to the user?

• Does the system provide for selective data feedback for operational needs and management decisions?

Modeling Techniques

The operations analysts are responsible for preparing an optimum information system based upon the analyses of the total requirements of the organization. Their output is a network simulation model with computer programs. The model and programs are then tested by management to assure their practicability and management's understanding and acceptance of them.

This effort need not start completely from scratch. Modeling techniques have already been developed, programed, and tested by various commercial and governmental organizations. As a result, various state-of-the-art modeling "disciplines" are available for use by the operations analysts. These include such networking techniques for both data and communications as PERT/Time/Cost-Performance methods; such operations research techniques as traffic analysis, queueing theory, linear programing, and the like; decision table techniques; and business simulators and gaming techniques such as the University of California's business game, the General Purpose Simulator, SIMPAC, SIMSCRIPT, and the like. Many of these management science techniques have been described at some length in previous issues of *Management Services.*

Use of these more or less standard tools will substantially reduce the time required for systems design and thus decrease its cost. With their aid the task becomes an applied science rather than a research and development project. The significant part of the effort will be to determine the fundamental requirements of the particular organization and its management's essential decision-making requirements and then to fit these requirements or parameters within the appropriate "disciplines."

Meanwhile the systems analysts have the mission of preparing, as an output, a network reflecting present mechanized data dependencies, data interactions, and data flow and of defining "essential" and "secondary" data. The use of source input/output analysis and data network analysis will greatly aid them in this effort—and will speed their work.

When both groups have completed their assigned tasks, their next step is to unite their efforts to produce the initial data network or preliminary information system. The operations analysts will attempt to adhere to their streamlined model while the systems analysts will attempt to utilize, insofar as is possible, the "best aspects" of the installed applications and subsystems that are currently in operation.

This preliminary design will be reviewed, analyzed, and modified as necessary. Then a second-cut data network, reflecting the anticipated equipment configuration and required equipment capabilities, will be produced in the final design phase. All three phases of the plan for systems design are illustrated in Exhibit 7.

A fundamental information system, designed with the aid of these new systems techniques, should go a long way toward solving the problem of the information explosion. Present-day data processing systems are pouring forth more information than anyone can ever hope to assimilate under present circumstances. The ability to generate information has outrun the ability to comprehend it.

Existing information subsystems and application-oriented techniques are not organized so as to permit effective study of the business complex in proper depth. Hence, it is nearly impossible to arrive at solutions revealing the optimum business decisions and the lowest-cost alternatives.

The time and money spent in designing a fundamental information system as outlined here should produce many benefits:

• By means of these techniques, the entire fundamental concept of operating the company is studied, perhaps for the first time. The result should be a single-thread flow of information.

• Previously unrecognized problem areas and bottlenecks will be uncovered. Data processing activities, manual or mechanized, which are now efficient and should continue despite the adoption of new methods will be isolated. The number of reports and the demand for meaningless data can be reduced, to everyone's relief.

• The study should produce a data processing system that justifies its cost since it will

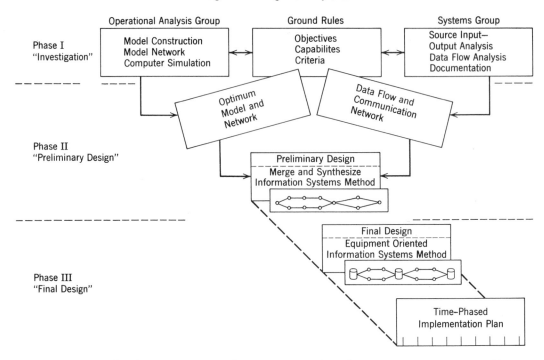

EXHIBIT 7. Plan for Designing an Information System (Final Design—Equipment Oriented).

be based on solid present and future requirements. One objective of the study must be to find that point of balance at which the payoff expected from the data, documents, reports, and analyses produced is at least equal to—if not greater than—the quantity and cost of data processing to be produced. Since every step taken to improve the accuracy of data transmission increases the cost, the study must include determination of the degree of data accuracy actually required for effective management.

• The study—as a catalyst—will help to initiate new systems thinking throughout the organization to match third-generation computer equipment capabilities. It will incorporate or at least foster such scientific techniques as simulation and decision tables, standards engineering, operations analysis, and cost/performance effectiveness analysis.

Management decision making in the new era can be made at a level of information availability never before dreamed of. This means not just more information faster but mathematically pre-analyzed and pre-selected information from which meaningless data have been culled.

To maintain control and measure the results of business activity is management's responsibility. To do this within a complete information system, the manager must understand the model construction so well that he can assure himself that the solutions coming from these models will reflect policies that will lead to minimum operational costs. Otherwise a manager may be forced into rubber stamping a computer solution. If management is to manage, the decision makers must take the lead in understanding, designing, and approving the model of the fundamental information system.

14. DESIGNING A BEHAVIORAL SYSTEM *

STANLEY YOUNG †

There is a growing realization that what has come to be called the systems approach can provide the manager with another valuable tool with which to perform his functions. This analysis, then, will have two purposes: (1) to ascertain the systems responsibility of management; and (2) to suggest how this responsibility can be exercised. As for the first purpose, it will be suggested that from a systems point of view, the management function can be considered as the design, installation, operation, maintenance and evaluation of behavioral systems. Before discussing this further, a behavioral system should be defined. This paper will be restricted to behavioral systems which are normative in nature.

DEFINITION OF A BEHAVIORAL SYSTEM

Although no complete agreement exists over the definition of a normative system, the following construct by Richard Kershner is representative. He notes, "A system is a collection of entities or things (animate or inanimate) which receives certain inputs and is constrained to act concertedly upon them to produce certain outputs, with the objective of maximizing *some* function of inputs and outputs." [1] Such systems are man created or inventions to serve specific human purposes.

They are purposeful, deliberate, rational and subject to modification in order to increase the value to be optimized.

Normative systems can be broadly classified in terms of the nature of the components or entities which comprise the system: these are (1) machine to machine, (2) man to machine, and (3) man to man. For the purpose of this analysis, the terms "man to man" and "behavioral systems" will be used synonymously. Meredith Crawford has observed, "A football team can be designated a man to man system in which man supplies the power, movement, striking force, information processing, memory and decision-making." On the other hand, he noted that a guided missile battery consists of machines that perform these same operations. [2]

Thus, in a man to man system, the hardware of the system is man himself. Moreover, just as with machine systems, behavioral systems can be thought of as social inventions. Social, economic and political institutions can be so categorized, as can organizational policies, procedures or methods that involve human behavior. This complex of social innovation and construction is presumed to lead to greater human satisfaction.

What is the relationship between the functions of management and the systems approach? If one accepts Professor Johnson's observation that organizations can be viewed as operating systems, [3] then one conclusion would be that these systems are composed of an intermixture of machine to machine, man to machine and man to man sub-systems. In the main, organizational sub-functions such as accounting, collective bargaining, personnel,

SOURCE: *Proceedings of the 23rd Annual Meeting,* Academy of Management, Boston, Massachusetts (December 27–28, 1963), pp. 76–83. Reprinted by permission of *Journal of the Academy of Management.*

* The author is grateful to Michael Witunski, Director of Long-Range Planning, McDonnell Aircraft Corporation, for reviewing this analysis.

† Professor of Management, University of Massachusetts.

[1] Richard Kershner, "A Survey of Systems Engineering Tools and Techniques," *Operations Research and Systems Engineering,* eds. Charles Flagle, William H. Higgins, and Robert A. Roy (Baltimore: Johns Hopkins Press, 1960), p. 41.

[2] Meredith Crawford, "Concepts of Training," *Psychological Principles in System Development,* ed. Robert Gagne (New York: Holt, Rinehart and Winston, 1962), pp. 304–305.

[3] Richard A. Johnson, Fremont E. Kast, and James E. Rosenzweig, *The Theory and Management of Systems* (New York: McGraw-Hill, 1963), pp. 50–52.

marketing, finance and purchasing can be viewed as man to man subsystems. The distinguishing characteristic of these subsystems is that their operations are performed by man components. The cracking of oil into subproducts, on the other hand, is performed by machine components.

Two different organizational subgroups have emerged that have systems development responsibility. Developing machine to machine subsystems is primarily the work of the professional engineer—electrical, mechanical, chemical and civil. However, the responsibility for developing man to man subsystems is that of the professional manager. Man to machine subsystems, for example the production function in manufacturing, is usually a joint responsibility of managers and engineers.

An analysis of the work of the professional manager and engineer illustrates that both groups perform essentially the same tasks—the design, installation, maintenance, operation and evaluation of systems. Their work varies only in the sense that the components of their respective systems differ.

The operation of human components can be arranged in an infinite number of patterns. Given the purpose of any behavioral system, management must design a pattern of human behavior that will optimize this purpose. The extent to which human welfare is optimized in regard to the operation of any given man to man system is, in part, a function of how well that system is designed. And if at times it is believed that certain behavioral systems are less than optimum, the fault may lie with the skills of the designer.

The significance of the systems approach is that it could provide for the professional manager a general purpose tool which would enable him to produce much more effective designs than he did in the past.

DESIGNING A BEHAVIORAL SYSTEM

If we intend to utilize the systems approach, through what process would the manager go and what techniques would he employ to design a man to man system? I would like to suggest that irrespective of whether one is going to design a human or machine system, the methodology one would follow would essentially be the same. It appears that much of the extensive literature on design relates by and large to machine systems; this means that it

must be translated into behavioral terms. Let us briefly review the essential aspects of the design process. The typical parts of the system that the professional manager will design, can be arranged into (1) input, (2) operations or handling, (3) control, (4) output, and (5) communication.[4]

Inputs have been classified with respect to their relation to the operations of the system. One input concerns that which enters the system upon which some operation is to occur. This input would affect the load of the system. Another input is environmental in nature and affects the operation of the system.[5] A third input relates to component placement and replacement. Inputs have been classified further in terms of their content: material, energy, information or any combination therof. Thus, in a man to man system, the material entering the system could be men—for example, a patient admitted to a hospital or a potential customer who enters a marketing system. Law can be viewed as an environmental input in the form of human force or constraint which may affect the operation of a business system. When human components quit a system and have to be replaced, this would exemplify another kind of input.

If we restrict our attention to those inputs upon which the system is to operate, these will generally be distributed in such a manner that they can be described statistically. Inputs may be multiplex. One usually must design an input source which will not only give rise to the inputs but will funnel them into the right channels for operation.

Another part of the system that has to be designed is the operations, process or channels through which the inputs must pass; these may also be mutiplex in both series or parallel.[6] A system has to cope with its inputs by assuring that the proper thing happens to each input at the proper time to achieve the desired output for a multiplicity of inputs.[7] Thus, if the input happens to be a patient in a hospital, this material will be passed serially along a channel from human operator to human operator. Human operators represent the hardware of the system and have to perform a

4 Harry H. Goode, and Robert Machol, *System Engineering* (New York: McGraw-Hill, 1957), p. 408.

5 *Ibid.*, p. 99.

6 *Ibid.*, p. 6.

7 *Ibid.*, p. 38.

set of tasks which have been assigned to them. The particular tasks which man is adept at performing are information processing and decision-making.

Decision-making relates to the selection of the appropriate responses, given a set of stimuli. Responses can be physical or mental. Task descriptions specify along a time scale the cues which the human operator should perceive in the task environment and the related response which he should make concerning the input.[8]

Another component of the system is control which provides direction in conformance with plan.[9] Man to man systems are adaptive, which means that they are capable of modifying operations to meet change in the values of input parameters with variable utilization to maintain a certain output.[10] The key to effective control is that one would not only have to predict the nature of all possible inputs but also establish the operating patterns of human components for each input. This pattern, which can be viewed as programmed action, is sometimes referred to as the systems logic or the rules under which the system operates. For example, new students may be thought of as an input into an educational system; and if the number of students increased over time, the systems logic would provide how the operation of the system is going to be modified in order to handle this augmented load, for successive increments.

In addition to the systems logic, one would require measurement devices and a power source for effective control. One would want to measure the system's (1) effectiveness or outputs, (2) inputs, and (3) operations. Measurement devices would provide information to a control unit, which would select the appropriate response that would already have been pre-programmed, given the variations in any one of these three parts of the system. The control unit would require sufficient power or influence over the behavior of the human operators to assure that when a command was given, human components would react correctly. For example, a supervisor may be thought of as a control unit. If the human operators have been pre-programmed to respond to a variety of inputs that would enter

this supervisor's unit, measuring devices would indicate to the supervisor a change in inputs. He would select the appropriate response and communicate it to his human operators, who in turn, would change their behavior to this directed pattern. If we return to the example of football, the quarterback performs this same control function.

Still another part of a system relates to information processing. There is little need for me to discuss information processing at length, except perhaps to note that channels, networks or information linkages should be provided to hold the system together. Such channels provide a flow of information among input, output, operations and control. Specific informational display forms have to be designed for various points in the system which would furnish information in a meaningful manner.

Yet another segment which has to be designed is the output of the system. Output is what the system is supposed to accomplish or produce. For the most part, one will be working with a subsystem of the organization. This means that the output of any given subsystem will be the input of another subsystem.

DESIGN PROCESS

What method would one employ to design these separate parts of the system? Harry Goode has suggested that the design process consists of (1) a statement of the problem, (2) the formulation of a model, and (3) the collection and application of data. In stating the problem, one would sketch the proposed system, either by starting with an existent system or beginning anew. Generally, one would consider at the outset, the output and payoff of the system. Payoff is the human utility or satisfaction that will result from system operation or that which the system is to optimize. In a man to man system, payoff is usually described in a cost ratio. For example, an educational system might be measured in terms of the number of graduating students which would be the output of the system per cost per student that would measure the extent of organizational resource utilization to achieve this output.

When we consider output, two operational criteria warrant attention, the stability and reliability requirements of the system. Requirements are standards of performance which the

[8] Robert B. Miller, "Task Description and Analysis," Robert Gagne, *op. cit.*, pp. 191–192.

[9] Richard A. Johnson, et al., *op. cit.*, p. 58.

[10] Richard Kershner, *op cit.*, pp. 143–145.

system must meet. Stability would mean the continuity of output. Given a variety of inputs, unless the system can adjust, the output can be affected adversely. Reliability refers to consistency of operation of components or error rate. Of particular concern are the minimum performance specifications to assure that the subsystems will be able to serve a total system.

Other aspects to consider are the description of the environment, general area of permissible or acceptable solutions and measures of effectiveness. Description of the environment would involve noting the different expected inputs that will either enter or affect the system. The area of acceptable solutions would relate essentially to a review of the present technology relative to the operation of the system. For example, in the selection of new employees, technology would refer to the existent techniques of interviewing, testing, and so forth. The measurement of effectiveness would relate to a determination of how various parts of the system are to be evaluated.

The next step in the design process is to formulate a model or representation of the proposed system. The key to effective design is the ability to simulate the system in its present state as well as any modifications that would be made. The development of a model serves as a conceptual link between the operation of the system and its environment. Such a representation can take a variety of forms from a relatively simple flow diagram to a highly sophisticated mathematical model. However, the block diagram, or flow chart is one of the basic tools in systems design. Because one attempts to improve the operation of an existing system, one might initially draw a schematic which reflected the present system in considerable detail, to include the subsystems that comprise the total system. For each subsystem, one would want to know the form of its input, operation and output. A single thread schematic which depicted the functional specifications of what occurs to a representative input would be a helpful starting point. This schematic could further be reduced to an equipment block diagram in which the interrelationships in operations between specific human components and the operation of each component are detailed.[11]

If it were advisable or possible, one would convert the flow diagram into a more rigorous statistical or mathematical form. In general, the output of the system represents the dependent variable and the input and operation are the independent variables.

If the system is linear, then we assume it will take the form $O = (I) \cdot (F)$ where (F) is operations and usually called the transfer function. This represents the operation of the system on its input. Although the input and transfer functions may be complex polynomials, they can still be subject to mathematical manipulation. In many instances, it is extremely costly, undesirable or impossible to develop a mathematical model. Frequently a simple block diagram may be sufficient for design purposes. Irrespective of the level of sophistication of the model, it is by and large more meaningful if the system can be symbolically represented. Managers need not be trained mathematicians or statisticians in order to simulate a system.

Whether or not the model is descriptive or mathematical, at this early model building stage, one would only have an approximation of its operation. Additional data would have to be acquired; and this is the third phase in design. One must determine what additional data are required and how they are to be obtained. For the most part, a constant feedback should exist between the collection and analysis of data and the completeness of the model. With these data, one would be able to assign realistic values to listed parameters.[12]

Of particular importance would be the ascertainment of the values to be assigned to the controlled variables. Control variables are those items which the control unit can modify to affect the operation of the system. For example, if employee motivation is considered the transfer function and the wages paid are a controlled input variable, then one would like to determine, given any variance in the amount of wages paid, what changes would take place in the output of the system. This could be defined in terms of the number of employee quits.

The ideal model would be able "to state exactly what will happen to every possible input at every stage of its passage through the

[11] Harry Goode and Robert Machol, op. cit., pp. 305–306.

[12] The use of a matrix to ascertain the parameter is illustrated in David O. Ellis and Fred J. Ludwig, Systems Philosophy (Englewood Cliffs, N.J.: Prentice-Hall, 1962), pp. 165–225.

system, or to describe every response which it will evoke in the system." [13] All possible outputs would, by definition, also be stated.

Given a model which is reasonably predictive, and given various inputs, by means of simulation one can modify the values of the controlled variables in order to establish those values which will optimize the operation of the system. This is essentially an iterative, yet heuristic process.

Because of the time limitation, what has been presented thus far represents a skeletal outline of the system design process. However, it will enable us to compare, at this time, man and machine system development as it characteristically occurs.

A COMPARISON OF SYSTEMS DEVELOPMENT

There is a widespread impression that progress in the development of machine systems has been much greater and more rapid than in human systems. For example, a common observation is that atomic energy has been harnessed via a machine system, but a social system has yet to be invented to utilize this energy properly. Why is this the case?

First, it seems to me that a greater differentiation of effort exists in the development of machine systems as compared to man systems. As late as the middle of the nineteenth century, the design, installation, operation and maintenance of a machine system more often than not, was the work of one individual, the inventor. Today, these functions have become largely separated. One group might concentrate upon research and development; another, on operations; while yet another, on maintenance. Moreover, a sequential procedure has developed whereby design precedes operation and maintenance.

Unfortunately, as respects the development of behavioral systems, we still appear to be in the stage of the early inventor of the machine. The manager frequently is expected to develop, operate and maintain a man to man system simultaneously. One would hardly expect the captain of a conventional submarine, during the operation of the ship's run, to experiment with his craft until the Polaris Weapons System evolved.

[13] Harry Goode and Robert Machol, *op. cit.*, p. 305.

What seems to be required is a subdivision of the management function; one group of managers would be responsible for the creation of behavioral systems, while another group would be accountable for their operation and maintenance. The line and staff division is perhaps developing along these lines.

Another difference between engineers and managers is that, in regard to the work of design, the level of sophistication exhibited by the engineer tends to be relatively higher than that of the manager. In the design of man to man systems, we rely too heavily on the intuition of the designer. This does not mean that the creativity factor will not remain critical in systems design, both for man and machine systems. Quantitative methods traditionally have been used in the engineering sciences but are relatively recent in their application to the management sciences. In the design of machine systems, standards of acceptable design are more rigorous. If one compares the actual physical designs of machine and man systems, machine designs as a rule are more detailed, complete and operational. It is disconcerting to note the frequent absence of model building in the planning of human systems.

Given all the variables in a situation, engineers want to be assured that if they take certain actions, they will obtain measurable, predictable results. On the basis of their analysis, a fund of usable knowledge is established which can be transmitted to other engineers who are faced with similar situations. Results are objective, impersonal and capable of reproduction. The engineer's personal opinion is not as significant a factor concerning the design, as is the specific body of tested knowledge.

A further difference is that the engineer places great reliance on the physical scientist whose work is a significant source of knowledge. On the other hand, the manager, who is an applied social scientist, relies much less on the progress made in the social sciences.

Another aspect relates to research and development. In comparison to machine systems, little expenditure is devoted to the development of improved behavioral systems. The potential payoff of human systems could be greatly enhanced with more research funds allocated to the improving of the design of man systems. In systems design of both man and machine, there are no easy, quick solutions.

Certainly this fact is accepted in regard to machine systems, and considerable engineering man hours will be expended prior to the achievement of acceptable designs. This same acceptance does not seem to exist concerning man to man systems, and too often the operating manager is expected to produce solutions for behavioral problems on demand. Unfortunately, we have come to think of research and development solely in terms of machine systems. Yet, given comparable research expenditure, there is reason to believe that the payoff from improved behavioral systems will be as great, if not greater, than with machine systems.

The final difference between the manager and the engineer is that the engineer tends to specialize in the operation of the components of the system, while the manager specializes in the system's output or purpose. For example, the electrical engineer concentrates on the operational capability of the various electrical components. How particular components will be arranged would depend on the purpose of the system. Consequently the engineer can design either a toaster or a radio, as required. He is a hardware or equipment specialist.

In the design of a system wherein all of its parts are composed of human hardware, a knowledge of behavioral sciences is critical. One must consider those functions or activities which individuals will perform skillfully, poorly or not at all. The role of man in systems development derives from his intrinsic properties. Very often, behavioral systems are designed with requirements that are inconsistent with human properties. If the system does not work, force is sometimes utilized to assure conformity to the design. This intolerance does not appear in the design of machine systems. Machine components will merely break down or halt if they are improperly used. Man is more adaptive than machines and although his failure to operate may not be as precisely indicated, nevertheless the same phenomenon occurs in a variety of forms.

Clearly, a more human use of human beings in systems design is required, in order to progress to more productive behavioral systems.[14] Moreover, if we focus on the components of the system, we will be working with fewer variables, so that a more generalized conceptual scheme can be developed. If human behavior is reduced to learning, motivation, thinking and motor skills, whether one were designing a personnel or marketing system, one would always be working with these particular variables.

I would like to conclude by stating that it is my belief that if we desire to improve our educational, economic and political systems, which are largely man to man constructions, as with machine systems, these improvements must be invented. The systems approach provides a general tool to facilitate this process. However, in order to progress, research expenditures should be available to support specialists who are trained in the designing of behavioral systems and who will devote their entire efforts to the improvement of our man to man systems. If this occurred, enormous strides can be made not only within the business firm, but for our entire social apparatus as well.

[14] Norbert Wiener, *The Human Use of Human Beings* (2nd ed., rev., Garden City, New York: Doubleday, 1954).

BIBLIOGRAPHY

1. Anshen, Melvin, and G. L. Bach (eds.), *Management and Corporations: 1985*, McGraw-Hill Book Co., Inc., 1960.
2. Bross, I. D. J., *Design for Decision*, The Macmillan Co., 1953.
3. Bruner, William G., Jr., "Systems Design: A Broader Role of Industrial Engineering," *Journal of Industrial Engineering*, March–April, 1962.
4. *Business Systems*, Systems and Procedures Association, 1965.
5. Dearden, John, "How to Organize Information Systems," *Harvard Business Review*, April, 1965.
6. Eckman, Donald P., *Systems: Research and Design*, John Wiley and Sons, 1961.
7. Ewell, James M., "The Total Systems Concept and How to Organize for It," *Computers and Automation*, September, 1961.
8. Goode, Harry H., and Robert E. Machol, *System Engineering*, McGraw-Hill Book Co., Inc., 1957.
9. Hall, A. D., *A Methodology for Systems Engineering*, D. Van Nostrand Co., 1962.
10. Jasinski, Frank J., "Adapting Organization to New Technology," *Harvard Business Review*, January–February, 1959.
11. Johnson, Richard, Fremont E. Kast, and James E. Rosenzweig, *The Theory and Management of Systems*, McGraw-Hill Book Co., Inc., 1963.
12. McDonough, Adrian M., and Leonard J. Garrett, *Management Systems, Working Concepts and Practices*, Richard D. Irwin, Inc., 1965.
13. McGrath, Joseph D., Peter G. Nordlic, and W. S. Vaughn, Jr., *A Systematic Framework for Comparison of System Research Methods*, Human Sciences Research, Inc., 1959.
14. McMillan, Claude, and Richard F. Gonzalez, *Systems Analysis—A Computer Approach to Decision Models*, Richard D. Irwin, Inc., 1965.
15. Malcolm, D. G., A. J. Rowe, and L. F. McConnell (eds.), *Management Control Systems*, John Wiley and Sons, 1960.
16. Stoller, David S., and Richard L. Van Horn, *Design of a Management Information System*, The RAND Corporation, P-1362, 1958.
17. Wohlstetter, A. J., *Systems Analysis Versus System Design*, The RAND Corporation, P-1530, 1958.

Part V.   Total Management Systems

It has often been stated that we are in the "era of systems." There are behavioral systems, communication systems, data processing systems, transportation systems, information systems, records systems, and innumerable others. And to further befuddle the layman utilizing operational systems, these have been categorized as closed, open, structured, unstructured, controlled feedback, uncontrolled feedback, deterministic, oscillating, man-made, real time, reproducible, isomorphic, simple action, and by an ever-growing list of other euphonious labels.

The concept of system will not only mean different things to different people but it can even mean different things to the same individuals. Proponents of the systems viewpoint have themselves to blame for much of the unintelligible jargon currently associated with systems. It would not be difficult to pinpoint the many and diverse orientations to management systems now in vogue. This diversity of orientations is certainly nothing to be deplored: the growth of any discipline depends upon it. Also it is but natural that one views any concept from his own intellectual landscape with its own peculiar value judgments. However the confusion has reached such proportions that it is necessary to attempt some clarification—if possible!

In Part IV it was pointed out that one of the systems approaches holds that "systems" is a frame of mind, a way of thinking, a philosophy, rather than any certain body of knowledge or of techniques. According to this viewpoint the systems concept can be equally applied to all types of organizational structures irrespective of size or type of industry. It is therefore not limited by its inherent nature to only those companies with computer capabilities but is applicable to virtually all companies.

For others, "systems" brings to mind a configuration of costly complex equipment comprising electronic computers, input-output devices and the usual auxiliary equipment used in conjunction with data processing systems. What is liable to be ignored is the fact that all of this "hardware" represents but *tools* designed to aid the manager in applying the systems concept to his own specialized operations. The computer cannot make his decisions for him; it can however provide him with meaningful predictions of results obtained by pursuing alternative courses of action. But in any event, the collection and processing of information should not be made synonymous with the systems approach.

The total systems approach has recently appeared under many labels such as integrated management, unified operations management, total information systems, holistic systems, macro systems, interrelated systems and subsystems, and complete systems. In addition, articles have been appearing linking the total systems approach to personnel, production, inventory control, scientific decision making, and even to the management of managers.

In this present section will be found several articles in which the authors take a hard look at the total systems approach from a more or less pragmatic viewpoint. The theoretical approach which is fundamental is, however, not overlooked.

In the selection by Asa Spaulding we have a theoretical as well as a practical approach to total systems. After underscoring the lack of clarity and consistency in the systems concepts, he prefaces his treatment of the conceptual approaches by a brief consideration of the evolution of the business enterprise. Historically, business progressed from the state where the owner was concerned with virtually all facets of the enterprise to the present state of the large complex organization where functional decentralization and delegation of authority are the universally recognized trademarks. The two basic problems of management, viz., communication and information, are continually under consideration in the remainder of the article.

The problem-oriented or the "piecemeal" approach to systems, though workable at times, has many inherent weaknesses, its chief defect being systems incompatibility. If practiced often enough, the piecemeal approach shows unmistakable evidence of being just "a thing of shreds and patches." After abandoning this approach as impractical, he defines the total systems concept and further elucidates some of the key words involved in this basic definition.

The dynamic processes of the business function are presented in three stages of increasing complexity, leading eventually to the total systems level. In the first, the simple straightforward procedural cycle is depicted from the initial decision to that of forecast, policy, design, action, results, evaluation, and back again to decision. The second stage employs in addition a somewhat unwieldy communication network that ties in all steps of the dynamic process with one another. The third stage is that of the total management information system with its automatic data processing medium for communication and control of the various functions.

Spaulding definitely does believe that the total systems concept is practical. Without it "we can't do today's job with yesterday's tools and techniques and expect to stay in business tomorrow." However he views as one of the prime problems of the systems man that of selling the idea for a total management system to management itself.

The next selection is replete with numerous instances where (total) systems have succeeded in real life and also where they have failed, and failed miserably. Allan Harvey believes that those chiefly responsible for propagating the systems concept have probably been its worse enemies, and for these reasons: (1) they have suggested to managers that systems somehow represented a "spanking new concept, sprung full-blown from the brow of Jove," when in reality the concept is based on traditional principles that marked the path to success of many of our great modern enterprises; (2) systems proponents have often clothed systems thinking in unnecessary technical jargon and elaborate mathematics. Mathematics of a sophisticated nature may be needed at the technical level but is generally not desirable at the managerial one; (3) overenthusiastic advocates of systems have given the impression or have done little to dispel the notion that systems are intended only for giant complex corporations. Although one can readily explain the probable origin of these misrepresentations, yet they have done an injustice to the systems cause.

Intelligent application of the total systems approach can provide practical, effective, as well as profitable solutions to managerial problems. To do this, realistic systems need not take into account, as is sometimes erroneously imagined, every possible contingency. Both short- and long-term variables can be identified by this approach and the total management system can coexist with real-life limitations since it is not a "cloud nine" or a pie-in-the-sky utopian scheme. Another important asset of the total systems approach is that it can be implemented stepwise for it is not an all-or-none one-shot technique.

However, total management systems must be applied realistically. This implies a sincere commitment to search out fundamental solutions and not to be satisfied with temporary *ad hoc* expedients. However, systems have failed in the past. This was due not to the inadequacy of the systems approach but to the fault of the designer, to the failure to implement the systems design, and to the all-too-pervasive human element involved in any business enterprise.

When reading W. M. A. Brooker's selection, "The Total Systems Myth," it might be helpful for the purpose of making comparative evaluative judgments, to keep in mind what Kenneth Boulding had to say about general systems theories and the various levels that unfortunately have not yet been realized, Moravec's stand rejecting the total information system in favor of what he calls a fundamental information system, Harvey's down-to-earth appraisal of the limitations and advantages of what amounts to the total systems approach, and Young's indictment of systems managers for ignoring almost completely the behavioristic elements involved.

In his article Brooker examines the total systems concept as presented in various journals and textbooks and finds the exposition sadly inadequate. He finds the total systems approach overrated from the pragmatic viewpoint, though he does concede that it seems to be a very powerful motivational force for those concerned with the theoretical viewpoint. He believes that basically what is wrong is the underlying assumption that the total systems approach is of all possible approaches the most adequate and hence the most fruitful. His pointed darts are hurled not at an imaginary target of his own making but at the specific target fabricated from the utterances of some total systems advocates.

In his outline of a basic theory of business Brooker as a sociologist rightly lays stress upon the human elements. A business, he points out, is primarily a social group and as a social group it can and ought to be considered from the same perspective as other social groups. This sociological emphasis is necessary in view of the current misrepresentations of total systems and of the underestimations of the behavioristic elements. The total systems approach, he concludes, is a myth, and not a holistic or total approach.

Konvalinka and Trentin's selection concludes this section on a predominantly pragmatic level. They expose some of the common fallacies associated with total systems, such as the identification of management information systems with electronic data processing and the inevitable computeritis. After treating briefly the concepts of information and decisions, they take up the nature, development, and the method of achieving management system. To provide the readers with a practical illustration of how a particular company might tackle the management information system problem, the authors have presented the case of the Able Manufacturing Company, a fictional corporation but one that represents a synthesis of actual cases experienced in their consulting capacities. They illustrate their treatment with well-designed charts and detailed tables.

15. IS THE TOTAL SYSTEM CONCEPT PRACTICAL?

A. T. Spaulding, Jr.[*]

Widespread attention is being given these days to the concept of a "total system" approach to the problem of information processing. At practically every conference and seminar held by the various management and data processing associations, considerable time is devoted to it. Almost every periodical that covers the systems and computer field includes numerous articles on the subject. And more and more talks and papers are being given on various aspects of it.

There seem to be differing opinions as to just what a total system concept really is. This fact is borne out by the lack of consistency in labeling it. A total system approach is often referred to as a "consolidated functions approach," or a "unified approach," or as an "integrated data processing system," and even as a "real-time system," as well as by a score of other presumably suitable names. The reason for this lack of consistency, perhaps, lies in the fact that the concept, as it has so far evolved, is very nebulous and has had meaning only in terms of its actual application to specific business information problems. Because it has been interpreted by so many people to mean so many different things, no clear-cut definition has yet been established or at least agreed upon.

Since this situation exists, it would be desirable for us to establish and agree upon a definition which will provide a basis for common understanding before an attempt is made to evaluate the practicality of the so-called total system concept. In this way, any evaluations we make or any conclusions we derive will be valid within the framework of our definition.

SOURCE: *Systems & Procedures Journal* (January–February, 1964), pp. 28–32. Reprinted by permission of *Systems & Procedures Journal*.
[*] President, Data Service Inc.

EVOLUTION OF THE BUSINESS ENTERPRISE

Before we consider our definition of a total system concept, let's look at the evolution of the business enterprise. It hasn't been very long since the modus operandi of almost every business enterprise was what might be considered a total systems approach. The owner of the enterprise, usually being the manager, salesman, and office clerk, as well as the janitor, conducted all or certainly most of the affairs of the business himself. Thus, every decision he made was based upon a complete knowledge of the overall business situation—from the community's economic and environmental conditions to his own firm's status of production and inventory.

As these organizations became larger and more complex, communication channels grew longer, slower and more difficult to maintain. Managers soon became aware of the fact that communication with and supervision of the various segments of the enterprise was almost impossible with the then existing organizational structures and systems. The outgrowth of this realization was the development of a new concept of organization, "functional decentralization." But even reorganizations and delegations of authority and responsibility which resulted didn't solve management's two basic problems:

1. Communication
2. Information

CONCEPTUAL APPROACHES TO SYSTEMS WORK

There have been a vast number of conceptual approaches to systems work down through the years. Unfortunately, these approaches have not kept pace with the tools

149

and techniques developed for use in the field. There are, perhaps, a number of reasons for this: lack of recognition of systems as a profession, specialization and loss of perspective by the systems man, lack of interest and receptivity on the part of management and so on.

Considering the various approaches, we find that the traditional and most prevalently used has been the problem-oriented or "piecemeal" approach. The procedure usually followed here is to call in a systems man each time a problem of either an operating or routine nature arises. Information is collected, analyzed and evaluated. Recommendations are made. These recommendations usually require only the revision of an existing system, although sometimes they require that a new system be designed. If it's the latter, the systems man may end up developing procedures which are not consonant with company policy. In fact, since it is a new system he is designing, there may not even be policy covering the situation. In which case, he may, in essence, have to develop company policy himself. (Of course we know that every good systems man develops his systems within the framework of company policy.) However, this is certainly not the most enviable position for a systems man to be in constantly.

While there are certainly some attractive features of the problem-oriented approach, it has the major disadvantage of creating a "patchwork" situation. That is, it only patches up the weak spots in the overall system. When this approach is used long enough with no attempt at basic or total system design, systems incompatibility usually occurs. The various systems end up cutting across each other. This creates duplication of effort, decreased efficiency, in short, increased operating costs.

N. L. Senensieb, International Vice President of the Systems and Procedures Association, in his paper "Systems, Functions, Concepts, and Programs" suggests several other conceptual approaches to systems work. Following are the common ones: [1]

The Manual-Writing Approach tends to document the status quo, i.e., the existing sys-

[1] N. L. Senensieb, "Systems Functions, Concepts, and Programs," draft of a college systems & procedures course outline, January, 1962, pp. 18–19.

tem, and ignores the other creative phases of analysis and design which permit establishment of optimum systems.

The Forms Control Approach tends to overlook the fact that forms are a data transmission medium, and concentrates, instead, on the narrower paperwork cost control techniques.

The Accounting System Approach concentrates on perfecting the accounting system per se, forgetting this is only one major subsystem of the overall management information system.

The Mechanization Approach implies that mechanization is the only means by which office operations can be improved, and that a mechanized method is always an optimum one.

Because of the positive impact that many of the earlier office mechanization attempts had on office systems and procedures, the first electronic computers to be used as management tools were looked upon as a panacea for the continuing rise in clerical costs and information processing problems. Early applications were put on these so-called miracle-workers with the same traditional approach that was being used in general systems work. Little or no attempt was made to take advantage of the vast capabilities of this new medium. While recent approaches to computer utilization for processing business information have considered more fully the present state of the art in ADP machine development, relatively little has been accomplished in the area of total systems.

TOTAL SYSTEMS CONCEPT DEFINED

Having taken a look at the business enterprise as it has evolved over the years and having considered some of the conceptual approaches used in general systems work, we can now view our total systems concept as it applies to the management problems of communication and information. First, let's consider a definition for the total system concept:

Total System Concept: an approach to information systems design that conceives the business enterprise as an entity composed of interdependent systems and subsystems, which, with the use of automatic data processing systems, attempts to provide timely and accurate management information which will permit optimum management decision making.[2]

For the sake of clarity, let us digress for a moment to define several key words and phrases as they are to be interpreted within the context of our total system definition:

System: ". . . a set of related procedures (or equipment) which provide the plan of action (or vehicle) for carrying out the basic objectives of organization."

". . . directed orderly plan of interdependent and sequential functions, the execution of which enables an organization to fulfill its purpose." [3]

Automatic data processing system: a configuration of equipment comprised of some or all of the following:

1. electronic computer(s);
2. input and output devices, both local and remote;
3. auxiliary equipment which directly supports or services the computers (exclusive of communications equipment), i.e., tabulating equipment; and
4. communications, i.e., data transmission equipment used in support of the data processing equipment.[4]

Management information (system): a system which provides ". . . the right information for the right people at the right time at the lowest possible cost." [5]

DYNAMIC PROCESSES OF THE BUSINESS FUNCTION

Every action program or project executed by a business enterprise follows a dynamic process. This process begins with the board of directors, for example, stating in abstract terms

[2] E. R. Dickey and N. L. Senensieb, "The Total System Concept," draft of entry for *The Encyclopedia for Management,* Reinhold Publishing Corp.

[3] *System and Procedures, Notebook for Systems Man,* rev. ed., Publication No. 460, U.S. Government Printing Office, 1963.

[4] *Preparation and Reporting Format of System Analysis Study on Potential Tactical Army ADPS Application,* USAEPG-SIG 940-25, U.S. Army Electronic Proving Ground, November, 1957.

[5] E. R. Dickey, "Total Systems," *Ideas for Management,* Systems and Procedures Association, 1963, pp. 331–345.

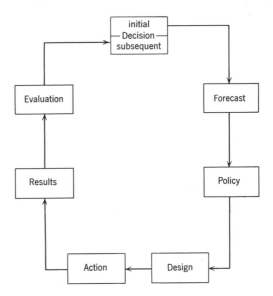

CHART I. Dynamic Processes of the Business Function. The dynamic process begins when management makes its initial decision and develops a forecast. Once policy is then established and a design effort is made, the action phase can be accomplished. Then come the results and evaluation steps.

the goals and objectives of the organization, i.e., the purposes for which the enterprise is being established. (We are excluding, for the moment, the profit motive which obviously is the underlying reason for the establishment of most business enterprises.)

Once these objectives have been established, they are communicated via the president, down through the executive and administrative officers, operating managers and supervisors, to the rank and file as management directives for accomplishing the specific programs and projects. This is where our dynamic process begins. (See Chart I.)

First, management makes its initial decision, i.e., it selects from among several alternatives what it wants to do; what type of program or project it wants to initiate. After this decision has been made, the next step is to develop a forecast. In other words, management determines the appropriate plans, i.e., what systems, etc., will be needed and their budgetary requirements. Not only financial budget requirements, but requirements for manpower, material, etc.

The next step in this dynamic process is the

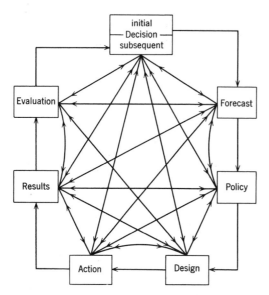

CHART II. Dynamic Processes of the Business Function. Command linkages among all steps of the dynamic process show an ideal network arrangement but no medium for transport of information back and forth nor a central control mechanism.

establishment of policy, i.e., the framework and guidelines for the accomplishment of the particular project. This is where specific individuals and activities are assigned their authority and responsibility for implementation, execution and follow through. Criteria which will serve as a basis for evaluating results are also established at this point.

The fourth step in our process may be referred to as the design step. This entails the actual detailed systems design effort; the development of the step-by-step procedures to be followed in carrying out the project; the selection of appropriate methods and techniques to be used; and the determination of rules to be followed within legal requirements.

Once the system has been designed, procedures developed, methods selected and rules actual implementation and execution of the determined, the action phase can be accomplished. This phase is nothing more than the project.

The next step in our model is the results step. This step is reflected by the information generated from the system in the form of records and reports.

The seventh step in our dynamic process is evaluation. Comparisons and analyses of the

statistics compiled in the preceding step are made, based upon the approved criteria, and trends are established.

We are now back where we started—at the decision step. The only difference is that we are now concerned with subsequent decisions as opposed to initial decisions. These are the decisions that management makes as a result of evaluation of the entire process. The specific decisions obtained usually fall into one of three distinct categories:

1. Decision to continue with the present project with no modifications or changes;
2. Decision to make modifications and changes in the present project and continue; or
3. Decision to cancel the present project and initiate another.

Once this choice is made, the cycle is repeated. This, then, is our dynamic process for the business function.

Quite often the elements of this process are not individually identifiable. They are obscured by the interplay of each with the other in management decision making. Because these elements are so easily obscured, we recognize that there is something missing from our model. There is no communication linkage, i.e., no network which ties in, for example, forecast with action; results with policy; design with evaluation. And this is what is usually missing from most basic systems. There is, as a rule, no communications network which ties in each step of the dynamic process with the other.

The Chart II version of our model depicts communication linkages between all of the steps of the process. While this is an improvement over the original model, in that it shows the ideal network arrangement, there is no vehicle or medium for transporting information to and from the various steps, nor is there a central control mechanism which permits interpretation of information received and decision making.

Chart III of our dynamic process shows a total management information system and considers ADPS as the medium for controlling and communicating with the various functions of the process. While highly theoretical and idealistic from a conceptual standpoint, this idea can be developed into a practical, working system. Whether or not this actually occurs, however, depends upon several things.

First, there must exist on the part of management a desire to have a management information system. It doesn't matter whether the impetus for such comes from operating personnel, systems specialists, or from upper management itself. The main thing here is that there be a genuine desire to have such a system developed. Management's interest in this connection can usually be measured by its decisions on requests for the allocation of appropriate resources for accomplishing the task.

Second, management must be able to state in concrete terms, not in abstractions, what its objectives are and what the desired outputs from the system should be. If we consider this in the light of our management information system definition, management will have to decide what information it wants developed, for whom and when the information must be available. If this can be done in specific terms, development of the total system will be possible. Obtaining comprehensive information of this sort in a form which will permit basic systems design is by no means an easy task.

Third, the group selected to accomplish this task must have the ability, both in terms of its own technical competence as well as its knowledge of the overall situation, to take management's objectives and general systems requirements and convert them into related systems and subsystems which will comprise the total system.

ADVANTAGES OF A TOTAL SYSTEMS APPROACH

One might be justified in asking at this point, why go to all of the trouble of designing a total management information system? What are its advantages? Simply stated, the answer might be: to provide the right information for the right people at the right time at the lowest possible cost.

Some specific advantages that appeal to the writer from the standpoint of a life insurance company's operations are:

1. Permits the elimination of redundant files and duplications of clerical efforts;

2. Reduces the amount of manual handling of records, thereby minimizing the possibility of clerical errors;

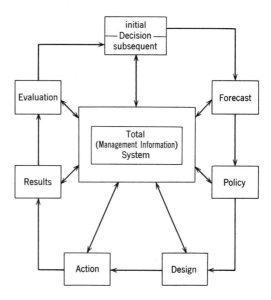

CHART III. Dynamic Processes of the Business Function. This highly theoretical information system can be developed into a practical arrangement if management has the desire for one and states what it desires from the system. Also, the group selected to accomplish such development must have ability.

3. Permits daily updating of records and files, providing current status information and identification of situations which may require individual attention and corrective action;

4. Relieves management and supervisory personnel of routine decision making through use of computer logic for the same; and

5. Permits better cost control and management of resources.

In answer to the question, "Is the total systems concept practical?", the author's personal opinion is that a total systems concept *is* practical. However, we as systems and data processing people need to have a clear understanding in our own minds of what we mean by a total systems concept, especially as far as it can be applied to our own organizations. After all, it's probably going to require a selling job in order to convey to management what the idea of a total systems approach is and what its advantages are. That is, selling the idea that we can't do today's job with yesterday's tools and techniques and expect to stay in business tomorrow.

16. SYSTEMS CAN *TOO* BE PRACTICAL

ALLAN HARVEY *

Early one recent morning, after the late, late TV movie had come to its flickering conclusion, I heard a ministerial voice extolling the superior values of what it called "the systems approach to salvation." As the speaker identified each of the elements of the good life and elaborated on their complex interrelationships, it gradually dawned on me that he was using the vocabulary used to expound the systems approach to business problem solving.

Listening to what I finally identified as the sign-off sermon on the local TV station, I realized how much the systems concept and all its themes and variations have become part of our everyday vocabulary. What struck me was the ease with which both the word and concept slip glibly into our talking and thinking; but as far as action is concerned, the systems approach has had surprisingly little impact on the way most managements go about running their businesses.

The reason for this is, I suspect, that those who have done the most to establish the validity of the systems point of view and promote its use have, in another sense, been its worst enemies. Starting with its origin in military problem solving, the systems concept was taken up by the "think" groups, from the Bell Laboratories in the East, where the term "systems engineering" was probably born, to the Rand Corporation on the West Coast. From these high-level foci, it moved down into university seminars, doctoral dissertations, and a few more or less learned journals.

But in the process of trying to define the systems approach and extol its virtues, its proponents have invariably made it sound too cosmic to be practical and too costly to be profitable.

As a result, the gap is widening between

SOURCE: *Business Horizons* (Summer, 1964), pp. 59–69. Reprinted by permission of *Business Horizons.*
* President, Dasol Corporation.

what we have learned about managing complex systems and the use to which we are putting this knowledge. We know much more today about systems involving rapid change, high degrees of uncertainty, and complex interrelationships than we did five years ago—much more than we are using in our business. Only a handful of companies have put the systems approach to work; their problems range from the production of ladies' blouses to the servicing of farm equipment, and from the distribution of beer to the filling of subscriptions to a magazine and a record club.

The evidence drawn from the successful experience of these few companies affirms categorically that the systems approach (1) has proven its ability to deal with many routine business problems, (2) produces solutions that are quite different from those offered by conventional engineering, and (3) provides a solution that is almost invariably the most profitable one to these everyday management problems. By examining available case material to see how the systems approach has been applied, why it has worked in some cases, and why it has failed in others, we can establish some guidelines for management's use of this approach to business problem solving.

SYSTEMS DOWN TO EARTH

To close the gap between our ability to understand and manage systems and our use of this capability in solving day-to-day business problems, the following observations are an elementary but necessary point of departure.

Practical Solutions

Businessmen inevitably find it hard to accept the fact that anything as abstract as a new approach—nothing is more abstract or harder to define than a system—can move mountains. It is much easier for the man of action to acknowledge the problem-solving power of a machine tool or a conveyor. Even market research statistics or the data spewed out of a computer have a much earthier appeal than something as intangible and immeasurable as a new approach. If a problem persists, the hard-headed realist can even find the services of a flesh-and-blood consultant more acceptable than a new concept. Yet from a score or more of successful experiences with the systems approach, examples of the practical power of this concept can be found in any industry, even in one not distinguished by the sophistication of its prevailing management practices.

A manufacturer, whose ladies' garment factory of modest size was located in the downtown section of a large city, was suffering from serious bottlenecks in his warehouse at the height of each of his five merchandising seasons. The head of this company, a much better manager than most, had introduced improved layouts, palletizing and conveyorizing, and a substantial amount of additional mechanization in his warehouse and order-filling operation. Thus the situation improved substantially, but, as business increased, the bottlenecks not only recurred but worsened; customer complaints mounted, and profit margins dropped.

A systems approach to this problem began with an analysis of how products moved through the factory. This showed that the warehouse and order-filling problems actually resulted from the way the goods were produced and the manner in which they were marketed. It was apparent that no changes were justified in the warehouse or order-filling operation; therefore, modifications were made in the way the product was packaged, and a basic change was effected in how it was marketed. These made it possible to completely redesign the warehouse and order-filling operations and integrate them into a smoothly operating man-machine system through which the product flowed without interruption.

The resulting system combined a high degree of mechanization and an efficient use of people, so that costs were cut sharply. The bottleneck problem no longer existed because its causes—rooted in production and marketing—were completely eliminated. Both in its general design and in every detail, the solution that resulted from the application of the systems concept was different from the succession of operations and procedures that had resulted from the application of alternative approaches. Not only were management's objectives dealt with forthrightly, but the investment in engineering and equipment was paid off in thirteen months from the saving in costs. More important, the system increased the sales potential of the company, improved its customer service, and thus substantially added to its profitability.

From a purely practical point of view, no amount of mechanization or computerization and no additional warehousing space, no matter how efficiently laid out or equipped along conventional engineering lines, could have solved this management problem, or moved it so far along the road toward achievement of its objectives.

Effective Solutions

The systems approach can also bring high levels of effectiveness to the solution of business problems. An antimissile defense that could intercept 98 per cent of an enemy's nuclear warheads would be of small survival value. A space vehicle that could come within 1 per cent of getting into orbit, or comes that close to returning an astronaut safely to earth, would do small credit to its designers. The need for 100 per cent effectiveness is the reason why the systems approach was developed as a management tool for complex military operations and the penetration of space.

Business, however, does not need or want 100 per cent effectiveness; what it can use profitably is something between this and the quite imperfect answers that present approaches provide. This is conspicuously true in some of the complex business problems for which there have been no better answers than rationalization techniques or improved layouts provided by industrial engineering, or the increase in brute capacity and speed offered by advanced mechanization or computerization. The experience of a major publishing enterprise is an example of the superior effectiveness of systems solutions.

This company, with a well deserved reputation for outstanding management and an excellent earnings record to support that reputation, was faced with an increasingly troublesome order-filling problem. The sheer excellence of its products and of its promotional efforts was generating a rapid growth in its subscriptions and sales. This was in turn producing increasing delays in its ability to respond to incoming mail, fast approaching an average of 50 million communications a year.

The highest levels of industrial engineering sophistication had been applied to each stage in the processing of orders, payments, and other correspondence from customers. The company had, for example, completely computerized the handling of billing and labeling. Yet these measures had not provided an effective solution to increasing costs, increasing delays, and mounting customer dissatisfaction. In fact, neither additional space nor added equipment and manpower promised any major improvement. A systems analysis identified the factors responsible for the problem—factors quite different from those on which the company had been focusing its efforts—and defined the criteria for a complete redesign of the operation. The resulting system cut the time from the receipt of a communication to its entry into the computer by 30 per cent and reduced the time for communication from one department to another by 91 per cent. In addition to important improvement in customer service, an expenditure of about $400,000 in engineering time and equipment reduced operating cost by about $150,000 a year.

Profitable Solutions

Thus systems engineering cut its eyeteeth on activities that are effectiveness oriented rather than profit oriented; this does not mean, however, that systems approach solutions are not profitable. On the contrary, this approach properly applied can define the most profitable solution to many of top management's most challenging problems. We need to be reminded of this fact because of the preoccupation of alternative management approaches with cost reduction rather than profit improvement. As one refreshingly hard-nosed commentator on this point has recently put it, "Our goal is, after all, to make money, not to save it." [1]

When any problem is isolated and dealt with more effectively, its cost can be cut. We

can computerize data processing, conveyorize materials handling, introduce numerical control into production, and in every case pare down the costs of the particular function. But how that affects the profits of the business can be determined only when we consider the effect of this function on all the others, on the interrelationships between them and on the ability of the business to achieve its growth and profit objectives. That kind of thinking is the very essence of the systems approach.

This profit preoccupation of the systems approach is seen clearly by looking more closely at the two examples described previously. In the case of the ladies' goods manufacturer, the systems solution did much more than cut costs. Because it could assure shorter delivery time to the customer in each of the five seasons, management was able to postpone strategic style decisions for an additional week, giving the company an important competitive advantage. It also added an additional week of effective selling time during each season, and, because of the way the business was now organized, the amount of merchandise returned due to late delivery was reduced, and so was the amount of broken-lot merchandise left to be sold at distress prices at the close of each season.

In the publishing company, it is of course important that a $400,000 investment in systems engineering and implementation is reducing costs some $150,000 a year. But the system accomplishes a great deal more. The subscriptions of many customers will now begin a full month earlier than before. Furthermore, a large but as yet unmeasurable amount of promotional material that would have been wasted on customers who had already responded to previous mailings will now be saved, as will the cost of processing that material. The mounting delays had been generating an increasing interchange of letters with subscribers who had not received a response to their original communication; this highly personalized correspondence was the most costly to handle, not only because of the expense of the individualized letter writing, but also because of mounting customer dissatisfaction. By overcoming these serious obstacles to continuing growth in volume and profits, the systems approach, in our best estimate, added more than $2 million in profit potential per year.

[1] Daniel D. McCracken, Harold Weiss, and Tsai-Hwa Lee, *Programming Business Computers* (New York: John Wiley & Sons, Inc., 1959), p. 8.

SYSTEMS LED ASTRAY

Principles Not New

If systems are so effective and profitable, why has management not been more eager to embrace this approach? Its proponents, I believe, have led management astray. First, they have presented this idea as a spanking new concept, sprung full-blown from the brow of Jove. Practical businessmen, who have little affection for abstract ideas, are particularly suspicious of brand-new concepts—and rightly so. Advocates of the systems approach, however, exaggerate its newness, for if the systems term is a new one, the principles on which it is based are actually time-honored. They are, in fact, the principles on which many of our great businesses have been built.

If we dig into the history of many of the great builders of our giant corporations— from Theodore Vail of AT&T to Alfred Sloan of General Motors, and any other outstanding architects of corporate managements—we will find that these business leaders had the ability to view the business as an integrated whole, that is, as a system. They were able to identify strengths and weaknesses, and to see how these defined the factors that were critical for success. This approach was the core of their genius for organizing the business and developing its management capabilities.

Vail, for example, saw the telephone not as an invention to be exploited or a product to be sold, but as a communications system— and a long-distance, world-wide system at that —the services of which were to be leased, and from the beginning, the logotype of this enterprise has borne the words, "Bell System." How deeply this thinking is ingrained into this business is suggested by the fact that it was the Bell Laboratories which contributed the phrase "systems engineering" to our language.

Similarly, at a time when his giant competitors were concerned either with the engineering of the automobile or its mass manufacture, Alfred Sloan looked at the business and saw that its essence was neither the factory nor the product. In the total range of factors that could produce success or failure, he saw that the critical ingredient was the dealer structure. With a strong dealer organization, it became possible to think of the business as an integrated system in which engineering and production were only elements.

Those who have since tried to compete with General Motors have learned the power of systems thinking, though they may not have identified it by that name.

Along the same lines, members of the consulting profession would do well to look closely at the contributions of the late James O. McKinsey, who, in revolting against the limited and limiting outlook of industrial engineering on the one hand and accountancy on the other, was among the first modern management thinkers to insist on the integrity of the business as an organic entity. This gave each corporation its own individuality in terms of which decisions had to be made.

Jargon and Mumbo Jumbo

The proponents of systems thinking have done their brainchild a second injustice by clothing it in unintelligible jargon and elaborate mathematics. These tools of the trade may be necessary at the technical level, but there is no reason why the approach cannot be translated into the familiar terms in which management thinks, listens, and makes decisions. Only in the analysis and definition of intricate interrelationships that precede the system design are advanced technical concepts and mathematics used. In the implementation, sophisticated data processing, electronic controls, and automation may be applied. But the system design—and that is all top management really cares about—can actually be expressed more simply than can other solutions. Ultimately, the system solution draws its strength from the application of sound common sense. There is good reason for this. Even the simplest living, growing organism is made up of many parts that interact with each other in complex ways; this is also true of any growing enterprise, in which finance and production, research and development, and marketing are all intertwined. Management has wrenched this entity apart and divided it into functions, authorities, and responsibilities; when the systems approach puts it all together again, it is only restoring to the business its real and inherent unity.

In one company, for example, goods received by a warehouse came packed in cartons of unlimited variations of size, shape, and description. This decreed that every operation in that warehouse had to be an inefficient batch operation, which prohibited smooth integration or mechanization. That all changed when suppliers were required to ship in modular size containers, which could then be handled mechanically and controlled electronically. All the various functions could then be integrated with other operations into a tightly knit system.

One fact is that the systems approach has been surrounded by obscure mumbo jumbo. This has tended to transform systems engineering into some sort of cult. Little effort has been made by the technical in-group to make top management or operating management familiar with the applicability of systems thinking to everyday business problems.

The Question of Size

Of all the damage that the expositors of systems thinking have done, none is so serious as the fact that they have permitted the impression to persist that systems are only for giant complexes. In part, this misconception flows naturally from the scope of the military and space applications that spawned our systems thinking and the related problem solving techniques. The research expenditure spurred by the needs of World War II has provided us with concepts, techniques, and hardware capable of dealing with complex interrelationships; some are similar to those that many business problems involve. They have provided us with people capable of thinking in systems terms, and of putting the hardware, the concepts, and the techniques together into integrated systems. What needs to be done, therefore, is to clarify the fact that the systems approach can be applied to problems that are modest in size and scope.

WORKABLE SYSTEMS

Fortunately, without in any way violating the systems approach, there are some practical shortcuts that make the application profitable in many common business situations.

1. *A realistic systems approach does not have to take into account every contingency.*

Exponents of systems have the bad habit of scaring management by insisting on using the impractical sounding word "optimum" to characterize the kind of solution they promise to deliver. A chief executive has gotten to that high estate by virtue of his ability to dis-

tinguish between the *best* solution and the *best possible* solution. Management decision making can go no further than developing as imaginatively as possible the range of practical alternatives and then making a choice among them. What a systems study does is identify variables and interrelationships that have to be taken into account in developing practical alternatives. This does not involve any pie-in-the-sky optimum.

Warehouse problems are typical. It is invariably possible to improve the efficiency and to lower costs in the warehouse by improved layout and more effective organization of equipment and people. A systems approach to a warehouse problem, however, acknowledges that the inefficiencies and bottlenecks can be eliminated only by analyzing purchasing, production scheduling, and transportation. Taking these variables into account, the flow of information and paperwork becomes inseparably linked to the flow of the product. In a valid systems approach, all of these have to be considered, not only historically but also dynamically as they relate to corporate growth.

From this viewpoint, management deals realistically with the warehouse problem as a manageable system. But it does so without any "cloud nine" exploration of irrelevant contingencies.

2. *Both short- and long-term variables can be identified.*

It is not necessary to deal here and now with every relevant variable. The critical ones can be considered first, and, if the system has been properly described, other factors will fall in line. If some do not, an appropriate modification of the design should make it possible to deal with them at a later date.

3. *The system can live with "real-life" limitations.*

Systems, as they are discussed in the theoretical literature and as they operate in some space-age applications, must operate without compromise. A capsule hurtling through its orbit has to be able to cope with every possible eventuality. Fortunately, most business problems do not have to be dealt with in this way. A sophisticated systems approach can sometimes lead to a "best possible" solution that simply acknowledges the need to live with limitations.

In designing a materials handling system for the arrival building at what is now Kennedy International Airport, we wanted to consider a number of sophisticated solutions. Our systems study, however, showed that none of them was practical because of space limitations. The area where passengers claimed their baggage was rigidly confined on one side by customs and immigration inspection areas, and on the other by the ramps for the planes. Our study also took into account the fact that this cramped baggage area was going to have to handle an increasing number of passengers and bags crowded into shorter and shorter periods of time. The capacity of planes is increasing and so is the percentage of seats occupied on each trip. At the same time, the number of airlines with international routes is increasing, all intent on arriving at New York at the same popular hours.

It was possible, however, to design a system that would substantially improve the service. The study had shown that the milling about of passengers looking for their luggage was the major cause of the problem. The key to the solution was to organize the area so that people whose baggage was not yet available were removed from the space needed for handling. They could then be called to the appropriate claim area when their baggage was available. This made enough space available to introduce a rather simple conveyor installation. Thus, within the severe limitations of space, it was possible to design a system that efficiently integrated the flow of people and baggage.

4. *Practically applied, the systems approach can be implemented step by step.*

Management too often gets the impression that the systems approach has all-or-none, take-it-or-leave-it implications. Just the opposite is true. The systems approach can identify the critical factors affecting growth and profits today as well as those that are likely to exert an important impact in the foreseeable future. They can relate these past and prospective critical factors to corporate objectives. This makes it possible to decide what needs to be done today, and what can validly be deferred. Only the systems approach can ensure that what is done now does not impede steps that probably will have to be taken to allow for change and growth in a dynamic business environment. Any other approach—the viewing of each decision as a separate transaction—locks companies into rigid situations that are only partial

solutions for today's problems and are totally inconsistent with the requirements of tomorrow.

WHEN SYSTEMS FAIL

In practice as well as in theory, the systems approach has success built into it. By its very definition, this method of problem solving takes into account every factor that relates in any critical way to the cause of a problem or to its profitable solution. Yet systems—or what are carelessly called systems—have failed, and the wide publicity given some of the more dramatic failures causes management to look askance at the systems approach. These failures should serve to temper the impractical enthusiasm of some systems propagandists. Certainly those who have worked in this field since its infancy have learned much from an analysis of systems efforts that have gone awry. Such an analysis can also provide management with guidelines to the practical and profitable use of this approach.

Obviously, the engineering of a system involves a more thorough analysis of the factors and the interrelationships contributing to the problem at hand than a conventional engineering approach. This means that more time is required and, of course, a larger expenditure, though not as large as some managements seem to think. In any case, accumulated experience now enables an engineer with a practical background in this approach to judge whether the additional effort is likely to be profitable. The nature of the problem, the number of items and the volumes involved, and the efficiency of the present mode of operation are critical in determining whether the incremental gain from the additional effort will earn a reasonable return on the investment of time and money.

Excessively elaborate studies are inexcusable where the likelihood of commensurate accomplishment is just not in the cards. But even more critical for a hard-nosed evaluation of whether the systems approach will pay off is the attitude of top management. Unless there is a commitment to search for fundamental solutions, to insist on something more than comfortable palliatives, a systems study can be money down the drain. One of the virtues of a well-designed system is that it irons out loose-jointed operations and closes the gaps between operations hitherto only loosely linked together. In the process, some corporate cliches of long standing may require stern reexamination.

Even where the advance indications were favorable, however, the outcome has been unsatisfactory in some cases. These failures were caused by faulty systems design, faulty implementation, or the fact that a company has tried to move too rapidly to a higher level of sophistication than it could sustain.

Designs for Disaster

One instance of a disastrous outcome in systems design is the well-known "Gertie," the electronically controlled order-filling installation designed several years ago for the Brunswick Drug Co. The company was facing constant pressure from its customers for faster delivery. At the same time, its distribution costs had been mounting. The decision was reached to attempt to resolve this problem by developing an automatic order-picking operation. Briefly, Gertie proposed to do this by translating orders onto punched cards, which were then used to trip gates controlling stock bins, so that the required quantities of each item in an order were automatically released onto a conveyor. The items, untouched by human hands, were conveyed to a packing station.

Gertie, an ingenious piece of engineering, worked flawlessly. The only trouble was that this costly complex of equipment was inconsistent with the nature of the problems it was designed to solve. In order to justify the considerable capital investment, all of the order filling had to be done at a central location. This one location made it impossible to substantially shorten delivery time to customers who were moving farther and farther out to the suburbs. The order-filling speed of Gertie could not make up for this lengthening delivery time, so that in a sense the system design actually aggravated the problem it was meant to solve. In order to cope with competitors located nearer the customers, secondary warehousing in suburban areas had to be set up. But this cut down the volume flowing through the central system, and the cost of running Gertie could no longer be justified.

Gertie proves only that a systems study exposes the fundamental factors that cause problems, and systems solutions deal with the realities of the problem at hand. In this case,

a study of the dynamics of the market should have demonstrated the fallacy of a highly centralized operation and pointed to a decentralized system as the only valid solution. This would probably have meant less hardware and less sophisticated electronics, but it would have produced a system that worked.

Experiences like this have led some people to conclude that systems are inflexible, unable to cope with dynamically changing requirements. This point was widely made a few years ago when the highly automated auto frame factory of A. O. Smith proved to be one of automation's costly white elephants; the system was too rigid to handle the changes in body suspension that had been introduced by A. O. Smith's customers.

To the extent that systems fail because they are inflexible, their inadequacy is the fault of the designer, not of the approach. Obviously, for a system to make any sense, it has to provide for a wide range of possible future developments. The systems approach, properly applied, should provide much more flexibility than traditional engineering.

Failure of Implementation

Experience also points to the fact that there is many a slip between the best system design and its implementation. The most common problems flow from the temptation to take advantage of new developments in equipment, forgetting that people are rather efficient mechanisms, given half a chance. Several attempts at mechanized order-picking systems have proved less than spectacular, for example, when compared to systems that require people to do the actual picking, but use them efficiently by bringing the work to them and by eliminating much routine decision making.

Closely related to problems of design are those instances in which the system's implementation violates an important need of the business. A system designed for a large variety chain validly took into account the fact that the stores in this chain have different characteristics, and that the items handled in these stores also have important differences. In an imaginative manner, the system provided for different stocking procedures for each combination of store types and merchandise categories. The distribution facility and the related materials handling and transportation operations were skillfully engineered.

However, to keep work loads even and minimize congestion in the warehouse and in the stores, the implementation called for matching the layout in the stores with the layout in the order-filling operation. Unhappily, this rigid layout conflicted with the merchandising practices in the stores, where, to maximize point-of-purchase impact, items and even departments are shifted from location to location, depending on the season, fashion trends, and other marketing considerations. This flaw in the implementation reduced the effectiveness of the operation so sharply that a fundamental redesign had to be undertaken to take into account this need for flexibility.

Human Failure

The most serious issues raised by the systems approach have to do with the ability of companies to accept the human requirements of operating an integrated system. Systems, by virtue of their tautness, impose new disciplines on people, and these are not easy for companies used to less tightly knit operations.

A major candy manufacturer, faced with chronic congestion in his warehouse and resulting deterioration in customer service, appropriated the money to build a new and larger facility. We were asked to study the needs and determine the size and design of the new warehouse and its equipment. As facts were gathered to define the system requirements, it became apparent that the problems of this company had to do with the top management organization and the impact of that structure on production scheduling procedures. Only when these matters were dealt with directly could a systems approach to the warehouse problems produce any real improvement in profitability. When this was done, it was found that a change in marketing policies would eliminate most of the customer service problems and that the existing warehouse was more than adequate for the company's needs.

As in the variety chain case, moving into an integrated system would have caused enough stress and strain to make a successful outcome unlikely. In addition to its implementation problems, operation of this system demanded of store managers and warehouse supervisors a level of sophistication they simply did not have. This was apparent from the company's previous mode of operation, which should have

served as a warning to the systems engineer. As a result, this sophisticated system never came close to the efficiency expected of it. What this company needed was a less ambitious systems design that would lead the company surely—if slowly—into a more sophisticated future. Of course, the elements in this intermediate system had to be usable, insofar as possible, in the more sophisticated operation.

WHAT A SYSTEM ACCOMPLISHES

What does systems approach accomplish for management in its effort to deal with the pressures of competition and the squeeze on profits?

First, it frees the corporation from the perils of its organizational straitjacket. In order to function, the business has to be organized by functions, by divisions, by products, or by geographical areas. Organization serves its purposes, but it inevitably violates some basic interrelationships that stand in the way of solving certain critical problems.

Recognition of this fact led the military and its major weapons suppliers to fly in the face of orthodox organizational theory and practice and adopt the systems manager concept. It is the job of the systems manager to put Humpty Dumpty's pieces together again. Many outstanding companies have found the same problem in managing products and have similarly adopted the product manager concept. Since the successes of a product may depend on purchasing, engineering, manufacturing, facilities planning, marketing, physical distribution, and a host of other organizationally distinct functions, it is up to the product manager to put these back together again into a meaningful and hard-hitting whole. Systems thinking acknowledges the integrity of these interrelationships.

Second, the systems approach makes it possible for management to make decisions with full knowledge of their impact on total costs. Partly because of the way our businesses are organized, and partly because of the way we assign profit responsibility to people with hemmed-in areas of authority, many decisions are made on the basis of how they affect partial costs.

Nowhere is this clearer than in the problem of managing inventory. In our experience, few companies can give the total cost of inventory. In almost any company, if different executives are challenged to estimate the value of inventory and the cost of carrying that inventory, their estimates will differ so much that any president can prove to himself that no one in his company really knows the total cost. How, then, can they decide whether a particular change will cut total inventory costs? This, of course, explains why so many decisions are made to reduce inventory levels or raise them without any real knowledge of how over-all costs and the net profit after taxes of the company will be affected.

Third, the systems approach makes it possible to put to profitable use new techniques and new technology. It is characteristic of rapidly advancing management techniques and the accelerating rate of technological change that they do not respect the arbitrary lines of demarcation in the business.

It is no accident, for example, that a recent study by McKinsey & Company shows that two out of three companies sampled in the study have failed to turn a profit on their computer after four years. In addition, many of the experiences with high-flying applications of operations research have been disillusioning. These circumstances help to explain the current wave of unpopularity that the term "automation" is experiencing.

The fact is that full advantage of these opportunities can be accomplished only by taking a hard-nosed look at the business of thinking through the systems interrelationships of the relevant elements.

Fourth, the systems approach puts a firm foundation under the corporate information and control procedures. Both things and facts flow through a company. The things are raw materials or purchased components, in-process materials or parts, and finished products, which end up in the hands of a customer. The facts are historic statistics, current data, and quantified forecasts of future events. When these are processed, they become information on the basis of which management makes its decisions, whether day-to-day operating decisions or judgments about what has to be done today that will affect future operations.

These two flows, when integrated, make the business an integrated entity. Only when these two flows are organized as a dynamic system does management know what information it needs to control that system. When there are gaps in the flow of materials and products, it cannot be controlled, and it is through these gaps that profits leak out. When there are gaps in data or in the flow of information, then management does not know what it needs to know to control its destinies. Only the systems approach can give management the kind of information and control it needs to maximize growth and profitability.

17. THE TOTAL SYSTEMS MYTH

W. M. A. BROOKER *

The purpose of this article is to examine critically the value of the total systems concept and to make predictions on the effects of its application. As is implied in the title, the author does not regard the concept itself as having the practical value claimed by its followers. On the other hand, the belief in this concept is a powerful motivating force among those who have accepted it as a frame of reference.

Why and what is untrue about the total systems concept? The basic error in the total systems concept is the assumption that the total systems approach is the most fruitful; that systems analysis in any situation is the most powerful kind of planning that can precede planned and profitable change for a company.

This article will discuss the foundations of the systems concept, the value of this concept and the limitations of its application. These limitations amount to an inadequacy as to the totality of pervasiveness of the approach, notwithstanding its value in an auxiliary role. We shall then discuss the requirements of an overall approach and outline an alternative in which systems theory occupies a significant but auxiliary role.

FOUNDATIONS OF THE SYSTEMS CONCEPT

The foundation of the systems concept seems to rest on the work of von Bertalanffy, who apparently coined the term "general systems theory." Hall, who is referred to by Bertalanffy, defines the system as . . . "a set of objects with relationships among the objects and among their attributes. Objects are simply the parts or components of a system." [1]

SOURCE: *Systems & Procedures Journal* (July–August, 1965), pp. 28–32. Reprinted by permission of *Systems & Procedures Journal.*

* B.A. M.Soc.Sc., University of Cape Town.

[1] Arthur D. Hall, *A Methodology for Systems Engineering*, Van Nostrand, Toronto, 1962, p. 60.

More specifically, systems are defined in terms of flows. According to Forrester: The business system is . . . "a system in which the flows of information, materials, manpower, capital equipment and money set up forces that determine the basic tendencies towards growth, fluctuation and decline." [2]

The flows of business system, according to Optner, are in the form of a closed system which . . . "can be defined as one which is free of variation or disturbance . . . the concept of the black box" [3] of which the basic model is thus:

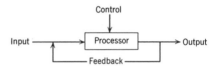

In its business form, this model becomes:

An advantage of the systems approach is that it focuses attention on broader issues than may be contained in a single department. This is because of the emphasis on inputs and outputs. What goes on *inside* the black box is of secondary importance. Naturally this has a healthy effect on any departmental narrowness of viewpoint.

The second advantage of the systems approach is that it aids in the formulation of purpose or objectives for a particular depart-

[2] J. W. Forrester, "Industrial Dynamics: A Major Breakthrough for Decision-Makers," *Harvard Business Review,* July–August, 1958, p. 52.

[3] Stanford L. Optner, *Systems Analysis for Business Management,* Prentice-Hall, Inc., 1960, pp. 3–15.

ment or operating area. The reason for the existence of any operating area can very neatly be expressed in the formula:

$$P = O - I$$

where P is purpose, O is output and I stands for input.

A third advantage of the systems approach is that it can sometimes be related to decision making. Forrester, for example, in his model for industrial dynamics, shows information flows controlling valves in material and money flows.*

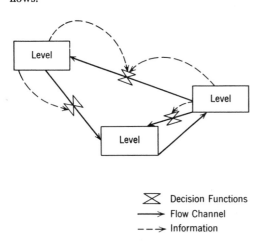

$\bowtie$ Decision Functions
$\longrightarrow$ Flow Channel
$--\rightarrow$ Information

Forrester, incidentally, develops this theme very well in demonstrating the effect of varying sales volume on inventory levels.

DISADVANTAGE OF THE TOTAL SYSTEMS APPROACH

The author's main quarrel with the approach is that many of the followers of systems theory seem to have translated *general* systems into total systems; they give the impression that if systems are omnipresent they must somehow, like God, be omnipotent. General systems theory is a valid field of interdisciplinary study. Those who profess general systems theory realize its limitations, which are not recognized by those who take the *total* systems approach. As an example of an understanding of the limitations of the approach, let's refer again to Hall. Following his definition of a system quoted previously in this article he continues:

"Systems may consist of atoms, stars,

* From J. W. Forrester, *Industrial Dynamics*, John Wiley & Sons, New York, 1961, p. 67.

switches, springs, wires, bones, gases, mathematical variables, equations, laws and processes." [4]

Nowhere in this list does he refer to businesses or people; nowhere in his book does he suggest the use of systems engineering models in business.

Bertalanffy remains conservative:

"General systems theory in its present form is one—and still very imperfect—model among others." Even then, this organismic picture would not claim to be a 'nothing but' philosophy: it would remain conscious that it only presents certain aspects of reality . . . but never exhaustive, exclusive or final." [5]

In contrast is the Forrester definition quoted above. Later, in his book, he says:

"Industrial dynamics models in their purpose and origin will be . . . similar to models of engineering systems . . . concentration must be on those factors that determine the characteristics of information feedback systems—structure, amplification and delays."

Even more ambitious is Wiener:

"It is the thesis of this book that society can only be understood through a study of the messages and the communication facilities which belong to it. . . ." [6]

THE ERROR IN THE "TOTAL" APPROACH

In a nutshell the objection to the "totality" of systems approach is that there is an assumption that this approach is the most important one. [7] This assumption is translated into practice by writers who define the role of change agents such as systems analysts in terms of the total systems concept.

In terms of this concept, the role of the change agents is to design the business system in terms of *flows* of information, materials, money and people, and to persuade members of the enterprise to adopt the system or subsystem so designed. The author has never come across a situation where this has actually been achieved nor has he read an account of where

[4] *Ibid.*, p. 60.

[5] Bertalanffy, *General System Theory—A Critical Review*, Yearbook of the Society for General Systems Research, Vol. VII, 1962, p. 10.

[6] Norbert Weiner, *The Human Use of Human Beings—Cybernetics and Society*, Doubleday-Anchor, New York, 1954, p. 16.

[7] The reason for the error lies in what the author calls the Magical Fallacy.

this has been done. This may be coincidental or it may be because of the following:

1. The total systems approach in business makes no attempt to explain, predict or understand why the human members of the business system act the way they do. It is concerned with components of a business system in the same way as communication theory is concerned with electronic components in a communications system, but it offers little or no understanding of those components either as individuals or as members of business organizations.

2. If it cannot explain the way things are, the total systems approach cannot be expected to explain the way things are going to be. Insofar as the total systems approach is weak analytically with regard to the most significant aspects of the business system (viz., the people), it must also be weak in predicting future developments with regard to people.

ILLUSTRATIONS OF THE MYTH

In order to demonstrate the points we have been making we are going to discuss two articles, both heavily influenced by the total systems concept.

The first is "Analyzing an Overall System" by Charles J. Berg.[8] Early in his article he defines a business system as a:

". . . set of policies, rules, and procedures which defines the actions, responsibilities, and authorities of all elements of a business organization in the day-by-day conduct of its normal activities."

This is all-encompassing, and justifies us as classifying it as being a holistic or total approach. How does Mr. Berg use it? The core of his article is concerned with the stepwise "analytical technique for defining our present position and for use as a systems reference point. Step One is the use of the conventional flow chart of the existing system, with each step analyzed and measured showing the amount of time, money and physical distance required in each processing component. It is not unusual to find at this stage that unnecessary transportation, time and money are incorporated into the system. Step Two relies on the information previously produced, but

it is a modified form of the same information. This is the input-output analysis chart. This technique clearly depicts the multitudinous uses of various data. Generally it can be stated that where many inputs are used to devise many outputs, potential systems improvements are of a high order. Step Three is to relate the present system as described in steps one and two above into financial terminology. What lines on the statement are affected and what are the potential improvements available? Step Four is the allocation of people responsibility for the planned systems improvement, along with specific financial objectives to be attained. Step Five is to accomplish the improvements resulting from the analysis of the above information."

Diagramatically Berg expresses his approach as shown in Figure 1.

But the author does not fulfill his promise. In terms of his own definition of a business system his analytical technique is mainly concerned with "procedures and actions." He refers to policies, rules, responsibilities and authorities *of all elements of a business organization* in his definition of a business system quoted above, and says precious little about them in his analytical technique. Under which of his stepwise analytical techniques could one consider the following problems which have to be considered in any business organization?

What business should we be in? For example, should we diversify our operations, or consolidate? Should our business be divisionalized along product lines, customer grouping, or geographic areas? Should our engineering function be centralized or decentralized or along some combination of both?

In fact these problems cannot be subsumed under the techniques proposed because they are too narrow. The promise of total systems—evident in the definition—remains unfulfilled in the proposals for its creation.

Similar objections come to mind with a second article by Dr. R. L. Martino.[9] But in this case the gap between promise and proposal is even more blatant. The promise lies in the title: "The Development and Installation of a Total Management System."

Most business people are inclined to accept the simple notion that management is con-

[8] *Systems & Procedures Journal,* November–December, 1963.

[9] "The Development and Installation of a Total Management System," *Data Processing for Management,* April 1963, p. 31.

cerned with governing and controlling of the activities of a company, somewhat analogous to the executive branch of the government of a state. To enlarge "management" to "total management system" emphasizes the pervasiveness of the phenomena and also its completeness and orderliness. This promise is not borne out by the following:

". . . The primary objective in developing a total management system should be the production of detailed up-to-the-minute summaries of the past and the use of these summaries to project future activity. In essence the functions of a total management system are: (1) To predict; (2) To compare the prediction with actual results; and (3) To produce the deviations between the predicted and the actual."

In other words, the total system conceptualizers, when they really get down to it, talk of designing flows of information to enable management to do its job better. Martino represents this diagramatically in Figure 2.

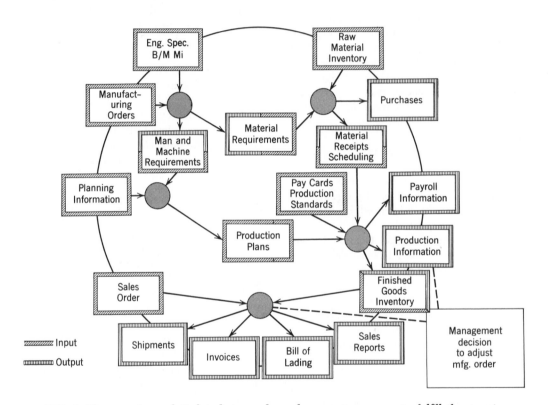

FIG. 1. The stepwise analytical techniques shown here are too narrow to fulfill the promise evident in the definition of total systems.

ONE: If you have a manufacturing order and this is combined with an engineering specification, bills of material and manufacturing information, these can be combined and materials information, manpower and the facilities required can be determined.

TWO: With material requirements being compared to raw material inventories, purchases and material receipts schedules can be derived.

THREE: Returning now to the manpower and facilities requirements, combining and comparing this with planning information, we can evolve specific production plans.

FOUR: Material receipts schedules and pay cards, along with production standards and the production plans, can be integrated to produce payrolls, production data and finished goods inventory.

FIVE: Coordinating the information of a sales order with that of the finished goods inventory, we can produce shipments, invoices, bills of lading and sales receipts.

SIX: Finally, we can build management decisions into the system which are necessary to operate it most effectively.

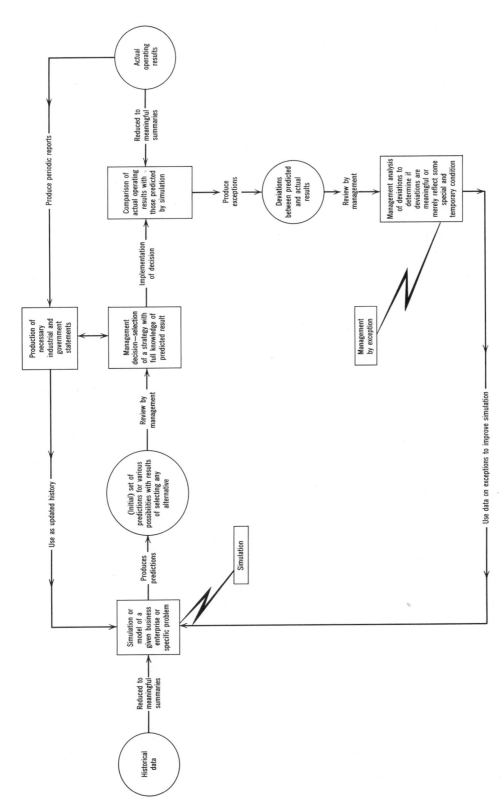

FIG. 2. This diagram shows what management does with various kinds of information. Management itself, however, is not part of the total management system, for nowhere is there any phase where management looks at itself or the organization of which it is a part.

The figure shows what management does with various kinds of information. In Martino's model, management *itself* is not part of the total management system, for nowhere is there any phase where management looks at itself or the organization of which it is a part. It is as though management were something like the driver of a car, detached; as though, like a car driver, management made the decisions, the "system" carried them out.

Factories, warehouses and saleshouses and other industries, services, utilities—whatever the business exists for—consist of much more than information handling systems glorified into some state of "totality." Just as a map of a country may cover the whole of it, it is not a "total" depiction of it, because in a country there are other dimensions and features that cannot be shown on a map. Similarly, in a business there are other dimensions and features which cannot be subsumed under the kinds of total systems we have been discussing.

REQUIREMENTS OF A GENERAL BUSINESS THEORY

What, then, are the theoretical requirements of change agents in business? The following thoughts are offered as criteria for basic theory:

A. Understanding for Action

1. It must be capable of understanding current problems of business. Therefore,

2. It should be capable of realistic predictions on consequences of proposed actions.

3. It should provide a basis for establishing direction for proposed change.

B. Basis for Theoretical Development

An acceptable basic theory should be broad enough to include other more specific theories. If, for example, we reject total systems theory as a basic tool, the basic tool we do adopt should be capable of covering the valuable aspects of such a theory.

OUTLINE OF A BASIC THEORY

What follows is a skeletal account of a theory which meets these requirements:

1. A business is primarily a social human group. The machines, however vast, are origi-

THE MAGICAL FALLACY

A danger in the development or use of symbols is due to the fact that they are selective; ". . . they do not express all that is given but only the aspects and relations considered important for the purpose at hand; hence there is always an aspect of hazard and adventure in the symbols from which the hypotheses are built . . .

"Symbols thus, by their selective nature, readily take on a normative role; being abstract, they tend to contain only that aspect of the referent which the selecting and symbolizing agent considers important or useful . . .

"The magical use of symbols is a natural but illogical development of this normative valuation function . . . magic imputes to the symbol itself an operative force . . . magic ignores the limitations imposed on symbols by their symbolic character." [1]

This error, which might well be called the magical fallacy, is present in the total systems concept. Battersby, in criticizing Forrester's *Industrial Dynamics*, says:

"Yet another source of disquiet on reading this book is the feeling that the author has fallen in love with his theory. The Galatean complex, like the deification of computers, is well known in the scientific world, its main symptom being the urge to conceal or excuse the loved one's blemishes and shortcomings." [2]

Geisler, in reviewing the *Theory and Management of Systems*, by Johnson, Kast & Rosenzweig (McGraw-Hill, New York, 1963), says:

"This is a disappointing book because it presents a glossy and superficial picture . . . the book seems to be a sales brochure trying to persuade the reader that the magical introduction of the systems approach opens the way to the wonders of modern management." [3]

[1] Leroy E. Noemker, *Symbol and Myth in Philosophy* in Altizer et al.: *Truth, Myth and Symbol*, Prentice-Hall Spectrum, 1962, Englewood Cliffs, N.J., p. 118.

[2] A. Battersby, "Book Reviews," *Operational Research Quarterly*, Vol. 14, No. 1, March 1963, p. 98.

[3] Murray A. Geisler, "Book Reviews," *Management Science*, Vol. 9, No. 4, July 1963, p. 702.

nated by and operated by human beings. Therefore, the theoretical basis should be human oriented.

2. There are three aspects of human groups which are important to the understanding of a business. They are objectives, or purpose; activities, or the actual work performed; and relationships which include cooperative and functional as well as the ever-present man/boss relationship. In addition, there are three corresponding concepts pertaining to the individual: values, status and activities.

3. The basis of the approach suggested is, first, that there are certain desirable or healthy conditions for these group and individual aspects, particularly in their relationship to one another. Second, it can be assumed that these conditions do not necessarily apply at all times. Third, it is suggested that the lack of desirable conditions applying will lead to the occurrence of certain effects or symptoms. Fourth, the approach envisages the use of various techniques to reveal these symptoms. Fifth, it is suggested that the symptoms can be used to identify the *causes* of malfunction, and sixth, that planning and executing projects which rectify causes are the proper work of systems analysts, or other change agents, in business.

4. The activities of business are only one of many aspects. Only when this aspect is viewed against its proper background of group purpose (or objectives) and structure, and individuals' values and status, should it be elaborated into a "totality" of system.

5. It is entirely possible to make use of the valuable aspects of systems theory (discussed in the early part of this article) within these other concepts, but then the systems aspect is no longer "total" but ancillary.

A PROPOSED ROLE FOR SYSTEMS ANALYSIS

How can the role of the systems analyst be met in view of these criticisms? The senior systems man in a company may be analogous to a cabinet minister in charge of communications (embracing, for instance, tele-postal-road-rail and air-communications). A minister of communications is concerned with the development of channels for the transmission of information in whatever form. Similarly, the VP of communications with a firm should be concerned with the development and maintenance of communication networks which best achieve company, and divisional if necessary, purpose(s).

This is far-reaching in that it would be extending throughout the whole but it is not holistic or "total" in the Wiener or Forrester sense. Systems departments, therefore, are not analogous to the management of a *real* whole (e.g., a company, a plant or a division).

Let us again take a geographic analogy. All the cities in North America are connected by a system of roads, but urban development—as in the case of corporate development—means working with the wholes in the situation.

City management and development undoubtedly requires auxiliary and parallel development and modification in the road system, and occasionally cities have to adjust to a road development program under the control of a wider authority which constitutes a natural whole,[10] such as a state government.

Roads in this way are analogous to the communications networks of business. Corporations as natural wholes are composed of other, smaller wholes (divisions, operating departments, staff functions, etc.), and the role of management is the continuous mutual adjustment of these parts to one another in order to achieve company goals. This process of continuous adjustment requires the continuous development of new communications transmittal, reception and storage, and it is the role of the systems analyst to carry out this development.

Sometimes, as in the case of a city having to adjust to the road development by a wider authority, the natural wholes (e.g., divisions, departments) within a company have to adjust to the communications system imposed upon them by the company as a whole.

The total systems concept implies—indeed some of its exponents, as we have seen, are quite explicit—that the communications system is the basis for understanding and changing society, or the micro-society that the corporation forms. This is not true; the systems concept is not that "total."

[10] J. C. Smuts, *Holism and Evolution*, Compass Books, New York, 1961.

18. MANAGEMENT INFORMATION SYSTEMS

J. W. Konvalinka * and H. G. Trentin †

In a day when words are used with no real attempt to define them, it should be no surprise to find that some people are puzzled by the term "management information system." For one thing, people tend to confuse a management information system with an electronic data processing (or computer) system. Are they the same? If so, are all computers management information systems? If not, can you have a management information system without a computer?

Another series of questions surrounds the concept of the so-called "total" system. To what extent can all the managerial and decision making processes of a business be systematized? How necessary is it that all systems of the business be combined into one "total system"? In short, does a management information system (M.I.S.) have to be a total system? Finally, whether or not this is so, can an M.I.S. help you in planning and controlling your business?

All this confusion is blocking progress in the development and application of many of the newer management tools. This article is an attempt to put these questions into perspective and to suggest answers based on our experience in assisting clients to design and install management information systems. To do this we have divided the subject into four sections: (1) information and decisions, (2) development of M.I.S. concepts, (3) what an M.I.S. is, and (4) how you get an M.I.S. The emphasis is on the practical rather than the theoretical aspects of the question, and we have drawn examples from our experience to serve as illustrations wherever possible.

Information is vital to good decisions. The more pertinent and timely the information the better the decision—if the decision maker is equally capable in each case.

Military strategists will tell you that armies run as much on intelligence as they do on food. They will also tell you that no general ever has all the information he feels he needs before making a decision. An example: the decision General Eisenhower made to cross the English Channel in the face of an unexpected period of stormy weather and uncertainty about the disposition of the German forces in France. The winning general makes his decisions on a timely basis, using the best information available to him at the time and important intangible elements like experience, judgment, nerve, and an intuitive feel for people and situations.

Business managers operate in the same way. They continually make decisions regarding purchases, sales prices, products, people, acquisitions, and many other things which involve uncertainties of varying degrees about all of the pertinent facts and about all of the probable consequences of their decisions.

Let us not forget, though, that the amount and nature of the information desired by business managers vary with their personalities. Some are impatient with elaborate detail study and preparation and like to make quick decisions based on the information at hand as they begin their deliberations. These men get their best results when historical or environmental data are not the major influencing elements in the decision, for example, with a decision involving the introduction of a new product. Other managers delay decisions too long waiting for information that may be helpful but actually is not vital. Between the two extremes fall the vast majority of business managers, who generally achieve the right balance between waiting for more information and making quick decisions—but, like General Eisenhower, wish that more pertinent and timely information could somehow be made available on an economically feasible basis.

SOURCE: *Management Services* (September–October, 1965), pp. 27–39. Reprinted by permission of *Management Services*.

* Arthur Andersen & Co.
† Arthur Andersen & Co.

This important relationship between information and decisions has led to the great preoccupation with management information systems. The question has become an increasingly pertinent one in recent years. Tremendous information pressures have been exerted on every business by such external forces as rapid technological change, improved communications, and increased competition and by such internal stresses as interdepartmental rivalries, misdirected effort, and a general lack of control.

But if the pressures have grown, so have the means of coping with those pressures. The advent of high-speed data processing equipment and better communications (which also help to cause the pressure) offer an adequate solution to the problem. So do modern management techniques and scientific assistance such as operations research. The problem then becomes one of facing up to the information challenges and selecting the right combination of modern tools to respond effectively.

DEVELOPMENT OF M.I.S. CONCEPTS

Business literature in recent years has abounded with discussions of the need for and nature of management information systems.

The management scientists and operations researchers have made valuable contributions to better management decisions by the development of logical analytical approaches and specialized techniques. The operations researchers in particular have emphasized the importance of viewing the business as an integrated system and understanding the relationships among the various company functions. For instance, in tackling an inventory control problem, they have been more inclined than some of their predecessors to consider the impact on inventory decisions of forecasting methods, raw material purchasing strategies, production leveling requirements, and finished goods storage and distribution economics.

An example will illustrate. A highly fashion-oriented manufacturing company (whose M.I.S. will be described later), experienced heavy annual inventory losses because of markdowns of slow-moving styles at the end of the year. After various unsuccessful attempts to correct this condition, the problem was turned over to an operations researcher.

The losses were traced to faulty forecasting based on salesmen's estimates, and a forecasting system was recommended which improved performance by a significant margin in its first full year of operation. Sales activity for several years was analyzed in complete detail to determine patterns of cumulative order build-up during the year. Based on the relation of early orders in the current year to the historical patterns, a system of projections of additional sales for the balance of the year was developed. A range of probabilities was determined at each reorder point which gave management an indication of its chances of selling various additional quantities of each style. This was expressed in dollars over the range of probabilities by applying unit profits anticipated if the additional goods were sold during the season and unit losses that would be realized if the additional styles had to be marked down at the end of the year.

After installation of this forecasting system, attention was turned to improving the system of buying raw material. Here the problem was one of reflecting the sensitivity in the demand for the finished product back into the purchasing commitments for material. This was done through an explosion of the material requirements for manufacturing and introduction into the final decision of such other factors as economic order quantity and the proper balance of inventory carrying costs.

With these two basic segments in place, the rest of the management planning and control structure was developed. Using similar approaches and enlisting the aid of specialists in data processing and production control where needed, the analysts made improvements in systems for deciding the desirable number of styles to be carried in the product line, scheduling and balancing operations, and developing data for short-range and long-range financial budgeting.

You can see from this example how logical it is to evolve an integrated information system to service all of the planning and control systems of a business. Sales and purchase figures, among others, are vital inputs to many of such systems and may readily be captured in suitable form in a well designed computer system and revised as required in the processing of data.

Management and research associations and electronic computer manufacturers have probably been more responsible for whetting the appetite of the businessman for an M.I.S. than any other source. We have all read the glowing promises in business literature and particularly in ads announcing new equipment. These seem to imply that computer systems are synonymous with management information systems and that management decisions can be automated.

Take the following excerpt from a recent newspaper ad of a computer manufacturer:

"The (blank computer) is a total management information system. It can give you a sure grasp of your business. The control of it. The understanding of it. That's what we mean by the best management control for your computer dollar.

"It can be analyst, planner, forecaster, designer, scheduler, controller, order processor, even customers' man. It can keep you informed, on line and in real time. It can free you to plan and work creatively. To focus on key decisions."

"COMPUTERITIS"

Computers have made possible the collection and dissemination of more information more quickly and economically. If used to process properly designed information flows, they will help achieve better management information systems—but they are not the automatic answer to the business manager's need for decision information. As a matter of fact, the cause of the computer has been unjustly hurt because it has too often been contracted for prematurely.

We have come to recognize the early signs of this condition. They involve undue preoccupation with how data will be processed and the characteristics of the hardware. We usually suggest at this point that hardware should be the last matter considered when thinking about an M.I.S. We tell the businessman who appears to be afflicted with "electronic computeritis" that he should first decide what kind of information he needs—how soon and often—and that what kind of equipment will do this best is a secondary, although an important, consideration. It is surprising to hear of the many early wrong notions that are dispelled by concentrating on the information requirements, with a consequent shrinkage to realistic size of the computer and communications plans.

Furthermore, large centralized data processing centers connected with areas of operation by wire communications facilities, sometimes called management information centers, are not necessarily a prerequisite to or concomitant of an M.I.S. The desirability of such large "figure factories" depends more on the size and nature of the business operation than on the nature of the M.I.S. Many excellent management information systems are serviced by local data processing centers, and the most common arrangement involves a combination of local and centralized centers.

Before leaving the role of computers as processors of integrated data for management information, we should emphasize their ability to use such data in specialized operations research techniques. For example, consider the use of linear programing, which is an analytical or computational technique for solving a general class of optimization problems involving many variables related in a complex way. The solution of these problems involves the attainment of a measure of effectiveness such as profits, costs, or quantities produced for a given set of restraining conditions, including material availability, production capacity, and government regulations. In a specific case, the linear programing technique may systematically search through unit cost and quantity tables of hundreds of alternatives for making products at various plants of a national company, shipping to and storing at various warehouses, and ultimately shipping to customers in order to arrive at an overall minimum cost solution. These many trial computations can be made by hand, but standardized computer programs are now available that reduce the time and cost and thereby extend the area of applicability of linear programing.

WHAT AN M.I.S. IS

In order to appreciate the significance of an M.I.S., we should explore the basic functions of management, namely, (1) planning, (2) execution, and (3) control.

The first function, which deals with company objectives and policies, covers the time period of, say, five or ten years forward. It is concerned with such things as total demand, share of market, new markets, new products, new plant sites, personnel sources and development, and capital requirements.

Execution, which involves carrying out the plans in the present, is what most of us in business do every day. We sell our products, manufacture more, build plants, hire people, pay our vendors and employees, and react to unplanned developments such as strikes and price cuts by competitors.

Control involves monitoring our execution by feedback techniques to determine that we are proceeding in accordance with plans and standards. The reports of our activities tell us how we are doing against sales quotas and expense budgets, whether we are in line on our capital appropriations expenditures, whether our manning tables conform to our standards, and so on through all phases of the business.

The management information system must provide the necessary intelligence on a timely basis to help management plan, execute, and control. Simply stated, an M.I.S. is a system of reports specially designed for this purpose, which means that they are position- or department-oriented to meet specific requirements. Incidentally, it was under the stress of this personal requirement that accounting and reporting of financial data were broadened over the years from a one-dimensional focus of "what did we spend our money for?" to a second dimension designed to show "who spent it and how does it correspond to budget?"—now referred to as "responsibility reporting."

Examples of some of the important elements which comprise an M.I.S. are the following:

1. Reports of historical company and environmental data for long- and short-range planning
2. Long- and short-range financial and operating budgets
3. Monthly financial and operating statements on a "responsibility" basis
4. Sales and order entry statistics, which provide input to many other systems such as sales quotas, salesmen's compensation, purchasing, manufacturing, shipping, and others
5. Reports to service the various control systems such as these:

   (a) Sales forecasting
   (b) Shipping and warehousing
   (c) Finished goods replenishment
   (d) Production control
   (e) Materials management
   (f) Manufacturing cost control
   (g) Personnel skills and manning control
   (h) Management incentives

6. Feedback which shows what should be done to the financial plan in view of actual results to date or what would happen to net income if hypothetical changes were made in the plan.

HOW DO YOU GET AN M.I.S.?

How to get an M.I.S. is the question many managers are grappling with today. And the question is a perplexing one for a number of reasons. For one thing, even though the basic concept of a "total" system is not difficult to understand, as a practical matter it poses a number of problems. How far should a company go in striving for a total system? Should it attempt to systematize and automate every possible function, stopping only at the highest policy and decision level? Or should it settle for something less, which might bring only an organized network of different systems sharing certain inputs and certain outputs? Then again, what effort is required to achieve a total system, and should the project be tackled in one phase or in several intermediate phases with the ultimate goal removed several years?

We are convinced that there is no easy answer to these questions. There is a finite limit to which systems development can be carried, and every company must decide for itself at what point that limit will be reached. You cannot simply transplant a system from one company to another. Not only are the systems requirements different from company to company but also the ability to perfect all management skills, including systematization, will not be the same in any two companies. Models from other companies, books, or computer manufacturer manuals may be helpful as checklists or guides, but the major portions of the system have to be especially designed to meet the needs of your business and its managers.

To provide an illustration of how a particular company might approach the M.I.S. problem, we have developed a hypothetical example that represents a synthesis of several of our assignments. The objective here is to portray graphically what types of systems can be combined to provide a "total" system and what the output of the system should be in terms of management control and information reports. In addition, we want to demonstrate how the M.I.S. project was organized. Our experience has led us to the conclusion that anything short of the approach outlined below will give inadequate results.

Able Manufacturing is a highly fashion-oriented company with manufacturing plants in various parts of the United States and nationwide sales and distribution facilities. A change in management prompted a critical new look at how the company had been faring.

Although the company was one of the leaders in its field, this position was the result of its pioneering effort. Competition from more vigorous young companies had leveled Able's rate of growth and reduced its rate of return to only tolerable percentages.

Typically, Able's new management embarked upon a profit improvement program which involved the introduction of many modern management techniques, including a management information system. After careful consideration of the alternative ways in which the project might be carried forward, Able's president accepted the recommendation that well organized interdepartmental teams be commissioned and given responsibility for the project, which was titled "Management Information System Development" (M.I.S.D.). This approach had the advantage of keeping the M.I.S. an entire company project, not just one organized by finance or administration. It also brought the right mixture of talents to bear on the problem, since Able felt that the basic information requirements should be set by the user of the information. Representation on the team from sales and production as well as the service departments helped assure that all information users would have a voice.

Organization of the effort was accomplished in the following way. A policy committee was appointed to plan and review M.I.S.D. activities on a broad basis. This committee met about once a month to authorize projects, hear progress reports, and make decisions. It consisted of the president, the executive vice president, the vice president of manufacturing, and the vice president of industrial relations and personnel. The selection of these men was made primarily on the basis of personal qualifications and characteristics rather than their functional responsibilities.

The policy committee selected an M.I.S.D. steering committee and approved its charter. This committee met as often as required, usually not less than once a week. The vice president of finance was appointed chairman, and with his participation a representative group of top and middle managers was selected from the various functional areas of the business, including the vice president of marketing, the comptroller, the newly appointed director of Management Information Systems, and others.

The charter of the steering committee (1) set forth the objectives in broad terms; (2) identified areas of special concern in developing an M.I.S. such as organization structure, management policies, and profit and cost center concepts; and (3) provided for the organization of task forces to conduct the required studies and make recommendations.

TASK FORCES

Personnel of the task forces were assigned, for the most part, on a full-time basis from the particular areas under study. Although the task force leader was usually a representative of middle or top management, most of the task force personnel were selected for their technical skills. To ensure that the data processing requirements of the M.I.S. would receive proper emphasis, members of the data processing staff were assigned to each task force. Technical representatives of our firm were attached to some of these task forces and were the means by which our consultants at the steering and policy committee levels helped plan and execute the M.I.S.D. effort. Each task force was charged with a specific task and timetable for reporting to the steering committee.

As the M.I.S.D. project developed it necessarily covered all areas of the business. It required approximately three years to complete. Its scope can be visualized from the following M.I.S.D. organization structure:

Policy Committee—
  Steering Committee—
    Task Forces
      Company organization
      Management and operating policies
      Budgets
      Monthly reporting
      Expense management
      Standard cost accounting
      Data processing
      Customer accounting and statistics
      Long-range planning
      Inventory management

As one of its early actions under this program the company placed orders for computing equipment of an advanced line announced by a manufacturer that had serviced the company's data processing needs in the past. This

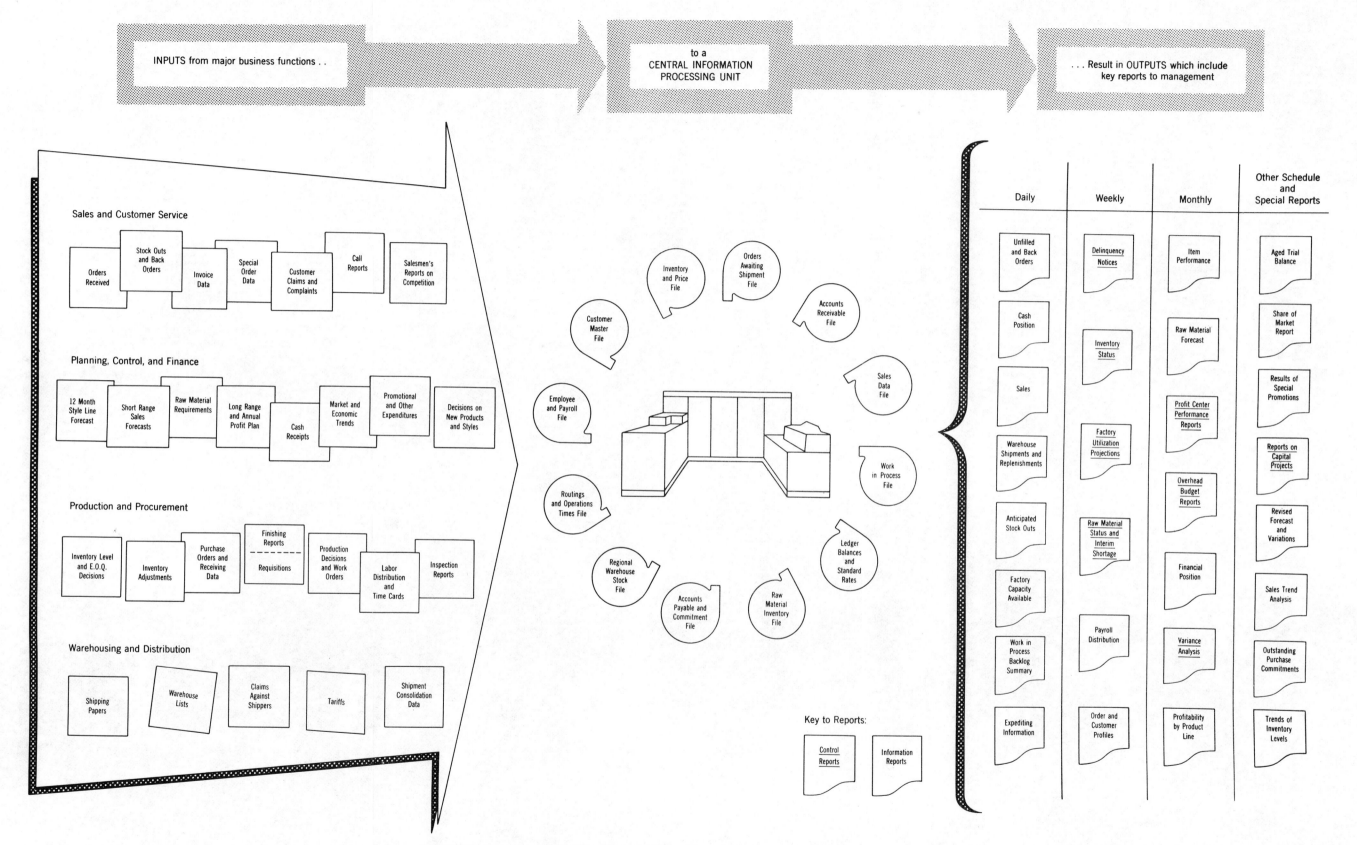

INPUTS from major business functions . .

to a CENTRAL INFORMATION PROCESSING UNIT

. . . Result in OUTPUTS which include key reports to management

Sales and Customer Service

Orders Received | Stock Outs and Back Orders | Invoice Data | Special Order Data | Customer Claims and Complaints | Call Reports | Salesmen's Reports on Competition

Planning, Control, and Finance

12 Month Style Line Forecast | Short Range Sales Forecasts | Raw Material Requirements | Long Range and Annual Profit Plan | Cash Receipts | Market and Economic Trends | Promotional and Other Expenditures | Decisions on New Products and Styles

Production and Procurement

Inventory Level and E.O.Q. Decisions | Inventory Adjustments | Purchase Orders and Receiving Data | Finishing Reports / Requisitions | Production Decisions and Work Orders | Labor Distribution and Time Cards | Inspection Reports

Warehousing and Distribution

Shipping Papers | Warehouse Lists | Claims Against Shippers | Tariffs | Shipment Consolidation Data

Inventory and Price File | Orders Awaiting Shipment File | Customer Master File | Accounts Receivable File | Employee and Payroll File | Sales Data File | Routings and Operations Times File | Work in Process File | Regional Warehouse Stock File | Accounts Payable and Commitment File | Raw Material Inventory File | Ledger Balances and Standard Rates

Daily
Unfilled and Back Orders
Cash Position
Sales
Warehouse Shipments and Replenishments
Anticipated Stock Outs
Factory Capacity Available
Work in Process Backlog Summary
Expediting Information

Weekly
Delinquency Notices
Inventory Status
Factory Utilization Projections
Raw Material Status and Interim Shortage
Payroll Distribution
Order and Customer Profiles

Monthly
Item Performance
Raw Material Forecast
Profit Center Performance Reports
Overhead Budget Reports
Financial Position
Variance Analysis
Profitability by Product Line

Other Schedule and Special Reports
Aged Trial Balance
Share of Market Report
Results of Special Promotions
Reports on Capital Projects
Revised Forecast and Variations
Sales Trend Analysis
Outstanding Purchase Commitments
Trends of Inventory Levels

Key to Reports:
Control Reports | Information Reports

EXHIBIT 1. Overview of Able Manufacturing Company's Integrated Management Information System.

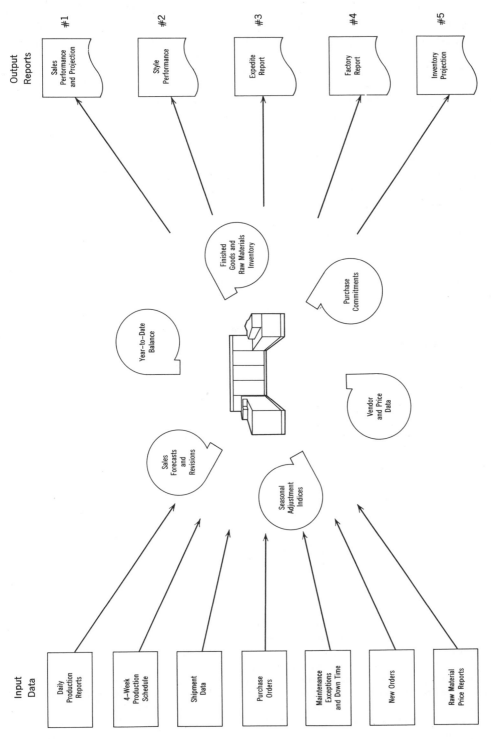

Input
Data

Daily Production Reports	
4-Week Production Schedule	
Shipment Data	
Purchase Orders	
Maintenance Exceptions and Down Time	
New Orders	
Raw Material Price Reports	

Sales Forecasts and Revisions

Seasonal Adjustment Indices

Year-to-Date Balance

Finished Goods and Raw Materials Inventory

Purchase Commitments

Vendor and Price Data

Output
Reports

Sales Performance and Projection #1

Style Performance #2

Expedite Report #3

Factory Report #4

Inventory Projection #5

EXHIBIT 2. Able Manufacturing Company—Detail of Inventory Planning Information Flow Showing Selected High Level Reports.

was done on a generalized basis before the full requirements were known in order to reserve favorable delivery time, and the orders were particularized as the various task forces completed work in the assigned areas of the business.

In the exhibits you will see, in broad terms, the end product of the M.I.S.D. effort. Our objective is to show how the teams were able to organize virtually all of the company's procedural and information systems into one integrated M.I.S. utilizing common files or a "data bank." We also want to show how the reports generated by the new system brought many of the key variables in the business into a new focus to aid in prompt and decisive management action. Please bear in mind that not all of the subsystems were integrated at one time and that the ultimate usefulness of the reports was attributable to a strong management planning function as well as to a well organized information flow.

Exhibit 1 shows how the major business activities create data input to a central processing unit on a daily, weekly, and monthly basis. Such inputs of data in previous periods have resulted in master files of data relating to customers, employees, inventories, and all other phases of the business, accumulated from previous processing cycles. As current information is processed, the applicable master files are updated, and the prescribed control and information reports and documents are prepared automatically. The types and volumes of planning and control reports generated from the basic data are limited only by the needs of management and the creativity of the systems analysts assisting management in the definition of requirements.

In Exhibit 2 we have taken one segment—inventory planning—and illustrated in more detail how this process works. Exhibit 2 is followed by five typical reports that would be produced by the processing cycle in this area.

Able Manufacturing Company, Sales Performance vs. Plan
September 30, 196X, (000 omitted)

| | | Year to Date Sales | | | This Month Sales | | |
| | | | Deviation from | | | Deviation from | |
	Amount	Original Forecast	Latest Revision	Amount	Original Forecast	Latest Revision
Product Line A	$ 778	$ 58	$ 4 *	$ 86	$ 7 *	$ 2 *
B	907	21	5	98	6	1 *
C	829	19	2	90	3	3
D	786	9 *	2 *	85	4 *	2
E	800	15	6	86	6 *	3 *
F	691	11	1	75	9	6
G	850	12 *	3 *	92	3	1
H	1,123	17	4	122	11	4
I	878	9	1	95	2	6 *
J	987	25 *	7	107	5	4
Others	43,868	329	54	4,899	178	8
Total **	$52,497	$433	$71	$5,835	$200	$16

* Below plan
† Based on year to date sales after seasonal adjustment
Note: As well as reporting monthly sales by product line, this report shows the expected and actual results against the original forecast and all revisions. By the application of standard gross profit rates, the profit effect of all deviations can be measured, and revisions in the profit and production plans can be recognized and made on a timely basis.

** Total is arrived at by summing the positive deviations and subtracting the deviations below plan (the numbers with asterisks).

REPORT 1

CONCLUSIONS

In this hypothetical example we have digested the results of our experience in many management information systems consulting assignments. Some of you may be questioning the suggested scope of such an undertaking. You may have had the impression that such projects involved largely the installation of a computer with some peripheral activity concerned with determining needed statistical data and reports. It may be that some management information systems assignments stay confined to this relatively simple pattern, but the inevitable tendency to expand is easily explained.

The first expanding influence is the computer itself, which is identified with so many of the M.I.S. projects. Most observers dealing with the computer field have come to recognize that its scope and potential is such that the old compartmentalized notions of de-

cision responsibilities and data processing interfere with efficient utilization of the new equipment and related techniques.

Secondly, the nature of a management information system leads naturally to a re-examination of many basic management approaches. The starting question, "What information do the various managers need to accomplish their missions?" evokes "What is their mission?" In most cases the answer to the second question is not readily forthcoming, for on probing you do not get articulate or unanimous answers to questions such as the following:

• Who has profit responsibility? Top management, marketing management, or manufacturing management?

• Who has responsibility for the size of inventories and obsolescence losses thereon?

• Should marketing management or manufacturing management make the final de-

Able Manufacturing Company, Sales Performance vs. Plan
September 30, 196X, (000 omitted)

Projected Deviation of Future Sales †							Expected at Year End	
October		November		December			Deviation from	
Original Forecast	Latest Revision	Original Forecast	Latest Revision	Original Forecast	Latest Revision	Total Sales	Original Forecast	Latest Revision
$ 8 *	$ 3	$ 5 *	$ 2 *	$ 15 *	$ 2	$ 1,011	$ 30	$ 1 *
3	1	7	2	10	6	1,180	41	14
5	2 *	3 *	1	12	4	1,078	33	5
9	3	15	3	8	4	1,022	23	8
7	4	6	1 *	11	5	1,040	39	14
6	3	9	4	2 *	3	898	24	11
2 *	2	7	2	4	2 *	1,105	3 *	1 *
5	4	12	2	9	5	1,460	43	15
1 *	1	2 *	2 *	12	4	1,141	18	4
2	2	4	1	3	2 *	1,283	16 *	8
115	10	230	. 30	247	21	58,782	921	115
$141	$31	$280	$40	$299	$50	$70,000	$1,153	$192

REPORT 1 (continued)

Able Manufacturing Company Style Performance Report
September 30, 196X (week 39)

	Year to Date Deviations from Plan [1]			This Month Deviations from Plan [1]		
Style	Sales	Production	Ending Inventory	Sales	Production	Ending Inventory
XAGO	$ 300 *	$ 3,600	$ 3,900	$ 200 *	$ 500	$700
XDZG	600	—	600 *	350	—	350 *
YHQN	2,200	1,600	600 *	400	200	200 *
ZMVO	400	1,200	800	450	800	350
APET	1,900	4,000	2,100	200	400	200
DUFH	800 *	3,000	3,800	175 *	200	375
GBEN	1,100	—	1,100 *	250	—	250 *
JLMD	900	—	900 *	325	—	325 *
WBPN	100	2,400	2,300	190	680	490
PTSY	500 *	1,400	1,900	300 *	290	590
RVWB	1,000	2,700	1,700	510	470	40 *
Other styles	14,400	18,500	4,100	4,000	3,350	650 *
Total	$21,000	$38,400	$17,400	$6,000	$6,890	$890

* Below plan
[1] Based on year to date sales after seasonal adjustments
[2] And existing production plan

Note: This report expands on Report 1. It relates sales performance of a style to its production and inventory levels, to maintain maximum flexibility in production scheduling. Where a style is falling below its sales forecast, the basis is provided for curtailing production on that item and shifting the resulting available capacity to where it may be needed. (Total sales for the entire product line, Product Line B, are shown on Report 1.)

REPORT 2

cision on special product runs or unusual size of orders?

• Are the functions of staff and line management defined so that the responsibility for operating decisions is clear?

• Are the bases for measuring the performance of the various people in management specified?

Even in those cases where organizational responsibilities are clearly defined, the intense reappraisal of all activities occasioned by an M.I.S. project may result in changes in approach. For example, top management may well decide to change its approach on the assignment of responsibilities. Thus, we have heard it said that a company has been too manufacturing-oriented or too marketing-oriented or too research-oriented in the past and that the emphasis should be changed by giving more responsibility and authority to

another functional group. You can appreciate how the nature and flow of information required would change if more emphasis were placed on marketing control of decisions regarding product lines, for instance, or on size of inventory, location of warehouses and plants, or order sizes.

MANUALS

Decisions relating to these matters should be reflected in organization and management policy manuals, and if these do not exist it is generally deemed desirable to prepare them as a prerequisite to, or concomitant of, the M.I.S. development.

Questioning of organizational responsibilities and management policies often stimulates a re-examination or revamping of control systems such as cost accounting and production

Able Manufacturing Company Style Performance Report
September 30, 196X (week 39)

Product Line B

				Projected Inventory Level Using Latest Forecast [1,2]					
End of Week 40		41		42		43	
Units	Days' Sales	Units	Days' Sales	Units	Days' Sales	Units	Days' Sales
38	8	43	10	50	12	56	13
17	4	(6)	(1)	(2)	(1)	(6)	(2)
19	4	16	4	(20)	(4)	(24)	(5)
20	4	20	4	26	5	30	7
21	5	25	5	27	5	32	7
39	8	65	16	74	18	78	19
61	15	46	11	(53)	(13)	(60)	(15)
31	7	(8)	(1)	(2)	(1)	(5)	(1)
12	3	20	4	21	4	28	5
25	5	4	1	20	4	23	5
45	10	18	4	9	2	3	1
320	80	270	68	250	63	298	75
648	153	513	125	400	94	453	109

REPORT 2 (*continued*)

Able Manufacturing Company Weekly Expedite Report
September 30, 196X (week 39)

Style	Safety Stock (units)	Projected Stock-Out Next Six Weeks [1]		Item Now Running at Plants No.	Capacity to Cover Stock-Out Available at		Hours Needed to Restore to Safety
		Week	Quantity Short		Plant No. [2]	Line	
XDZG	25	41	31	1-6-3	4-6	1,7,15	192
YHQN	40	42	60	1-6-3	4-6	2,3,5	568
GBEN	100	42	153	2-7	—	—	791
JLMD	60	41	68	4-7	—	—	213

[1] Based on year to date sales (after seasonal adjustment) and existing production plan
[2] Based on existing production plan, subject to any prior special orders
Note: This report expands on expected stock-outs disclosed in Report 2, showing available plant capacity and amount of inventory and production hours needed to restore safety stock and cover planned requirements.

REPORT 3

Able Manufacturing Company Factory Report—September 30, 196X
(000 omitted)

| | Year to Date | | | | This Month | |
| | Earned Hours | | Plant Utilization | | Earned Hours | |
	Number	Deviation from Plan	%	Deviation from Plan	Number	Deviation from Plan
Plant 1	98	3 *	78	2 *	11	.4 *
Plant 2	139	6 *	84	1 *	15	.7 *
Plant 3	117	5	86	6	13	.5
Plant 4	81	2	61	14 *	9	.2 *
Plant 5	108	9 *	84	3 *	12	1.1 *
Plant 6	144	4	82	2	16	.5
Plant 7	126	1	90	1 *	14	.2

* Below plan

Note: This report focuses on plant utilization and pinpoints variations from plan as well as the major reasons for those variations. The information here comes from the same source as the information on Report 3 relative to plant capacity for certain lines.

REPORT 4

Able Manufacturing Company Weekly Raw Material Inventory Projection
September 30, 196X (week 39)

| Raw Material Code | End of Week | | Lead Time | Safety Stock | On Order Due in Week | | | | | | |
	Material on Hand	Deviation from Plan			40	41	42	43	44	45	46
281	2,758	204	2	1		600		450			
282	204	816 *	3	2			1,400		1,400		1,800
284	421	286 *	2	1		100		400		400	
290	575	55	1	1	75		75		75		75
301	1,008	122 *	2	1		350		450		550	
350	900	500 *	3	2			1,500		1,500		1,500
423	847	47	2	1		500		400		300	
424	3,100	100	2	1							1,500
500	290	90	1	1	40	40	40	40	40	40	40
501	1,949	49	1	1	900			600		600	

* Below plan
[1] Based on existing production plan
[2] For quantity sufficient to restore safety stock

Note: This report helps ensure that the production plan and finished goods inventory levels can be met. Changes in either of these plans are reflected in this report, and attention is drawn to any exceptions in the planned level of raw materials inventory.

REPORT 5

Able Manufacturing Company Factory Report—September 30, 196X
(000 omitted)

This Month					
Plant Utilization		Lost Hours Due to			Available
%	Deviation from Plan	Unplanned Down Time	Schedule Gaps	Production Balance	Hours Next Month
78	2 *	.4	—	—	11.9
82	3 *	.2	.4	.1	16.4
82	2	—	—	—	14.2
65	10 *	.1	.1	—	9.6
88	1	.5	.6	—	13.7
87	2 *	—	—	—	17.3
90	5 *	—	—	—	14.3

REPORT 4 (*continued*)

Able Manufacturing Company Weekly Raw Material Inventory Projection
September 30, 196X (week 39)

Projected Usage in Week [1]							Projected Stock-Out [1]		Indicated Purchase Price [2]
40	41	42	43	44	45	46	Week	Quantity	Variance
45	45	40	42	45			—	—	—
400	400	400	400	400	400	400	40	996	5.5¢
150	150	150	150	150	150	150	43	79	14.7¢
80		80		80		80	—	—	—
	600		600		600		—	—	—
500	500	500	500	500	500	500	41	600	11.2¢
	90		210		660		—	—	—
375	375		375	375		375	—	—	—
90		90		90		90	—	—	—
300	300	300	300	300	300	300	—	—	—

REPORT 5 (*continued*)

and inventory management. For example, if manufacturing management were to be judged solely on cost performance and if this were carried to the point of introducing an incentive system based on actual performance against standard, the company would require a rather sophisticated standard cost accounting system and a set of performance reports to reflect results of operations. In a manufacturing company the cost consequences of manufacturing operations constitute a major segment of any M.I.S., which explains why cost accounting systems installations so often accompany M.I.S. development. In the same way, questions about inventory policy and responsibilities very often lead to much needed improvements in the production and inventory control systems.

In summary, the great current popularity being enjoyed by management information systems development is responsible for improvements in management skills and techniques in many companies which would not have accomplished them so soon otherwise. If your company has not had this experience yet, you should ask the door-opening question at your next staff or management meeting: "Do we have the information we need to run our business?"

BIBLIOGRAPHY

1. Carasso, M., "Total Systems," *Systems and Procedures,* November, 1959.
2. Doherty, P. A., and J. G. F. Wollaston, "Effective Management of a Systems Project," *Management Services,* March–April, 1965.
3. Eckman, D. P., *Systems: Research and Design,* John Wiley and Sons, 1961.
4. Ewell, J. M., "The Total Systems Concept and How to Organize for It," *Computers and Automation,* September, 1961.
5. Goode, H. H., and R. E. Machol, *System Engineering,* McGraw-Hill Book Co., Inc., 1957.
6. Hoag, M., "What Is a System?", *Operations Research,* June, 1957.
7. Johnson, R., F. E. Kast, and J. E. Rosenzweig, *The Theory and Management of Systems,* McGraw-Hill Book Co., Inc., 1963.
8. Lach, E. L., "The Total Systems Concept," *Systems and Procedure,* November, 1960.
9. McDonough, A. M., and L. J. Garrett, *Management Systems, Working Concepts and Practices,* Richard D. Irwin, Inc., 1965.
10. McMillan, C., and R. F. Gonzalez, *Systems Analysis—A Computer Approach to Decision Models,* Richard D. Irwin, Inc., 1965.
11. Malcolm, D. G., A. J. Rowe, and L. F. McConnell (eds.), *Management Control Systems,* John Wiley and Sons, 1960.
12. Mayer, R. R., "Scientific Management or Management Science?", *Advanced Management— Office Executive,* July, 1963.
13. Optner, S. L., *Systems Analysis for Business and Industrial Problem Solving,* Prentice-Hall, Inc., 1965.
14. Shultz, G. P., and T. L. Whisler (eds.), *Management Organizations and the Computer,* Free Press, 1960.
15. Tilles, S., "Manager's Job: A Systems Approach," *Harvard Business Review,* January, 1963.

Part VI. Human Problems of Systems

One of the several previously discussed constraints that systems designers must take into consideration is people. It is a sad fact that too often many of them ignore the human element in systems design. Indeed, the remark, "It would be a great system if it weren't for the people involved," is more than mere witticism or facetiousness. In the man-to-machine but especially in the man-to-man systems it is the human element that merits greater attention. Though systems do involve materials, energy, and information flow, it is the impact of these on the individuals that tends to be either overlooked or underestimated.

It is the behavioral scientist who has especially concerned himself with the problems involved in effecting change. The agent of change must therefore familiarize himself with the findings from the fields of cultural anthropology, sociology, psychology, and social psychology, for these have much to contribute to the solution of those problems plaguing management. Specialists at times tend to overconcentrate on their own tightly circumscribed arena of investigation and to act as if nothing of importance could possibly transpire elsewhere. Ackoff noted this tendency when he warned systems engineers:

We must stop acting as though nature were organized into disciplines in the same way that universities are. The division of labor along disciplinary lines is no longer an efficient one. In fact, it has become so inefficient that even some academic institutions have begun to acknowledge the fact . . .

No single individual can be educated so as to be expert in all the disciplinary approaches to systems. It is difficult enough to make him expert in one. We can, however, educate him to an awareness of what others know and can do in systems work and motivate him to desire to work collaboratively with them. Scientific snobbery must go.[1]

The one aspect of human problems that has been stressed over and over in the literature and for which there is by now a voluminous bibliography is resistance to change. Problems of resistance to change have been present throughout recorded history and their most recent manifestation has been occasioned by the introduction of electronic data processing and automation. The classic study dealing with this is the article written by Coch and French.[2] Though this somewhat lengthy article has not been reprinted among the selections included in this reader, it is worth perusing. The shorter articles by Alvin Zander, Lawrence Williams, and Robert Schlosser, together with the selection "The Sociological Problems of PERT" in a later section highlight this important area.

In the first selection Bruce DeSpelder comes out strongly for the newer, human-centered philosophy favoring broader tasks (job enlargement), more involvement in decisions, self-discipline, and more demo-

[1] Russell L. Ackoff, "Systems, Organizations, and Interdisciplinary Research," *General Systems,* **5,** 1960, pp. 1–8. Quotations are from pp. 6 and 8.

[2] Lester Coch and John French, Jr., "Overcoming Resistance to Change," *Human Relations,* 1948, pp. 512–532.

cratic processes of supervision (participation). He champions this approach over the older, impersonal managerial approach based on rigidly defined tasks and work processes, specialization, and close discipline imposed from above. In general he stresses the need for finding more meaningful work situations where the worker's personal development and self-enrichment can flourish, where his emotional health is promoted, and where freedom of thought and action are values important in their own right. Case studies serve to illustrate the interesting treatment. The critical dichotomy of our times, DeSpelder believes, is not between democracy and totalitarianism but between a society dominated by material production and one laying stress on human personal values.

The psychologist, Lawrence Williams, advances the hypothesis that much resistance to change is based on attitudes that are largely emotional. Consequently, the "logical" approach that the systems engineer is to employ in overcoming resistance is not that of sheer logic or of brute force. However, he can learn much of the real cause of the attitude from an examination of the statements proffered in opposition to the proposed change.

It may be something less than a compliment to learn that resistance to change is probably more prevalent on the level of middle managers than on that of the rank-and-file employees. This may be due to the fact that these individuals have more at stake.

The bulldozer method of attacking resistance to change is shown to be devoid of almost all merit. Even when short-run results are obtained, the costs must be carefully weighed. Often it retards subsequent change-adoption and dries up the pool of goodwill that may have existed in the past.

Possible loss of status and of existing informal relationships that have proved satisfying are singled out as human features to be considered when planning change. Dif-

ferential motivation on the part of managers and employees, poor communication networks where top level managers learn of the resistance at lower levels only when it is too late, feasibility for change from both the technical and the human viewpoint, and the difficulty of translating the impersonal language of the technological system into the human language of the social system are succinctly but clearly discussed.

Alvin Zander continues the same line of thought in the third selection. He points out that not all opposition need be labelled resistance to change. Some opposition may be based on perfectly logical reasons. The rationale for this distinction is his definition of resistance to change as "all behavior intended to protect or insulate the individual from the consequences of real or imagined change." After discussing briefly the nature of this resistance he goes on to examine the conditions that seemingly are associated with its development. Though not intended to be exhaustive, his listing of six conditions conducive to resistance are presented as broad generalizations. Because of accompanying modifications these must be carefully examined. Thus resistance is said to be expectable if the nature of the change is not explained to those who will be concerned therewith. It is assumed that one is uncomfortable when he does not know exactly where he stands. Yet the important thing is not how much information is supplied by higher level management but what the information means to the recipients. Differential interpretation comes into the picture. Finally, means for decreasing and preventing resistance are also outlined.

Robert Schlosser in the final selection also underscores the need for a sound understanding of the basic principles of psychology if one is intent on averting or reducing resistance to change. The two psychological concepts that he focuses upon are motivation and learning. Among the many essential motivating factors that he lists are the biogenic and the sociogenic urges or drives. These must be carefully considered when planning change; otherwise a conflict of motivating forces or a sheer frustration of one impelling motive may create problems for the systems engineer.

In the learning process, which is defined as "a change in behavior as a consequence of experience," seven elements stand out as worthy of note: situation, personal characteristics, goal, interpretation, action, consequence, and reaction to thwarting.

Schlosser does not fail to remind the systems analyst that he must be realistic enough to know that the ideal cannot always be attained and should therefore work out ways to deal with nonadaptive behavior.

19. DESIGNING THE PARTICIPATIVE DECISION-MAKING SYSTEM *

Bruce DeSpelder †

What is the effect of systems and procedures work upon the individual human being or groups of human beings whose work patterns are being studied and changed?

It seems quite clear that the major stress is on work and not workers. Such subjects as work flow, work simplification, work sampling, work analysis, work measurement, forms design and control, space and facilities planning, time and motion study, records management, data processing, budgets, cost control, operations research, etc., keep recurring. But little stress is being placed on the fundamental that systems and procedures work is only an aid to human endeavor.

To be sure, you can find an occasional chance remark in current business literature that systems and procedures specialists should "sell" their ideas by being tactful and cooperative, or that workers will resist change. But, the issue of the human effects of systems and procedures activities cannot be relegated to such passing comments. It is a central problem. Perhaps the best way to point up this anomaly is to refer to the very words of a leading writer in the field of systems and procedures, Richard F. Neuschel, who in the preface to his recent book, *Management by System*,[1] quotes from Elton Mayo's pioneering human relations study, *The Social Problems of an Industrial Civilization*. Neuschel notes

SOURCE: *Systems & Procedures Journal* (January–February, 1964), pp. 20–24. Reprinted by permission of *Systems & Procedures Journal*.

* This article is based on a talk delivered by the author on February 10, 1962, to the Fourth Annual Mid-winter Conference of the Detroit and Motor City Chapters of the Systems and Procedures Association.

† Professor of Management, Wayne State University.

[1] Richard F. Neuschel, *Management by System*, McGraw-Hill Book Co., New York, 1960.

that Mayo identifies three persistent problems in industry. One is the application of science and technical skill to some material good or product. A second difficulty is the systematic ordering of operations. Finally, Mayo refers to the problem of organizing teamwork which is defined as creating "sustained cooperation."

Neuschel proceeds to build his entire treatise solely on the second of Mayo's persistent industrial problems—the need for a systematic ordering of operations; and rather completely overlooks the importance of the third issue—"organizing teamwork." To be fair, it is evident that he is engaging in the favorite pastime of using a quote from a very respected treatise in order to lend authenticity to his own effort.

However, and this is vital, he does fail to acknowledge that Mayo was writing about fundamental research work at the Hawthorne plant of the Western Electric Co. during the period 1927–32. Mayo's experiments showed quite conclusively that the traditional engineering approach to the motivation of workers failed to create attained cooperation. This traditional approach is based on what Mayo called the rabble hypothesis. The theory assumes that job holders merely tolerate their positions as a necessary evil which is demanded by the economic need to survive. Work is considered to be unnatural and something to be minimized and avoided, if possible. As a result, man must be driven and controlled by authoritarian methods and precisely defined work routines, so as to overcome his dislike for work and tendency to shirk his job.

Systems and procedures are, of course, a necessary part of a carefully designed work process. Neuschel, by his failure to indicate otherwise in his book, seems to countenance orthodox, impersonal management practices. However, other recent writers appear to follow this same tradition. For instance, Lazzaro's handbook, *Systems and Procedures*,[2] professes to give an A to Z coverage of the field but also ignores the effects of his topic upon human behavior.

Mayo, later to be dubbed the "father of human relations" in business, demonstrated that there are great social factors to be accounted for in explaining and managing on-the-job performance. Factors such as the creation of a feeling that one's job is significant were found to be much stronger elements in worker motivation than were usual concepts like incentive pay and better physical conditions such as heating and lighting of work spaces. In short, he gave great impetus to the concept that traditional methods of management should be questioned and could be improved.

Other social scientists have added their research findings. Together, they add up to a strong protest against authoritarian direction and control of workers. Extended research since 1947 by Rensis Likert and his staff at the University of Michigan's Institute for Social Research has indicated that the usual methods of carefully defining jobs, work systems and organizational patterns often result in unfavorable attitudes on the part of employees and a lesser feeling of job satisfaction. Oddly enough, the institute's investigations show that autocratic or hierarchically controlled methods of management will actually maintain or increase productivity in the short run.[3]

It is the longer term effects which are the most startling, however. Such things as increased labor turnover, grievances and strife may not be reflected in normal measures of productivity, but the cost consequences, apparent or hidden, are inevitable. In other words, satisfactory rates of production may be achieved only through liquidation of certain human values like favorable attitudes, interest in work and "general spirit of cooperativeness," which are vastly more significant to society, and far less susceptible to measurement in the normal accounting manner, than are other tangible business assets.

Chris Argyris, a professor of industrial administration at Yale, has taken a hard look at the effect upon the emotional health of employees of rigidly defined and controlled organizations which break jobs down into their most minute parts.[4] His conclusions are not flattering. In fact, he speaks very critically of the tendency for modern management methods to demand only childlike behavior from employees. The latter's jobs are so highly organized that they feel passive, dependent, and submissive. In Argyris' estimation, many organizations are creating mental health problems through failure to regard their employees as mature adults who can make great contributions to business effectiveness by releasing and fully utilizing their "mindpower." Too often they are merely regarded as hired "handpower" with inevitable consequences of apathy and frustration.

Perhaps the most outspoken of the behavioral scientists who are challenging traditional management practices is Douglas McGregor, professor of industrial management at MIT. His book, *The Human Side of Enterprise*,[5] has won the annual publications award of the Organization Development Council.

Ex-psychologist McGregor believes that, based on present social science knowledge, it can be theorized that work is not distasteful to the average human, and that given a proper work environment, employees will behave in a responsible manner. Further, he assumes that the average human has the capacity to exercise a relatively high degree of imagination, ingenuity and creativity in the solution of organization problems. This is an optimistic view of the value of human resources, to say the least. It is supported also by the views of a leading businessman turned educator who has had extensive experience in personnel administration and who likewise argues for the adoption of more enlightened managerial practices which enhance morale and productivity.[6]

There is still another issue to be faced. Do traditional management practices so "de-skill" jobs by transferring human abilities to mechanical and electronic devices that the individual often becomes a mere machine tender? The resulting relationship seems to the social scientist to indicate often a master-slave relationship between machine and man with the latter steadily losing ground in the process.

[2] Victor Lazzaro, *Systems and Procedures*, Prentice-Hall, Inc., Englewood Cliffs, N.J., 1959.

[3] Rensis Likert, *New Patterns of Management*, McGraw-Hill Book Co., New York, 1961, pp. 62–74.

[4] Chris Argyris, *Personality and Organization*, Harper & Bros., New York, 1957.

[5] Douglas McGregor, *The Human Side of Enterprise*, McGraw-Hill Book Co., New York, 1960.

[6] Thomas G. Spates, *Human Values Where People Work*, Harper & Bros., New York, 1960.

For instance, a number of studies of men at work on assembly lines have highlighted worker feelings with regard to their loss of human dignity, pride in accomplishment and a general sense of satisfaction from work.[7] Although these reports are based primarily on manufacturing-type operations, it is apparent that many office operations have similar characteristics and therefore, apparently comparable effects.

Thus, the full issue has been joined. Have you, through the use of standard systems and procedures practices, followed the typical, orthodox approach to solving management problems? Are you perpetuating the practice of dividing and subdividing jobs into such simple, elemental tasks that they offer little challenge to the incumbent? Do you believe that employees have to be prodded and pushed in order to get work out? Have you been unconcerned about the effects of changes in work assignments upon emotional health?

There are at least four issues which must be recognized as having a direct bearing upon whether or not we can tolerate traditional management patterns.

First, it is abundantly evident that the United States is faced with formidable opposition from different political and economic ideologies as well as general, worldwide business competition. Our system must be strengthened against this onslaught.

Second, the trend in this country is toward greater individual initiative and freedom at home, at school and in the community. This is the inevitable result of the rapidly rising educational level in our population. People are being exposed to more knowledge and thus are more prone to question established modes of society.

Third, rising standards of living, increasing governmental assistance and the monopoly power of unions allow employees the option of challenging orthodox managerial procedures.

Finally, in a more constructive vein, there are techniques which are based squarely on more job freedom and more job challenge which offer promise of successfully coping with the human problems in business. Because

they deal with what could be called a "human-centered" management philosophy, many advanced concepts which are now in successful practice should be mentioned. However, only two that relate directly to systems and procedures work are singled out: participation and job enlargement.

In designing the management decision-making system, there is one element which is being advocated generally by both social scientists and progressive, experimentally-minded business managers. It is the practice variously called "participative management," "consultative management," "multiple management" or "democratic management." The last term is perhaps unfortunate since it may have overtones of a new way of industrial life wherein employees select their bosses. Such is not the case. However, use of the term "democracy" does center attention on the fact, which is often overlooked, that our tradition in business and industry is one of authoritarian methods wherein employees often have little voice in their affairs. This stands in rather stark contrast to our cherished democratic ideals in the political process. Management's prerogatives have been modified, of course, by union intervention. Unfortunately, this social change has been marked too often by open warfare and economic waste.

Participation has to do with a voluntary decision on the part of management to create conditions wherein employees are intentionally made a part of the decision-making and policy formulation process. Technically, of course, this is in the nature of a staff rather than a line capacity, since the employee's role is one of advice and suggestion regarding factors that affect his job. Management decisions encompass more elements than simply worker welfare, and thus must be made by leaders who also represent the interest of consumers, owners and the community at large.

Participation pays off. It is a method of creating better understanding, better decisions, higher morale and greater productivity. Since employees are "in the know," it serves to reduce resistance to change by making them a valued part of the managerial process.[8] Office automation, or mechanization, if you prefer, which is daily causing major methods changes,

[7] See Charles R. Walker and Robert H. Guest, *The Man on the Assembly Line*, Harvard University Press, Cambridge, Mass., 1952, and William Foote Whyte, *Men at Work*, Irwin-Dorsey Series in Behavioral Science in Business, Homewood, Ill., 1961.

[8] For a more complete coverage of the problem see Lester Coch and John R. P. French, Jr., "Overcoming Resistance to Change," *Human Relations*, 1948, pp. 512–532.

has led to considerable employee resistance. According to a recent American Management Association research study, many companies have not realized expected cost reduction because of failure to recognize the human element in their plans for office automation.[9] The lesson for systems and procedures people, whose work inevitably results in new modes of work, is obvious.

Man's resistance to variations in his work patterns is based on his tendency toward habitual behavior. Habit in turn stems from the principle of least effort. It is no accident that short-cut paths appear across lawns when sidewalks force longer distances to be traveled. Similarly, the continuing enthusiastic consumer acceptance of mechanical creature comfort devices is simple witness to the same human tendency. Thus, changes in job routines will be opposed almost instinctively. Participation offers the opportunity to lead, anticipate and partially influence future events in such a manner as to minimize disruption and conflict.

Those who wish to examine actual business experience can be referred to any number of examples. Foremost among these would have to be multiple management as employed at McCormick and Co., and incentive management as practiced by the Lincoln Electric Co. Both of these organizations have utilized participative management for many decades. Undoubtedly the technique has been a major factor in their successful performance in their respective fields. McCormick is in the food industry and has a number of management boards which are open to those operative and managerial employees who demonstrate leadership capabilities. Based on the principle that many heads are better than one, the firm offers board members the opportunity to by-pass traditional channels of authority and to come to grips with sales, production, and general management problems. McCormick even goes so far as to have a junior board of directors which advises its senior board.

Lincoln Electric manufactures electric arc welders. Perhaps one of the key elements in its record of competitive performance is its long-time use of an advisory board composed of employee representatives and management officials. This council theoretically acts in a

staff role to the principal owner and chief executive of the company. As a matter of actual practice, however, it appears that the chief executive, who chairs the board and has a veto power over its decisions, has never had to exercise his normal legalistic prerogative. Apparently, mature discussion has resulted in the ability to solve employee-employer problems as well as other managerial difficulties.

Before one concludes that participative management is the cure for all labor-management problems, it must be underscored that both of the companies cited are managed by progressive leaders who many years ago adopted the enlightened philosophy of human-centered management. Participation is only one element, if not a key one, in McCormick's and Lincoln's continuing assault upon orthodox, traditional, management practices. Space does not permit a detailing of the full range of their beliefs as well as their innovations. This can be done at the reader's leisure since both industrialists have set forth their philosophies and methods in a number of publications.[10] Then, too, practically any of the previously cited research studies by modern social scientists contain additional evidence as to the benefits of creating greater mental and emotional involvement of workers in their work situation.[11]

Participation is an advance stage of employee-employer relations. It is quite superior to the stages of autocracy (employee has no voice), paternalism (management acts as a benevolent father) and information (employees told all events affecting their welfare). There is still another stage, that of employee ownership, wherein the rights of private property formally place final authority in the hands of the workers. Profit sharing is closely related to this latter stage. Both are means of creating more favorable conditions of industrial citizenship. However, they are beyond the scope of this discussion.

A second major development, which is very

---

[9] Ben Miller, "Gaining Acceptance for Major Methods Changes," *American Management Association,* New York, Research Study No. 44, 1960.

[10] See Charles P. McCormick, *The Power of People,* Harper & Bros., New York, 1949; *Multiple Management,* The Jacobs Press, Clinton, S.C., 1938, and James F. Lincoln, *A New Approach to Industrial Economics,* The Devin-Adair Co., New York, 1961; *Incentive Management,* The Lincoln Electric Company, Cleveland, 1951; *Lincoln's Incentive System,* McGraw-Hill Book Co., New York, 1946.

[11] For example, see Likert, *op. cit.,* pp. 39–43 and 62–69.

closely related to the philosophy of participative management, is that of job broadening or job enlargement. Here again, the challenge to traditional attempts of finding the one best way of performing a job by breaking it down into small elemental components comes from social scientists rather than industrial engineers.

As suggested before, the common practice is to de-skill the job so that it can be performed expeditiously by employees requiring little training. Not only have workers in larger enterprises steadily lost technical proficiencies to machines, but also abilities have been surrendered to all kinds of staff specialists. Such tasks as planning of work, control of quality, knowledge of costs, movement of materials, machine set-up, product design, process layout, etc., have been lost to specialists. Workers and even first-level managers have been reduced to a virtually empty shell of requisite job skills. Many employees have become largely unthinking and unchallenged automatons in many instances. As a result, countless numbers of production and office employees currently labor in almost a detached trance. Their thoughts are apt to be on anything other than the job at hand.

The emphasis in job broadening, then, is upon "re-skilling" jobs so that they furnish a sense of pride in accomplishment and a feeling of challenge and creativity. Insecurity fears are lessened. Full use is made of "mindpower" as well as "handpower." Emphasis is on what another industrialist, Henry L. Nunn, who has pioneered enlightened human relations in the shoe industry, has termed the "whole man." [12] Incidentally, Nunn has gone so far as to have two employee representatives on the board of directors—a very unorthodox practice, indeed.

The traditional deep-rooted belief that job specialization always lowers costs can be dispelled by examples of successful job enlargement which prove just the opposite. Since 1943, International Business Machines has made extensive use of the concept. This came about during a plant visit when Thomas J. Watson became curious as to why a young woman was standing idly by her machine. When questioned by him, her explanation was that she was waiting for the "set-up specialist" to adjust her machine for a new operation.

[12] See Henry L. Nunn, *The Whole Man Goes to Work*, Harper & Bros., New York, 1953.

This was company policy even though the operator was quite capable of making the necessary changes herself. Watson prevailed upon his production officials to change the practice and allow operators to make their own adjustments. Results were so successful that the idea has been expanded to allow operators to read blueprints, to inspect their own work and to rotate jobs so that they have the opportunity to run several different types of machines. Grievances, fatigue, labor turnover, work spoilage and absenteeism have been reduced. [13]

Turning to the office area, the Detroit Edison Co. under the leadership of J. Douglas Elliott has experimented with job enlargement in its customer billing activities. Installation of the simple procedural change wherein billers began checking their own work rather than sending it to separate checkers increased morale and reduced overtime work considerably. Impressed by the results, Elliott made a general survey of electric utility billing practices. His findings confirmed his own experience. Billing costs on the average were higher in the departments using the greatest amount of specialization, lowest in those with the least. [14]

Again, there are those who can take issue with the evidence which is still fragmentary and all-too-limited in scope. [15] This is fully admitted. Furthermore, no claims of a panacea are made. However, it is quite evident that something can and must be done to combat monotony and repetitiveness.

[13] Robert Saltonstall, *Human Relations in Administration*, McGraw-Hill Book Co., New York, 1959, pp. 192–193.

[14] *Ibid.*, p. 193. Elliott also found that enlarging supervisory jobs, by returning functions that had passed into specialized staff hands, also increases office productivity. See "Increasing Office Productivity Through Job Enlargement," *Office Management Series No. 134*, American Management Association, 1953.

[15] However, other studies can be cited. For example, Sears, Roebuck and Co., has found that jobs that are broken down too finely are more likely to be marked by both low output and low morale. See John K. Lagemann, "Job Enlargement Boosts Production," *Nation's Business*, Dec., 1954, p. 37. For a very comprehensive overview of both sides of the total issue, see A. C. MacKinney, P. F. Wernimont, and W. O. Galitz, "Has Specialization Reduced Job Satisfaction?" *Personnel*, January–February, 1962, pp. 8–19.

In the automobile industry, for instance, an "outright distaste for and revulsion to the job itself" often exists in the minds and attitudes of men on the assembly line.[16] Men working on motor assembly lines have stated that they feel trapped by their jobs and literally deprived of the ability to think because of the dulling effects of their assigned tasks.[17] The effects of such negativism do not speak well for our industrial system, no matter how productive it may be of material wealth. We cannot close our eyes to such social costs as mental illness, alcoholism and demoralized families which never enter into typical business accounts of profit and loss but which nevertheless have some of their genesis in the business system itself. After all, the only real asset a nation has is its stock of trained human resources. The mental debasement that is inherent in many jobs today seems reprehensible. How can we expect to produce energetic proponents of our industrial system and mature thoughtful citizens if we deliberately make many of them imperfect machine tools? It would seem that all too often the intent is to create productive systems wherein moronic behavior is encouraged and even desired, if not absolutely necessary.

The author can't help but be impressed by the fact that Neuschel's book *Management by System* (1960), and Likert's, *New Patterns of Management* (1961), were released only a year apart by the same publisher. Neverthe-

less, in concept they are eras apart. Neuschel seems to countenance the older, impersonal approach to management based on clearly defined tasks and work process, specialization and imposed discipline by close supervision. He is work-centered. Likert is strongly in favor of the newer, human-centered management philosophy which favors broader tasks, more involvement in decisions, self-discipline and more democratic processes of supervision. He is human-centered.

In attempting to decide between the two schools of thought, one may fall into the error of basing the answer on productivity alone. The writer is not arguing the merit of this criterion; there is evidence that either philosophy can meet such a materialistic test. However, it seems that the fundamental at stake cannot be sought in terms of output alone but in the need for finding more meaningful work situations wherein self-development, emotional health and freedom of both action and thought are significant values in and of themselves. Technology must be recognized fundamentally as the servant, not the master. The crisis of our time is not the struggle between democracy and totalitarianism but in reality between a society dominated by a concern over commodities and careers and one in which a high regard of mental health and humanness predominate.[18] Management emphasis should be on the key element in the term, "man."

---

[16] R. H. Guest, "Job Enlargement—A Revolution in Job Design," *Personnel Administration,* March–April, 1957, p. 11.

[17] Whyte, *op. cit.,* pp. 179–197.

[18] Alvin Pitcher, "The Importance of Being Human," *Harvard Business Review,* January–February, 1961, p. 47.

20. THE HUMAN SIDE OF A SYSTEMS CHANGE

LAWRENCE K. WILLIAMS *

The process of introducing complex systems into organizations is still part science and part art. The science includes the comprehension and design of the technical parts of the system, and the art involves the process of introduction primarily with regard to the human element.

The science has advanced to the point where nearly everyone describes procedural change in terms of its effect upon the total system rather than merely thinking of the introduction of another piece of "hardware." The large number of problems which grew out of early computer installations, when the computer was merely looked at as another piece of "hardware" rather than being looked at from the point of view of systems change, are now being anticipated to a much greater degree.

Most managements, for example, are now aware of the fact that the sponsoring agent for the computer in the organization will not be the only part called upon to make rearrangements. Rather, when the computer comes in the door, it usually affects a number of departments or units which are related to the sponsoring department and thus a total system is effected even though we may describe the change in terms of the piece of hardware or the technique that is being introduced.

There is still an art, however, to transferring a systems design into actuality. The process of making the new system acceptable to the human element and of modifying the human element so that it fits the requirements of the new system, if not an art, is certainly an inexact science. Perhaps one of the simplest ways of describing these problems in systems change is to note the fact that flow diagrams, new or-ganizational charts and manuals of operation do not reflect the human element. They essentially describe an inanimate organization, and if everybody in the organization were merely a robot, most of the problems of systems change would be mitigated or disappear.

Fortunately or unfortunately, an organization is made up of people. The problems on the human side of a systems change involve the fact that there is considerable resistance to change, that downright acceptance of a change is quite often unique, and that the number of unanticipated consequences in terms of communication failures and road blocks thrown in the way from unexpected sources in the organization form a minimal list of problems. This leads the procedures specialist to the conclusion that individuals are highly irrational.

ATTITUDES: THE CORE OF RESISTANCE TO CHANGE

Even the most primitive analysis of the failures of a systems change usually results in the observation of attitudes and values which run counter to those required for accepting and endorsing the change. The whole concept of resistance to change, to a large degree, can be recoded as a problem of attitudes. Parenthetically, it should be noted that probably the poorest attitudes, if one wants to use this statement in terms of resistance to change, come from managers, not other employees. The middle level manager can and often does offer more resistance to systems change than all the employees reporting to him.

There is a complete literature on attitude formation and attitude change which suggests that attitudes are not formed in a logical manner nor are they changed in a logical manner. To a large degree, an attitude is a matter of emotion and not logic. While we

SOURCE: *Systems & Procedures Journal* (July–August, 1964), pp. 40–43. Reprinted by permission of *Systems & Procedures Journal*.

* Assistant Professor, New York School of Industrial and Labor Relations.

195

would all like to think that we have arrived at logical conclusions with regard to our political preference to people we like and dislike, the kinds of jobs we prefer, etc., there is every evidence that our most basic attitudes and values have not come about through logical deduction.

The impermeability of many attitudes to logic is amply demonstrated in such areas as prejudice and attempts to change styles of consumption in the area of marketing. It is here that the systems engineer is perhaps the most illogical. In an attempt to change attitudes, he uses logic. The systems engineer convinced of the logic of his plan and the logic of the system usually operates on this basis: if he can explain this highly rational and logical system to someone, they will automatically accept his point of view in terms of the merit and necessity of the new system.

The line manager who states that the new computer won't work is usually quite immune to new information. Attempts to give him more booklets and more short courses on how a computer works, for example, or showing him that the same system has worked in other companies, and finally, recourse to saying it slower and louder as if somehow the manager was an imperfect receiver, usually are all to no avail.

What this resistant manager is really "saying," even though he may not be conscious of the fact, is that "it is impossible to think that most of the decisions which I have thought important for 20 years can now be put over on the computer;" and "not only am I not superior but you are suggesting that I am inferior with regard to decisions that will come out of a *machine*." He may also be "saying" that "I am terribly afraid I will never be able to understand this new system, and no matter how much you talk or how much information you give me, I will never be on top of the new system the way I was with the old."

He may also be "saying" that "I have had 20 years of getting used to things the way they are, and any thought of changing the system is a violation of who I am and what I have been." This is perhaps what he is unconsciously saying and which we may get out of him if we have the time and the skill to explore fully the statement, "It won't work." If we engage in debate and counter argument with argument, we can go on for days, but we will

probably never get close to the real cause of the attitude or the means of changing the attitude.

WHO WANTS TO LOSE STATUS?

The human side of the systems change also includes status. There is considerable status to being the oldest member of the work group who knows all the right answers. It is a considerable blow to have to start all over again and learn something new, and to be put perhaps at the same level or somewhat below the newcomers to the organization in terms of learning the language of the new technology or system.

It is also a blow when the responsibility of the unit that a person leads is transferred to another unit because it is logical from the point of view of the total organization. Get a person concerned enough about loss of status and he will commit himself to the antichange movement so strongly it is almost impossible to move him from this point of view. Again, the use of logic about the delights of the new system is to miss the point of the resistance.

THE UNSEEN ORGANIZATION CHART

The human side of the organization is also made up of a series of informal relationships. Many well-planned changes from the point of technology "go under" because of poor communications. Many organizational changes are based upon the belief that the organization works the way the organizational chart says it does. Very often, some of the best coordination and some of the best information in the system takes place in terms of informal connections that are not represented on the organizational chart. System changes which rearrange the relationships between units quite often assume that people communicate with each other and solve problems in keeping with the organizational chart. Operating under this assumption, systems practitioners make changes only to find that these changes are directly counter to a series of informal arrangements which have been making the organization work.

THE "LOGICAL" WAY TO HANDLE A CHANGE

The inability to cope with the resistance from the social system with regard to change often results in the "bulldozer approach." This school of thought advocates ramming the change through, for, after all, individuals can't resist completely as long as the company is paying the check. Many "successful" systems changes have been brought about in such a manner and, in fact, those who are concerned for the social side and for the minimizing of resistance are often viewed as missionaries who have somehow not seen what business and profits are all about. Before analyzing the results of the bulldozer approach, however, we should look at the causes.

Under the stress of production and time schedules, it is perhaps a natural consequence to resort to the use of formal authority and power in order to bring about change. Nearly every person responsible for change probably does become concerned with morale, resistance and the reaction of individuals; but under pressure, more often than not, the maxim is, "if logic won't do it, try force." Thus, one reason for the bulldozer approach is perhaps the fact that attempts to reduce resistance have failed.

This decision may also be coupled with the fact that those who are responsible for change often do not have complete communication with the top of the organization, which could be of assistance in countering resistance. If one looks at the cycle of major change in the organization, the usual observation is that once the top levels have made some major decisions about the nature of the change, cost and timing, the remainder of the work is delegated to lower levels in the organization. Very often, overt resistance does not come about until change is imminent. And even though the lower levels may be highly concerned, communication channels have been blocked with regard to communicating this to the top because the top is now unprepared to hear about these problems. Convinced that the system is logical and that the major decisions have been made, top management is often little interested and, until it is much too late, it does not hear about resistance at the bottom level where the change is being introduced.

Again, the inability to obtain attention from the top with regard to these problems results in an appeal for power and force which is usually forthcoming in order to protect the dollar investment, and again the bulldozer approach is in full swing.

Despite the fact that the adoption of the bulldozer approach can be readily explained, more investigation should be made into its implications. One of the more significant implications is the fact that after one change has been introduced, the system which has been subjected to the bulldozer approach is usually not ready for another significant change. Individuals who have not been forewarned, who have found their jobs done away with overnight, be they managers or nonsupervisory employees, are little inclined to accept. In fact, they go out of their way to reject any additional change.

While the bulldozer approach may work for one round of change, it increases the resistance for further rounds. Many system changes, particularly those which involve computer installations, involve a sequence of which the first round is only the forerunner of many changes. Even if additional changes are not contemplated, they are usually required as a function of making modifications in the first installation of change. It is highly questionable whether a systems change involving the bulldozer approach is really successful if it retards subsequent change and if it uses up any goodwill that may have been funded in the organization in terms of tolerance for change.

The bulldozer approach may also result in a resistance which spreads from the changed part of the system to that part of the organization seemingly unaffected by the change. If, for example, the managers in Sales feel that the managers in Accounting received a "raw deal," they tend to view any change coming into their own system with a great deal of suspicion and downright resistance.

In summary, the major disadvantage of the bulldozer approach is its effect upon subsequent changes. And it is still relatively easy for an outsider to predict the amount of resistance to change in an organization. He may merely use the following predictive hypothesis: *"The human element in an organization will react to change in terms of how the last one was handled."*

CAN ANYTHING BE DONE ABOUT IT?

While it may be all well and good to realize that much of the resistance to change is not necessarily logically based, or that it involves problems of status, or that we are dealing with informal systems not represented on the organizational chart, there is still a question as to whether anything can be done about it. Social science is of some assistance in this case, but its use is limited because the process of adjusting to change is probably still an art.

If we establish the premise that many of the individual fears are unfounded, then the notion of participation in the change can be of great assistance. Individuals are much more prone to adapt and actually work for changes when they have had a hand in the design of same. Moreover, they may be able to contribute to the overall design of a systems change at least with regard to the problems of introduction. Some forms of participation give individuals a chance to really understand the new system, and thus the fear of the unknown is mitigated; at least there is some feeling of control.

SELLING THE RIGHT PRODUCT

The system can also be sold in terms of objectives that are understandable and acceptable to those who must react to the change. The social system of the organization may not have any great degree of identity with the total organizational goals. People are interested in labor saving when it involves their labor, and they may be interested in their own efficiency. (For example, the sales department may be very much interested in a program that is going to lead to better relationships with customers.) Often, however, an attempt is made to sell the change in terms of the objectives that were used in getting the innovation accepted by the upper echelons of the organization. Yet there is no reason to believe that many of the lower levels can identify or indeed are necessarily interested in the phrasing of objectives of change in terms of how it appears to the total organization. They are interested in and are motivated primarily by terms of those objectives that are consistent with their own needs and activities.

While a certain procedural change may be one of the greatest things that has happened in terms of making the company important in the international market, this objective must be related to the objectives of some subpart of the system such as increased job security. Otherwise, it is doubtful whether anyone will really eagerly anticipate a change. It is primarily a matter of being receptive.

DON'T UNDERESTIMATE INFORMAL SYSTEMS

Those who are planning change cannot depend upon the organizational chart, but must become more conscious of informal communication and coordination systems. Much of this has to be a "seat of the pants" operation, and those responsible for the change must be sensitive to problems early in the introduction.

To assume that what is communicated is received and that if it goes through formal channels it will be received with the same reaction by everyone flies in the face of everything that nearly everyone knows about organizations but which too few take into account. Rumors should not be discarded because they are not consistent with fact; they should be analyzed in terms of what they indicate about the system. Assumptions about the formal organization must constantly be checked during a time of change much the way we would look at information loss in any other system.

Much more can be gained in understanding the nature of resistance if we do not assume that logic will effectively change attitudes and opinions. Challenging the resistant manager to debate may only be a greater way of entrenching rather than changing him. More adroitness in understanding the real causes of resistance by a fuller hearing and perhaps the offering of certain forms of assurances may be highly necessary in order to avoid certain forms of roadblocks.

MEETING FEARS HEAD-ON

All of the above assumes that change will be beneficial for the organization as a totality and also for the individual members. Often this is not the case; at least not to the degree people would like to think it is. Some individuals will have some of their authority stripped away from them; some will have to go through the strain of learning a totally new job. Assuming this as a cost of the change, and taking those steps necessary to find an alternative means of using the individuals or adjusting such problems on an individual basis may be far less costly in the long run than the amount of disruption, chaos and the resistances engendered by not anticipating and working with the problem.

It is just possible that some organizations are not prepared for change at the time it is suggested. Feasibility studies should look at not only the feasibility from the technical point of view but the feasibility from the human side. It is possible that some necessary arrangements and preconditioning are necessary prior to the introduction of the systems change. Most deadlines for introduction are based upon technical feasibility and not on any assumptions about the receptivity on the part of the organization's members.

Finally, much can be done by greater attention to predicting problems in the organization. The systems engineer who gives a complete hardware description to his change without suggesting or forecasting problems in the social system does a disservice to himself and to the organization. While it is true that even the most sophisticated technical descriptions do not necessarily lead to any predictions with regard to the impact on the social system, those in this position must find a language form and a means of describing their change that is closer to the problems of the social system with which they are dealing.

Instead of describing the computer in terms of its units of memory, one learns quite a bit more by describing the computer as an adjunct to decision making, and then asking about its impact on the organization in terms of those who have a role in the supporting decision-making structure. Describing the computer as a faster calculator also may raise more questions in advance about what will happen and what will be the consequences if we do away with those jobs where calculation is now being done by humans.

The language and variables of the technological system are quite unrelated in many instances to the language and variables of the social system, but more of us must become concerned with translating from one to the other if organizations are going to maintain the amount of receptivity required to continually introduce change into the existing establishment.

21. RESISTANCE TO CHANGE—

ITS ANALYSIS AND PREVENTION

ALVIN ZANDER *

In order to derive the benefit from research in industrial relations, someone must plan a program of action to apply them. When one begins implementing, he must change the social system in some way. The creation of this change can cause the development of resistance in those influenced by the change.

First, we shall look at what resistance is; second, the conditions that appear to be associated with its development; and third, some means whereby resistance may be prevented or decreased.

NATURE OF RESISTANCE

Let us look at some examples of resistance growing out of administrative changes.

A large number of foremen in a company were given training in how to treat their men like human beings. They liked the course and were eager to apply their learnings on the job. The company found, however, that relatively few of the foremen are really behaving any differently on the job. They know their stuff but do not use it.

In one of the paper-shuffling government agencies a new data form was developed which all admitted was briefer, more logical, and easier to use. Yet, this department found that the employees often omitted much of the data needed on this form, their speed of work decreased, and they objected to it on many insignificant grounds.

Our favorite example of resistance was furnished by a farmer in the TVA area. He assured us that he knew all about contour plowing, the rotation of crops, and the use of

SOURCE: *Advanced Management* (January, 1950), pp. 9–11. Reprinted by permission of *Advanced Management Journal.*

* Professor of Educational Psychology, Research Center for Group Dynamics, University of Michigan.

what he called "phosaphate" for improving the soil. He allowed as how these were good ideas, "But," he said, "I don't do it that way."

These examples have one common denominator which might serve here as a definition of resistance. They describe behavior which is intended to protect an individual from the effects of real or imagined change. This reaction might be to either real or imagined change since the resister might be reacting to things that were really not changed but he thinks were, or fears that they might be. If a person believes a change has been made, or fears potential change, it makes no difference whether or not it is true in fact. He will act as though there has been a change.

How can one recognize when resistance is working? Unfortunately, there is no list of typical behavior which can be described as the symptoms of resistance, which, if present, indicate that one is dealing with this phenomenon. It is the protective function which the behavior is providing which determines whether or not a person is resisting, rather than the kind of thing he does. By the same token, all behavior which opposes change is not necessarily resistance. Some opposition to change may be perfectly logical and grounded on well supported reasons. The behavior must be attempting to protect the person against the consequences of the change in order for it to be resistance. This may be clearer if we look at the origin of the concept.

THE HOSTILITY PATTERN

The term and the concept we are using here has been borrowed from psychotherapy. When a therapist is attempting to change the behavior of the patient, he expects resistance from him. The therapist takes the position that the pattern of behavior used by the patient (which makes him a "sick" person) is a means to some satisfaction for him even though it also may make him ineffective or unhappy. Resistance occurs in the patient when the process of change (therapy here) comes close to being successful. When faced with the unpleasant necessity of giving up the behavior he does not like, but somehow needs, he begins to balk. He becomes silent, blushes, changes the subject, tells fibs, comes late to appointments, becomes angry with the therapist, or any of a number of similar things. The therapist watches for the context in which these signs of resistance occur since these indicate the crucial problems in the way the patient sees and deals with his world.

For the administrator, resistance may occur under fairly similar conditions. When he attempts to create a change the administrator may develop, unintentionally, many threats to the person or groups with whom he works. The behavior used by the resister may take many forms.

It may take the form of hostility either openly expressed or obliquely implied. The aggression may be directed against the change itself or against the administrator. What is done depends on how the person can safely resist without further endangering himself in that situation. Other symptoms of resistance may be sloppy effort after the change has been made, or fawning submissiveness which is a hybrid of apple-polishing and apathy. It can occur by lowering the level of aspiration to an inefficient degree, discouragement, or the development of unhappy cliques and outspoken factions. It is important, however, to remind ourselves, that it is the function which such actions are performing for the person that makes them resistance rather than what they look like.

WHERE RESISTANCE STARTS

It will be helpful if we look at a few conditions conducive to resistance.

1. Resistance can be expected if the nature of the change is not made clear to the people who are going to be influenced by the change. In one of the largest government agencies, a change required one department which originally had the responsibility of processing papers involved in contacts with certain industries to share this task with another office. Announcement of the change was issued in a brief statement. The immediate reaction was violent objection, even though some of the workers privately admitted that it was a wise and necessary move. They were reacting to incomplete information. Many people fear incomplete information about changes which influence them. It is more comfortable to know exactly where one stands.

There is some evidence to support the hypothesis that those persons who dislike their jobs will most dislike ambiguity in a proposed change. They want to know exactly what they must do in order to be sure to avoid the unpleasant aspects of their jobs. Some administrators may attach too much importance to the value of information itself. Apparently they reason that people "ought not" to resist the way they do because the administrator has told them everything he thinks is important for them to know about the impending change.

2. Different people will see different meanings in the proposed change. Some of the resistant reaction described above came about because some workers saw the change as an indication that they had been doing a poor job, others assumed it meant their office would soon be abolished, still others were troubled since they were losing some of the power they had formerly controlled. We tend to see in our world the things that we expect to see. Complete information can just as readily be distorted as incomplete information, especially so if the workers have found discomfort and threats in their past work situation.

3. Resistance can be expected when those influenced are caught in a jam between strong forces pushing them to make the change and strong forces deterring them against making the change.

4. Resistance may be expected to the degree that the persons influenced by the change have pressure put upon them to make it, and will be decreased to the degree that these same persons are able to have some "say" in the nature or direction of the change. In a garment factory a change was required. The switch meant that workers would be asked to change their jobs and in many cases, to develop working relationships with new people. An experiment was made in which three different styles of introducing this change were tried out. One group of workers were simply informed about the change and were allowed to ask questions. They developed the most resistance as measured by turnover, absenteeism,

and slowness in learning the job. Resistance was *less* in those groups who sent representatives to a meeting in which the nature of the change was discussed and all persons present made plans to carry out the change.

Resistance was *least* in the groups in which those to be affected discussed the nature of the change, laid plans for making it, and as a total group made decisions which were satisfactory to the entire group. In this latter group everyone participated. They had an opportunity to develop their own motivation instead of making the change only on the basis of orders from the boss. The fact that they were able to develop their own understanding of the need for the change and their own decisions about how to do it, reduced resistance most effectively.

5. Resistance may be expected if the change is made on personal grounds rather than impersonal requirements or sanctions. A supervisor posted the following notice:

I have always felt that promptness is an important indicator of an employee's interest in his job. I will feel much better if you are at your desk at the proper time.

Employees responded to this notice by appointing a committee to get information which would justify their late arrival at the office. Many administrators can expect trouble in establishing a change if it is requested in terms of what "I think is necessary"; rather than making the request in the light of "our objectives," the rules, the present state of affairs, or some other impersonal requirement.

6. Resistance may be expected if the change ignores the already established institutions in the group. Every work situation develops certain customs in doing the work or in the relations among the workers. The administrator who ignores institutionalized patterns of work and abruptly attempts to create a new state of affairs which demands that these customs be abolished without further consideration will surely run into resistance.

These are a few of the conditions in which resistance might be expected to occur. There probably are many others.

DECREASING RESISTANCE

Some procedures on the part of the administrator might be useful in preventing or de-creasing the resistance which arises in a changed situation. Let us look at a major principle in preventing resistance and some of its basic implications:

Resistance will be prevented to the degree that the changer helps the changees to develop their own understanding of the need for the change, and an explicit awareness of how they feel about it, and what can be done about those feelings.

This principle implies that the administrator can use resistance as an important symptom. Specifically, he can use the nature of the resistance as an indicator of the cause of resistance. It will be most helpful to him as a symptom, if he diagnoses the causes for it when it occurs rather than inhibiting it at once. The same resistant behavior, for example, may indicate that one person feels that he has lost prestige by the change, to another it may mean that he has lost power over an area of influence which he formerly controlled, and to still another it may mean that he fears that his friends will think less well of him. An administrator must know what the resistance means in order that he may effectively lessen it by working on the causes instead of the symptom.

There has been a good deal of experience in recent years in staff meetings and in work conferences like the National Training Laboratory for Group Development with the use of a group observer. This observer gives to the group, and the leaders, information about the group and the nature of any resistance. In these cases, the data about itself is made common group property for all members to discuss and to use in planning better work relations.

This communication must go in both directions. If two-way communication is not maintained, negative attitudes created during resistance will tend to persist.

RESTORING UNDERSTANDING

In a utility company a new office was formed with a new set of supervisors. The entire staff of supervisors called the workers together and scolded them for shortcomings in their performance. The tone used by the supervisors was so aggressive that the employees found it difficult thereafter to discuss anything with them except those topics directly related to the effectiveness of production. The workers kept themselves at a distance from the supervisors and the supervisors made no move to close the gap. The result was that distance between these two groups made it impossible for them to come to any new understanding of each other. This mounting hostility was lessened only when the personnel department advised a number of "gripe-sessions" with small groups of workers in which the two levels developed a new understanding of each other.

Another implication in the above principle is that there is value in blowing off steam. The psychologists call this a "catharsis." There is good evidence that new attitudes can be accepted by a person only if he has a chance to thoroughly air his original attitude. Resistance to accepting the rigid, and often apparently meaningless, rules of military life, showed itself in flagrant violation of the rules, often in a most aggressive manner. Punishment only increased the resistance. Relief was provided by group sessions in which men were able to thoroughly gripe. After this relief of tension, they were able to turn to a reasonable discussion about what they could do to learn to live in terms of these requirements. It is as though new air can be put in the tire only after the old air is released.

A third implication of the earlier expressed principle is that resistance may be less likely to occur if the group participates in making the decisions about how the change should be implemented, what the change should be like, how people might perform in the changed situation, or any other problems that are within their area of freedom to decide. The experiment in which three ways of introducing a change were tried out showed that the workers, who had a chance to make a group decision about the ways in which the change should be made, developed much less resistance than did those who were simply called together to be told about the change and have all of their questions answered. What is important here is that the workers feel that they have a chance to discuss the major factors involved in the change, a chance to understand the nature of the fears they have in facing this change, and a chance to plan what they will do to calm their fears.

SELF-DIAGNOSIS GETS ACTION

Still another implication is that resistance will be less likely to develop if facts which point to the need for change are gathered by the persons who must make the change. A number of high level supervisors in a utility industry came to feel that the workers had many negative attitudes about their jobs which were due to poor supervisory practices. Each supervisor, quite naturally, felt that other supervisors were at fault. Top management set up a number of study groups in which the supervisors first learned how they could diagnose the causes of these negative attitudes. Each supervisor then returned to his own work place and gathered facts that would be necessary for him to analyse the causes of negative attitudes he could spot among his workers. Later the supervisors came together to report their findings. At this meeting their enthusiasm for change in their own practices was high because they had participated in gathering the facts which best described their problems. People will be more likely to act in terms of information they gather themselves than in terms of information gathered by others and delivered to them. If it is clear that a change is indicated in a given state of affairs, but the people who must abide by the change are resisting the shift, they can come to see it themselves by obtaining the facts which properly "case" the situation.

To summarize, we have said that resistance is a problem which any person who is responsible for social change must face. Even though it is strange and unexpected behavior, there are causes for the development of this phenomenon. These causes may be understood, and resistance may be prevented, if the administrator will help the changees develop their own understanding of the need for change and explicit awareness of how they feel about it, and what can be done about those feelings.

22. PSYCHOLOGY FOR THE SYSTEMS ANALYST *

ROBERT E. SCHLOSSER †

One of the greatest challenges to the systems analyst is the potential conflict between the business's need for change and its employees' resistance to change. As a business tries to adapt to changing conditions, its employees are required to accept new patterns of thought, new work routines, and new social relationships. Frequently, the psychological discomforts created by the new conditions cause good employees, regardless of position, to resist necessary changes.

One of the major tasks of a systems analyst is to reduce this resistance by bringing order and understanding to the process of change. To do this successfully, an analyst must have not only a grasp of the technical needs and resources of the business but also a sound understanding of the basic principles of psychology. He must understand how people behave and use that understanding to develop good human relations.

While there is no general agreement as to what constitutes an adequate listing of basic principles of psychology, there are two concepts that can bring the area into focus for us. These concepts are:

1. Motivation
2. Learning

MOTIVATION

The primary "principle" of motivation is that every human experience involves a causa-

SOURCE: *Management Services* (November–December, 1964), pp. 29–36. Reprinted by permission of *Management Services*.

* This article is adapted from a chapter in a forthcoming book, *Accounting Systems Theory and Practice*, by James B. Bower, Charles T. Zlatkovich, and Dr. Schlosser, to be published by Allyn & Bacon, Inc.

† Price Waterhouse & Company.

tion factor and an effect from that cause. The principle of cause-and-effect relationships in human behavior means that every motive produces some effect and that every response or effect is preceded by a motive. Motivation, as an activating force, affects every area of human behavior. Its field of influence ranges from the directing of a simple act where the motive is obvious to a complex, formal activity pattern, such as career behavior, which represents numerous detailed aspects of motivation.[1]

One list of essential motivating causes includes the following: (1) the urges arising from bodily needs, (2) the urge to succeed and to achieve, (3) the urge to avoid failure and disappointment, (4) the urge for recognition and approval, (5) the urge for sympathy and affection, (6) the urge for security, (7) the urge to experience the new and the different, and (8) the sex urge.[2]

The systems analyst should be aware of these motivating forces and use this knowledge in carrying out his assignments. Each one of the motivating forces cited can play a part in carrying a systems engagement through to a successful—or unsuccessful—conclusion. To emphasize this point, consider the following situations in which a systems analyst had to give thought to some of these forces.

CONFLICT OF MOTIVATIONS

In order to increase the efficiency with which receiving reports were processed, a systems analyst recommended, among other things, that the receiving department be relocated nearer the receiving dock and the inspection

[1] Lester D. and Alice Crow, *Understanding Our Behavior*, Alfred Knopf Publishing Co., 1956, pp. 53, 54.

[2] *Ibid.*, pp. 60–67.

department. The recommendation was accepted, and the receiving department was relocated in the receiving dock area. Within a short time after the move the supervisor of the receiving department complained that he could not see much improvement in efficiency. He also expressed his concern over the morale of his employees. It seemed to be much lower at the new location.

After looking into the problem the systems analyst discovered that the women's rest room was located a good distance from the new receiving department quarters and that to get there the women in the department had to "run a gauntlet" of men in the inspection department and in one factory department. Discomfiture caused by this arrangement was the root of the morale problem. Once rest room facilities were provided adjacent to the receiving department, the morale problem disappeared, and efficiency reached the level expected when the move was approved.

This problem arose from a conflict of motivating forces, the urge arising from bodily needs on the one hand and the urge for sympathy and affection on the other. The women could not avoid the use of rest room facilities, but they did not like the attitude of the men they had to pass to reach the facilities. In this instance, a systems improvement nearly failed because the analyst had either overlooked or failed to give sufficient weight to basic motivating forces.

FRUSTRATION

Everyone possesses the motivating urges to succeed and to avoid failure. These are forces of which the systems analyst must be aware in redesigning any system, in whole or in part. His efforts may be seriously jeopardized if suggested changes seem to reflect unduly on the competence of the very employees who are to be expected to carry out the revised operations.

For example, a systems analyst discovered, while on an assignment involving the investigation of the entire accounting system for a moving van company, that the manual journalizing and posting of transactions and manual preparation of payroll data were extremely inefficient. In recommending that a multiple-purpose bookkeeping machine be installed, with all of the attendant changes in forms and

procedures, he neglected to discuss this proposal with the bookkeeper, a person who had been with the company for several years and had been considered very competent. The bookkeeper reacted vigorously in opposing the recommendation, chiefly because of an assumption that the recommendation made by the analyst was a direct disparagement of his ability. The urges to succeed and to avoid failure were being frustrated. Often it is possible to avoid such frustrations of basic motivations if the analyst is sensitive to their existence and adjusts his approach accordingly.

USING MOTIVATIONS

One of the principal motivating forces with which a systems analyst must deal is the urge for recognition and approval. Almost invariably, when personnel are consulted and their opinions are given thoughtful consideration, changes to be effected by the systems analyst become joint projects. An effective approach that utilizes in a positive way both this urge and the urge to experience the new and the different could be called the team approach.

In most systems modifications more than one person and more than one department are involved. In lieu of attempting to make the complete systems review, design, implementation, and follow-up himself, a systems analyst will often enlist the help of a representative from each department to be affected. This is the team approach. Results from the group will be workable compromises, and the fact that departmental representatives helped draft the solution will in and of itself help in the acceptance of changes by all departments involved. Indeed, this approach can assist in offsetting deleterious effects from any of the motivating forces. By using this approach, the analyst is permitting various human urges to be expressed and solutions found, rather than ignoring the psychological reactions of the people in a system and thus in many instances dooming his efforts to failure.

LEARNING

Two sources define learning as follows:

1. ". . . a process of adaptation. Through the process of learning, men acquire new ways of behaving or performing in order that they

can make better adjustment to the demands of life." [3]

2. ". . . learning is shown by a change in behavior as a result of experience." [4]

In most assignments undertaken by a systems analyst, the degree of success he attains depends directly on how well the personnel understand the new procedures and methods that have been installed. The teaching of new methods and procedures can be effective only if the teacher understands the concept of learning.

Lee J. Cronbach discusses "seven elements in behavior." If we are to accept Professor Cronbach's definition (2 above) that learning is a change in behavior, careful consideration should be given to these "seven elements in behavior":

The elements in behavior are as follows:

a. *Situation.* The situation presents alternatives requiring choice.

b. *Personal characteristics.* A person's abilities and attitudes limit the ways in which he can respond.

c. *Goal.* The person sees some possibility of acting on the situation so as to gain satisfaction.

d. *Interpretation.* The person interprets the he expects will lead to the greatest net satis-situation.

e. *Action.* The person takes whatever action faction.

f. *Consequence:* confirmation or contradiction. The response is followed by consequences which confirm or contradict the person's interpretation.

g. *Reaction to thwarting.* If a response does not satisfy the person's wants, we say that he is blocked or thwarted. He may reinterpret and try a new response. He may decide that his goal cannot be reached. If he doubts that he can reach his goal, he is likely to become emotionally upset. [5]

[3] G. Lester Anderson and Arthur I. Gates, "The General Nature of Learning," *National Society for the Study of Education—Forty-Ninth Yearbook, Part I, Learning and Instruction,* University of Chicago Press, 1950, p. 16.

[4] Lee J. Cronbach, *Educational Psychology,* 2d ed., in consultation with Ernest R. Hilgard and Willard R. Spalding, Harcourt, Brace & World, Inc., 1963, p. 71.

[5] *Ibid.,* p. 69.

At this point the intimate relationship between the concept of motivation and the concept of learning should be obvious. A goal is an objective that an individual wishes to reach. The urges that spur individuals toward goals are contained in the concept of motivation.

GOALS

Goals can either be proximate or remote. A proximate goal to an employee may be the finishing of a particular work assignment. A remote goal may be self-advancement. The employee has been led to believe that good work will be rewarded by professional advancement. Another proximate goal may be the employee's desire to finish so that he can leave to attend a twilight double-header baseball game.

If the systems analyst is to initiate and maintain effective employee learning processes, he must be able to create attainable goals for the employees involved in the system. For example, in a job shop manufacturing plant it is imperative that the time spent on each job be accurately reported if the direct labor cost per job is to be computed. When direct laborers are being asked to report their time in this way for the first time, something more than just instructions must be issued to them. A goal must be created. They must see in their own way that a worthwhile goal is being reached.

In one manufacturing plant the systems analyst talked first with the foremen of the various direct labor departments involved, convincing them that his request would lead to more meaningful information that would not only help general management but would have beneficial results for each foreman as well. Those foremen who were convinced that their ultimate goal of self-advancement would be helped by this change in procedure became staunch allies of the systems analyst. Those who could not translate this change immediately into a worthwhile personal goal had to be approached differently. The analyst had to probe to find the argument which would convince these foremen that the proposed change was necessary and worthwhile.

After the immediate on-line supervisors of the direct laborers had accepted the new procedure, some time was given to them so that they could convince the men under them that the change was necessary. Many of the foremen relied quite heavily on the urges to succeed and to avoid failure. Once the men realized that the completion of accurate time tickets was a means to success, most resistance to the new procedure ceased. The new procedure had become a worthwhile goal.

PERSONAL CHARACTERISTICS

Personal characteristics include "all the abilities and all the typical responses that the person brings to the situation." [6] This element of behavior specifically involves the frame of mind of the individual and what he has already learned from previous experience.

The approach that the systems analyst used in the previous example, in which he convinced the laborers through their supervisors that the new labor reporting procedure was necessary, would have been doomed to failure had not the men in each department already learned through prior experience that cooperation with their boss was far more beneficial than opposition or disobedience. These men were ready to be convinced by their foremen that the new procedure was necessary.

Quite frequently the systems analyst must study the personnel in a department that is to be affected by a new or revised procedure to determine whether their personal characteristics place them in a state of readiness to accept the suggested change. In some cases he will find it necessary to create certain experiences for the employees in order to get them into the desired state of readiness.

The element of personal characteristics in human behavior may need special attention by the systems analyst in situations where increased mechanization of a data processing system is being recommended. Employees who have not been properly introduced to the idea of working in a data processing system centered around an electronic computer, for example, often resist the proposed innovation because they are not personally ready to embrace the new concepts and the new approach to data processing made possible by the computer. A major part of the systems analyst's work is to get employees ready to accept the highly mechanized system so that they can learn to operate it properly. Many systems revisions or new installations have been set back or could not be effected because the sys-

tems analyst did not recognize personal characteristics as an element of human behavior and failed to give sufficient weight to the human factor in a systems engagement.

SITUATION

"The situation consists of all the objects, persons, and symbols in the learner's environment. Experience in one situation prepares a person to respond to similar situations in the future." [7]

A systems analyst who realizes that the situation in which certain employees have found themselves during their normal working hours will affect both their current behavior patterns and those toward which he would like to see them move is in a better position to judge what effect new or revised data processing procedures will have on these employees. Employees who have been taught that systems changes are good and that there is a thrill in experiencing new and more efficient data processing procedures will welcome the new and the different situations when they are confronted with them. Employees who have been encouraged by their employer—either actually or implicitly—to resist change normally resist systems changes without listening to the merits of the proposal. Thus, the systems analyst must recognize or discover the experience level that he must work with during his engagement.

During a systems investigation at a fairly large medical clinic in the Midwest a systems analyst found that employees were not reluctant to try new and different procedures. The reason was that the clinic management did an excellent job of employee training. Employee goals were effectively tied to organization goals. Because the employees had been exposed many times to new and different situations and had been expected to choose alternatives that advanced their own goals as well as the clinic's, these employees were in a personal state of readiness for the new procedures recommended. Unfortunately, this situation exists in too few companies.

INTERPRETATION

"Interpretation is a process of directing attention to parts of the situation, relating them

---

[6] *Ibid.*, p. 73.

[7] *Ibid.*

to past experience, and predicting what can be expected to happen if various actions are taken." [8] It is important to know that once a learner is confronted with a situation he will make certain interpretations, based on previous experience, from which he will predict what will happen if various alternatives are chosen.

In any systems engagement changes in routine will be proposed to certain employees. Depending on how the employees interpret these changes, they will either be convinced that the changes are worthwhile or will be opposed to them. If the systems analyst has sufficient depth of understanding of human behavior, his presentation of proposed changes will be such as to permit favorable interpretation of the proposals.

On one systems engagement the analyst discovered that a certain department supervisor interpreted most problems or situations by asking himself this question, "Which alternative will make me look the best—to my boss and to my people?" To capitalize on this discovery the systems analyst utilized an interesting approach.

One problem to be solved in this part of the engagement was the redesign of a customer charge ticket so that it could be used more effectively by the accounts receivable clerks and accounting machine operators. The analyst spent most of his time helping the supervisor redesign this document. When the task was completed, however, all of the credit for the new form design was given to the supervisor. There was no question about the acceptance of this form when the new procedures were installed. The supervisor convinced his people that far more benefits would accrue to the department through the new procedures than through the continuation of the old. In this instance the analyst was skillful enough in presenting the situation properly to insure that the desired interpretation was drawn from it.

RESPONSES

"*The person's actions include movements and statements; they are observable responses.* A person chooses whatever action he expects to give him the greatest satisfaction.*" [9] The example just cited illustrated both interpretation and action. The supervisor not only in-

terpreted the use of the new form properly but also responded to or acted on an alternative in the situation by convincing his subordinates that the change was desirable.

To some extent the elements of action in human behavior is dependent on the other elements. If enough facts are known about the status of the other elements, the kind of action that an individual will take can quite often be predicted. In recommending a proposed systems innovation, the analyst can be reasonably sure that it will be received favorably if he has done a good job in preparing the individuals affected by this innovation. If acceptable goals have been outlined for them, if they are in a proper state of personal readiness to accept this change, and if the situation has been presented properly so that the desired interpretations will be made, the systems analyst should be able to expect a favorable response from them.

CONSEQUENCES

"*Consequences: confirmation or contradiction. Some events that follow the action are regarded by the learner as the consequences of it.*" [10] This element, too, contributes to the analyst's ability to predict or expect certain actions. The learner inevitably predicts the consequences of actions that he is about to take. If the consequences are favorable, this assists the learner in choosing among alternative courses of action when a similar situation is presented to him.

Employees who have had favorable experiences when working with a systems analyst are far more willing to work with him again. Employees who have had no such experience tend to be a bit hesitant and "stand-offish" until they are motivated and willing to accept this new experience as part of their learning process.

An absolute must for a successful systems analyst is to see to it that the consequences of his proposals are salutary. To be assured of this result the analyst must have the support of top management. Employees must see that he has this support. They also should be able to see from past experience that cooperation is far more beneficial to them, in terms of their own long- and short-run goals, than opposition to or rejection of new proposals.

[8] *Ibid.*
[9] *Ibid.*, p. 74.

[10] *Ibid.*

THWARTING

"Reaction to thwarting . . . thwarting occurs when the person fails to attain his goals." [11]
Up to this point in the discussion of the elements of human behavior little doubt has been expressed that the systems analyst can, in every instance, create proper goals, induce a proper state of personal characteristics, and present the situation so that the proper interpretation will be made and desired action will be taken. Unfortunately this is not always the case. Systems analysts are as imperfect as anyone else in properly utilizing the various elements of human behavior. Furthermore, not all actions result in favorable consequences for the employees who must accept new procedures and must be taught how to use them, nor are the consequences always favorable for the analyst himself.

Usually, when an individual's first response is thwarted, one of two reactions occurs. He may re-assess the situation and try another action, or he may give up and refuse to respond at all (nonadaptive behavior). A successful systems analyst should never be guilty of the latter reaction to thwarting. He should believe "that the mountain can be moved" and should act accordingly.

Another problem presents itself, however, when the analyst encounters a nonadaptive reaction from the individuals who will be responsible for effecting the new or revised procedures that are being recommended. How should this be handled? The ultimate solution, if the new procedures have been approved by management, is to reassign the nonadaptive employees or separate them from the company. Such a solution should be resorted to only if the individual's reaction to thwarting is definitely and firmly nonadaptive.

One systems analyst reported the following example: He had been asked by the owners of a small trucking company to review the accounting system to see whether a more mechanized system was feasible. Even after doing everything he could from a human relations point of view, he was not able to convince the bookkeeper that she could learn to operate a general purpose accounting machine. When this person realized that her employer was convinced of the desirability of the more mechanized procedures and that her resistance would not forestall the change, she asked to be relieved of her duties. The management was sorry to see her react this way but was instrumental in placing her in another company in the same city in a similar position.

SUMMARY

People are an essential part of any business system. No matter how heavily mechanized data processing systems become, people will be part of these systems and will present a series of problems to systems analysts that are very different from those posed by the communications media and machines that are also essential physical elements of a data processing system.

The systems analyst must understand two important concepts of psychology—the concept of motivation and the concept of learning. The concept of motivation embraces the idea that every human experience involves a causation factor and an effect from that cause. The essential motivating causes are sometimes classified as the urge arising from bodily needs, the urge to succeed and to achieve, the urge to avoid failure and disappointment, the urge for recognition and approval, the urge for sympathy and affection, the urge for security, the urge to experience the new and different, and the sex urge. The systems analyst must always be aware of these motivating forces and must use his knowledge of them in carrying out his assignments if he is to be successful.

The concept of learning centers around the idea that ". . . learning is shown by a change in behavior as a result of experience." Since a good deal of the effort put forth by a systems analyst is in the area of teaching, it is imperative for the systems analyst to understand the various elements of human behavior which are the basic aspects of learning: goals, personal characteristics, the situation, interpretation, action, consequences: confirmation or contradiction, and reaction to thwarting. These seven aspects function in this way: Every individual strives for goals. His previous experience has prepared him in certain ways to be personally ready for new experiences. When a new situation is presented to him, he will interpret this new situation and respond in a way he thinks will meet his goals, based on the consequences that he has experienced in similar situations before. If consequences in

[11] *Ibid.*

previous similar situations have brought him closer to his goals, this will have increased his personal readiness to accept the new situation. However, favorable consequences do not always result, and then the individual is said to be thwarted.

The systems analyst must concentrate on teaching employees to accept and to operate new procedures in such a way that none of them feel that they have been thwarted. He must also be realistic enough to know that this ideal cannot always be attained and should work out ways to deal with nonadaptive behavior.

BIBLIOGRAPHY

1. Cartwright, D., and A. F. Zander (eds.), *Group Dynamics,* Row, Peterson, 1953.
2. Coch, L., and J. R. P. French, Jr., "Overcoming Resistance to Change," *Human Relations,* 1948.
3. Haire, M., *Psychology in Management,* McGraw-Hill Book Co., 1956.
4. Jacobson, H. B., and J. S. Roucek (eds.), *Automation and Society,* Philosophical Library, Inc., 1959.
5. Jacoby, N. H., "Impacts of Scientific Change Upon Business Management," *California Management Review,* Summer, 1962.
6. Jasinski, F. J., "Adapting Organization to New Technology," *Harvard Business Review,* January–February, 1959.
7. Johnson, R. A., *Employees–Automation–Management,* University of Washington, Bureau of Business Research, 1961.
8. Johnson, R., F. E. Kast, and J. E. Rosenzweig, *The Theory and Management of Systems,* McGraw-Hill Book Co., 1963.
9. McGregor, D., *The Human Side of Enterprise,* McGraw-Hill Book Co., 1960.
10. Miller, B., "Gaining Acceptance for Major Methods Changes," *American Management Association, Research Study No. 44,* 1960.
11. Postley, J. A., *Computers and People,* McGraw-Hill Book Co., 1960.
12. Ronken, H. O., and P. R. Lawrence, *Administering Changes,* Harvard University, Graduate School of Business Administration, 1952.
13. Spates, T. G., *Human Values Where People Work,* Harper and Row, 1960.
14. Strauss, G., and L. R. Sayles, *Personnel: The Human Problems of Management,* Prentice-Hall, Inc., 1960.
15. Thompson, V. A., "Hierarchy, Specialization and Organizational Conflict," *Administrative Science Quarterly,* March, 1961.

Section B.   Management Controls

Part VII.   Management Control Systems

Throughout the ages, down to our own Space Age, man has been ceaselessly searching for and achieving an ever greater degree of control over his environment. It is this control that has enabled him to create civilization as we know it. It is this control by which management hopes to implement ever more fully the short-range and long-range goals of the business enterprise. It is precisely for this that the marvel of modern science, the electronic digital computer, is being increasingly utilized by enlightened, progressive management.

In nearly all previous chapters, control has figured as an important element in management systems. In Part II Daniel rightly related information to both the planning and control functions of management. Young listed control as one of the essential aspects of all systems and we saw self-regulating feedback presented elsewhere as paramount to the closed-loop control of the cybernetic system. PERT, real-time, and the whole field of computer science are oriented to management control. It is nigh impossible to conceive of this area without touching upon nearly all the other topics mentioned heretofore.

For this reason, the selection by D. G. Malcolm and A. J. Rowe provides a review of much of what has already been treated in previous chapters dealing with the many and diverse facets of systems management. Although specifically directed at management *control* systems, it includes such topics as a total systems approach, information flow and organizational structure, information feedback, and real-time; computers and their use, language, and applications; and computer simulation and the role of models. In fact, the greater part of the reading is devoted to these latter topics. One special aspect of their treatment is its orientation to military control systems like SAGE and SACCS, possibly because these have been the most highly developed and the most outstanding examples that we possess. Since models of management control systems are concerned with information, decision making and control, none of these, especially control, must be viewed as an end in itself but as a means of improving the performance of the total system.

The separate article by Alan J. Rowe on the "Research Problems in Management Controls" certainly raises more questions than it answers. For him control includes such things as objectives, decision criteria for evaluating performance, decision rules for remedial action, and some measures of performance, while the control problem involves information on all of these, information so quantified as to be amenable to computer simulation.

Computer simulation Rowe views as a most fitting means of studying the dynamic response characteristics of business systems. For this end he describes business systems as a matrix of activities and responses with elements susceptible to computer simulation.

In shifting emphasis from computer simulation to feedback considerations, George Weinwurm both restricts and sharpens Rowe's field of view. He projects his brief discussion against the background of experience gained in military control systems (e.g., SAGE), for these are highly complex man-to-machine systems similar to those found in the world of business.

Since the most characteristic aspect of systems in general is feedback, Weinwurm distinguishes four distinct types of feedback in man-to-machine systems: feedback within the computer, between the computer and the system environment, between man and the machine, and between man and the system environment. Combinations of these may also occur. An interesting feature of these types is that they are characterized by time-cycle discriminants. While the first of these (intracomputer feedback) can be measured in fractions of a second (milliseconds, microseconds and now nanoseconds), the other three involving extracomputer interactions consume much more valuable time. Where human decision making is involved, the use of faster and faster computers does little to solve the problem. The progress made in military applications has been due primarily to having more and more decisions programmed internally. However, before this can be done, decision rules will have to be more explicitly and more formally expressed. These rules must, moreover, cover every relevant situation and optimally every possible contingency. These rules must then be translated into a language that the computer can understand, another formidable task indeed. Most difficulty however will be encountered in the twilight area where no general rule suffices to cover a particular situation. However, it is in reducing this "circle of confusion" that the payoff for control systems takes place but the price thereof is compromise.

In the final paragraphs some thought is given to the exciting idea of adaptive automata, of machines capable of learning from experience how to solve the problem with which they are dealing. The problem of having the machine adapt itself to increasingly complex environments under controlled conditions is however currently under consideration. The degree to which the machine simulates the real world will be only an approximate one but the further

question then arises: What approximation is reasonably sufficient? A test of the sufficiency of the real-time man-to-machine SAGE system would be to have a war, an expensive and not humane proposition. But even this would not suffice for little of statistical significance could be derived from a sample of one.

In the final selection Edward Roberts takes up for consideration the intriguing topic of industrial dynamics and its interrelationship to management control systems. The Massachusetts Institute of Technology, with which he is associated, has generally been recognized as the cradle of industrial dynamics, and it is here that the management-tool aspects and the teaching-device feature of industrial dynamics have consistently been stressed. The present selection weds both features and the results achieved are worth the study.

Every organization is itself a kind of control system. There are the inevitable objectives to be reached, the decision-making processes that mediate the idealized goals and the apparent progress of the company toward these goals, and the implementation of the policy-making decisions that translate the objectives from the realm of the potential to that of the actual—all of these in one continuous, complex, and interrelated feedback system.

As a philosophy industrial dynamics views organizations from this control system type of perspective, and as a methodology it aims to redesign organizational structures and policies consonant with this viewpoint. If a company's likelihood to succeed depends on such features as the flow of information, men, money, materials, orders, and capital equipment, then in insisting that each of these be viewed as an essential part of a total system and not in isolation, industrial dynamics reveals its own total systems approach to the problems of management control.

The traditional approaches to management control systems have too often proved inadequate. Many fail to solve the problems for which they were designed, and the least successful even manage to create other insoluble problems of their own. This unfortunate situation, by no means an archaic phenomenon, is illustrated by telling examples from the field of R & D projects, production-inventory-employment control, logistics, and quality control systems. Both facets of the situation are convincingly portrayed: that in which management control systems proved inadequate for the task for which they were designed and that in which they compounded an already perplexing situation by giving rise to additional problems.

Three general principles are inferred from the examples: the boundaries of a management control system design study must not be drawn to conform with organizational structure merely because of that structure since key factors may lie outside the conventional structure; management control system design must be viewed as a form of man-machine system design; and an effective total systems approach to management control will necessarily be one involving many departments and levels beyond that of middle management.

23. AN APPROACH TO COMPUTER-BASED

MANAGEMENT CONTROL SYSTEMS

D. G. Malcolm * and A. J. Rowe †

In an era of automated information technology, the ability to formulate decision criteria precisely and process information electronically should prove valuable in the design of management control systems. One can look forward to organizational structures which more nearly conform to the communication and informational requirements.

In an attempt to explore the problems facing management of large organizations and persons responsible for the design of management controls, the authors have embarked on an intensive research program in this area. Started in April of 1959, the research has been primarily concerned with studying computer-based management control systems.[1] By examining the flow of information and decision processes using computer simulation, insights into the behavior of these complex systems appear possible.

NATURE OF THE PROBLEM

Examining the problems confronting designers of management control systems, one is readily aware of the magnitude of the task. Although management and organizational specialists have been concerned with these same problems for many years, there still remain a large number of questions to be answered. For example:

• To what extent should top management go in developing a philosophy of "management by system"?

SOURCE: *California Management Review* (Spring, 1961), pp. 5–15. Reprinted by permission of California Management Review, Copyright 1961 by the Regents of the University of California.

* President, Malcolm Associates.

† Professor of Quantitative Business Analysis, University of Southern California.

• How can top management determine the depth in the organization to which it should extend day-to-day personal influence?
• How can management evaluate proposed computer-based, information-processing, decision-making systems?
• How should management plan the development of an organization to achieve control?

These in turn raise a number of questions for the researcher as follows:

• What is a suitable method for determining the cost and effectiveness of management information or control systems?
• How can appropriate systems be designed prior to their actual installation?
• By what method can various types of information be expressed in terms of a company's over-all objectives?
• What is the best configuration of an integrated management control system?

Specialists have applied a wide variety of answers and approaches to these problems. Examples of traditional methods include: organizational planning, scheduling of operations, inventory control, quality control, and cost control.

It is significant to note that each of these is a component or single aspect of a business and the concept of an integrated total-system control remains practically unexploited. However, it is possible that concise, quantitative, and unequivocal answers to these questions may not be found for a long time.

DEFINING MANAGEMENT CONTROLS

For the purpose of this paper, a management control system is described as a set of policies, procedures, and associated information processing designed to give direction to corporate activities in the following ways:

- By clearly establishing goals;
- By measuring progress in achieving these goals;
- By indicating the need for corrective action.

To achieve an optional set of management controls, however, it is necessary to "design" a management system in much the same way that equipment itself is designed. As part of this design process, it is a basic requirement that the system designer clearly understand the objectives of the business.

In this regard the traditional statements of maximizing profit or return on investment are not sufficient guides. Modern business is conducted to serve many diverse objectives, making the problem of control more sophisticated than attempting to have each and every action directed toward such goals. Management, therefore, can be considered as the custodians of the resources of an organization with the mission to organize the effort to achieve purposeful objectives and to assure survival of the business.

As part of the control process, a communication network is used to link management with the resources of the business and to provide the information needed for feedback control. The information available to the manager is therefore used as the basis for control and operating decisions. The core of the design problem, therefore, is in determining which operating decision rules can be reduced to a routine, computerized approach.

The characteristics of information flow and decision rules provide the basic inputs for a study of management controls. It is obvious that the interlinkage between decision points, as well as the density of information flow, has a direct effect on the nature of the organizational structure required for successful operation. Thus, the constraints of the existing organization must be ignored, and the specifications for an effective organization to-make required decisions should be based on the system design activity.

CURRENT APPLICATIONS OF COMPUTERS

Although there is an ever-increasing use of electronic data-processing equipment in the automating of existing information systems, the need to integrate the over-all informational requirements and to redesign a given system is often overlooked.

More generally, applications are made in one area of the business, such as finance or manufacturing, and little more than checks for compatibility are made with respect to the total system problem.

This piecemeal approach is most frequently justified on the grounds that one must build gradually in developing a total system. However, there is a growing recognition that this approach leads to suboptimal results.

In current applications, the use of electronic computers does not tap one-tenth of their ultimate potential. Although this condition is particularly true of industrial, as contrasted with military, applications, it is a situation that will become a matter of increasing concern to those who use computers, especially as they realize the nature of this potential. The situation, conceivably, could become worse before effective long-range programs are designed and in use.

APPLICATIONS IN MILITARY SYSTEMS

If one examines the Air Defense Command, it is readily apparent that the prototypes of highly automated information systems are currently being established for management use. Examples of such systems which operate with extremely short feedback time, often referred to as operating in real-time, can be seen in SAGE [2] (Semi-Automatic Ground Environment) and SACCS (Strategic Air Command Control System). Both of these systems are computer-based, command-control systems.

In the course of the design and implementation of these Systems, a number of changes were made in the Air Defense Command structure. The computer control system itself was used as the basis for organizational changes which led to the centralization of many activities.

A further development which was necessitated by the requirement for design and implementation was the concept of a system manager. The ESSPO (Electronic Support Systems Project Office), was given the mission of properly managing the joint efforts of system analysis, system design, computer manufacturing, computer programming and system training.

REAL-TIME CONTROL

In military applications, the computer has been used as an integral, on-line controlling device. In this context, the terms, "real-time control," "communication," and "information system," emerge as system design concepts.

"Real-time" is used to mean that the desired information is transmitted into a centralized computer instantaneously and without conversion. The significance of "real-time" control lies in the fact that information is used as it is developed and that elements in the system are controlled by the processed information immediately, not after the fact, or by making periodic forecasts of the expected future state of the system.

To achieve "real-time" control, the computer processes information, compares it with predetermined decision criteria and issues instructions to men or machines, or both, for corrective or purposeful action. Further, the computer, by means of direct outputs, informs affected parties of this information as it is developed. This is "real-time management information."

By examining the best known examples of systems of this type currently found in the military, one may find some guidance in design approaches that may be useful in evolving better on-line management control systems for industry.

MILITARY SYSTEMS

The experience gained in the development of military command control systems can be summarized under the following topics:

- Use of the Systems Analysis Approach,
- Problem Formulation for Computer Programming,
  - Use of New Computer Applications, and
  - Use of Formalized System Training.

While the following are broad generalizations, it would appear that the quickest route to effective development of a truly integrated management control system involves a proper point of view on the part of management in regard to the possible effects of information flow on the organization structure. That is, the possibility of recentralizing and the eliminating of certain functions must be within the system designer's scope.

Further, to perform a system analysis there must be proper organizational status for the design function and top management must plan for the necessary lead time to perform its activities. Finally, while it should be evident, it is worth emphasizing that top management participation and support is vital to obtain desired results.

SYSTEMS ANALYSIS APPROACH

In reviewing the development of a system such as SAGE, one is impressed with the magnitude of the design process. The design of this system necessitated spelling out precise system requirements. This, in turn, provided the basis for more effectively meeting the needs of the air defense system.

In contrast to the systems approach, the question that is often asked is, "What can be done to improve or automate existing practices?" In looking over the process of creating new management control systems, it becomes obvious that this latter approach is often the easiest to justify and, thus, has been the route traditionally followed.

In essence, the design process is based on answering the question, "What is the best system?" and is generally called the systems analysis, or systems engineering, approach. Thus, one principle in creating a new system involves a careful look at the requirements of the system via the systems engineering approach. A brief description of the steps generally involved is as follows:

1. *Establish criteria for management information needs:* (a) Establish the objectives or mission of the system. (b) Determine current information, decision, display, and report practices, by use of graphical flow analyses.

2. *Develop the preliminary design:* (a) A preliminary statement of system requirements; i.e., specific reporting frequencies, types, and routings of reports, type of equipments, displays, etc., should be established. (b) Determine what can be automated using computer programming and what to leave as currently performed. We must remember here that technology is changing rapidly. Simon [3] predicts that by 1984 it will be technically possible to automate any and all functions in an organization. (c) Balance current requirements with growth considerations.

3. *Evaluate the preliminary design:* (a) Determine the cost of hardware and applicable

costs. (b) Assess training implications and requirements. (c) Establish the nature of the improvements to be gained.

4. *Develop a revised model of the proposed system:* (a) Use of systems analysis or an experimental approach involving simulation or gaming, to test the design. (b) Obtain the participation of the ultimate users.

5. *Determine system specifications:* (a) Evaluate alternative means of achieving the proposed design. (b) Consider the relationship to other system requirements.

6. *Install, de-bug, modify, extend the system:* (a) Provide for maintenance and updating. (b) Allow for flexibility in operating and modifying the system.

COMPUTER PROBLEM FORMULATION

In the application of computer-based systems, it has become evident that there is a need for precise formulation of the computer program. Descriptive statements are not sufficient, rather, quantitative or analytic formulation of problems is required.

Furthermore, factors such as kind and size of memory, speed of computation, manner of indexing, and rounding must all be taken into account in computer programming. Methods of filing information, data accumulation, and reporting requirements are also significant aspects of program design.

It is often necessary to reformulate a problem to conform to the computer requirements; although this consideration is becoming less important with the availability of large-scale digital computers.

At the outset of a given computer program, a decision must be made whether to have a flexible, general purpose program or one designed for the immediate specific use. Modular programming which treats each section of a program separately provides considerable flexibility at only a small cost in computation time and storage.

COMPUTER "LANGUAGE"

Probably the most difficult aspect of the problem is the actual coding or programming language. Not only is the coding a time-consuming and difficult process, but the system designer must convey the intent of his work

to programmers, thus compounding the problem.

Considerable effort is currently being expended in the development of computer languages which can be used more readily by system designers. This, in part, recognizes the fact that as much time is often spent in coding a problem as in the formulation. In this regard, then, considerable work remains to be done to develop computer languages which will simplify the operational instructions for the computer programming task.

USE OF NEW COMPUTER APPLICATIONS

The capability of the computer to process information rapidly, store information conveniently and provide accuracy has made significant inroads on long-standing problems. Some of these computer applications are:

1. *On-line control:* As has been mentioned previously, on-line, direct read-in and read-out, integrated computer operation has been used in military systems. The importance of this technical achievement should not be underestimated. However, the feasibility of utilizing this on-line control feature for industrial application requires research and analysis to determine the cost and effectiveness of a given application.

2. *Management-by-exception:* [4] The data processing capability of high-speed computers, as used in the military, has made possible centralized operations using large masses of data which have been carefully sorted by built-in criteria. Only the exceptions requiring attention are presented to decision makers by the computer. This feature could be extended to provide centralized control in management systems. PERT (Navy Polaris program) is an example.

3. *Interrogation, or fast-simulation possibilities:* Using a computer-based system, the human monitor can, in a sense, ask "What would happen if I issued this command?" This interrogation feature, often called "fast-simulation," requires the building of analytic models which incorporate desired predictive capabilities. Appropriate computer models for business situations may eventually provide the potentiality of on-line management control systems.

USE OF FORMALIZED SYSTEM TRAINING

In the course of developing major new military systems, it has been found that provision for training people in the on-going operations of the new systems is needed. The training in a system such as SAGE involves elaborate simulations of a predicted attack environment. This represents a new concept to the management world. The justification for this elaborate training stems from the fact that there is no other way to adequately train the people to perform under an attack situation.

However, a significant additional value in this approach should be pointed out. The proficiency of a system is determined by its operation as a whole, involving the communications and interrelations of many people and machines. Therefore, the proficiency of individual acts must be judged by measures appropriate to the system context.

It would hardly be desirable to emphasize performance at one part of the system that would be detrimental to the total system performance. In short, each person should be trained to act in an optimal way from the total system point of view.

Therefore, to adequately provide for proper performance in such broad systems, a comprehensive means of training using simulated exercises is required. Furthermore, the need for this training is not dependent on whether the environment is real or hypothetical.

SIMULATION MODELS ESSENTIAL

It appears that when radically new concepts in management control are installed, quite likely simulation models will be required. The installation time, the acceptance, and therefore even the ultimate efficiency attainable by the control systems will be considerably enhanced by appropriately designed simulation exercises along with proper criteria for measuring performance in relation to the total system.

Using a systematic design approach, as shown in the preceding discussion, it is possible to develop improved, total, computer-based management control systems. In view of the requirements of current air defense systems, the need for computer-based systems was readily justified. However, industrial systems have not reached the point where objectives can be set forth in clear and unequivocal terms and thus it is difficult to evaluate a given system design.

In short, the only feasible means for meeting the military requirements for rapid, high volume, and accurate data handling was the use of computer systems. Given these requirements, one could systematically design a feasible system. On the other hand, the capability of rigorous evaluation of a number of alternative designs has generally been considered too costly. However, the acceptability of the military approach for the business world will undoubtedly be predicated on the ability to evaluate control concepts prior to actually installing new systems.

If the advantages of information recentralization are to be achieved in practice, they must first be proved beneficial to the organization; and secondly, they must be both desired by and acceptable to management.

In practice, however, these two requirements are often in conflict. Although it is difficult to assess the value of a new system, it appears desirable to develop a design approach that is both evaluative and instructive. Such an approach can be instrumental in the realization of promised benefits of an integrated management information system. An approach which appears to be the most suitable, and perhaps the most effective in the long range, is the use of computer simulation.

COMPUTER SIMULATION

As a problem-solving tool, computer simulation has been used for a number of years. It has enabled management to experiment with and test certain types of policies, procedures and organizational changes in much the same way an engineer tests new designs. With the use of computers and the development of probability methods, computer simulation can also be applied to complex operating plans or management controlling systems in addition to day-to-day operating problems. The method is similar to war gaming techniques used by the military and the paper and pencil techniques used by systems and procedure specialists.

In a sense, simulation is a synthetic means used to imitate the behavior of a system for the purpose of studying the response to specific changes. Where the problem is entirely physical in nature, such as in testing aircraft, a physical model can be used. However, in studying management control systems, which deal with the flow of information and decision networks, an exact analogue of the problem may not be possible.

An approximation, usually in the form of a mathematical or symbolic model, is used which describes the elements and properties of the system under study. Thus, a model for a management control system is a means for providing a formalized statement of system behavior, rather than a physical analogue of the system.

A DESIGN TOOL

Simulation has only recently been considered as a useful tool for the design of management control systems.[5] A similar approach has been taken in the research program conducted by the authors,[6] where computer simulation is used as a laboratory for examining system behavior. To conduct such experimentation, an analytic model of a total business system has been developed which explicitly characterizes the information flow, decision rules and physical processes of a business system.

To the extent that this model describes the behavior of the elements of the system in a realistic manner, the conclusions drawn should prove useful in the design of management controls as applied to large-scale, complex organizations and their associated information processing.

However, in view of the intricately complex nature of a total business system, intuition alone cannot be considered sufficient to evaluate new concepts or designs. While on the other hand, extensive experimentation directly in an actual plant to evaluate alternate designs poses almost insurmountable problems.

Aside from the inevitable disruptions and possibly unrealistic results, valuable time would be lost in gathering performance data. In addition, costly mistakes might result if the consequences of actually carrying out a given experiment cannot be predicted in advance, and there is no control. These considerations, therefore, strongly support the use of computer simulation both as a research and design vehicle.

EXPERIMENTS WITH MODELS

Research in Management Controls implies experimentation; however, the manner of experimenting is dependent upon the results desired. An exploratory type of experimentation is possible by simply changing parameters of the simulation model and observing the resultant system behavior.

Thus, insights into the response characteristics of the system are obtained by examining the results shown in the computer output. Another manner of experimentation is to specify given system designs and subject these to many conditions and observe the effects. This latter method is principally used to test the significant differences among alternative designs.

"POLICY LABORATORY"

Since the computer output provides a summarization of information reflecting system behavior generated during simulation, it is possible to obtain a continuous time trace of the changes in system performance and the interdependencies among the elements of the system. It is this capability of being able to examine, in considerable detail, the changes which result from alternate system designs that has led to the term "policy laboratory" being applied to computer simulation.

THE MODEL AND ITS ROLE

To simulate management controls, then, it is necessary to have a model which provides a formal statement of the business system's behavior. Computer simulation, however, is seldom an exact analogue of the operation of an actual system. Rather, simulation performed on a digital computer can only approximate continuous, simultaneous activity. If the elements and properties of the system have been properly defined, then the parameters and variables can be readily controlled and measured.

The model may be symbolic, mathematical, or descriptive; however, it should be constructed so as to include properties which are sufficient to define the behavior of the system.

FORCING FUNCTION

The variables describe behavior for a given set of parameters. The forcing functions provide the external stimuli which cause the system to react—for example, orders which enter a system cause men to work, machines to run, and so on. In this way, orders become a forcing function for the system. Whatever particular form is used, a model provides the frame of reference within which the problem is considered.

A model often indicates relationships which are not otherwise obvious. However, it should be noted that a model need not duplicate actual conditions to be useful. A model should be designed to predict actual behavior resulting from changes in the system design or application of new decision rules. Such prediction implies an understanding of the manner in which the system reacts; that is, being able to specify the outputs for a given set of inputs. This approach differs from the conventional concept of treating the system as a "black box."

Since a simulation model is merely a means for testing new ideas, the simpler the model, the more effective for research or design purposes. It is not necessary to incorporate all possible aspects of system behavior in the model; rather, only those variables which contribute substantially to system response characteristics need be incorporated.

To this end, a model can be considered as an initial experiment to determine what factors are most significant in a business system. The model can be refined or expanded as experimental data describing the system performance and sensitivity to various factors become available.

DEVELOPING A BUSINESS MODEL

For the purpose of studying management controls, modeling should be centered about the information, decision-making and control aspects of the business. The majority of simulations to date, however, have been concerned with the physical activities within a business, such as scheduling of products,[7] control of inventory, movement of vehicles, and maintenance of aircraft, to name a few.[8]

On the other hand, since management control is concerned with the more intangible aspects of the business, modeling is a far more difficult problem.[9] Reviewing some of these modeling considerations in detail indicates the task involved:

DECISION-MAKING PROCESS

If the decisions in an organization are associated with the physical points where they occur, then the decision-making process can be characterized by the decision rules and associated information. Interlinkages among the decision points represent the communication channels.

To simulate an organization with an appropriate degree of reality, it is necessary to establish a suitable communication network. In addition, the many decision criteria and decision rules have to be stated analytically to be amenable to computer programming.

QUEUING EFFECTS

If a decision maker is viewed as a processor of information, the rate of arrival of information and the time taken to process decisions will result in an average delay or queuing effect. Analysis of such delays will provide one important measure of system effectiveness.

The speed of information transmission, as well as the number of decision points, however, must be closely coupled with the capability of the system to respond to varying inputs. By assigning costs to alternate means of information transmittal, the cost of on-line controls can be assessed.

ORGANIZATIONAL CONSIDERATIONS

Since delays in decisions are a function of information flow and queuing, they have a direct effect on the organization structure. For example, introducing alternate decision channels to permit more effective information flow might lead to radical changes in an organization. A simulation model could thus examine different forms of organization structure and evaluate the effect of changes on the system performance.

Decentralization in an organization leads to the possibility of distortion in information due to the number of levels through which the information must pass; whereas this effect may be avoided in a more centralized organization.

Therefore, the modeling must treat with this consideration in order to provide a suitable basis for studying management control systems.

USES OF THE COMPUTER MODEL

Up to this point, the discussion has been primarily concerned with the modeling process itself. Let us now turn to some of the specific problems which can be studied using such a simulation model.

PRINCIPLES OF SYSTEM DESIGN

An important consideration in management control is the relationship of the total business system to the control methodology employed. In a sense, management controls are embedded in the broader consideration of total system design.

In view of the sparsity of knowledge in this area, computer simulation provides a means for examining a multitude of alternate designs with the possibility of developing basic design principles.

TESTING SYSTEM OBJECTIVES

As has already been discussed, the formalizing of business objectives is probably one of the most difficult aspects in establishing useful management controls. This aspect of the problem is particularly important since there are a number of competing objectives in any system which must be taken into account to avoid suboptimization.

Using a computer model, the possible consequences of different combinations of objectives can be examined. It is evident that there may not be a set of universal objectives which apply to all businesses; rather, actual objectives are generally dependent upon the willingness of managers to take action in the face of uncertainty and with inadequate information.

MEASURING SYSTEM PERFORMANCE

During the course of running a computer model, a means for explicit measurement of system performance must be provided. In actual practice, methods of measurement have involved long delays from occurrence to reporting of events due to the lack of high-speed data-processing equipment. However, with the increased use of computers, processing and summarizing data will prove a less formidable task, and measures of system performance can be based on actual operations.

Using fast simulation as discussed for the SAGE system, managers will have the option of periodically introducing real-time control. In addition, using a simulation model new measures of performance can be developed and tested.

DESIGN OF MANAGEMENT CONTROLS

A number of design concepts that should be explored in the development of new management control systems are:

* The use of information feedback loops, providing on-line control;
* The use of variable control limits in place of arbitrary standards as the basis for corrective action;
* Inclusion of formalized decision rules in the control system to (a) provide for optimization of the business system, (b) provide for improved response characteristics of the system;
* Use of a sampled-data approach for providing information on system performance. This is similar to the "exception principle."

Although these four items do not constitute an exhaustive list of all considerations, they do provide some idea of the complexity of designing management control systems.

All too often, management controls are treated as ends in themselves rather than as the means of improving total system performance. In the case of corporate budgeting, for example, funds may be spent unnecessarily to forestall budget cuts at a later date.

Another illustration of the misuse of the control concept is traditional costing practices that force the business to conform to arbitrary standards. As stated by Warren Alberts of United Airlines,[10] controls should be considered as guides for obtaining improved performance and not as a means of restricting performance.

If the design process, as discussed here, is at the system level, there is greater assurance that management controls will truly be integrated. The process of modeling and formalizing the structure of the business system should itself bring clarity to the interdependency of management control with planning, policies, objectives, and decision rules. As our understanding of the behavior of business systems improves, we should be in a position to develop effective design principles for management control systems.

REFERENCES

1. A. J. Rowe, "A Research Approach in Management Controls," *Journal of Industrial Engineering*, May–June 1960, Vol. XI, pp. 251–258.
2. A computerized air defense system using data automatically correlated with known flight plans to detect presence of unknown aircraft. Also provides automatic guidance of interceptors.
3. H. Simon, "The Corporation: Will It Be Managed by Machines?" *Management Review*, Nov., 1960.
4. D. G. Malcolm, J. H. Roseboom, C. E. Clark, W. Fazar, "Application of a Technique for Research and Development Program Evaluation," *Operations Research*, Vol. 7, September–October 1959, pp. 646–669.
5. D. G. Malcolm, "A Bibliography on the Use of Simulation in Management Analysis," *Operations Research*, March–April 1960, Vol. 8, pp. 169–177.
6. *System Simulation Symposium Proceedings*, American Institute of Industrial Engineers, New York, May 16–17, 1957.
7. D. G. Malcolm and A. J. Rowe, *Management Control Systems*, the proceedings of a symposium held at System Development Corporation, John Wiley and Sons, 1960.
8. A. J. Rowe, "Toward a Theory of Scheduling," *Journal of Industrial Engineering*, March–April 1960, Vol. II, pp. 125–136.
9. C. W. Cragin, et al., "Simulation: Management's Laboratory," Simulation Associates, Bradford, Mass., April 1959.
10. W. E. Alberts, "The Concepts of Management Control," *Management Control Systems*, New York, John Wiley and Sons, 1960, p. 14.

24. COMPUTER MANAGEMENT CONTROL
SYSTEMS THROUGH THE LOOKING GLASS

GEORGE F. WEINWURM *

A discussion of three aspects of the introduction of real time computer executive control systems into the world of business, using as a frame of reference the experience acquired through the design and operation of a similar military system, SAGE, over the past several years. In particular, consideration is given to the relative effectiveness with which the system communicates with its environment, the necessary compromises in the definition of the rules by which the system will function, and certain difficulties in the concept of executive control systems which are in some sense adaptive.

INTRODUCTION

The advent of electronic data processing equipment into the world of business has, as predicted, been followed by an increasing stream of practical applications. Perhaps the greatest challenge to the management scientist is presented by the concept of a *real time* man/machine system, of the type which would be involved in the actual decision processes essential to the everyday conduct of an industrial enterprise. This sentiment is not unreasonable, since developments in this area involve the deepest and most subtle considerations about the nature of automata and the practical business environment, as well as the men through whom the system must interact.

The diversity of endeavor which characterizes the world of business is a barrier to those seeking measures which remain significant from one field to another, or even within a single enterprise. Furthermore, the techniques of conducting a business, which historically have developed along lines peculiar to the needs of a specific organization, may be quite at odds with any effort at definition in terms of a machine-like program. The various considerations involved in balancing a system between the desires of a customer, however

SOURCE: *Management Science* (July, 1961), pp. 411–418. Reprinted by permission of the Institute of Management Science.
* Systems Development Corporation.

"non-optimum" they may be, as opposed to undertaking a revision of the customer's operating procedures, with the inherent risks implied, have been discussed and could easily fill many volumes (1).

Let us say that whatever experience has been acquired in the general area of executive man/machine systems is of real value, particularly since such systems are of comparatively recent vintage operationally. It is in this context that we will consider a widespread complex of computers, weapons, and men which since 1956 has been charged with the integrated defense of increasing portions of the continental United States against manned bomber attack, namely, the SAGE system. (The acronym represents the words Semi-Automatic Ground Environment.)

When compared to the multitude of computerized military command and control, or "L" systems now in various stages of development, SAGE appears as an earlier effort. Its significance lies in the fact that it represents the first occasion that an automatic man/machine system on the scale of conception of the cybernetic pioneers was actually built and operated in a live environment over an extended period of time. I am referring here to the work of men such as Wiener (2), von Neumann (3), and others.

It seems worthwhile to consider some general questions concerning the application of real time computerized executive control systems to the problems of business, using the SAGE system, and some of the experiences acquired in its design and operation, as a frame of reference.

FEEDBACK

Perhaps the most characteristic aspect of systems in general is the notion of feedback, the measurement and comparison of output with some standard in order to affect future outputs. In the realm of real time man/machine complexes this concept appears in a number of ways:

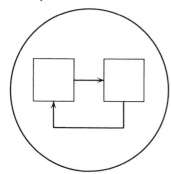

- Feedback within the computer—
  Checks on the progress and validity of certain calculations or events, etc.

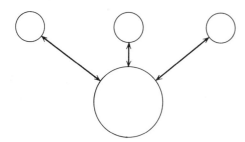

- Feedback between the computer and the system environment—
  Direct or circuitous automatic communication between the computer and other machinery in the system.

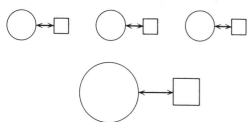

- Feedback between the man and the machine—

Decision problems presented to an operator through some audible or visual indication, for his response through the means provided.

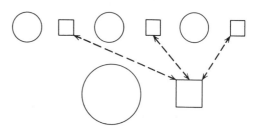

- Feedback directly between the man and the system environment—
  An operator may communicate directly with another operator by phone or radio, and subsequently insert information into the computer as desirable.

In all of the above cases we are seeking to minimize an error function of some kind, but the context of the communication involved greatly affects the way in which the problem is expressed, perhaps the fineness with which it may be considered, and certainly the approach to be taken toward its solution. Although all these feedbacks are in some sense discrete, many may, for all practical purposes, be considered as continuous or at least cyclic. In general, the more sophisticated problems will involve several types of feedback, even to the extent of using all four varieties many times over.

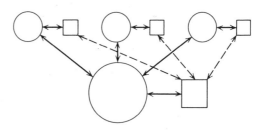

The most striking differentiation between these aspects of feedback is shown by considering the time required for one loop in the cycle. In general, checks within the computer will not exceed the order of a millisecond in SAGE. The three types of feedback necessitating interaction outside the computer will require 15 to 30 seconds, on the average: a ratio in time of at least 10^4. This has some rather interesting implications for real time systems. In the first place, a feedback loop which is discrete to the extent of the latter three varieties is difficult to analyze meaningfully within the existing tools of mathematical modeling, particularly in those areas involving human discretion (4). Secondly, a class of problems whose characteristics demand a relatively quicker feedback will not be within the capabilities of this system. Note that the situation will not necessarily improve with the introduction of a "faster" computer: in fact, the ratio will increase unless marked improvements are made in the general communication problem external to the machine.

In other words, we are emphasizing that the capabilities of a system, its "flexibility" in responding to various problems and environments, is dependent on more than the speed of the central computer. In terms of a present day complex such as SAGE, the hindrances which prevent the consideration of certain classes of problems probably have more to do with communicating with the environment than computing within the machine. Of course there have been significant advances in volume information transfer equipment in the past few years, and some of these devices will be available to improve the situation in future systems. In many cases, however, providing special equipment for a system of any magnitude may prove prohibitively expensive when compared to the use of existing telephone and teletype circuitry. In addition, for military applications, questions of security and survivability enter into the picture.

But the previous discussion has been rather mechanistic. A likely question is this: is not the communication problem described due largely to the need for human intervention; in other words, would not a greater degree of automaticity be the solution? The quick answer would be . . . in theory, yes; practically, not quite! The more complete answer involves a consideration of the way in which a real time program is prepared for operation in its environment.

RULES FOR DECISION

An early conception of an electronic digital data processor, as seen by Wiener (5), was described as follows:

The ideal computing machine must then have all its data inserted at the beginning, and must be as free as possible from human interference to the very end. This means that not only must the numerical data be inserted at the beginning, but also rules for combining them, in the form of instructions covering every situation which may arise in the course of computation.

The difficulty in realizing this ideal is found in the reference of the ". . . rules . . . covering every situation which may arise. . . ." Certainly one of the characteristics of executive operation which the advent of computers has brought sharply into focus, if any further emphasis was needed, is the difficulty in establishing the ground rules in almost any situation, not to speak of all possible situations. Even in such a practical field as accounting, which one would think consisted of algorithms for counting value (what could be easier for a computer?), the incompatibilities which may arise between the rules used within an enterprise, or between several branches of the same company, are well known (6). The situation is no different in areas involving the operation of a business in a competitive environment, or in a war game, or in SAGE.

The evolution of a set of rules is, however, only a prelude to translating them into a language which may be manipulated by the machine. The supposition that all such expressions can be represented by a sufficiently lengthy string of yes/no propositions avoids two rather practical considerations:

• We must formulate exactly the right questions.
• We must ask them in exactly the right order.

Those who have attempted to evolve such a sequence of questions will verify that it is not as easy as one would assume. In fact, many of the "technical difficulties" exposed in checking out a program stem from a wrong question erroneously asked at a certain point in a sequence, or perhaps for some reason, by an inability to ask the proper question at the required moment. This latter situation is sometimes referred to as a "control problem."

Perhaps the greatest difficulty comes from dealing with the inescapable "maybe's"; those circumstances which fall outside the bounds of the rules which have been provided, either through some error or unforeseen circumstance, or because no general rule covering the situation could be agreed upon. For these cases, the real time program may follow one of a number of courses:

- Stop.
- Resort to some arbitrary solution which has nothing to do with the problem at hand, e.g., throw away the data and start somewhere else.
- Utilize a general problem solving routine, particularly in the case of a routine data error.
- Let an operator intervene.

The existence of "maybe's" in any but the most abstract or restrictive systems would not seem to require much substantiation, nor would the assumption that the first three alternatives to a situation falling outside the explicit rules for decision have a limited application. In other words, for any system approaching the complexity of an executive data processor, the kind of system we have been referring to, the intervention of an operator will certainly be required somewhere along the line.

But we have only approached the real problem. It is not overly difficult to provide a negative sort of logic by which problems are routed to an operator: in other words, anything other than the situations bounded by certain rules will be so referred. Now, we must define the ways in which we will permit the operator to respond to the machine, and furthermore, the ways in which the machine will consider the operator's response. Some extreme examples follow:

- We may require the operator to insert his responses into the computer via punched cards, using some machine language.
- We may provide a unique mechanical switch action to cover each response which the operator may desire to make.
- We may require the computer to stop until the operator's response has been received.
- We may permit the computer to continue with other problems, but wait for a response in the troublesome area.

Note that the answers in *these* areas, and the compromises which will necessarily be made in each case must be *specified in advance*. Even though we have been able to refer the "maybe's" to an operator with relative freedom, he will be restricted in his ability to respond by the equipment at his disposal, and by the computer program, both of which have been defined to some degree arbitrarily in advance.

In an operating system such as SAGE, experience has shown that the continual iterative process of defining the allowable boundaries of interaction between the operator and the machine, in terms of equipment, programming, training, and of course monetary restrictions, is of the greatest importance and is responsible for a major share of the effort required to keep the system running from the point of view of both the designer and the operating personnel.

Some mention should be made of the compromises which have proved useful in defining these man/machine interactions. A number of typical SAGE approaches would include the following:

- The operator is provided with a series of category selection switches by which he may discriminate between standard displays available at his console position.
- Certain displays are forced to an operator's position for his attention.
- The operator may respond through several general alphanumeric push-button modules which have been tailored to his individual task.
- Some processes are initiated solely by an operator.
- In other cases, the program will hold a problem for the operator's response although the computer continues to function in other areas.
- For certain critical situations where a delay may be significantly harmful, the program will wait a pre-set time for an operator's response, and failing to receive an indication, assume a pre-programmed case and proceed.

These types of man/machine interaction are clearly applicable to business situations. Consider, for example, a hypothetical *Air Freight* enterprise whose operations are controlled from a computer facility located at the home office, and tied by leased digital data lines to district offices throughout the service area. An operator at the central office would require a computer-driven visual display capability, and several general purpose push-button modules. Given this equipment, several types of interaction are possible:

- Displays indicating the present position of all company aircraft might be always present. By depressing the proper combination of buttons, an operator may request summary informational displays on a particular aircraft, freight order, or district office.

- Displays pertaining to an incoming request for freight routing would be forced to an operator's console.
- The computer will continue to display a forced request for freight routing until acknowledged by the proper button response, although continuing to function in other areas.
- An operator may choose to take button actions causing the computer to calculate and display several alternative routings for a specific freight order, based on combinations of least cost and time criteria.
- Confirmation of a selected routing must be initiated by an operator's button action, although the computer will transmit the appropriate messages to the requesting district office.
- If a position report indicates that an aircraft has landed at a location not specified on the flight plan, a special display will be forced to an operator. The absence of a proper button acknowledgement within a pre-set time will cause the computer to automatically transmit alert messages to all district offices having freight on the aircraft involved.

Although some rather complex decision hierarchies have been based on similar categorizations of interaction, the *technology* of computer systems has certainly outrun an appreciation of the broader aspects and subtleties of the man/machine relationship and the nature of the intercommunication which is desirable (7). The many rather arbitrary solutions which have been found to work for a multitude of specialized problems should not obscure the great need for a more general understanding, which is yet to come.

But a more visionary aspect of executive control systems remains to be considered, particularly with regard to the increasing number of references in recent years to so-called "adaptive" machinery, "general problem solvers," and the like. Is it not conceivable that a machine with a degree of "intelligence" and a broader view of the problems at hand could, in fact, circumvent many of the difficulties suggested earlier by "learning" its way to a solution, no matter what the problem? We will dwell upon this question somewhat further.

ADAPTIVE AUTOMATA

Certainly the present emphasis on parallel operation, which is found in many of the newer computer systems, begins to suggest the presence of a higher type of organization. The executive routines which evaluate tasks and assign priorities not only within a machine, but often for several machines, and the increasing amount of direct intercommunication between computers of various types suggest in some sense the theory of von Neumann mentioned earlier (8) which proposes that out of a "pool" of elementary machines, computers of certain special kinds could assemble automata of arbitrary complexity. Some of the work in pattern recognition (9) and general problem solving (10) is also of great interest.

But all this does not seem to be enough, at least in the foreseeable future. One reason is that although the theory of communication provides a measure for the information content of a message, in the sense of its degree of organization, or unexpectedness, it does not follow that this criterion necessarily provides an indication of the relative importance of a message. In other words, the information of greatest importance does not have to be contained in the message occurring with the lowest frequency. A system could be flooded with messages with the highest degree of organization, all containing information which was irrelevant to the problem at hand.

This situation casts some doubt on our ability to select a valid live environment to which our machine may adapt. There is a great deal of difference between training a machine to recognize the shapes of certain letters, and teaching it to separate more meaningful information from a flood of available literature than can the machine designers themselves—although this too has been postulated (11).

One approach is to simulate the real world to some degree of exactitude, and then permit the machine to adapt itself to increasingly complex environments under controlled conditions. The sufficiency of approximation, that is, a determination of the order of simulation which should be considered, may itself be a limiting factor for certain systems which cannot easily be made to "fail safe." Two examples which come to mind are a discussion of a computing machine with appropriate sensors which would perform the duties of a surgeon (12); and the control systems which function in a wartime environment, such as

SAGE. In spite of the best of simulated exercises, some say the only way to really evaluate a military system against the improbabilities of war is—to have one, at which point some one will surely complain that the sample was insufficient.

There is a diminishing requirement for "selling" the efficacy of simulation. In general, any environment can be simulated to some extent, and quite likely, the model can be improved over a period of time. An urgent need is for the development of a theory dealing with the order of simulation which is sufficient for a particular problem, whether the model is to provide a classroom for an adaptive man or machine. The question to be answered is not "why," or even "how," but "how much."

The potentials of adaptive automata are certainly impressive, and have been well documented in a number of fields. The general understanding of the manner in which these systems are to be brought to reality is, once again, a question which is largely unanswered.

SUMMARY

Charles Pierce has said that we do not want a logical machine to do its own business, but ours. The realization of this aim has been the topic of this discussion. In particular, we have tried to relate the overall capabilities of a computerized real time executive control complex to some of the compromises which must be made if the system is to function in a live environment, and to do this from the point of view of the experience which has been acquired through the operation of a similar system, SAGE, over the past few years.

The exciting future which awaits these systems is not altered by emphasizing the practical considerations involved in their design. On the contrary, herein lies the foundation for any subsequent realization of the hopes and plans of our day.

REFERENCES

1. C. West Churchman, "How Is Planning Possible," *Operations Research for Management,* edited by McCloskey and Coppinger, Baltimore: Johns Hopkins Press, 1956.
2. Norbert Wiener, *Cybernetics,* New York: John Wiley & Sons, 1958; and *The Human Use of Human Beings: Cybernetics and Society,* Garden City, New York: Doubleday & Co., 1950.
3. John von Neumann, "The General and Logical Theory of Automata," *The World of Mathematics,* edited by James R. Newman, New York: Simon & Schuster, 1956. Also, *The Computer and the Brain,* New Haven: Yale University Press, 1958.
4. Franklin V. Taylor, "Four Basic Ideas in Engineering Psychology," *The American Psychologist,* Vol. 15, No. 10, October 1960.
5. *Cybernetics,* p. 139.
6. See T. A. Wise, "The Auditors Have Arrived," *Fortune Magazine,* Vol. 62, Nos. 5 and 6, November and December 1960.
7. Taylor.
8. von Neumann, "The General and Logical Theory of Automata."
9. Frank Rosenblatt, *The Perceptron: A Theory of Statistical Separability in Cognitive Systems.* Cornell Aeronautical Laboratory Report VG-1196-G-1, January 1958; ASTIA Document No. 204-076.
10. Allen Newell, J. C. Shaw, and Herbert Simon, "Elements of a Theory of Human Problem Solving," *Psychological Review,* Vol. 65, No. 3, 1958.
11. W. Ross Ashby, "Design for an Intelligence Amplifier," in *Automata Studies,* edited by C. E. Shannon and J. McCarthy, Princeton University Annals of Mathematics Series, No. 34, 1956.
12. S. Gill, "Possibilities for the Practical Utilization of Learning Processes," *Proceedings of the Symposium on the Mechanization of Thought Processes,* National Physical Laboratory, Vol. II, 1958.

25. RESEARCH PROBLEMS IN MANAGEMENT CONTROLS *

ALAN J. ROWE †

The purpose of this paper is to present a number of concepts pertaining to management controls and to discuss information requirements, decision rules and feedback mechanisms. The use of computer simulation as a means for studying the dynamic response characteristics of management controls in a business environment is also presented.

INTRODUCTION

The complex nature of modern day business gives rise to the need for effective means to study and design such systems. Since computer simulation has been applied to the problem of system design and study of management decision rules (1), it appears to be a suitable means for examining business system behavior and the associated management controls. In fact, the use of simulation to evaluate system designs has led to the term "policy laboratory" (2). Furthermore, the use of computer simulation will undoubtedly have profound effects on the design of real-time management control systems.

Managers are concerned with organizing the available resources subject to constraints such as capital structure, physical facilities and market position, to achieve purposeful objectives and assure survival of the business. In carrying out the control function, management uses an information and communication network which provides a direct link to persons concerned with utilization of the resources. Operating decisions, in turn, are based on information describing the status of the system as resources are used to produce goods and services. This information and the associated

SOURCE: *Management Technology* (December 1961), pp. 6–15. Reprinted by permission of the Institute of Management Science.

* A paper prepared in October 1960 at the Systems Development Corporation and received for publication in March 1961.

† Professor of Quantitative Business Analysis, University of Southern California.

decision rules are seldom made explicit in an actual business; nonetheless, the informational aspects of the management control problem should be amenable to study via computer simulation.

DEFINING MANAGEMENT CONTROLS

In current business systems, measurement is often mistaken for management control. Although measurement is implied, control includes objectives, decision criteria for evaluation of performance, decision rules for corrective action and, of course, suitable measures of performance. To clarify the definition, we might consider the problem from the point of view of three separate systems: the data processing system, the management information system, and the management control system. These are shown in Figure 1.

Data processing is generally considered as carrying out the activities shown at the second level; whereas a management information system includes levels 1, 2 and 3. However, a management control system implies that all four levels are included. This manner of structuring the problem is similar to the familiar servomechanism feedback loop; however, in a business system we are dealing with a man-machine system, and, as yet, mathematical transfer functions have not been developed to describe human decision-making behavior. Thus, servo theory is not sufficient as the basis for the design of a complex man-machine system, although some progress has been made in dealing with specific physical responses (3).

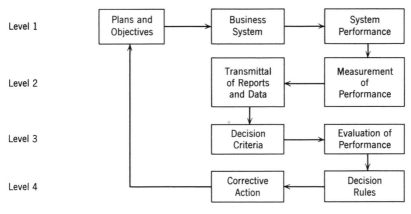

FIG. 1.

DESCRIBING A BUSINESS SYSTEM

A business consists of numerous activities such as sales, design, fabrication, etc., which, in effect, define its capabilities. However, the effectiveness with which these activities are executed depends to a considerable extent on the human organization charged with these responsibilities and their knowledge of the interactions among the system activities. A study of management controls should therefore explicitly consider these interactions.

One manner of characterizing a business system is as a matrix of activities and responses, as shown in Figure 2.

The elements of this matrix define the relationship between system activities and the decision rules which determine system responses. For example, element a_{11} is the budget allocation rule that determines the system response to sales requirements. The element a_{ij} refers to the delays incurred during the manufacturing process as a result of using

priority decision rules to choose work from queues at machines. The element a_{mn} defines the manner in which information is used to achieve system control. Obviously, there would be many elements required for this latter activity in describing an actual business.

INTERACTION OF CONTROL AND SYSTEM BEHAVIOR

The behavior of a complex business system can be described in terms of the basic business phenomena and the decisions made by managers. In order to simulate a business, however, it is necessary to formalize the decision rules used by management and to use transfer functions that describe the basic phenomena. The simulated system behavior is a combination of both factors and can be viewed as in Figure 3. Thus, changes in system behavior may be due to modification of the basic structure or simply to the interaction of the phenomena with control decision rules.

In a computer model, information is generated whenever the simulated physical system changes from one state or condition to another.

	System Responses			
Activity	Allocate Funds	Assign Personnel	Incur Delays	Generate Information
Sales	a_{11}	a_{12}		a_{lm}
Engineering	a_{21}			
Manufacturing			a_{ij}	
Planning				
Control				a_{mn}

FIG. 2.

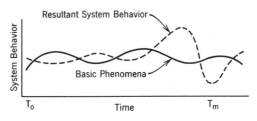

FIG. 3.

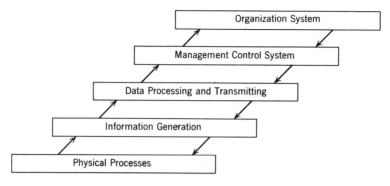

FIG. 4.

This is shown schematically [1] in Figure 4. This information is selectively updated and made available to the management control system which uses various decision criteria and decision rules to change or correct the state of the physical system. A number of these decisions may, however, be dependent upon the organizational level. Thus, tactical or operational decisions are made in the control system, whereas strategic or long-range decisions are generally made at the organizational system level (4).

THE CONTROL FUNCTION

For purposes of this paper, control is directly related to the decisions made in the system. If we examine the typical decisions made in a business, we find that there are decisions (such as budgeting) which affect the entire system; and other decisions that do not have an appreciable effect on the entire system. The former decisions are generally long range; whereas the latter tend to be operational in nature. However, the majority of decisions directly affect a number of other system activities. Because of interdependencies, these decisions are difficult to formulate explicitly. Thus, one of the major advantages of computer simulation is that the dependent relationships can be generated by continuous updating of interacting variables in the system.

Turning to the question of control itself, it should be capable of assuring the following system response characteristics.

• Adapting the system to changing conditions

[1] The manner of viewing the problem resulted from a discussion with Professor Daniel Teichroew of Stanford University.

• Stabilizing system response under variable demand

• Allowing maximum effectiveness of the system rather than imposing restrictive limits

• Providing a minimum time lag in correcting deviation in performance commensurate with the desired objective

• Implementing real-time control

The possibility of achieving real-time control appears very likely in view of the capability of computers to rapidly process data. However, the review frequency in real-time control systems should be matched with the response capability of the system. For example, if corrective action requires a minimum of one day, a review frequency of once a minute would be unreasonable. Since business systems often have long delays between measurement and corrective action, the significance of real-time control may differ radically from that used in military control systems.

In business, there are many interacting subsystems, and response depends on factors such as the status of subsystems, speed and amount of their changes and time dependencies. The time dependencies are important in the design of error correcting controls, as shown, for example, in Figure 5.

where t_0 = time that error of forecast is observed

t_r = time that error of forecast is reported

t_m = minimum time after t_r that the system can respond to a given correction

$p = t_m - t_r$ = minimum response period

The response period p is dependent both on the magnitude and the rate of change re-

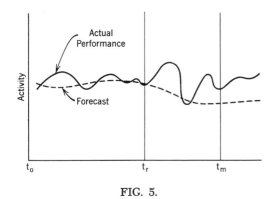

FIG. 5.

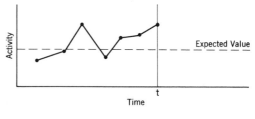

FIG. 6.

quired. Where the response period has to be made extremely short, as in military control systems, computer-based controls are often the only solution. Short response periods, however, are generally prohibitive for business systems due to cost and the design requirements. The cost of control is often overlooked; however, it is a significant factor and should be balanced with operating efficiency in the control system.

Another consideration in the design of control systems is the accuracy of error sensing techniques. Where there is loose coupling between system response and the forecast, extreme accuracy is unnecessary. However, where accuracy is required and the demand is a time series, the forecast can be improved by considering the current state of the system as the base point for predicting future demand. This is based on the assumption that the system is in a state of activity at time t and that the best estimate of the state at the time $t+1$ can be obtained by a form of exponential smoothing using both past history and anticipated events (see Figure 6).

A first attempt at explicit formulation is the following:

$$S_{i+1} = aS_{i-n} + (1-a)S_i + bE + (1-b)F,$$

where S_{i+1} = forecast state of the system for time $t+1$

S_i = present state of the system

S_{i-n} = past history of the system

a = a smoothing constant, which could be made a function of the variance of system activity

b = a smoothing constant such that the ratio a/b is made a function of time and error of forecast

E = environmental factors such as condition of the economy, etc.

F = forcing functions used by the business such as advertising, etc.

Although this formulation may lead to improved forecasts, the manner of responding to forecast is still not completely solved. A paper has been written which considers the problem of changing production and inventory levels in response to forecast demand (5). However, such decisions, like many in a business, interact with other system activities. Where there is a significant interaction, the decision rules controlling system response should take this into account.

Another consideration in the question of accuracy of forecast is the response mechanism. Since business is stochastic in nature, the error correction should hold performance within a specified band rather than directed toward an exact objective. In addition, the correction can be made as shown in Figure 7. First a large correction (from A to B) is made, and then only minor adjustments are made within the variance band, which is similar to the quality control technique.

Decision rules used as control mechanisms can affect performance by inducing fluctuations in an otherwise stable system. For example, consider a classical inventory problem, where the usage rate is constant and the replenish-

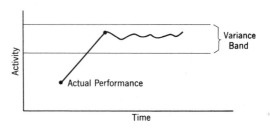

FIG. 7.

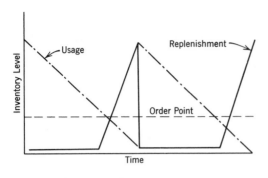

FIG. 8.

ment rate has a lag imposed by a reorder point rule as shown in Figure 8. The decision rule which leads to periodic replenishment will cause fluctuations in employment if the plant is producing a single product. Thus, labor productivity would follow the replenishment curve despite constant demand.

Often, due to considerations such as the physical processing, production cannot match consumption. A better understanding of the interaction of decision rules and physical processes is a prerequisite to the design of effective management control systems.

CONTROL SYSTEM DESIGN CONSIDERATIONS

The design of management control systems should take both variability of system performance and response characteristics into account. We can anticipate that the control would change radically for different types of business, if the variability of performance is assumed to increase as a function of the complexity of the business. Variability in the system is a measure of the error in predicting performance. Furthermore, it is assumed that the quantity of information required for control varies inversely with the stability of the system. Thus, a system which exhibits considerable variability would require a larger amount of information to maintain a given level of control. Of course, it is assumed that variability is caused by underlying phenomena rather than induced fluctuations resulting from the control system employed.

Since complex business systems will probably require large amounts of information for control purposes, the use of computer-based controls appears likely. However, the specific control system design is still subject to further

research. An example of the use of computers for R&D control is the PERT (6) technique. This technique is used to schedule the vast interconnected number of components for the Polaris missile. Although the PERT system was initially designed for control of the many contractors working in the Polaris program, it is now being applied to the internal operations of a single business. This is but one of a class of computer-based control systems for use in business.

A significant design principle of real-time control through continuous monitoring has been demonstrated by computer-based control systems. Stated another way, the computer now provides the capability of continuously updating critical systems variables. In the PERT system, this would be the minimum slack path, while for other applications it can be extended to include a number of critical variables. If the variables are ranked in the order of their impact on the system, we can anticipate the curve shown in Figure 9.

Thus, a computer-based management control system could continuously monitor variables 1 through m which have the major impact on the system. The variables m through n could then be treated by exception reporting or other techniques. One means of determining which are the critical variables is by the use of computer simulation. Furthermore, since the variables which have a major impact could be continuously monitored in an actual business, this should lead to improved system control.

Another problem is that of local vs. total system control. Stated another way, the question is, what is the optimum combination of subsystem controls where there is interdependence? One approach to this problem which may be suitable is the joint optimization

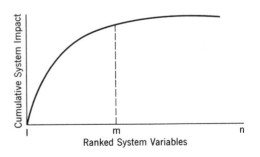

FIG. 9.

proposed by Markowitz in his book on port-folio selection (7). This approach uses quadratic programming to find the optimum which is defined in terms of expected values, variance and co-variance estimates.

Thus, the control system can be designed to achieve a given expected value with an associated risk. Since survival of the enterprise is an important management objective, this manner of formulating the problem of joint optimization should be useful in the control system design.

An integral part of any control system design is the measurement of performance. Not only must there be suitable measures, but these should be a function of the level of management. Since top management is primarily concerned with long-range decisions, there is loose coupling with the actual business processes. Thus, the amount of aggregation and frequency of information transmission should be appropriately designed into the measurement system. Rather than continuous reporting of system status to top management, periodic reports are generally sufficient. However, a computer-based system would provide the capability of random access to updated information on detail system status as the need arose. In this sense, then, top management would have real-time control.

A related problem to reporting of system status is the communication network in an organization. In current management control systems, measurement of performance is reported successively upward in an organization and is aggregated at each level. For example, consider the flow as shown in Figure 10. Each level summarizes performance and reports it to the next higher echelon, until the information reaches the top. At each level, summarization and biasing occurs. Although the levels

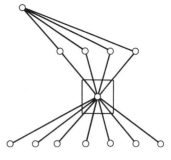

FIG. 11.

act as filters in one sense, they can also introduce distortion in another sense. Furthermore, at no time does anyone but the top executive level have access to all of the information in the system. Contrast this with the concept of a system staff reporting to the top executive which acts as the summarizing medium using the computer for rapid, random access to detail system information. This would appear as in Figure 11.

In this kind of application the computer would have direct access to all system information and have as much as 30% reported automatically. Not only is the information on system performance more timely and accurate, but the system staff as a team has an overview of the entire operation. Thus, we can anticipate that the organization design in computer-based control systems will be more closely matched with the information requirements of the system.

In a like manner, the design of the decision network poses a number of formidable problems. Current organizations lead to a cascading effect of decisions as a result of interpretation at each level and generally differing measures of performance. In addition to the cascade effect among levels, there are the conflicting objectives at any given level. Thus, there is a need for a design mechanism which treats the problem as a whole rather than the fragmented approach prevalent in industry today.

One attack on the problem which may prove worthwhile is the use of a decision matrix and mathematical operators to generate solutions. That is, rather than enumerate all possible combinations of a given set of decisions and system variables, heuristic rules can be used to select good solutions. Consider the following example:

There are four kinds of information, I_1 to

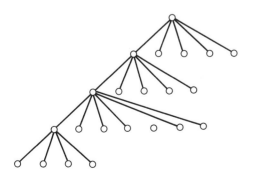

FIG. 10.

	D_1	D_2	D_3
I_1	e_{11}		
I_2	e_{12}		e_{23}
I_3		e_{32}	
I_4			e_{43}

FIG. 12.

I_4 which are used to make decisions D_1 to D_3 as shown in Figure 12. The number of possible combinations is $2^n - 1$, which equals 4095. If a particular combination of decisions and information is required to execute a given activity, then a rule can be used to choose from the twelve elements in the matrix to arrive at the solution. For instance, a rule might appear as follows:

Given conditions XYZ, use e_{11} and e_{12} for D_1, e_{32} for D_2 and e_{23} and e_{43} for D_3, where the D's themselves may be complex functions.

Thus, the rule chooses a particular combination based on a set of conditions XYZ. This decision matrix approach is similar to the associative lists of Simon and Newell.

There are obviously many additional design problems which must be studied in management control systems. To experiment with these problems, however, it is necessary to have a suitable laboratory. Although there are some severe limitations to computer simulation, especially in regard to studying human behavior, nonetheless there are many facets of the control problem which can be profitably examined. Hopefully, as there is a better understanding of basic system phenomena, the design process itself will reach the point where management controls are no longer based on judgment alone.

CONCLUSION

Although this paper has undoubtedly raised many more questions than have been an-

swered, the intent was to explore the problems associated with the study and design of management control. Since research is enhanced by experimentations, computer simulation has been proposed as the vehicle. A model of a business system (8) is now being programmed at the System Development Corporation (9) which should provide the means for studying many of the problems and questions raised in this paper. It is hoped that useful knowledge will be forthcoming from this effort in the attempt to design effective management controls.

REFERENCES

1. A. J. Rowe. "Application of Computer Simulation to Production System Design," SP-85. System Development Corporation, September 14, 1959.
2. D. G. Malcolm and A. J. Rowe. "An Approach to Computer-Based Management Control Systems," SP-145. System Development Corporation, August 3, 1960.
3. P. M. Fitts. "Engineering Psychology and Equipment Design," in S. S. Stevens (ed.), Handbook of Experimental Psychology, New York: John Wiley and Sons, 1951, Ch. 35.
4. A. J. Rowe. "Modeling Considerations in Computer Simulation of Management Control Systems," SP-156. System Development Corporation, March 3, 1960.
5. C. C. Holt, F. Modigliani, and H. A. Simon. "Linear Decision Rule for Production and Employment Scheduling." Management Science, Vol. 2, No. 1, October 1955.
6. D. G. Malcolm, J. H. Roseboom, C. E. Clark, and W. Fazar. "Application of a Technique for Research and Development Program Evaluation," SP-62. System Development Corporation, March 1959.
7. H. M. Markowitz. Portfolio Selection. New York: John Wiley and Sons, 1959.
8. R. C. Crawford, et al. "Simulation of a Firm: The Mark I Model," TM-528. System Development Corporation.
9. J. B. Heyne. "Mark I Operational Specifications," TM-536. System Development Corporation, September 23, 1960.

26. INDUSTRIAL DYNAMICS AND
THE DESIGN OF MANAGEMENT
CONTROL SYSTEMS

Edward B. Roberts *

The usual approaches to management control system design often fail to be effective, sometimes creating problems more significant than those they resolve. Such failures result from lack of total system understanding, from use of subsystem constraints, and from inadequate or improper treatment of the human decision-making elements of the system. Examples drawn from Industrial Dynamics research studies illustrate these problems and provide some pointers for remedying the difficulties.

THE ORGANIZATION AS A CONTROL SYSTEM

Every organization is a control system. Each has direction and objectives, whether explicit or implied. Each has beliefs as to its current status. Each has policies and procedures whereby it reaches decisions and takes actions to attain its goals more closely. Every organization actually contains a myriad of smaller control systems, each characterized by the same goal-striving, but not necessarily goal-attaining, behavior.

The organization as a whole or any one of its component subsystems can be represented by the feedback process shown in Figure 1. Four characteristics of this diagram are noteworthy. First, the transformation of decisions into results takes place through a complex process which includes a basic structure of or-

SOURCE: This article is based on studies supported by grants of the Ford Foundation and the National Aeronautics and Space Administration. The computer simulations were carried out at the M.I.T. Computation Center. The paper was presented at the Stanford University Seminar on Basic Research in Management Controls, February 20, 1963. The writer is grateful to Professors Donald C. Carroll, Jay W. Forrester, and Donald G. Marquis for their many helpful comments.

* School of Industrial Management, Massachusetts Institute of Technology.

ganizational, human, and market relationships; this structure is sometimes not apparent because of its numerous sources of noise or random behavior and due to its often lengthy time delays between cause and effect.

The second aspect to be noted is the distinction between the achievements that are apparent in the organization and those which are real. The real situation is translated into the apparent through information and communication channels which contain delays, noise, and bias. These sources of error may be the inadvertent features of an organization's communication system, or they may result from the chosen characteristics of a data-processing system which sacrifices accuracy for compactness. In any event, however, the bases of actual decisions in an organization may be assumptions which bear but little relation to fact.

The third feature of the diagram is that the decision-making process is viewed as a response to the gap between objectives of the organization and its apparent progress toward those objectives. Although both the objectives and achievements may be difficult to define precisely and measure accurately, such a goal-seeking behavior is nonetheless present in all organizations and in every subsystem of the organizations. At any level of an organization, many similar decisions are being made. The real problem of the management control sys-

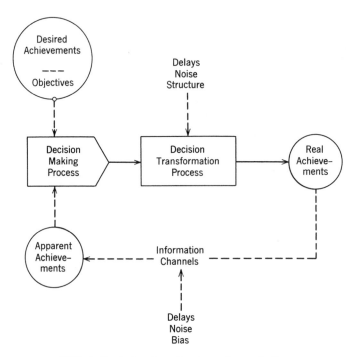

FIG. 1. Control system structure of organization.

tem designer is to recognize these multiple decision loops and their interrelationships, and to develop policies and an organizational structure that will tie these activities into progress toward total organization objectives.

The fourth characteristic of Figure 1 is the continuous feedback path of decision-results-measurement-evaluation-decision. It is vital to effective system design that each element of this feedback path be properly treated and that its continuous nature be recognized. Whether the decision in the system is made by the irrational actions or logical deductions of a manager or by the programmed response of a computer, the system consequences will eventually have further effects on the decision itself.

INDUSTRIAL DYNAMICS—PHILOSOPHY AND METHODOLOGY FOR CONTROL SYSTEM DESIGN

Industrial Dynamics is a philosophy which asserts that organizations are most effectively viewed (and managed) from this control system perspective. It is also a methodology for designing organizational policy. This two-pronged approach is the result of a research program that was initiated and directed at the M.I.T. School of Industrial Management by Professor Jay W. Forrester. The results of the first five years of this program are described in Professor Forrester's book, *Industrial Dynamics*, which also discusses a variety of potential applications to key management problems.[1]

Industrial Dynamics recognizes a common systems base in the flow structure of all social-economic-industrial-political organizations. This perspective ties the segmented functional aspects of formal organizations into an integrated structure of varying rates of flow and responsively changing levels of accumulation. The flow paths involve all facets of organizational resources—men, money, materials, orders, and capital equipment—and the information and decision-making network that links the other flows.

Industrial Dynamics views decisions as the controllers of these organization flows. Such decisions regulate the rate of change of levels from which the flows originate and to which they are sent. In the flow diagrams drawn as part of an Industrial Dynamics study, decisions are even represented by the traditional con-

[1] Jay W. Forrester, *Industrial Dynamics* (Cambridge: The M.I.T. Press, 1961).

trol valve symbol of the engineer. Figure 2 shows such a decision, based in part on information about the contents of the source level, controlling the rate of flow to the destination level.

The system structures and behavioral phenomena that are studied by the Industrial Dynamics methodology are present at all levels of the corporation. The top management of the firm is involved in a system that can be studied and aided in the same manner as the middle management of the organization, and again in the same fashion as the physical operating system of the plant. The potential payoff from changes derived from system studies increases greatly, however, as the study is focused higher up in the organization. For all studies the pattern of forming a dynamic verbal theory, developing mathematical equations, computer simulation of the model, and derivation of improved policies is followed. The problems encountered in these phases do not significantly change as we move from the bottom to the top of an organization. Only during the final stage of implementation of system change does the problem complexity get significantly greater the higher the level of organization involved. But the impact of improved corporate-level policy on company growth, stability, and profitability can readily justify this added effort to renovate top management policy making.

PROBLEMS OF MANAGEMENT CONTROL SYSTEMS

The preceding discussion has focused on the nature of organizational problems as management control system problems, and on the intended applicability of Industrial Dynamics to these problems. Observation of several different types of management control systems and a survey of the literature in this field lead to a belief that a new attack on control system design is needed. The traditional approaches to management control systems have mushroomed in number and sophistication of applications as operations research and electronic data processing have developed during the post-war era. Although these systems have made significant and successful inroads, many fail to cure the problems for which they were designed; other management control systems even amplify the initial difficulties or create more significant new problems. All this is tak-

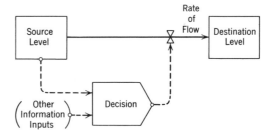

FIG. 2. The decision as a controller.

ing place even as we derive enhanced but misplaced confidence in the systems.

Several examples will help to illustrate these problems and lead us to some findings about the design of management control systems.

Systems Inadequate for Their Problems

Sometimes the management control system is inadequately designed for the problem situation. In such a case the control system may improve performance in the trouble area, but be far short of the potential gains. At times the limited effectiveness may transform a potentially major benefit to the company into but a marginal application.

The Control of Research and Development Projects

One example of an area in which the traditional approach to control system design has proven inadequate is the management of research and development projects. The intangibility, lack of precise measurements, and uncertain character of R and D results are partly responsible for this failure. But a more basic lack of system understanding has implications of even greater significance. All systems of schedule and/or budget controls that have been tried till now have failed to achieve success in R and D usage. These techniques have included Gantt charts, milestone schedules, and computerized systems of budgetary and manpower control.

The latest approaches to control of research and development projects are based on PERT (Program Evaluation Review Technique) or PERT/COST. The management control systems implied by the methods used can be represented by the diagram of Figure 3. As shown here, the basis of the current sophisticated methods is a single-loop system in which

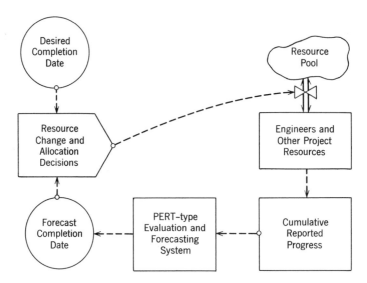

FIG. 3. Assumed basis of current R and D project controls.

the difference between desired completion date and forecast completion date causes decisions to change the magnitude or allocation of project resources (manpower, facilities, equipment, priorities). As these resources are employed, they are assumed to produce the progress that is reported during the project. These reports are processed through a PERT-type evaluation and forecasting system to create the forecast completion time.

But the design of a management control system based on such a set of assumptions is doomed to failure, since some of the most vital aspects of the real system have been excluded from the underlying analysis. For example, the lack of tangible, precise measurement sources is entirely ignored. Yet these factors contribute much of the error between the *real* situation in the project (its true scope and actual progress to date) and that which is *apparent* to those doing the engineering work.

Another part of the real system which appears to be ignored by current R and D control system designers is the human element in the project actions and decisions. The attitudes and motivations of the engineers and managers, their knowledge of the schedules and current estimates in the project, the believed penalty-reward structure of the organization—all affect the progress and problems that are reported upward in the organization. Furthermore, these same factors even affect the rate of real progress toward project objectives. All systems of measurement and evalua-

tion (in R and D, manufacturing, government, universities, or what-have-you) create incentives and pressures for certain actions. These interact with the goals and character of individuals and institutions to produce decisions, actions, and their results. For example, a system which compares "actual to budgeted expenditures" creates an incentive to increase budgets, regardless of progress; one which checks "proportion of budget spent" creates pressures on the manager or engineer to be sure he spends the money, whether or not on something useful. The presence of such factors in research and development ought to be recognized in the design of systems for R and D control.

Adding these two additional sources of system behavior to the earlier diagram produces the more complete representation of a research and development system that is pictured in Figure 4. But even this is an incomplete representation of the complex system which interrelates the characteristics of the product, the customer, and the R and D organization. A proper characterization of research and development projects must take into account the continuous dynamic system of activities that creates project life cycles. Such a system will include not just the schedule and accumulated effort, costs, and accomplishments. Rather, it will encompass the full range of policies and parameters that carry a research and development project from initial perception of potential need for the product to final

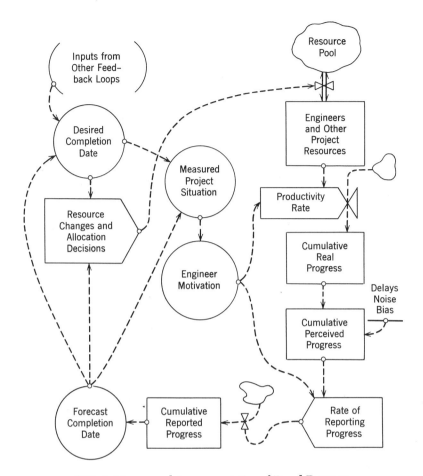

FIG. 4. More complete representation of R and D system.

completion of the development program. The fundamental R and D project system is shown in Figure 5, from which we have developed an Industrial Dynamics model of research and development project dynamics.

Some of the results of simulation studies of this model are of particular interest to designers of management control systems. They demonstrate the importance of taking cognizance of the complete system structure in at-

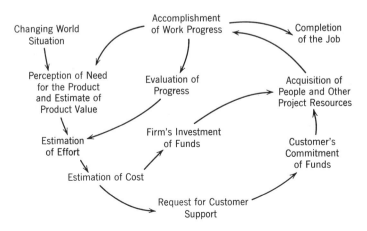

FIG. 5. Dynamic system underlying R and D projects.

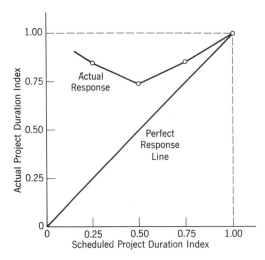

FIG. 6. Scheduled versus actual project durations.

tempting to create and implement methods of system control. For example, one series of simulations of the general project model was conducted in which only the scheduled project duration was changed in the various runs. Within the model the effort allocation process *attempts* to complete the project during this scheduled period. However, the actual completion dates of the projects seem only remotely responsive to the changes in desired completion time.

Figure 6 demonstrates the nature of this response, using the outputs of four model simulations. The horizontal axis is an index of the scheduled project duration as a percentage of the maximum schedule used; the vertical axis shows actual completion time in a similar percentile manner. If changes in schedule produced corresponding changes in actual completion dates, the curve of results would have followed the diagonal "perfect response" line; that is, a 50 percent reduction in scheduled duration should produce a 50 percent reduction in actual duration, if control is *perfect*. But the actual response is far from perfect; a 50 percent schedule change effects only a 25 percent actual change. And at the extreme, the actual change is even in the opposite direction, taking longer to complete the urgent crash project because of the resulting organizational confusion and inefficiencies. Of course, this response curve does not present the simulation data on the manpower instability, total project cost, and customer satis-

faction changes that also accompany shifts in the project schedule.

Some of the implications of Figure 6 are more clearly presented in the next curve. Here the slippage in project schedule is plotted as a function of the scheduled duration, the points on the curve coming from the project model simulations. A completion time slippage of 242 percent of schedule was incurred in the crash project, with a rapid decrease in this percentage completion date overrun as the schedule is dragged out. When the project is slowed too much, the slippage increases again as lack of enthusiasm induces further stretch-out during the project life.

The principal point made by these two illustrations is that many factors other than desired schedule determine the resultant actual schedule of research and development projects. *Control systems for R and D which resort to schedule and effort rate control without full understanding of the system structure of projects are bound to be ineffective.* The current PERT-based project control systems seem guilty of this error in design philosophy. In fact, many aspects of our government contracting program suffer similar faults of inadequate system understanding, producing ill-conceived policies with attendant poor results. For example, increased risk-taking (i.e., greater willingness to invest company funds prior to contract receipt) and higher bidding integrity by R and D companies would act in the best interest of the government customer of research and development. However, our simulation studies show that neither policy is in the short-term best interests of the R and D companies, under existing government regulations and practices. Thus the contracting policies, a

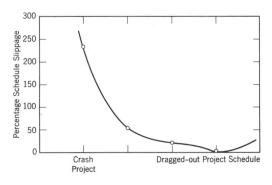

FIG. 7. Schedule slippage as a function of schedule.

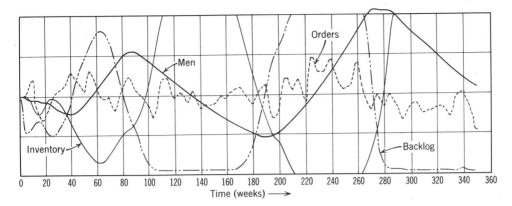

FIG. 8. Management by crisis.

government control system for R and D procurement, act to the detriment of national objectives by inducing company behavior which produces unsatisfactory project outcomes.[2]

The proper design of research and development control systems, for both company and customer, should take into account three things: (1) the source of internal action, information, and control in a project is the individual engineer; measurement and evaluation schemes and the internal penalty-reward structure must be designed with him in mind; (2) the total results of research and development projects are created by a complex dynamic system of activities, which interrelates the characteristics of the product, the customer, and the R and D firm; control systems which ignore vital aspects of these flows cannot succeed; (3) institutional objectives of R and D companies (profits, growth, stability) can be aligned with the objectives of government customers; procurement policies constitute the system of control which can effect or destroy this alignment.

A Production-Inventory-Employment Control System

As another example, let us take the case of an industrial components manufacturer who

[2] A general theory of research and development project behavior, a model of the theory, and extensive simulation studies of parameters and policies influencing R and D outcomes are reported in the author's book, *The Dynamics of Research and Development* (New York: Harper and Row, 1964).

initially has no formal production-inventory-employment control systems. Such a firm operates by its response to current problems. It follows the example of the firemen trying to use a leaky hose—as soon as one hole is patched up, another leak occurs elsewhere. A company operating in this manner does not keep sufficiently close tabs on changes in sales, inventories, backlogs, delivery delays, etc. Rather, when customer complaints build up on company delivery performance, people will be hired to increase production rate and repair the inventory position. Similarly, when a periodic financial report (or the warehouse manager's difficulties) shows a great excess in inventory, workers will be laid off to reduce the inventory position. Despite the obvious faults, the majority of our manufacturing firms have these problems. The dynamic behavior of such a firm (as here illustrated by simulation results of an Industrial Dynamics model) has the appearance of Figure 8, with wide swings in sales, inventories, employment, order backlog, and correspondingly in profitability. The potential for a well-designed management control system in such a firm is enormous.

The traditional approach (some may prefer calling it the "modern approach") to the design of a control system for such an organization will recognize that: (1) better information on sales is necessary; (2) such information should properly be smoothed to eliminate possibilities of factory response to chance order-rate variations; (3) inventories should be periodically (perhaps even continuously) checked, and reorders generated when needed to bring stocks into line with target inventories; (4) order backlogs should not be allowed to drift

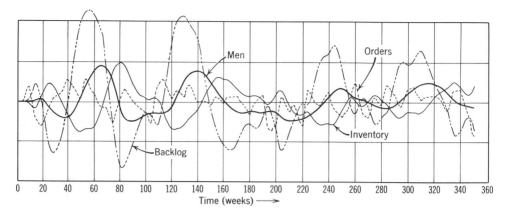

FIG. 9. Effects of management control systems.

too far from the normal levels; and (5) work force should be adjusted to meet the desired production rate that stems from consideration of current sales volume and the manufacturing backlog situation. Using our earlier company model, we can readily build into the model a management control system that incorporates all these features. The modeled company would then be a leader in its use of management control techniques. And, as Figure 9 illustrates, the company would have benefited by this approach. With the new control systems installed, fluctuations in the business have in general been reduced in magnitude as well as periodicity. Yet the basic dynamic pattern observed in the earlier diagram is still present—periodic fluctuations in sales, larger ones in inventories, and corresponding variations in production rate and work force. The latter situation is similar in character to that which we encountered at the Sprague Electric Company, at the beginning of our Industrial Dynamics study program with them several years ago.

Let us briefly review their case. The Sprague Electric Company is a major producer of electrical components, with an annual sales volume of approximately 75 million dollars. The particular product line which was selected for Industrial Dynamics research is a relatively mature industrial component, developed by Sprague several years ago and now past its market introduction and major growth phases. The principal customers of the product are manufacturers of military and high-grade consumer electronic systems. The industry competition is not price-based, but is rather dependent on product reliability and delivery time.

The work structure of the company, including its inventory and manufacturing control aspects, is diagrammed in Figure 10. Orders arrive from the customers, and a determination is made as to whether or not they can be filled from existing inventories. Orders for those catalogue items not ordinarily stocked, or for those which are currently out of stock, enter into the backlog of manufacturing orders. The customer orders for which inventory is in stock are processed and shipped from inventory.

The inventory control system of the company attempts to maintain a proper inventory position for the product line. Target inventories are adjusted to take into account average sales, and inventory reorders are generated to reflect the shipping rate from inventory and the desired inventory corrections. The orders for inventory replacements enter into the manufacturing backlog.

Production rate in the company is determined by the level of employment, with manufacturing output being sent to the customers or to inventory in reflection of the relative production order backlogs. Control of both backlog size and employment level is attempted by means of the employment change decision of the company.

As the curves of Figure 9 demonstrated, inventory, backlog, and employment all had sizable fluctuations, despite the existing controls in these areas. They seem to reflect, with some amplification, the variability in incoming orders. Given this situation of fluctuating sales, the traditional management control designer would either express satisfaction with the system performance or perhaps seek additional improvement by parameter adjustment. Neither approach would get at the source of the difficulties, and this source is not the fluctuations in incoming customer orders.

To determine the real system problem, let us examine our next diagram (Figure 11). Here we have duplicated the manufacturer's organization of Figure 10 and added a representation of the customer sector of the industry. The customers receive orders for military and commercial electronic systems. These are processed through the engineering departments, resulting in requirements for components. Customer orders for components are prepared and released as demanded by the delivery lead time of the component manufacturers. Delivered components enter into the system manufacturers' component inventories and are used up during production of the systems.

Having added this sector to our diagram, we now discover the presence of another feedback loop in the total company-customer system: changes in the company delivery delay will affect the customer release rate of new

orders, which in turn will influence the company delivery delay. This loop amplifies the system problems of the company, being able to transform slight variations in system orders into sustained oscillations in company order rate, producing related fluctuations in company inventories, backlog, employment, and profits.

Let us follow through a possible dynamic sequence that will illustrate the full system interactions. If, for any reason, system orders received by the customers temporarily increase, the customers will soon pass this along to the component supplier as an order increase. Since, even under ordinary circumstances, weekly fluctuations in order rate to the component manufacturer are sizable, some time will elapse before this order rate change is noticed. In the meantime, the component manufacturer's inventory will be somewhat reduced, and the order backlog will be increased. Both of these changes tend to increase the delivery delay. The smaller inventory allows fewer incoming orders to be filled immediately; the larger backlog causes a longer delay for the now increased fraction of orders that must await manufacture. As the customers become aware of the longer lead time, they begin to order

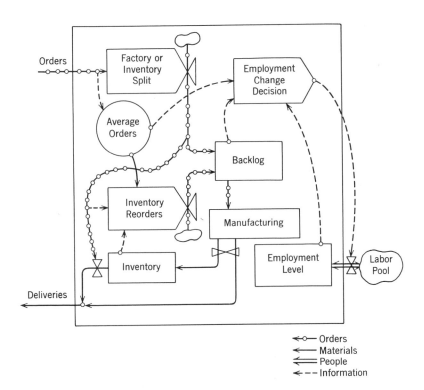

FIG. 10. The manufacturer's organization structure.

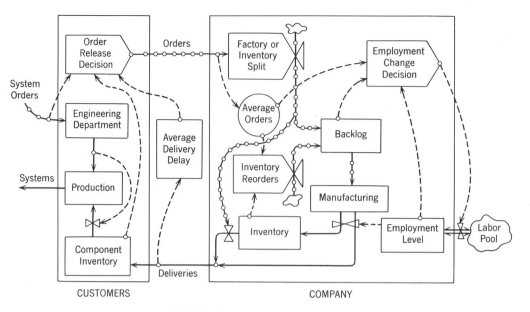

FIG. 11. Company-customers systems.

further ahead, thus maintaining a higher order rate and accentuating the previous trend in sales.

Eventually, the component manufacturer notes the higher sales, larger backlog, and lower inventory, and begins hiring to increase his factory employment. The employment level is set higher than that needed to handle the current customer order rate, so that backlog and inventory can be brought into line. As the increased work force has its gradual effect on inventory and backlog, the changes tend to reduce the delivery time. The information is gradually fed back to the customers, lowering the order rate even below the initial value. This set of system interactions can produce order rate fluctuations unrelated to the basic demand pattern for the customer products.

To dampen the fluctuations in customer order rate, the component manufacturer must control not inventory or backlog or employment, but rather he must stabilize the factory lead time for deliveries. This can readily be accomplished once the nature of the need is recognized. System behavior can also be improved to a great extent when the component manufacturer becomes aware that his inventory control system does not really control inventory, but it does contribute to production overshoots of any change in orders received.

The details of the Sprague case, the model for its study, and the new policies now being

implemented at Sprague are discussed fully in Chapters 17 and 18 of *Industrial Dynamics*. It is sufficient for our purposes to show the effects of the new policies applied to the same situation shown earlier in Figure 9. The curves shown on the next graph (Figure 12) demonstrate a higher degree of stability achieved in all variables except inventory, which is now being used to absorb random changes in sales. In particular, the enployment swings have been dampened significantly. The simulation results forecast significant benefits to the company deriving from the application of this new approach to management policy design. Our experiences during the past year of system usage at Sprague seem to support the initial hypotheses, and the product line is currently benefiting from higher productivity, improved employment stability, higher and smoother sales, and lower inventories.

SYSTEMS CREATING NEW MANAGEMENT PROBLEMS

The two control system areas discussed above were intended to demonstrate that many management control systems are designed in a manner that makes them inadequate to cope with the underlying problems. In each example, however, certain aspects of the systems were described which actually aggravated the existing problems. Our discussion of research and

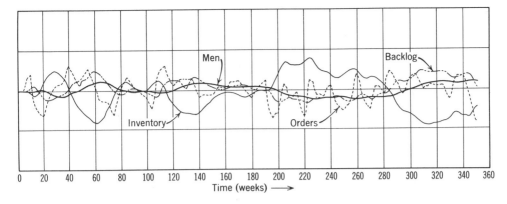

FIG. 12. Effects of industrial dynamics policies.

development project control indicated that government contracting policies often create resulting behavior that is contrary to the government's own interests. In the Sprague case, the inventory control system amplified sales changes to create wider swings in production and employment than actually existed in orders received from the customers. Other examples can be presented which have similar effects: the attempt to achieve management control leads to situations in which initial difficulties are amplified or significant new problems are created.

Problems of Logistics Control

One apparent instance of this type occurs in the Air Force Hi-Value Logistic System. This inventory control system was developed over a long period of time at great government expense by some of the nation's most sophisticated control system designers. The Hi-Value System is intended to provide conservative initial procurement and meticulous individual item management during the complete logistic cycle of all high-cost Air Force material. Yet an Industrial Dynamics study of this system by a member of the M.I.T. Executive Development Program concluded that the system behavior can result in periodic overstatement of requirements, excess procurement and/or unnecessary repair of material, followed by reactions at the opposite extreme.[3] These fluctuations produce undesirable oscillations in

[3] Max K. Kennedy, "An Analysis of the Air Force Hi-Value Logistic System; An Industrial Dynamics Study" (unpublished S.M. thesis, M.I.T. School of Industrial Management, 1962).

the repair and procurement work loads and in the required manpower at Air Force installations, supply and repair depots. The study recommended changes in policy and information usage that tend to stabilize the procurement system behavior.

Quality Control Systems

A commonly utilized management control system has as its purpose the control of manufacturing output quality. The feedback system apparent to the designers of such quality control systems is pictured in Figure 13. Component parts are produced by a process that has a certain expected quality or reliability characteristic. The parts are inspected for flaws and rejects discarded or reworked. Statistically designed control charts determine when the production process is out of control, and reports are fed back to production to correct the problem sources.

The effectiveness of such quality control systems becomes questionable when we view the performance curves generated by a typical system. Figure 14 plots component production rate and inspection reject rate over a period of two years. Wide periodic swings in reject

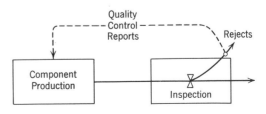

FIG. 13. Theoretical quality control system.

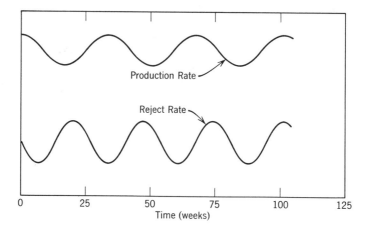

FIG. 14. Quality control system performance.

rate produce violations of the control system tolerance limits which cause machine adjustments in production and temporarily lower production rates. But what causes the oscillations in the reject rate? Its periodic nature suggests seasonal fluctuations in production quality, often strangely encountered in many manufacturing plants. The manager has almost no way of checking the validity of such an assumption. Therefore, since the explanation seems reasonable, it would probably be accepted under most circumstances.

This situation illustrates one of the key problems in quality control—the lack of an objective confirming source of information. We are in a more favorable position to understand the phenomenon, however, since the results were produced by a computer simulation. The surprising fact is that the actual production

quality was held constant, without even random variations, throughout the two years of the run. This means that the oscillations of reject rate and production shown in Figure 14 are not responses to outside changes, but rather are internally created by the behavioral system.

Let us examine a more complete picture of the total factory system, as shown in the next diagram. Components are produced, then inspected, rejects being discarded. The accepted components are forwarded to an assembly operation, where they enter into the manufacture of complete units. In an electronics plant, for example, the component production and inspection might correspond to a grid manufacturing operation, with the assembly operation putting together complete electronic tubes. When the tube is put through a life test, tube

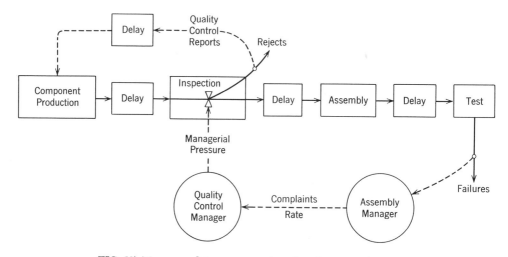

FIG. 15. More complete representation of quality control system.

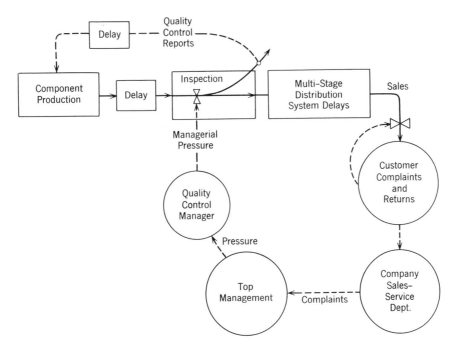

FIG. 16. Total quality control system.

failure and the source of failure are far more obvious than are the grid imperfections during the component inspection. Should too many imperfections get through component inspection, eventual tube failure rate will produce complaints by the assembly manager to the quality control manager. As these complaints continue to build, the quality control manager puts pressure on his inspectors to be more careful and detect more of the poor grids. In response to this pressure, the inspectors reject far more grids. Without an objective measure of grid quality, the reject rate tends to be a function of subjective standards and inspection care. Under pressure from the manager, the inspectors will reject any grid which seems at all dubious, including many which are actually of acceptable quality. As the rejects rise, fewer poor grids enter the assembly process, thus causing fewer tube failures in test. The assembly manager's complaints drop off and, in fact, soon switch to a concern for getting more grids for his assembly operation. Without pressure from the quality control manager and with counterpressure to get more grids to the assembly operation, the grid inspectors tend to slacken gradually their care and their reject standards. Eventually, the number of reject-able grids getting into the tube assembly

creates the problem of tube failures again, and the cycle repeats. Given normal delays in such a process, the entire cycle takes on a seasonal appearance. Thus, a system intended to assure control of product quality actually creates serious fluctuations of rejects, component production, and tube failures, all attributed to unknown factors "out of our control."

The consequences of such a situation are even more serious when the inspection output is distributed to eventual customers through the normal multi-stage distribution system. In this case the customer complaints and store returns also affect sales. These influences combine after a long delay to produce significant top management pressure on the quality control manager in reflection of a situation which existed many months before. In both Figures 15 and 16, the quality control manager's response is a key to system behavior. Here the manager of the formal quality control system is himself the most important aspect of the total system of quality and production control.

SOME PRINCIPLES OF MANAGEMENT CONTROL SYSTEM DESIGN

The examples discussed represent a wide range of management control systems. Study of these applications produces some general principles of management control system design.

A. The key to effective control often lies outside the boundaries of *conventional* operational control systems; in fact, it is sometimes outside the *formal* boundaries of the company organization.

Too many organizations give up altogether too soon the battle for mastering a management problem caused by factors apparently "out of our control." Government changes in project funding of research and development, the cyclic swings in customer orders in the production-inventory case, seasonal variations of product reject rate in the quality control problem are all examples of such factors. Yet in each case successful control system management rests within the access of company policy.

Project success in R and D is strongly influenced by company integrity and risk-taking. Yet the customer can affect these results by redesigning his own policies to achieve more desirable company behavior. Again, in the Sprague case the system requiring control included the ordering decisions of the customer, certainly not part of Sprague's formal organization. But the basis for system control exists in the stabilization of the input to the customer decision, the component delivery delay. And the key to quality control involves recognition of the total system of product flow to assembly (or to customers) and the resulting feedback of complaints and pressures.

The boundaries of a management control system design study must not be drawn to conform with organizational structure merely because of that structure. System boundaries cannot ignore vital feedback channels for information and action if the system is to be effective.

B. The proper design of management control systems often requires inclusion of the effects of intangibles; in particular, the role of decision makers who are part of the total system of control must be treated carefully.

Control system designers who are working with computers often have as their end product a computer model for calculating (or searching for) an optimal control decision. Yet while being willing to model a decision for a machine, they seem unwilling to include in their studies any models of man—of human decision making within the control loops. Our initial

example emphasized that a properly designed R and D control system should be based on models of engineer and manager decision making in both the company and customer organizations. In the production-inventory control case, the modeling of aggregate customer decision makers is a vital part of the system. Finally, we observed that the decision making and responses of both managers and inspectors are crucial aspects of the quality control case.

These illustrations emphasize the usual failure to recognize and cope with the nature of human response in organizations. The decision makers, single or aggregated—their motivations, attitudes, pressures, and models of response—must be included in management control system design. *The man (and manager) is part of the system of control, and management control system design must be viewed as a form of man-machine system design.*

C. A true understanding of total system basis and system behavior can permit effective design of both operational control systems and top management policy, without differences in philosophy or methodology of approach. In fact, most significant control system applications inherently require supra-functional or multi-departmental organization.

In the Sprague case, for example, successful control involved consideration of such aspects as customer service (marketing), inventory and production rate (manufacturing), and employment policies (personnel). Thus what often gets treated as a middle-management problem becomes resolvable only at the top policymaking level of the firm. The important elements in research and development tend not to be middle-management concerns for schedules, but rather top management policy affecting investment planning, customer relations, and company-wide attitudes. Management control systems can therefore seek to achieve the major goals of the organization as a whole, and not just the sub-optimizing aims of individual segments. A great present hazard, in fact, is the common planning and programming of control systems at the wrong level of the company, by people who lack total system perspectives and the authority to achieve broad system integration.

The Industrial Dynamics program has demonstrated the possibilities of examining and treating system problems of great variety and scope of complexity. We have dealt with many situations in which stabilization was needed and more recently with other cases in which balanced growth was the objective of the policy design efforts. The potential advantages to companies who pioneer in this work are significant and may become the basis of our future industrial competition. In this regard, it seems fitting to close with the implied advice of the Japanese scholar who said: "When your opponent is at the point of striking you, let your mind be fixed on his sword and you are no longer free to master your own movements, for you are then controlled by him." [4]

[4] Takawan, as quoted by Charles H. Townes, "Useful Knowledge," *Technology Review,* January, 1963, p. 36.

BIBLIOGRAPHY

1. *Advances in Management Information Systems Techniques,* American Management Association, 1962.
2. Bellman, R., "Control Theory," *Scientific American,* September, 1964.
3. Bross, I. D. J., *Design for Decision,* The Macmillan Co., 1953.
4. Diebold, J., "Application of Information Technology," *Annals of the American Academy of Political and Social Science,* March, 1962.
5. Emery, F. E., and O. A. Oeser, *Information, Decision and Action,* Cambridge University Press, 1958.
6. Ewell, J., "The Total System Concept and How to Organize for It," *Computers and Automation,* September, 1961.
7. Hitch, C. J., *On the Choice of Objectives in Systems Studies,* The RAND Corporation, P-1955, 1960.
8. Hopkins, R. C., "Possible Applications of Information Theory to Management Control," *IRE Transactions on Engineering Management,* March, 1961.
9. Johnson, R., F. E. Kast, and J. E. Rosenzweig, *The Theory and Management of Systems,* McGraw-Hill Book Co., Inc., 1963.
10. Johnson, R. A., "Designing Management Systems," *The Business Quarterly,* Summer, 1964.
11. Kast, F. E., and J. Rosenzweig, "Planning: Framework for an Integrated Decision System," *Washington Business Review,* April, 1960.
12. Lathi, B. P., *Signals, Systems and Communication,* John Wiley and Sons, 1965.
13. McDonough, A. M., and L. J. Garrett, *Management Systems; Working Concepts and Practices,* Richard D. Irwin, Inc., 1965.
14. McDonough, A. M., *Information Economics and Management Systems,* McGraw-Hill Book Co., 1963.
15. Machol, R. E., and P. Gray, *Recent Developments on Information and Decision Processes,* The Macmillan Co., 1962.
16. Malcolm, D. G., A. J. Rowe, and L. F. McConnell (eds.), *Management Control Systems,* John Wiley and Sons, 1960.
17. Malcolm, D. G., and A. J. Rowe, "Computer-based Control Systems," *California Management Review,* Spring, 1961.
18. Morse, G. E., "Pendulum of Management Control," *Harvard Business Review,* May, 1965.
19. Optner, S., *Systems Analysis for Business and Industrial Problem Solving,* Prentice-Hall, Inc., 1965.
20. Stoller, D. S., and R. L. Van Horn, *Design of a Management Information System,* The RAND Corporation, P-1362, 1958.
21. Tilles, S., "Manager's Job: A Systems Approach," *Harvard Business Review,* January, 1963.
22. Tou, J. T., "Information Systems: Learning, Adaptation and Control; Report of Computer and Information Science Symposium," *Science,* September, 1963.
23. Weinwurm, G. F., "Computer Management Control Systems Through the Looking Glass," *Management Science,* July, 1961.
24. Wilson, I. G., and M. E. Wilson, *Information, Computers and System Design,* John Wiley and Sons, 1965.

Part VIII.   Cybernetics

For many years now automatic control systems, which have been largely confined to governors, servomechanisms, and the like, have had their greatest impact and application in the field of engineering. This is not a thing to be wondered at, for ever since the 1790's when James Watt invented his "governor"—the mechanical regulator for stabilizing the speed of rotation of the steam engine, the field of cybernetics has been almost wholly dominated by the mechanical engineer. Even today many of the guidance and control systems employed in missiles are based on fundamentally the same principles that were enunciated decades ago. While it is true that automatic control systems are being used more extensively year by year, still there is relatively little application of such systems outside the realm of mechanical devices. Until the recent contributions to cybernetics of such men as Norbert Wiener, W. Ross Ashby, and Stafford Beer (to name but a few), the all-important idea of feedback, so vital to a cybernetic system, has only with extreme difficulty been transferred to the political, economic, social, and managerial fields.

Historically cybernetics dates from the time of Plato who, in his *Republic*, used the term *kybernetike* (a Greek term meaning "the art of steersmanship") both in its literal sense of piloting a vessel and in the metaphorical sense of piloting the ship of state, i.e., the art of government. In time the metaphorical sense became the predominant one to be replaced by the literal mechanical sense, and it is only now that the meaning of the term has come full circle.

The various selections in this section will be concerned with the concise exposition of the field of cybernetics (often characterized as the science of communication and control) and with its application to several "orthodox" areas of investigation. It is not surprising that the social scientist as well as the industrial manager exhibit more than a passing interest in the science of cybernetics. Because of the tremendous technological advances of modern times, especially with regard to the high-speed electronic computer with its data processing potential, only now are the formal aspects of cybernetics being seriously applied to the man-to-machine and man-to-man systems.

One important characteristic of all control systems is feedback. Regardless of the particular type of control we are interested in, whether it be quality control, budgetary control, production control, inventory control, missile control, social control, etc., the idea of feedback permeates the entire control spectrum. Since control always implies the existence of some basic plan to be implemented or some standard to be applied and of some reliable means of measuring and correcting deviations from the plan or standard, feedback is essential if a steady state or equilibrium is to be achieved and maintained.

From the point of view of the business manager an understanding of feedback is vital and yet the appropriateness of this has often not been sufficiently recognized. An earlier section elucidated the role of the computer in providing timely, up-to-date feedback. And with the advent of the computer the behavior of even extremely complex systems can now be predicted.

Cybernetics is a new interdisciplinary

science. As such it makes use of older concepts peculiar to several disciplines, concepts which have performed admirably in the service of the older sciences, and attempts to weave them into one general hybrid discipline centering around the information and control functions.

In the first selection, Charles Dechert outlines the history of the discipline from its early beginnings down to modern times, sketching rapidly the contributions of the mechanical engineers, mathematicians, and physiologists.

Every cybernetic system has three basic components, viz., a detector or sensor, a selector or decision-making element, and an effector. The detector is the component sensitive to the state of the particular quality to be controlled. The selector or control unit is the element capable of selecting from among several possible responses on the basis of information sensed by the detector or by the preset condition of the selector itself. Finally, the effector is that component that can bring about some change in the condition sensed by the detector. Consequently self-regulation demands that the three functions of perception, decision-making, and action be at least conceptually distinct.

It is however the control loop that characterizes any self-regulating system. Control necessarily involves the communication of information, here understood as any input data capable of influencing the behavior of another. Thus cybernetics is, in the words of Wiener, the *"control and communication* in the animal and the machine." Progress in communications and control theory has advanced so far that it is today one of the chief factors in the modern technological revolution.

In the popular imagination cybernetics and the digital computer have been wedded, and rightly so, for it is the computer that has made possible the automatic factory, and the myriad forms of automated activity that characterizes modern civilization.

In the man-machine system the machine is viewed as a projection of the human personality, subject normally to human control. In the simplest type of such a system the person serves both as the source of energy and the source of control. In more advanced types prime movers provide the energy while man provides the control. In still more advanced types the machine is more or less self-regulating and man controls the programming phase alone. As we advance up the hierarchy of systems we thus notice a gradual shift in the concept of control. The same is true as we move from the realm of machines controlling machines, men controlling machines, and men controlling men.

It is in the field of the social sciences that the author believes great possibilities exist for cybernetics. Many of the basic concepts of cybernetics are relevant to an understanding of social groups and social organizations. For years now political science, cultural anthropology, and social psychology have analyzed social groups as complex communications networks characterized by a multiplicity of feedback loops. However, much progress still remains to be made in the field of the behavioral sciences.

In Joseph Bonney's selection the major emphasis is on the quality of the feedback reports that should characterize an effective management information system. Such a system should have as its objective that of supplying the manager with the amount of information needed to make decisions easily, quickly, and with a reasonable degree of accuracy. To have perceptive feedback the reports should have these characteristics: (1) They should be oriented toward the user and the function for which they are intended. The *who* and the *why* must be uppermost since the amount and type of information needed varies drastically with the user, top management needing less detail and lower and middle management more. (2) Also information reports should flow downward for direction, upward for feedback for managerial decision-making. (3) These reports should be brief, analyzed, accurate, and timely. Accurate, timely information is a must but the gathering of such information is also expensive. (4) These reports should be based on a system flexible enough to allow for quick changes to meet new conditions.

To illustrate the decision-making process and perceptive feedback, Bonney contrasts the manager of a small business with one in a larger firm in the process of making a decision involving the addition of minor capital equipment. The processes of judging, evaluating, appraising, and projecting are scrutinized. In either case, however, good decisions are the product of a manager with a keen mind, with updated experience and with the necessary information. The information requirement will be somewhat different in each instance. The importance of exception reports on general activity and of detailed information relating to the specific problem to be solved is highlighted. Also stressed is the need for employing the newer available techniques made practical by the computer, such as more refined mathematical and statistical approaches, operations research, linear programming, business games.

Stafford Beer's 1958 paper presented to the Operational Research Society of London is an admirable example of clear thinking and of straightforward presentation. He attacks the problem very logically, first exposing for view the nature of cybernetics, then that of operations research, and finally tying both ends together.

Cybernetics is seen as the science whose object of study is control. It aims to study the nature of control *per se*, control common to many fields of investigation. Hence its interdisciplinary nature, hence its relevance to industrial, social, economic, mechanical, and biological systems.

Control is an essential attribute of a system which he then goes on to define in a relativistic way as "a collection of entities that can be understood as forming a co-herent group." Relatedness is but the structural element of systems.

Every cybernetic system has three essential features. It is extremely complex, probabilistic, and self-regulating.

"Operational research," Beer affirms, "is the attack of modern science on problems of likelihood which arise in the management and control of men and machines, materials and money in their natural environment. Its special technique is to invent a strategy of control by measuring, comparing, and predicting probable behavior through a scientific model of a situation." Note that operations research is not considered to be a science; it is a method of science, a subset of the scientific method so appropriate for analysis of activity. As such it is nothing more or less than logical induction. The characteristic tool of operations research for dealing with problems of control is model construction.

Operations research and cybernetics have very much in common. They share the same general common concern for control, the same complexity and probabilistic nature, a common level of sophistication, reciprocity of method, and an interdisciplinary approach.

In Beer's view communication is nothing else than employing the language of the structure that makes the system what it is. The languages that can be used for this purpose are logic, mathematics, statistics, and metamathematics. Because cybernetics is interdisciplinary it must talk in the language of some science. The language of physiology so often employed is a language of identities, not merely of metaphors or analogies.

In summary, operational research is a body of methods which provide a powerful investigative tool. Cybernetics, on the other hand, is a body of knowledge enjoying the status of a science. The two are methodologically complementary; operations research is the natural technique in research of cybernetics, while the latter is the natural embodiment in science of the former.

27. THE DEVELOPMENT OF CYBERNETICS *

Charles R. Dechert †

The term "cybernetics" derives from the Greek word *kybernetes* which means steersman. Plato uses it to describe the prudential aspect of the art of government.[1] Ampere in his *Essay on the Philosophy of Science* used the term *cybernétique* for the science of civil government.[2] The Latin term *gubernator* is derived from the Greek, and hence also our word governor. In English we use the term governor in at least two ways: first in the traditional sense of a public steersman or political decision-maker; second to refer to the self-adjusting valve mechanism on a steam engine which keeps the engine at a constant speed under varying conditions of load. In the steam engine governor, a valve linked to the engine's output shaft increases steam flow into the engine as the output speed decreases, raising the speed to the level desired, or reduces steam flow if the speed exceeds the pre-established level. Maxwell analyzed this control phenomenon mathematically in his paper on governors published in 1868.[3] What is essentially involved in steering behavior or control behavior of the type illustrated by the steam engine governor is a feedback loop through which the output of the system is linked to its input in such a way that variations in output from some pre-established or "programmed" norm result in compensatory behavior that tends to restore the system output to that norm.

An analogous process occurs in organisms subjected to internal or external changes that might disrupt metabolism. By the turn of this century physiologists such as Claude Bernard were fully aware of this process of "homeostasis" whereby an organism acts so as to restore its internal equilibrium. Cannon's *Wisdom of the Body* is a classical exposition of these phenomena in the autonomic processes of men. The self-regulatory aspect of neurophysiological phenomena was treated by such men as Sherrington in his work on reflexes, McCulloch in his analysis of neural networks, and Rosenblueth in his studies of psychomotor disorders. By the early 1940's physicists, electrical engineers, and mathematicians were all at work on servomechanisms, self-regulating systems that could be used for such military purposes as gun laying. A broad range of disciplines had been at work on analogous problems of self-regulation. Institutionally, the interdisciplinary study of self-regulation in the animal and the machine began at a meeting held in New York in 1942, sponsored by the Josiah Macy Foundation.

BEHAVIOR AND PURPOSE

One result was a paper on "Behavior, Purpose and Teleology" which serves as a watershed in which the breadth of the analogy was realized.[4] In 1943 *Philosophy of Science* published this article by Norbert Wiener, Arturo Rosenblueth and Julian Bigelow. The authors distinguish between the "functional analysis" of an entity and a "behavioristic approach." In the former ". . . the main goal is the intrinsic organization of the entity studied, its structure and its properties . . ." ". . . The behavioristic approach consists in the examination of the output of the object and of the relations of this output to the input." Wiener in his subsequent works largely restricted himself to ". . . the behavioristic method of study [which] omits the specific structure and intrinsic organization of the object." The authors assign the term "servomechanism" to designate machines with "intrinsic purposeful behavior." Purposeful behavior is directed at ". . . a final condition in which the behaving

SOURCE: *The American Behavioral Scientist* (June, 1965), pp. 15–20. Reprinted by permission of *The American Behavioral Scientist*.

* The original version of this paper was presented at a symposium on the Social Implications of Cybernetics held at Georgetown University, Washington, D.C., November, 1964.

† Professor of Political Science, Purdue University.

object reaches a definite correlation in time or space with respect to another object or event." All purposeful behavior may be considered to require negative feedback, that is, ". . . the behavior of an object is controlled by the margin of error at which the object stands at a given time with reference to a relatively specific goal." The authors conclude on the note that "purposefulness [is] a concept necessary for the understanding of certain modes of behavior . . . ," and define teleology as "purpose controlled by feedback." The authors reject the concept of teleology as implying a "cause subsequent in time to a given effect."

In this model the key elements of self-regulation were reduced to a form amenable to mathematical analysis, and the knotty problem of consciousness so relevant to human behavior was bypassed. The novelty of this mode of conceptualizing purposive behavior lies in its implicit distinction between energy and information. " 'Control' is a special kind of relation between two machines or parts of machines, such that one part regulates the operation of the other. . . . The essential point is that the source of energy is dissociated from the source of instructions." [5] The transformation of relatively high energic inputs into goal-oriented outputs is subject to relatively low energies characterized by a formal content whose programmed interaction with these high energies produces the purposive transformation.

The principal characteristic of a self-regulating system is the presence of a control loop whereby system comportment may be modified on the basis of information inputs regarding performance and the comparison of performance with a criterion value. The control loop may be a "closed loop" existing within the boundaries of the system, or it may be an "open loop." In open loop feedback, part of the control information flow takes place outside the system boundary. The interaction of a self-regulating system with its external environment characteristically involves an open loop. Effector elements on the system boundary manipulate the environment to achieve certain objectives. Sensor elements (receptors) perceive environmental changes which are transmitted to a decision-making element that compares this percept with the objective and transmits new orders to the effector elements in terms of the difference between objective and achievement.

Basically, self-regulation requires a functional distinction between perception, decision-making, and action. This is normally achieved by a structural distinction between perceptor elements, control elements and effector elements in the system. Behaviorally, system may be defined as a "black box" characterized by a given set or range of inputs and outputs. Adequate knowledge of any system requires both structural-functional analysis and behavioral analysis. Where very large numbers of inputs and/or outputs are involved or where the system is composed of a large number of components, statistical techniques are required and behaviors are analyzed probabilistically. It is entirely possible, of course, that structurally diverse systems may effect identical transformations, and that structurally identical systems of a sufficient degree of complexity may produce very different outputs on the basis of identical inputs. The "sensitivity" of a system refers to the degree of departure of the output from a programmed norm that invokes an adjustive response. "Rapidity of response" refers to the speed with which a given system will correct behavior that does not correspond to the norm. "Stability" refers to the ability of a system to maintain a given behavioral posture over time. Normally there is a rather close formal relation between these aspects of systems behavior. The more sensitive a system, the less likely it is to be stable over a broad range of inputs and outputs. The more rapid the response of the system to an error signal, the more likely it is to overshoot the norm—to overadjust, and so invoke a counter-adjustment, to overadjust, and so forth. This behavior may lead to oscillation destructive of the entire system.

INFORMATION AND MESSAGES

It is clear at this point of our discussion that control involves the communication of information. In an operational sense, information is that which can or does influence the comportment of another. Information is conveyed as a message, that is, as a configuration of signal elements borne by a medium having actual or potential meaning for the recipient (destination). By the late 1920's communications engineers, concerned with the problems of interference (noise) and channel capacity, had begun to develop measures of information.[6] This work culminated in 1948 in a paper of

Shannon entitled, "The Mathematical Theory of Communication."[7] Shannon's study does not concern itself with meaning, that is, with the semantic aspects of communication but with the technical problems of the accuracy of transmission of various types of signals. Clearly, the purely technical problems of coding, transmitting, and decoding signal sequences are of critical importance in designing and understanding self-regulating systems. The actual comportment of such systems, however, is a function of the semantic content of these signal sequences. The "quantity of information" as a measure of the improbability of a signal sequence has no *necessary* relation to the amount of semantic information conveyed by a statement.[8]

In 1948 Wiener published *Cybernetics or Control and Communication in the Animal and the Machine* which formalized much of the thinking up to that time and suggested potentially fruitful areas for further inquiry. With the quantification of signal transmission and the formalization of control system theory a new and broadly applicable science of communications and control had become a reality. In its strict applications, communications and control theory has become a major factor in contemporary technology and lies at the base of the "second industrial revolution." In the "first industrial revolution" prime movers largely replaced human energy while men performed a control function. Under automation, process and production *control* is relegated to servomechanisms while the human operator programs, monitors, and maintains the automated system.

SCOPE OF CYBERNETICS

In the United States, scientists and engineers working in the theory and applications of self-regulation tend to avoid the term cybernetics which deals to a considerable degree with isomorphisms among various types of self-regulating systems. Since only a very limited range of systems and communications processes are presently amenable to mathematical formalization and manipulation, there has been a tendency to institutionalize fairly narrow disciplines concerned with limited formal or material applications of these concepts, such as computer engineering, bionics, and control systems engineering. In the Soviet Union, on the other hand, the term "cyber-netics" is used quite broadly, ". . . not as the doctrine of Wiener, Shannon, Ashby, *et al.*, but as the general science of the control over complex systems, information, and communications. . . ."[9] Elsewhere in the Soviet literature we find cybernetics defined as ". . . the new science of purposeful and optimal control over complicated processes and operations which take place in living nature, in human society, and in industry."[10]

Cybernetics extends the circle of processes which can be controlled—this is its special property and merit. It can help control life activity in living nature, purposeful work of organized groups of people, and the influence of man on machines and mechanisms.

We shall divide cybernetics into three large subdivisions: theoretical cybernetics which includes mathematical and philosophical problems; the cybernetics of control systems and means which includes the problems of collecting, processing, and output of information, and also the means for electronic automation; finally, the field of the practical application of the methods and means of cybernetics in all fields of human activity.[11]

Many of the basic concepts of this science are relevant to an understanding of social groups. Norbert Wiener realized their applicability and suggested many insightful applications, but was concerned about potential abuses owing to the complexity of social processes and the limited applicability of existing methods of mathematical analysis. On the other hand, he also pointed out that the application of cybernetic concepts to society does not require that social relations be mathematicizable *in esse*, but only *in posse*—that is, the conceptual clarification of the formal aspects of social relations can make a positive contribution to the science of society.[12]

More recent definitions of cybernetics almost invariably include social organizations as one of the categories of system to which this science is relevant.[13] Indeed, Bigelow has generalized to the extent of calling cybernetics the effort to understand the behavior of complex systems.[14] He pointed out that cybernetics is essentially interdisciplinary and that a focus at the systems level, dependent upon mixed teams of professionals in a variety of sciences, brings one rapidly to the frontiers of knowledge in several areas. This is certainly true of the social sciences. The term "cybernetics" is used here in the more extended sense discussed above. It is entirely appropriate that this should be done, not only because of the traditional political and social connotation of the term governance, but because of the role played by the social and behavioral sciences in the explication and development of models of social control and decision-making. The first modern calculating machine was made by Charles Babbage, whose classic study (*On the Economy of Machinery and Manufactures*) was published in 1832 and anticipated by fifty years or more the beginnings of scientific management.[15] Organizational theory, political science, cultural anthropology and social psychology have for many years analyzed social groups as complex communications nets characterized by a multiplicity of feedback loops. Organizational decision-making was given a quantitative base, again at the time of World War II, by the development of the techniques of operations research. Von Neumann and Morgenstern succeeded in analyzing strategic optima in certain types of decision processes. In 1936 Leontief produced the first input-output matrix. Von Bertalanffy has pointed out analogies (isomorphisms) characterizing all systems, including social systems.[16]

ROLE OF COMPUTERS

Let us now examine certain aspects of the popular view of cybernetics. In one view, cybernetics is identified with the development and use of large digital computers. Computers are, of course, of fundamental importance to cybernetics, first because they embody so much communications and control technology, and second because they oblige us to sort out vague ideas and feelings from clearly formulated univocal ideas and relations if we wish to manipulate them by machine, and finally because once ideas are clarified the machine permits the rapid execution of long and detailed logical operations otherwise beyond human capability. In many cases these logical operations performed by machine permit a rationality in decision-making or precision of control hitherto unattainable. Until a few years ago it was impossible to compare very large numbers of decisional alternatives to find an optimum. Decision techniques and aids such as linear and dynamic programming, critical path analysis, large scale input-output matrices, network analysis, factor analysis, simulation, and so forth are largely dependent upon computers.

Computer technology, of course, lies at the base of the automatic factory, of sophisticated inventory control systems, and of the increasing automation of routine paper work. Fundamentally, any information handling operation that can be reduced to rule and rote is amenable to computer performance. Considered abstractly, this means that virtually every human job activity that does not require intellectual or artistic creativity or some human emotivity in its performance is potentially susceptible of automation. Under our existing institutional "rules of the game" the only limiting factor will be the cost of the machine as opposed to the cost of people.

It now seems increasingly likely that computer networks will be formed, first on a local, then a regional, and finally a national scale which will make unused computer capacity available, perhaps on a rental basis—and which as a unit will be capable of data processing tasks of hitherto inconceivable magnitude. Eventually each citizen may have access to computers and a vast complex of data storage centers on a rental-use basis. Computers might be used to handle such routine chores as tallying adding machine tapes, making out Christmas mailing lists and preparing income tax returns. At a more sophisticated level perhaps our citizen may use his machine to analyze interpersonal relations in his office sociometrically in order to optimize strategies for personal effectiveness. He may have access to a wide range of factual or bibliographic information; he may, perhaps, run machine searches of newspaper files or gather genealogical data. From a purely practical economic viewpoint there would be obvious benefits to American business to be gained from centralized insurance files, credit reports, accident reports, academic and job records, public opinion surveys, market surveys, and so forth. All of these would enhance predictability, and so also increase business' capacity for rational decision-making. The principal question that will arise in this process of increasing centralized information storage concerns the values in terms of which the information will be utilized in making decisions. Profit maximization? a politically imposed values-mix? or might new institutional forms permit more decentralized decision on the basis of widely varying criteria? In the not very distant future some hard public decisions must be made regarding who shall have access to what information and for what purposes, and perhaps as to what types of information may legitimately be collected and employed.

APPLICATIONS TO SOCIAL SYSTEMS

Let us return to our basic model of a self-regulating system, examine some of its fundamental operations a little more closely, and try to see wherein it is applicable to the study of social relations.

A system is an organized collection of interrelated elements characterized by a boundary and functional unity. The concept of system emphasizes the reality of complex relational networks and permits the analysis of mutual causal processes involving large numbers of interacting entities. Although systems of ideas and systems of symbols play a critical role in human society, we shall here treat of social systems as real composite entities in continuing self-regulated interaction with their environment(s). Social systems comprise every level of complexity from the family or primary work group through large scale formal organizations to the nation-state or even the whole human race conceived of as an interacting human community. Primary groups and ultimately all groups are composed of self-regulating persons as their components. Large social systems normally consist of functional groups as their component subsystems. The integrated activity of large social groupings is the product of effective internal communication and a willingness on the part of decision-makers in their component social subsystems and ultimately of their component persons to respond in a predictable and programmed manner to a defined range of perceptual inputs.

Fundamentally, a model of self-regulation requires a functional distinction between perception, decision-making, and action. This is normally achieved by a structural distinction between receptor elements, decision-making elements, and effector elements in the system. As social systems increase in size and complexity, these functions and the related communications functions tend to become concentrated in component social subsystems.[17]

If we apply these basic concepts in a very much simplified way to the political sphere they may help to systematize certain basic relations that are the traditional matter of political science, such as the constitution and the separation of powers.[18] Basically, a constitution is a program defining the nature (activities) and interrelations of the formal loci of political power. The outputs of the political system are enforceable laws defining the interrelations of persons and groups within the society. Demands on the political system are communicated by petition, by representatives of organized groups, by publicists, and other means including elections. Legislative decisions are made in the form of laws and resolutions. The executive puts the laws into effect and the judiciary serves a control function by comparing specific individual actions with the law that programs such action. Even judicial review in the United States is fundamentally a comparison of legislative action (output) with a constitutional norm.

Similarly in the conduct of foreign affairs, information on the international environment in the form of foreign intelligence is communicated to the foreign policy decision-makers—ultimately, in the United States, the President. The challenges of the environment are met by policy decisions allocating resources of the state to effector elements of the executive branch for the achievement of national objectives by various techniques: diplomacy, foreign assistance, propaganda, military action, and so forth.

If we apply the concepts of sensitivity and stability to political systems we see distinct analogies even at an elementary level. The founding fathers of the United States wanted the legislature (decision-maker) sensitive to public opinion, so they introduced a House of Representatives elected biennially on the basis of population. But they did not want the decision process too sensitive to public opinion, so they introduced a Senate elected on a different basis for a different term of office whose concurrence is necessary to legislation. In order to introduce further stability into the system they decoupled the legislative (decision-maker) from the executive (effector) branch and introduced an independent control element in the form of a Supreme Court. The inherent stability of the system has been proved over the past 175 years. It is interesting to note that most of the proposals for "reform" recommended by political scientists are directed at increasing the sensitivity of the system to public opinion.

Each entity in our experience, whether physical object or person or social group, exists in time and interrelates with others in time. In the temporal order what will occur cannot provide a real input into antecedent action—but as a foreseen possibility it may provide an imputed information input. If we conceive of the current state of a system as determined by its antecedent states, the future states of that system are a set of probabilities dependent on the possible future states of its environments, and for self-regulating systems upon their actions in the "now." Insofar as the self-regulating system can know not only its actual state and the state of its environment in the "now," but can project and "know" alternative trajectories that are possible as realizable in the future, to this extent the future can be an input into decisional processes. While recognizing and attempting to predict the future states of key variables over which there is no effective control, individual and social planning consists essentially in: a) projecting alternative trajectories as functions of direct action by the system and of the indirect effects of action by the system on its environment; and in b) choosing the set of actions which, on the basis of past experience or subjectively assigned probabilities, seems most likely to bring about a future state conceived of as desirable. It is perfectly clear that the actions undertaken to achieve a future state of the system may *determine* to a considerable degree that future state. Hence it follows that in the reality of human affairs means and ends can never be separated.

Social systems not only respond to an existing environmental challenge, but they may foresee such challenges and plan to forestall them or cope with them in the future. In brief men and societies are provident—they respond not only to perceptions of reality but to the extrapolation of reality into possible future states. Much social choice depends upon the image of the future deemed desirable by a society and it is for this reason that the abstract ideology or the utopia expressed in concrete terms plays a critical role in defining social purpose and hence in conditioning social decisions. The range of possible response to an existing challenge is normally quite limited, while the range of autonomous action becomes increasingly broad as increasingly long future time-spans are anticipated. As given future goals become increasingly clear, that is, concretely defined, social behavior may increasingly resemble that of a servomechanism in which guidance is reduced to control ". . . by the margin of error at which the object stands at a given time with reference to a relatively specific goal." Action may then become a routine problem of technical administration.

Action upon the environment is regulated by a continuing process of perception in which the perceived external reality is compared with an end state to be achieved. Now in this process it is clear that we are dealing with focused perceptions, that is, a set of sensory inputs to which attention adverts selected from the innumerable alternative sets to which the person or group might advert. In an evolutionary sense only reasonably adequate criteria of perceptual relevance permit survival of a given biological species. For men whose criteria of perceptual relevance are largely cultural, only cultures having reasonably adequate criteria of relevance can survive. Similarly the norms of behavior of the person, the criterion values on the basis of which action is undertaken, are crucially important to behavior and to survival. These too are largely a matter of culture. In the history of mankind certain patterns of value have proved to possess a higher survival value than others. Within the range of viable systems of value and perceptual relevance (ideologies) there have been diverse degrees of success as measured by the extent of their diffusion and survival. In man we are dealing with a broad range of potential criteria of action and the possibility of self-conscious choice among sets of alternative criteria. Hence in dealing with social systems in which men form the ultimate self-regulating components, we must deal with the problem of the adequacy of perception and of value to effective action within a natural and human environment. The analysis of men and societies as self-regulating systems brings us back to the perennial philosophic problems of the Good and the True.

MAN-MACHINE SYSTEMS

Let us now conceive of the individual's environmental system in terms of a man-machine relationship. The machine is essentially a projection of the personality, normally subject to direct or indirect human control, capable of converting a given input or set of inputs into an output or set of outputs having greater imputed utility.

In its simplest form this is the man-tool relation in which the person serves as both a source of energy and of control. In more sophisticated man-machine systems prime movers may provide energy and man the control. At a more advanced stage the machine is in whole or part self-regulating and human control is exercised only in the programming phase. As we move to "learning machines" the human control interface may be reduced to the direct or indirect construction of the machine (indirect construction might involve programming a machine to produce a machine) and the direct or indirect programming of the criterion values on the basis of which decisions affecting output will be made. There is also a man-machine interface at the output since, presumably, the machine serves some human value. The most sophisticated man-machine systems today are basically extenders of human perceptive, data processing, and motor capabilities.

In some sense complex organizations, especially economic organizations, are man-machine systems in which the components are both men and artifacts in programmed interaction to convert input values into output values having a higher (ascribed) value. Within such an organization both persons and things are subject to decisions and the output values may or may not directly serve the human component of the system itself.

As we move from the realm of machines controlling machines, to men controlling machines, and to men controlling men in society we subtly shift the meaning of the term "control." In machine controls the message either actuates some multiplying device such as a relay or by combining with energic inputs modifies their characteristics. In human control of a machine, the person observes directly, or indirectly through an instrument display, the comportment of the machine in its environment and manipulates control devices. Here our man-machine "interface" basically consists of displays and controls. Social control is the capacity (often based on control of material or financial resources) to manipulate the internal and/or external environments of other persons or groups so as to achieve a preconceived end. This normally involves selected changes in their

information inputs designed to change in some way their perceptions or values so that they respond in the desired manner. It is largely concerned with "evoking" an "autonomous" response. Even the social effectiveness of negative sanctions in controlling behavior is contingent upon their being perceived and then evaluated more negatively than noncompliance. Basically, when dealing with objects as complex and autonomous as persons, control is reduced to presenting a challenge so structured that it evokes the desired response. Since social action normally involves a feedback loop, the socially controlled in some sense also control the controller; indeed this is the major characteristic of political decision-making in a democracy. Greniewsky points out: ". . . all control is communication. But on the other hand all communication is control. . . ." [19]

SYSTEM INTERFACES

A system interacts with its environment at the system boundary. Inputs move into the system across this boundary. Outputs move across this boundary into the system's environment. The area of contact between one system and another is termed an "interface." Operationally systems, and subsystems within systems, may be identified by the transactional processes that occur across their boundaries. For social groupings these transactional processes may involve the transfer of energy, material objects, men, money, and information.

The outputs of one social system are normally inputs for one or more other systems. These interrelations are amenable to analysis for economic sectors (and even for firms) by the use of input-output matrices. Quesnay in his *Tableau Economique* saw the national economy as an integrated system of monetary exchanges and exchanges of goods and services. The political system may be analyzed in terms of input demands and supports and an output of authoritative decisions that program the interrelations of persons and organized groups within the state. By extending our analysis to comprehend the five categories of exchange noted above, we are in a position to view the entire world as a (relatively) closed system of interrelated social components linked together by these transactional processes.

Communications and control technologies are already being extensively applied for purposes of social organization within the more advanced countries. The Soviet economy is now being organized on the basis of very extensive input-output matrices and computer programs designed to optimize resource utilization. These techniques may also help resolve the problem inherent in the limited use of market mechanisms to determine prices. By ascribing more or less arbitrary value to primary resource inputs (including the categories of human labor) all other prices in the economy can be made consistent. In the French indicative plan, a political decision, based on a consensus among all interested groups as to a future national mix of economic values, is reduced to an investment program that generates a high level of business confidence. The result has been an increasing tendency to reduce government to administration in terms of the technical achievement of concrete objectives. In the United States, the Social Security system has provided a means for national population control and is at the base of the new Internal Revenue Service computer system in which wage earners and salaried persons are posted on a biweekly or monthly basis. Given the increasing use of electronic data processing in our banks, plus the sophistication and widespread use of credit facilities, it is quite conceivable that all monetary transactions over say twenty dollars could be posted in a national accounting system (at least aggregate) through the use of cascaded computers. This would, of course, largely do away with the possibility of robbery—but above all would provide a rapid running account of interregional and intersectoral exchanges that would permit the use of indirect controls at strategic points to effect very rapid adjustments of the economy in terms of programmed goals such as full employment and planned rates of economic growth. Such a system would also permit more equitable taxation by doing away with unrecorded transfers.

I would suggest that cybernetics today possesses great relevance for the social scientist. First it has begun to provide conceptual tools of the greatest importance for the analysis of complex systems and their interrelations. It establishes a focus on the critical importance of control and communications relations, of individual and institutional modes of perception and values. Certainly this view of men and societies as complex self-regulating systems, interacting among themselves within complex environments should prove conducive to a more holistic approach to the social and behavioral

sciences in all their multivariate complexity, and provides us with a more solid foundation for systematic scientific formalization than existed in a past in which "science" *par excellence* comprised the simplified model of a clockwork universe governed by the laws of classical mechanics. Second, the social scientist must examine closely the actual and potential relations of cybernetic modes of thought and technologies to social institutions. Cybernetics has profound implications both as an ideology and as regards ideology. This is already abundantly clear in the works of both the Russians and the Anglo-Americans. Cybernetic technologies lie at the root of the quantum shift in economic relations called automation and cybernation. Computer based "optimum" decisions based on cost-effectiveness analysis have begun to replace the interplay of interest in some key areas of political decision—specifically in U.S. military spending. These techniques are potentially applicable to the whole budget process.

Certainly the political sphere will be a major forum for the resolution of the problems of value and social philosophy that can no longer be ignored. Even in the absence of sophisticated competitive economic and social systems and competitive concepts of a good life, such as those of Russia and France, these decisions cannot long be postponed. What must now be demonstrated is the capacity of a democratic society to understand, confront, and resolve very complex problems of social organization in such a way as to retain traditional freedoms and consultative political institutions while moving into new patterns of economic and social relations in which we realize that our relation to the machine has become quasi-symbiotic.

REFERENCES

1. Plato, *Republic*, I, 346 B.C.
2. Ampere, A. M., *Essay on the Philosophy of Science* (1838).
3. Maxwell, J. C., *Proceedings of the Royal Society* (London), 1868, XVI, 270–83.
4. Josiah Macy Foundation Conference on Cerebral Inhibition, May, 1942. Rosenblueth, A., Wiener, N., and Bigelow, J., "Behavior, Purpose and Teleology," *Philos. Sci.*, 1943, 10, 18–24.
5. Guilbaud, G. T., *What Is Cybernetics?* New York: Grove Press, 1960, p. 11.
6. Nyquist, H., "Certain Factors Affecting Tele-

graph Speed," *Bell System Technical J.*, April, 1924, 324; "Certain Topics in Telegram Transmission Theory," *A.I.E.E. Transactions*, 47, April, 1928, 617; Hartley, R. V. L., "Transmission of Information," *Bell System Technical J.*, July, 1928, 535.

7. Shannon, C. E., and Weaver, W., *The Mathematical Theory of Communication*. Urbana: University of Illinois Press, 1949.

8. Bar-Hillel, Y., "An Examination of Information Theory," *Philos. Sci.*, 22, 1955.

9. Bershteyn, N. A., "New Lines of Development in Physiology and Their Relation to Cybernetics" in *Problems of Philosophy*, 1962, 8, 78–87 (JPRS; 17,117).

10. "Biological Aspects of Cybernetics," Moscow, 1962 (JPRS; 19,637, p. 17).

11. *Ibid.*, p. 19.

12. Wiener, N., *God and Golem, Inc.* Cambridge, Mass.: M.I.T. Press, 1964, p. 88.

13. *Encyclopedia of Science and Technology*. New York: McGraw-Hill, 1960. "Cybernetics: The science of control and communication in all of its various manifestations in machines, animals, and organizations."—"An interdisciplinary science."

14. Bigelow, J., Address at Founders' Dinner, American Society for Cybernetics, October 16, 1964, Washington, D.C.

15. Babbage, C., *On the Economy of Machinery and Manufactures*. London: 1832. For a very recent application of advanced analytic techniques to management see: Beer, S., *Cybernetics and Management*. New York: Wiley, 1959; "Toward the Cybernetic Factory" in Von Foerster and Zopf (eds.), *Principles of Self-Organization*. New York: Pergamon, 1962, p. 25.

16. Von Bertalanffy, L., "General Systems Theory," *General Systems*, vol. I (1956); "General Systems Theory: A Critical Review," *General Systems*, vol. VII (1962); Miller, J. G., "Toward a General Theory for the Behavioral Sciences," *Amer. Psychol.*, 10, 1955.

17. See Deutsch, K., *The Nerves of Government*, p. 258; Dechert, C., "A Pluralistic World Order," *Proceedings* of the American Catholic Philosophical Association, 1963, pp. 167–186.

18. See Easton, D., "An Approach to the Analysis of Political Systems," *World Politics*, 9, 1957, pp. 383–400; Dahl, R., *Modern Political Analysis*. Englewood Cliffs: Prentice-Hall, 1963.

19. Greniewsky, H., *Cybernetics without Mathematics*. New York: Pergamon, 1960, p. 52.

28. PERCEPTIVE FEEDBACK

Joseph B. Bonney, Jr.*

The words "management information system" imply the application of an overall management approach to bring the essential information out of the various report systems of a business. Information must be based on sound material or data and be effectively translated into a meaningful form designed to assist managers in fulfilling their responsibilities to the business.

The owner or manager of a business employing 20 to 100 people, making one or two products and marketing these locally or regionally, can with good transportation, a long day and a quick mind keep well informed on the important factors affecting his business. His dependence on memos, reports, or records is minimal and for most decisions he goes into the plant and into the market place to get "what he decides he needs" as a basis for decision. Let's face a simple problem with him, such as the determination of the production level for the next quarter. He can increase his production 10 percent next quarter by the addition of some minor capital equipment that will also give him a slightly lower per unit production cost. When faced with such a decision, what will the manager do? He will review the proposed production savings and *judge* whether or not the savings will occur. He will review the capital expenditures both to *evaluate* if it will actually cost what the proposal indicates and to *appraise* the cost in relation to the present and ex-

SOURCE: *Data Processing* (August, 1964), pp. 11–15. Reprinted by permission of Data Processing Magazine, The Publication of Computers and Information Technology.

* Weyerhaeuser Co.

pected financial position of the company. He will *speculate* on whether the 10 percent increase will be sold at present prices, or whether he will have to increase his advertising or add a salesman, etc., to sell the 10 percent increase.

There are other points he will consider in his review and judgment process. His familiarity with the aspects of the problem enable him to reach a decision without much difficulty. After all, yesterday after talking to three of his six major customers he knows they want more of the item. This morning, while making one of his frequent trips through the shop, he noted that with the addition of a new lathe and the shifting of the old for easier maintenance, a production increase will occur. With crops beginning to be harvested, collections will pick up and cash needs will ease a little in the next quarter. He remembers that the shop uptown put in one of the new lathes last month, he will check with the owner during the weekly luncheon, and he should be ready to decide whether to immediately order or wait until the first of the year.

He was familiar with all aspects of the problem; he obtained the necessary new information and made a decision. Only men, not machines or techniques make decisions—machines and techniques only reflect and use previous decisions by men. What factors, both within and outside the manager, contribute to turning a man into a decision making system capable of turning out good decisions? The manager starts with a quick mind and when experience is added he is ready to make good decisions as fast as he receives the necessary information.

Symbolically this appears—

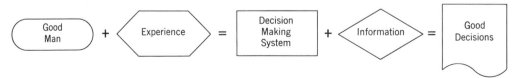

270

Turn to the manager's counterpart in a larger business which makes several product lines in multiplant operations and markets nationally. Deed him the quick mind, sound legs and good judgment, then give the same problem to the large firm manager: a 10 percent production increase in one product line based on minor capital outlay. Unfortunately, it is a larger problem now with all problems our first manager had plus the secondary effects on his other products, markets, and plants that the initial change will have.

The larger company manager starts by reviewing the costs of the expenditures to *judge* whether or not the savings will occur. Even as he takes the time to look he cannot, in a quick look, get the same depth of feeling or understanding that our first manager with his constant familiarity did. Similarly, how can he talk to half of his major customers to be sure they want more of the item at the current price? Our large firm manager cannot take a week to find out and he doesn't have this answer at his finger tips before the question arises. When he turns to production and sales reports to gather more information (it is mid-November and he has the third quarter reports) he gets another piece of the picture. But none of the reports tell him what *will* happen, only what happened some time back. After this he gets partial *judgments* from his subordinates (i.e., sales from sales managers, production from production managers) none of whom can see the whole picture.

What is missing here? It is not information on the costs of the new action; it is information on the effect of it on the business and no one person has the whole story. The large firm manager can rarely rely on personal observation as a major source of information.

The manager is not able to maintain the depth of recent experience with all aspects of the problem that the small firm manager had. The lack of recent experience is the result of his job (he can't keep current on all problems). Many people feel this problem is resolved by the normal reporting and advice received from subordinates and specialists (e.g., market research, production troubleshooters, etc.). No real argument here, the point is that the manager's information sources should be designed keeping the two purposes in mind. First, he will need the facts regarding the new

projects and second, a modest but steady stream of information to keep his experience level current. Such a stream should be monitored to prevent pouring repetitious information at the manager by a "report by exception technique" or the manager will probably shut it off and lose this recent experience based on new information.

The large firm manager needs information for two purposes: (1) exception reports on general activities to keep him familiar with the changing status of the business, and (2) specific detailed information relating to the problem being resolved.

GOAL OF SYSTEM

Here then is a worthwhile objective for a management information system. It should be designed to give the manager the amount of information (comparable to what his small firm counterpart has) he needs to make decisions both easily and quickly, with a reasonable degree of accuracy.

Business big or little cannot live long with consistently incorrect management decisions. Further, when the correct and necessary information is gathered and assembled, the making of sound decisions is simplified. The gathering of information, like the making of mistakes, is expensive. It may come that tomorrow's manager will be judged less on the poor decisions he may have made based on incomplete or distorted information but will be evaluated more on his ability to obtain and use the minimum sufficient amount of information necessary to make sound decisions.

For some managers such an approach would mean doubling the present supply of information. Others will balance their dependency on quantitative information with personal observation and halve their present supply. The man responsible for decisions must have what he deems to be sufficient information to keep current and on which to make decisions. A manager who completely ignores the responsibility for selection and/or maintenance of his information sources must approach his decision points like a blind man approaching an arterial highway relying on secondary senses or someone else to lead him across.

After a decision is made many managers self-evaluate and measure the results of their decisions: (1) to be ready for any corrective actions, and (2) because the evaluation process itself adds to their experience storehouse. Such evaluation is, in effect, repeating the decision process as new information is reviewed.

Symbolically, the manager's decision-making process is now a bit more complicated. It includes responsibility for controlling information input and for the establishment of measures to evaluate decisions. Frequently, the out-

The amount and types of information required by these people vary drastically. The system must serve them not only as a group but individually. The best reports are those designed for the people who must use them. The amount of detail needed regularly at top levels is less than that needed at lower and middle management levels. This results in a pyramid of report information.

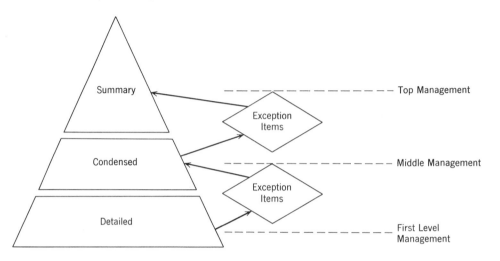

put items of an information system are reports and for them to serve as tools to aid management in making decisions they should have certain qualities.

This does not mean that the president needs less information to run the business than the foreman does to run a department. It is rather that the information normally reported to the

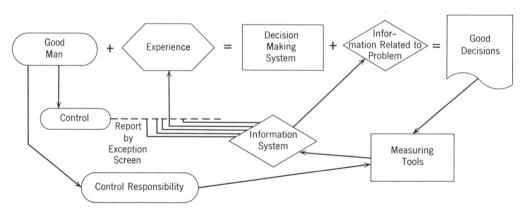

REPORT EFFECTIVENESS

Effective reports should be oriented toward the user considering both the management level of the user and the function of the individual using them. Many people need facts and reports of a various nature taken from the information system. Information users come from members of both line and staff.

president is of a summary nature so that he can judge results to see that subordinates have properly controlled the detail operations. A critical factor in a good information system is to be sure that exceptional items (both positive and negative) are automatically selected from each level of reports and included in the information normally reported to the next higher level of management. For example, a foreman's basic report might include productivity per hour for each employee on standard operations, whereas the middle manager's report would not show productivity by employee but only productivity per hour rates for employee groups. However, if an employee has an exceptional production rate, the report should bring this to the attention of middle management by reporting it as an exception item in the next level of management reports.

Effective reports giving information in quantitative terms must flow both ways in the organization. Information must flow down to serve as direction and, as feedback, flow up to show customer and end user demands to supply information for future policy decisions.

Information flows down because business organizations are directed from the top, and quantitative records of performance against standards or desired goals are necessary. This requires records of production or sales to be maintained for comparative and directional purposes. In customer sensitive organizations substantial information from field forces and customers flows up for use in inventory management and product planning. It is not enough to know that a customer in some location wants a product. What is required are more absolute measures of the size and reliability of the demand there. Then as these demand bits and pieces are summarized, checked in other areas and translated into production, they represent increased opportunities for the profitable marketing of the companies' products.

Effective reports must be brief, analyzed, and accurate. It should be unnecessary for higher levels of management to be required to analyze, compare, and compute the facts and figures shown in reports to determine the real meaning of the figures. Managment people have many demands on their time and cannot digest hundreds of pages of reports looking for the significant changes so that they may take action on them. Compare, in your own firm, the total costs of information system tools (including the costs of a modern high speed data processing machine) with the total costs to the firm of members of management, even ignoring the costs of bad decisions based on poor information, and determine in the best interest of the firm whose time should be saved.

It seems more desirable that management be advised by reports of four situations where problems exist and of three situations where an outstanding job is being done rather than for management to get 27 reports and dig out the seven special cases while filing the other 20. To be accurate, reports should not only be free of arithmetical errors and be based on reliable entries but should use figures that have no distortions. For example, a reported increase of 10 percent in sales realization for a commodity may look favorable until compared with figures showing that the cost of the commodities' production has risen 20 percent in the same period. If approaches of this type violate accounting principles, then the accounting reports using only these principles cannot serve as management information tools.

Effective reports must be based on a flexible system that allows quick changes to meet new conditions. Businesses and economic systems are not static but rather subject to constant changes. Yet many of the more effective statistical tools require data from extended past periods. The need is for flexible information, that can be reclassified or regrouped when new problems are recognized, to provide a history of previous data in such form that it contributes to the solution of the new problem. To do these things the system should gather (and record that source in machine language) all the material that will be needed later. Data should be gathered in full, establishing a separate classification for each significant factor for each transaction. Current summaries in machine language should be maintained reflecting the current status of products and their distribution. These summaries should be designed to serve the periodic report needs and to carry a background of detailed information that can quickly (within hours) provide complete information.

The goal for reports should be to publish regularly only what is used regularly. Other information would be maintained in a current state so that important, frequent, but irregular, distribution questions can be answered quickly. For example, it would not seem desirable to publish monthly a report giving a product breakdown of some 500 major products for 4,000 customers. There will be information frequently needed, however, on selected products by customer or location; these must be promptly satisfied so actions affecting profits can be taken. Also needed are records of major product groups by customer and/or end user groups. Quite probably new product development or a problem product may require a regular published report showing distribution.

The examples illustrate how general marketing information in summary form is used for both the publishing of minimum regular reports and the timely satisfying of irregular needs.

Effective reports must be timely. Studies have shown that the function of sales direction requires prompt records but allows a reasonable latitude in stating absolute quantities or dollars. For example, for most sales direction purposes it doesn't make any appreciable difference whether it is known that an account was sold exactly to the penny. However, care must be taken in accumulating figures that have been "rounded off" or significant total errors can develop. The essential point for sales direction is to have available current information. With the normal time lapse between orders booked for future production and shipments it is considered important in directing sales to know at least in early February what the important parts of the January order picture looked like.

Compare the sales direction control function to the quality control techniques used in keeping a production system within certain predetermined limits. Here it would be a poor system that told you in February that production in January was running out of control. What is needed is an information system to tell you at 2:16 P.M. that production from 2:14 to 2:15 P.M. was too heavy in rejects. Similarly, sales managers need prompt information to effectively direct and control sales activities. An information system must serve more than the function of sales direction (sales direction has been used as an example).

What is needed in a management information system and what is possible to achieve in the short run are often irreconcilable due to the practical limits of any existing system. For maximum effectiveness, the short run system should be highly flexible so facts from it can be easily converted into usable form in the new long range system. However, care should be taken in discarding an existing system until the new system is producing results.

MEASUREMENTS

Other important tools and techniques are part of a modern manager's kit in addition to reports. Modern computers have made practical the application of mathematical and statistical approaches to solving old problems. Operations research, linear programming, management games, correlation and regression analysis, analysis of variance, factor analysis, time series studies, all may contribute to an information system. Interestingly, in practically all cases in the applications of these techniques to business problems, the first problem to be faced was that insufficient information (distorted considered insufficient) existed for these tools to be applied effectively. The result being that the biggest costs of applying the technique were devoted to getting the information to serve as an input.

A related part of an information system is developing better means of activities measurement. As man progresses, he has found continuing need to improve his ability to measure both in a physical sense and as a measure of activities. Tolerances of ± ten thousandths of an inch were common and acceptable in components of transportation vehicles a few years ago. Today accuracy is often required to the ± one millionth of an inch; to achieve this goal new production techniques were required and new measuring techniques were needed. In physical measurements the problem is concentrated in determining the distance between two clearly defined points; in activity measurement one must first establish a starting point, then an ending point, before even beginning to measure the "distance" between them. To improve activities we must measure to determine both the direction and the magnitude of changes.

Today, all firms record the amount of money their customers owe them. How many also record "gross margin" per transaction per customer so that at the end of the period they can have a measurement not only of the top 50 customers in dollar billings but of the top 50 customers in "gross profits"? This is one beginning to measuring activities that can provide information to improve decisions about which customers (or customer groups) deserve better service or a larger part of the firm's influencing or merchandising dollars. Measuring begins by determining a starting point. With a flexible information system the firm can choose a point back in time as a starting point and measure through today, Those firms with inflexible information systems must choose today as a starting point and wait the passage of time to establish measurements. The foundation for information systems, decision making tools, and measurement systems is input. Oversimplified, the effect of poor input is often referred to as GIGO or garbage in—garbage out. Today, when accurate, timely detailed data (input) is accumulated it can be handled by techniques and tools available to provide sound information (output) for decisions.

In summary, a management information system is the means of bringing to each level of management the necessary and complete information that is accurate, timely, and sufficient, but not in excessive detail, so that the manager can fulfill his responsibilities in the business. Such information must flow both up and down in the organization. It must be based on sound data in a flexible system, allow new techniques to be used, and operate at a minimum cost commensurate with the overall information system results.

29. WHAT HAS CYBERNETICS TO DO WITH OPERATIONAL RESEARCH?

STAFFORD BEER *

Part 1 of this paper answers the question "What is cybernetics?" A brief historical review introduces a somewhat formal statement about the nature of systems and the way they are controlled. The unifying topic in the study of control in every context is an underlying identity of system: an example is taken from learning machines.

A comparably brief treatment of the question "What is operational research?" is given in Part 2. Operational research is thought to be the latest exemplification of scientific method rather than "a science." What is important about operational research is brought out through a description of an actual case study, and some of the activities which look like operational research but are not are mentioned. This leads to an attempted definition of operational research.

Part 3 tries to draw the answers to the first two questions together, and to show how operational research and cybernetics are related. It is possible to pursue each activity in its own right; but it is also possible to practise operational research with essentially cybernetic models, and to study cybernetics by operational research techniques. This thought is generalized into the idea that cybernetics is the science of which operational research is the method.

INTRODUCTION

"The Department of Operational Research and Cybernetics." This phrase is, I regret to say, rather a mouthful; and from what I hear some of my operational research colleagues find it too much to swallow. The last bit is not regarded as very respectable.

Now ten years ago operational research itself was not a particularly respectable activity. Today by contrast, the advertisement columns of the newspapers week by week attest to the fact that operational research is now highly respectable—and respected. It can only be a matter of time before cybernetics too achieves the status which it must have: I am quite confident of this.

Now you will gather that my mood is not very apologetic. In fact this address is meant to be polemical. That is why I have given it the aggressive title that I have; that is why I am wearing a bullet-proof waistcoat.

SOURCE: *Operational Research Quarterly* (March, 1959), pp. 1–21. Reprinted by permission of the *Operational Research Society*.

* The United States Companies Limited, United Kingdom.

WHAT IS CYBERNETICS?

Cybernetics is the science of control; or, to expand it into Norbert Wiener's own words: [1] control and communication in the animal and the machine. Like most definitions, this one does not seem to say very much at first sight. To understand what cybernetics is about, one just must look at the origins of the work. As you probably know from Wiener's book, cybernetics originated in the work of a group of people representing a number of sciences. And the point I want to make, the first point, is that they did not get together to discuss the question of control in the first place. They had noted that the whole range of human thinking had been developing over the centuries into a pattern, a pattern represented today by a large number of subjects each generally discussed as if it were a valid object of study in its own right. Here was a pattern which represented the historical development of human thinking; could it be, however, that it might not represent the real world very accurately at all? Whole topics of enquiry might fall neatly between the stools of the established sciences.

The problem of control emerged from these early discussions as something which is common to every science. Soon it was discovered that the nature of this problem for scientists in every field was uniform in many respects. What I should like to call "the theory of organic control," which is applicable to mechanical and social systems as well as to biological, grew from this impetus. So the essence of cybernetics is to be interdisciplinary.

Now it is very easy at this stage to talk about uniting the body of thinking, to speak of the unity of science and the indivisibility of knowledge. I am as aware as anyone of the pitfalls of this kind of speech. One can quickly throw oneself open to a charge of being some kind of alchemist, of having naïve and probably egotistical views about the complexity and wonder of nature and the amount of insight into it that one brain can possibly acquire and comprehend. But if you look on this concept of the unity of science simply in terms of the dimension of control, which is the way the subject of cybernetics arose historically, such charges prove baseless. Cybernetics is not an attempt to comprehend the whole of science and knowledge in one glorious confusion, but rather an attempt to see whether the understanding of control problems so far acquired in many disparate sciences is being properly shared. Although a great deal is known about control in various departments of learning, little has been done about the nature of control *per se*. In attacking that problem, cybernetics must inevitably borrow the available information about its subject wherever that seems to be available; in this sense it is certainly a unifying influence on science at large.

Just as the concept of control appears in every science, any conclusions which can be reached about it must be applicable to many contexts. Very soon, Wiener and his associates realized that they were discussing something which was relevant to industrial, social and economic systems, as well as to the mechanical and biological ones. Now it is extremely difficult to talk scientifically about a topic which has so many utterly different origins, and also so many widely varied applications. For this reason, the essence of a developing science is that it has some formal technique for discussing the basic nature of its subject and of ridding itself of the trappings which make up the specific detail. Can we find a formal language in which to talk about problems of control wherever they arise?

I do not think there is any doubt about the answer: we can. In logic, in mathematics, in statistics, and in metamathematics, there are formal systems that we know how to manipulate. But in a general paper like this I must confine any formal analysis, not to some recondite algebra, but to a verbal version. Even in English, it is possible to discuss the nature of control formally, and without bringing in the details of many different sciences. But I must do this quickly, because it is rather a tiresome set of aphorisms that must be presented.

Control is the attribute of a system. A system is any collection of entities that can be understood as forming a coherent group. The fact of their being capable of being understood as a coherent group is precisely what differentiates a system from a meaningless collection or jumble of bits and pieces. Now that statement does not sound very important, but I think it is; because at once it reveals the relativity of this concept of a system. This means that we might have a series of numbers on the blackboard which to an uneducated man, or a savage, or indeed most of the general public, would appear to be a meaningless jumble of figures; but to a mathematician this would be at once recognizable as a binomial series.

Therefore the property of being a system is as much a property of the observing system, which is I, or you, or whatever we use for the purpose as extensions of ourselves, as of the observed system itself.

The structure of a system is its relatedness. A description of the way in which the system is interconnected *defines* its structure. The system and the structure are formal components of the analysis I wish to make, and are words which I shall henceforth use in this special way.

It seems to me that there are three main characteristics of a cybernetic system. The first is that it is extremely complex, to the point of indefinability. It may be that no real system is in principle indefinable; but many certainly are in practice, because (like the brain) they disintegrate once they are probed too closely. The reason for this characteristic of a cybernetic system is that the connectivity of its structure, of which I was speaking just now, is initially very great and changing continuously. Thus the brain, the economy, the industrial company; all these things are cybernetic systems under this first heading at the very least—the heading of extreme complexity.

May we note in passing that operational research itself often claims to deal with complex systems, and so it does. But when we talk about an operational research model we like to think, I suspect, that we are creating an isomorphic representation of our problem. If we use linear programming, for instance, to study a problem of the allocation of materials from five different sources to five different consumers, it may well be true that we can do this. But once we try and use it ouside the context in which the straightforward matrix of small order can be constructed, and turn to game-theoretic analysis of the entire operations of a company, we are in very great difficulty. This is more than a practical problem, it is a methodological one; because we can no longer determine in any sense that our model is an isomorphism. To be quite formal: we must end up with a homomorphic representation—by which I mean, of course, that there is a many-one relationship from every segment of the situation being described to each element of the matrix which is describing it. This is a very severe methodological limitation on the analysis by operational research techniques of extremely complex systems. Cybernetics tries to answer the problem by the use of Black Box theory. This is the theory which specifically begins by accepting the situation as indefinable in detail.

Now the second feature of a cybernetic system is its probabilism. Again, operational research deals with indeterminate systems. But we normally say this in the sense that *within* a rigid framework of related parts, most of the quantities which characterize the parts are not constants, they are distributed. For example, the relations which connect a queue to the machine which has to serve it are quite clear, distinct and unchanging. It is the waiting time and the service time that are the variables which lead us to call the system probabilistic. In cybernetics, however, the very structure of the system is indeterminate. The existence of connexion between entities which make up the system is itself problematic; the network of connectivity is itself defined by variables to which levels of probability can be assigned. If the levels fall below the threshold of statistical significance, then the system disinte-

grates and ceases to be recognizable as a system at all. If the level of threshold changes, the system itself changes, and is no longer describable as the system that it was.

The third major feature of cybernetic systems is the feature of self-regulation. How, after all, is a system to be controlled? In operational research, it is customary to design controls which can be operated within certain fiducial limits. This approach is a great advance over the less sophisticated notion that it is possible to have rigid error-free regulators. But consider the kind of system we have so far designated as cybernetic. It is to be so complex as to be indefinable; it is to be probabilistic not only in its operational parameters but in its very structure. It follows that no control at all designed to be imposed upon the system from outside could possibly work. A little reflection shows this must be the case, and that a regulator can only be designed in the sense that the system will operate it itself. Systems can in fact be designed as machines for self-regulation. Homeostasis is of course the example of this in biology and physiology; and thanks to Ross Ashby it is further exemplified in his kind of topological mathematics and ultrastable machines.

With these explanations, let me now try to finish my formal verbal statement. Control is the attribute of a system which tends to sustain the system's structure, to reinforce its cohesion. Control is the dynamics of the structure. To exert control in a new direction in a given system is to discover the language in which new structure may be discerned. To exert control in a recognized direction, on the other hand, is to facilitate the speaking of the language of a recognized structure. This is what communication means: the talkativeness of a structure within itself, the ease of association inside its relatedness. So to manage the system you must be able to talk to it, to talk inside it, as a competent conversationalist.

A system, and now I am speaking emphatically of any system, can be made responsive if it is talked to in the right language, the language of its own structure which makes it the system it is. By communication inside the system, it comes to be conditioned; this is to say that the probabilities which quantify the internal relatedness of the structure begin to change. Circumstances can be created in which the system becomes conditioned to suit the behaviour we require of it; circumstances in which, with perfect propriety, the system can be said to be learning and discriminating. As management of this kind goes on paths of facilitation inside the structure become established, certain languages become more fluent than others, and certain translations from one language to another become more readily available to the system itself. In this way the system comes to exhibit memory.

At this point we have arrived knee deep in the language of physiology, and I expect a lot of complaints about this. May I at once attempt to dispose of the problem about the free use of the languages of one science in the languages of another, a practice which is always so very unpopular. When, in cybernetics, we use machine language to talk about animals; when we use biological language to discuss machines; it is then that the trouble starts. We are breaking down inhibitions of language, we are breaking through habits of thought; we are accused of a facile rhetoric, and a mere glibness of tongue. What is the point of this polyglot language, and what is the validity of the comparison it implicitly makes?

Let us arbitrarily distinguish three levels of comparison. Firstly, there is the metaphor. Perhaps when we speak of memory and learning in machines, this is the level of comparison we intend. Now the validity of a metaphor is poetic; it can offer science no more help than its verbal facility. Secondly, there is the comparison of identity itself. Perhaps when we speak of a complicated logical gate made of electronic components as a neuron we mean that it is literally the same thing as a neuron in a nervous network. But the validity of the comparison of identity between things which are not one and the same is a mystical validity. Mysticism is not generally regarded as useful to science; it may offer insight, but the vision is cloudy. Thirdly, there is analogy. This comparison has a logical validity. If we choose to say that a machine has a neurosis, perhaps we mean that its behaviour is like the behaviour of a human neurotic. Such a comparison is useful in science although it is edged about with problems of the delineation of its application. Any argument which we do not particularly like can be said to be "pushing the analogy too far." Nonetheless, analogical thinking is extremely useful in operational research; and I think that many operational research men who object to cybernetic discussion do so because

they imagine the thinking is analogical—by analogy with operational research!

Now I am extremely anxious to assert that the physiological language of cybernetics is neither metaphorical nor analogical. Despite the mystical connotations of the assertion, I contend that the comparisons of cybernetics are identities. If a mystic were to say that two things which are manifestly not the same are the same, we would say that he had perceived, or dimly understood, some kind of ultimate identity. I am claiming that in cybernetics we are trying to pinpoint that perception scientifically. And the identity we can pinpoint is the identity of structure—as I have already defined that word. Let us take an example.

We talk about learning in the animal and the machine. It is customary to take the example of a rat running a maze for the demonstration of animal learning: the maze has two outcomes and eventually the rat learns to go to the cheese rather than the electric shock. You have perhaps heard the story of the maze-running rat who said to his colleague: "I have that chap in the white coat conditioned. Every time I run to the end of the maze he gives me a piece of cheese." But let us take this maze-learning more seriously, and consider that the maze is so constructed that there is (on a basis of random running) an equal probability of getting a piece of cheese or an electric shock. Therefore the system begins in a state of even probability over these two outcomes. And as the experiment proceeds the rat begins to approach the cheese more often than the shock until after some considerable experience he almost invariably reaches the cheese. We call this process learning; and I refuse to be impressed by the kind of special significance which some people wish to give this word. They speak of learning as if it were a prerogative of animate things; in so doing they are being dragooned by a mere word. Our rat-maze system begins in a state of even probability over the two outcomes; ultimately it approaches a state of unit probability on the cheese outcome. I choose to label this behaviour "learning." Now if we do this experiment repeatedly, we find that the initial and final outcome of the experiment, designated 0.5/0.5 and 1.0/0, are connected through time by a curve which is reproducible —and what is more a curve to which statistical significance can be given.

Now there is the formal language and there

is the abstraction of the structure of the system of learning. It is expressed in mathematical terms as a stochastic process. Once that structure is understood, there is no reason why a machine should not be built, which is a probabilistic machine, to do the same thing. And indeed, as you no doubt know, this has been done. The result is an artefact of a learning rat, which will produce experimental learning (by a Monte Carlo procedure) and provide behavioral statistics which are indistinguishable to the animal physiologist from the real results. There is an example, an elementary one, of what a cybernetician would call a learning machine. The rat running a maze is a learning machine. The mathematical specification of this stochastic process is a learning machine. The mechanical artefact is a learning machine. This illustrates quite well the idea of the structural identity of all three things. There is neither metaphor nor analogy here: there is identity in a formal sense.

So that is the kind of process that cybernetics studies, that is how it analyses what is going on, that is the heuristic mechanism of cybernetics. The result of such studies is, inevitably, that we seek to build machines: and cyberneticians have built machines that learn. They have built machines which carry out many other functions normally attributed to animate systems by a similar process of reasoning. Let me now pick up three examples of actual machines which I choose to illustrate the three main features of cybernetic systems which I began by discussing. The feature of structural probabilism is exemplified in a small way by the learning machine already described. A learning machine is essentially a conditional probability mechanism. Secondly, there is the idea of self-regulation; this may be exemplified by Ashby's homeostat,[2] where the same process of finding the structural element that is common to all self-regulating systems is pursued. In this case, the discovery is of that formal structure which leads a system to fall into an equilibrial state when perturbed by unspecified causes. And thirdly, the idea of extreme complexity is very well illustrated by one of Gordon Pask's brilliant machines [3] which formally identifies the structural elements of a process of growth.

This is what I take cybernetics to be about, and this is what cyberneticians do. But please note that because of the definitions which I have already given about systems and their structure, and the account I have given of the formal languages by which they may be described, any collection of entities which is cohesive can be described as a machine. Thus whether cybernetics deals with animals, or hardware, any other kind of system, is irrelevant. It is always possible to journey into the problem of describing the behaviour of a complex, probabilistic, self-regulating system in this way. And therefore there is no necessity to characterize cybernetics by the building of machines in the metal. They may equally exist in the flesh. Above all, they may arise in economic and social relationships. If the description of a social system can be mapped into the formal structure of a learning machine, then that society is a machine for learning. There is no more to be said.

WHAT IS OPERATIONAL RESEARCH?

Having probed the nature of cybernetics, I would now like to probe the nature of operational research. I am really rather tired of the situation where, whenever anyone speaks on operational research, we have to make all these coy jokes about not really knowing what it is. What is our present approach to this question of the nature of operational research? I will tell you as I see it.

We say that this is a new and a young scientific endeavour, and that it would be very unwise to be dogmatic about it. Operational research is a sort of high-level activity; it involves studying things scientifically. Now this is a very estimable line to take. Consider how *mature* it is: one is not making any wild claims about what can be done, and what cannot be done. Consider how *safe* it is: the best of all worlds is ours to command. If someone says: "What about this operational research job, it just did not work," we may reply: "Oh, *that* was not really operational research." They may say: "Look at this wonderful job"; and we reply: "Yes—yes—*that* is operational research." Consider further how *comforting* this approach is: we sit in an esoteric coterie, hugging ourselves, and keeping warm together, which is a very superior sort of thing to do. Yes: our attitude is estimable: mature, safe, and comforting.

What price do we pay for this charming situation? We pay the price of utter confusion. There is today total confusion about the status, aims, and abilities of our work. Management has no idea of what we are trying to do, and is getting tired of trying to find out.

Recently I agreed to give a lecture on linear programming, and I was introduced by a senior and well-known industrialist who said: "Mr. Beer will give a lecture on linear programming, or as it is sometimes called, operational research." Management does not yet understand what operational research is about. Do our junior operational research people themselves? Most of the people at this meeting are fairly senior in operational research. I ask them what sort of future we can offer our staffs, what sort of professional status they will have in the years to come, in the brave new world? We, the Operational Research Society, have not managed to agree what operational research is, and have refused an authoritative definition to enquirers. Perhaps for this reason the Society is unable to give our staffs the professional distinction of the letters M.O.R.S. (or K.I.M.B.A.L. for that matter) to their names. And what about the national level? We have totally failed, as far as I can see, and despite some very distinguished senior men in our organization, in making anything like the right impact on the national problems to which operational research might offer a solution.

Now this is a very high price to pay for our present outlook, and I am boldly going to suggest that this outlook is simply cowardice masquerading as wisdom. For of course we know what operational research is. We have been doing it for years.

Let me quote. "Operational research may be regarded as a branch of philosophy, as an attitude of mind towards the relation of man and environment; and as a body of methods for the solution of problems which arise in that relationship." You will recognize that; it was our President speaking to the Operational Research Society.* Now I hope Professor Kendall will not think it an impertinence in me to say that I consider this is one of the best descriptions I have ever seen. It gives us an excellent start. Please notice that he did not say anything about queue theory, or search theory, or the inventory model. He gave us a description of a new man-oriented science. This is indeed what we are trying to do.

I would like to urge this point of view.

* Presidential Address on 23 October, 1958.

Operational research is not *a* science, for it is not *about* anything; it *is* science.

Now the Newtonian universe has given place to several more sophisticated universes in succession. They are universes in which man has projected a greater maturity of his own intellect. In physics, the billiard-ball atoms have gone; in physiology, the reflex arcs have gone; in economics, the Robinson Crusoe economy has gone. We have replaced these elementary descriptions by those more advanced. In turn, operational research for me has replaced the "objectivity of science." It is the modern embodiment of "the scientific method." That phrase is one we use in the Society's constitution. But what is *the* scientific method? I gather that nobody ever seems able to define that either. For me, again, it can be nothing more or less than induction, which is part of logic.

This induction has three main principles which I should like briefly to review. Perhaps we can learn from the way these three principles are being recast, what is really happening in the attack of applied science. First, there is the old principle of the uniformity of nature—associated with John Stuart Mill. This principle insisted that nature is a connected whole, within which changes occur; it led to the notion of "physical laws." By today, the same notion has led us in our work to what I have always called the operational research of "organic wholes." You all have your names for this, but the idea is the same. It is not the job of operational research to investigate the fiddling details of industrial processes, nor the pin-pricking worries of management. The operational research job is to get the problem in perspective in its proper environment; in other words, we do not suboptimize. And the second lead that the principle of the uniformity of nature gave us was the notion that what is true this time will be true next time if the conditions are the same. That notion originally led to the whole of the nineteenth century idea of the laboratory experiments, controlled experiments. And to what has that outlook matured? It has matured straight into operational research, where we have rejected the laboratory investigation with its belief that variables can be altered one at a time. We have said: real life is not like this, we have statistical techniques and the design of experiments to help us in studying more natural patterns of variation. And so this thread unfolds, until we find ourselves with the modern idea of active applied science—being precisely operational research.

Causation, the next principle of induction, is the most important exemplification of the principle of uniformity. Not only is there relatedness in the universe, there is causal relatedness. That lead, through the nineteenth century again, gave us "objectivity in science." It gave us nature as an inexorable machine, working out its answers deterministically—if only we could discover how. But the large clockwork toy has changed. The raw notion of cause has given place to the principle of indeterminacy. It was Sir Owen Wansbrough Jones whom I first heard in a broadcast talk comparing the problems of operational research with the problems of a physicist looking at the discoveries of Heisenberg. That was a useful idea, which I myself pursued in another paper.[4] We find it summed up again by Professor Kendall in his Presidential Address, when he said: "There is a broad movement against the nineteenth century attitude towards objectivity in science." We have learnt that the observer is part of the situation. In work study there is the spotlight effect. In the introduction of new ideas there is the Hawthorne effect. These are examples of a point made earlier tonight about the observer affecting the definition of the system he seeks to describe.

Finally, the third principle of induction: limited variety. This is the idea that properties go in sets; the idea that variety does not proliferate, as it could do in theory, by permutation and combination, but that attributes hang together in families. And for the Victorians that provided the argument from analogy. Already this evening we have had to dig ourselves out of the muddle which this testament has bequeathed. And already, I have tried to show how the concept of analogy in logic has grown and developed into the idea of structural identity. Today we have a new version of limited variety. We say: "Here is a ɬream of ingots coming from a melting shop, and the stream breaks up into six streams feeding six soaking pits." This model could equally well be a warehouse from which flows a stream of goods to six retail shops. Is this an analogy? No; these two things are identical in a formal sense. They are identified in a structure given by the statistics of queue theory.

In short: the universe has gone over from the motionless universe of Zeno, where nothing ever happens, to a Heracletian flux in which things are happening all the time. And the methods of science have gone from the stationary, one-variable-at-a-time kind of treatment to the treatment of operations conceived operationally—and what could that be but operational research? We no longer imagine ourselves to be using the three inductive principles to discover "what a thing is really like"; that is a pious hope belonging to the old conception. We use instead new versions of these three principles to say what makes an assembly of things tick. These new versions are essentially the operational research techniques; their object is to discover the strategy of the assembly. Thus I contend that operational research emerges as a subset of scientific methods appropriate to the analysis of *activity*, just as chemical methods of analysis from titration to spectroscopy are a subset appropriate to chemistry. And these sets of methods do not form a science—nor does operational research. And so I am saying let us do away with the idea of *"the* science of operational research"; and let us also do away with the idea "but we do not know what it is." There is really a wonderful ambivalence about these two statements anyway, is there not?

Let me now make these comments about the nature of operational research more specific by reference to a particular operational research job. I shall do this very briefly, because this is not intended as a specimen case history, but is put forward as revealing a number of important features of our work. This project identifies some of the things I take operational research to do, and which I would like to see incorporated in a definition.

The job arose in this way. What should the maximum demand for electricity be in a steelworks? Maximum demand is the greatest load of electricity you expect to call from the grid at any one time; you fix this level with your supplier in the summer, and say that you will not go beyond this figure at peak loading during the winter. The higher this figure is fixed the more safe you are, but the more expensive the contract is because the supplier has to cover himself against this load as a potential demand. The lower the figure is fixed, the less expensive the contract; but the greater risk is then run of exceeding it. Once the works comes up against its limit, it must either shed its load and thereby ruin its productivity, or must exceed its maximum demand and pay a severe fine for doing so.

We were told what the maximum demand figure operated the previous winter was; that it had in fact been exceeded more than once; and what the contractual terms and the excess levy had been. The question naturally was, what should the limit be set at now, having regard to the extra cost involved in diminishing the risk and the extra risk involved in diminishing the cost? This, you will agree, was very rightly conceived as an operational research job.

You will also agree that the main difficulty in operational research is the definition of the problem. The one we were given which I have outlined seems clear enough. But is it the real problem, or is it perhaps no more than the symptom of the real problem? We argued in this way. Electricity is a source of energy; but a steelworks has many sources of energy: coke-oven gas, blast furnace gas, steam, and oil, as well as electricity. And all these sources interact; because gas or oil can be burnt to make steam, and steam used to make electricity. Therefore, just as you can buy electricity from the national grid, you can sell electricity to the national grid (though for less money than you pay for buying it). Still further, gas can be stored in a gas holder; but if you have a contract to supply the local township with gas, the store must take that commitment into account. In fact, this is an exceedingly complex interacting system with many constraints.

It is now clear that to consider the original problem of maximum demand in a vacuum would be to suboptimize the larger problem. Effective operational research would study the whole energy system, and this is what we did. A large scale mathematical model of the system as a whole was constructed, and from a study of this a strategy for operating the whole energy system was evolved. This strategy had then to be expressed in terms which could be understood on the shop floor. There, one cannot discuss a strategy in set-theoretic terms; one must say: "If the reading on this meter has reached this point, then providing that reading on that meter has reached that point, pull this handle." The strategy, translated into these operational terms, was accepted by the management, explained to the operatives, and installed by the operational research team.

What was the answer to the original question? From the study just described, it was possible to evaluate the optimum level for maximum demand. Far from proposing to raise the previous level, and we had originally thought that we should have to do just that, it proved possible to *halve* it. The extra power to justify this had been obtained from degrees of freedom imported to the problem from the rest of the energy system. This recommendation was accepted, the strategy adopted, and the whole job was a success.

Several critical points about an operational research study emerge from this example. First, operational research involves an environment. In the case quoted, the issue is to decide what *is* the problem and what the environment. The answer was that the other energy systems had to be incorporated in the study of the first. It is always possible to bite off an arbitrary amount of a problem's environment, and to include it in the problem: the question is, how much? The first great characteristic of the operational research man is the ability to see this fact, to delineate his problem on that basis, to persuade the management that he is right, to find the method which will handle this organic structure; all this comes before the ability to solve the problem.

The important fact is that problems are simply not respecters of the official organization. A problem is first observed as a kind of outcrop; it appears in one cell of the business. There is a tendency to assume that the problem is completely contained in that cell: the cost office, a particular works department, a specific sales office. If it has ramifications elsewhere, then surely it is possible to make representations and to expect a little collaboration from "the other side." This is not the approach of operational research, which is essentially a problem-oriented activity. The real nature of the problem must be uncovered, and this requires a very general authority to investigate the state of affairs without being contained in the organizational locality where the outcrop first appeared. If operational research men cannot be trusted with this generalized authority, then either they are not fit people for the work or the management does not understand what sort of work it is.

The specimen study concerned a dynamic interacting state of affairs which must certainly be described as both complex and probabilistic. How did operational research seize hold of the problem? Its method was to construct a model; and my next point is to ask: how ubiquitous is the idea of a model in operational research? I have often tentatively proposed that no operational research job has ever been done without the use of a model, and since this has never provoked a counter-example I will now risk the statement that this is indeed a characteristic of the work. Should anyone seek to deny this, may I warn him in advance of my defence. He says of a given job: there was no model. I reply that a model of the situation must have existed in his brain before he could do the thinking required to solve the problem. A model is no more than a description into which the real situation can be mapped. If the mapping can be done inside the skull, so much the better. But if the situation is too complicated, then the brain cannot hold the structure and its owner must go on to paper with an elaborate scheme. But the idea is the same, I contend.

The final point to be brought out is the obvious one that mixed disciplines were playing their parts in the study quoted. This point must be made but need not be laboured; for no one has ever denied that the interdisciplinary attack is characteristic of operational research.

If this is the kind of approach which we would agree constitutes operational research, there are other kinds of activity which I feel we ought steadfastly to eliminate from that classification. In the first place, to plot a set of empirical results from the works, and to note that they form a normal distribution, and that therefore a specific probability can be allocated to the likelihood that values greater than a certain parameter of the variate will occur, is not in itself operational research. It is trivial. It may be perfectly good statistics to make this observation, but it is not operational research. To ensure that I am not misunderstood to say that industrial statistics is trivial, let me take the example further. Just look at some of the models for inventory control which have been published. They are not trivial statistics, they are very advanced. But should you come to *use* such models in the works, you find that you are speared and impaled on the assumptions implicit in the model. "Since this delay is likely to be exponentially distributed"

has got into the script in small print; it seems innocuous enough. But should we plot the actual distribution as derived from an empirical study—why, it looks like the sunset silhouette of a file of camels walking down the Valley of the Kings. This is not to deny that academic model-building is useful; of course it is. But the *operational research* has hardly begun at the point when the proud author goes into print with his piece of mathematics.

The second class of cognate activity which I should like to segregate from operational research is what I classify as erudite fun-and-gamesmanship. Consider this example of model-building for the analysis of decision procedures.[5]

N is a sequence of decision rules applied to the decision situation d. We made this specific by applying a particular starred sequence to the decisions typified as d_i; and where u is the pay-off the outcome may be written:

$$u(N^*(d_i))$$

But other decision sequences are possible; let us designate another set N^1. The first sequence is preferable to the second if their difference is positive when this has been evaluated for all i. And so we get:

$$\sum_{i=1}^{n} \{u(N^*(d_i)) - u(N^1(d_i))\} > 0$$

which is called "the axiom of long-run success."

So far, so good. Say rather: so far and no farther. There is nothing much else we can do with this, but at least we have got a fine name. But I forget: there is another step after all. Put Lim in front of the expression, where (I $n \to \infty$ quote) "the limit is assumed to exist." If I am going to take an infinite number of decisions I most certainly *expect* long-run success.

Let us have science, and mathematics; let us think deeply; let us be abstruse in our arguments where necessary. But let us relate operational research to operations and the possibility of improving them.

On the strength of this analysis, may I now attempt the definition of operational research for which I have been pleading. This one consists of two sentences including eight clauses:

(1) Operational research is the attack of modern science

(2) on problems of likelihood (accepting mischance)

(3) which arise in the management and control

(4) of men and machines, materials and money

(5) in their natural environment.

(6) Its special technique is to invent a strategy of control

(7) by measuring, comparing and predicting probable behaviour

(8) through a scientific model of a situation.

THE CONNEXION

The Shared Aspects. We have reviewed the nature of the science of cybernetics, and the nature of the modern scientific method that we call operational research. I have made no attempt as we went along to relate the two, but now is the time to show how much these topics have in common.

There is a shared general intention. Cybernetics studies control as its object; operational research is normally concerned with control problems. That is implied by clause 3 of my definition. Elsewhere [6] I have tried very hard to show that operational research jobs always involve control, and that therefore they must always involve a cybernetic model. Secondly, there is the shared nature of the problem; complex and probabilistic. The only difference between the two topics in this dimension is that cybernetics stands for the problem itself, and operational research stands for the approach made to it.

Thirdly, there is the shared level of sophistication. In cybernetics, this appears as the mapping of an inanimate system into the physiological model which makes it viable. In operational research the outlook is manifested in a refusal to isolate the system from its environment, together with the important idea that the observer himself is inextricably involved in the system.

Fourthly, there is the reciprocity of method between the two subjects of which I will say more in a moment. And fifthly, there is the shared organization: which is simply the interdisciplinary attack.

So there are all these points of contact, these shared characteristics. Therefore we may next ask: is cybernetics itself the same thing as operational research? The answer is: no, it cannot be. Would any operational research man really contend that his job in life is to build thinking machines? Does operational research really have the pure structure of control as the object of study? No again: it may involve the idea of control, but the object of study is (to put the point as precisely as possible) the improvement of an operation. Nevertheless, the relationships are there, and we must consider in what way they actually work.

Operational Research (cum Cybernetics). In the first place, there is the notion of characteristically operational research work which has a basically cybernetic model. In our Department, there are now some seventy people. More than fifty of these are scientists and technicians, working on twenty-seven different projects at the moment. No less than eighteen of these projects are in the area of production control (as we call it). This means the field of planning, progressing, programming, stockholding, the flow of material, and so on. All eighteen projects could be described as cybernetics, if we choose to define the object as the study of control itself. But if we concentrate on the mode of attack and the general intention to improve the state of affairs, no one here would dispute that we are doing operational research.

In being specific, I think there is no need to repeat to this audience an account of the servomechanistic model used years ago in our early work on production control in United Steel. There was an operational research attack, based on a definitely cybernetic model. Consider further, however, two more recent jobs in different works on the progressing of orders. A logical model of priority has been built which includes organic feedbacks from the plant and from the customer, so that the logic changes continuously as environmental events unfold. That is a cybernetic model. The job of quantifying the model, of transforming the logic into an arithmetic of priority numbers which can be handled as if they were natural numbers, and of installing this system to procure better deliveries, is a piece of thoroughgoing operational research. In the second works, the same problem has the different characteristic that it concerns jobbing engineering; a fact which results in a difficulty about commensurable facts. It is a typical operational research problem to find coherent measures for incommensurables, and to achieve the outcome of controlled production and accurate deliveries. But the model for this work is again entirely cybernetic. We are concerned with orders which *grow* from raw materials to completion—and growth is essentially an organic process in an organic world. It is also typified by a familiar sigmoid curve. This curve is our model, against which the growth of capital built into engineering products can be contrasted. Managerial decisions are based on fiducial control limits built on to the sigmoid curve. Finally, think of the concept, discussed elsewhere,[7] that the diversified management structure of a large industrial combine constitutes a learning machine for investing capital in stocks. There is no time to expand this point here; but I seek to implant the notion of a cybernetic machine having no hardware, no paperwork system, no automatic data processing; a machine whose operations can be studied solely by operational research.

The basis of these ideas about operational research in production control on a cybernetic model may be found in a paper entitled "The Cybernetic Analogue of Planning and Programming,"[8] which I wrote three years ago. I am very proud of this paper. The review in the *Operational Research Quarterly* was admirably succinct. It was: "Curious rather than important." Now curiosity is the essence of enquiring science; importance is the essence of conforming orthodoxy.

Cybernetics (cum Operational Research). Secondly, we come to the thought that in "doing cybernetics" the only methods available to the scientist are precisely those of operational research. I will give just one example of this, although the story of cybernetics is full of such illustrations. This one derives from a paper by Ross Ashby.[9]

Habituation in animals is the phenomenon whereby the response to any regularly repeated stimulus decreases. By analogy with neg-entropy it could be called neg-learning. Making a study of habituation is assuredly a job for the cybernetician: it is not an apparently operational research job. But Ashby's attack on it has many features of the operational research attack.

To begin with, he built a model of habituation, in terms of the special kind of topology

he has derived from the French school known as Bourbaki. In studying this model, he came to the very surprising conclusion that habituation is a property of a wide class of general systems, and not uniquely a property of living ones as most people would suppose. Startling conclusions are typical of well-conceived operational research, and so is the result that the problem has been completely misapprehended. Moreover, Ashby finds that the habituating system is not independent of the observer: again a typical operational research result. The observer is muddled up with the system and cannot be detached. According to Ashby, to say "I tested this system for habituation, and I eventually found it to show a diminished response" is to verge on the tautologous.

As if this cybernetic study had not already revealed the operational research nature of its approach its author next proceeds to check his results by nothing other than a Monte Carlo simulation. He takes as his system a set of random numbers from Kendall and Babbington Smith, and by applying the rules of his model proceeds to show these numbers undergoing transformations in which habituation can be detected. This fittingly completes a beautiful example of the relationship I have been trying to demonstrate.

Conclusion. Now I must conclude, and I do so by answering the initial question: "What has cybernetics to do with operational research?" The answer will be given in two parts. First, as to subject matter, both topics are concerned in the main with control. This contention may be expressed in a Venn diagram (Figure 1) as follows:

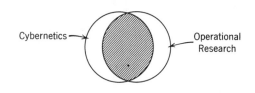

FIG. 1.

The overlapping area is where the subject matter is concerned with control. Secondly, as to methods, I cannot conceive an operational research technique which could not be applied in the field of cybernetics, and I think that most cybernetic studies must invoke operational research techniques. This conclusion is portrayed in another Venn diagram (Figure 2):

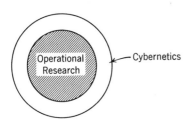

FIG. 2.

The unshaded portion of the diagram which belongs to cybernetics alone includes such methods as the dissection of the brain and the construction of electronic machinery.

It must be made clear that these over-simplified conclusions and the diagrams are offered simply as a résumé of these arguments. They are not meant to be logically demonstrable conclusions, as are the conclusions to be drawn from Venn diagrams in logic itself. I accept that they are arbitrary; by which is meant that a means of representing the existence of a dinosaurus or the relationship of church and state could doubtless be found and added to them. They are neither unique nor logically necessary: they are there to say what I mean.

Three years ago, I did try to educe the relationship between cybernetics and operational research in a formal way. This was done through the concept of causation which both subjects also share, and the method used was analysis by symbolic logic. I would like to quote from that part of the paper [10] which was written in ordinary English:

Operational research comprises a body of methods which cohere to provide a powerful tool of investigation. Cybernetics is a corpus of knowledge which might reasonably claim the status of a science. My contention is that the two are methodologically complementary; that the first is the natural technique in research of the second, and the second the natural embodiment in science of the first.

By definition, each is concerned to treat a complex and interconnected system or process as an organic whole. By methodology, each is concerned with models and analogies from every source. By science, neither is departmental. By philosophy, each attests to the indivisible unity of knowledge.

Three years and a good deal of research in both these fields later, I am more convinced than ever that cybernetics is indeed the science of which operational research is the method. Thus, as long as this profession treats "cybernetics" as a rather dirty word, and as long as the universities in the main ignore a new science which has the audacity not to fit into the hallowed academic structure; so long will operational research practitioners, their beards growing greyer and their eyes more wild, have to pretend that they do not really know what their subject is all about.

REFERENCES

1. Norbert Wiener, *Cybernetics.* John Wiley, New York (1948).
2. Ross Ashby, *Design for a Brain.* Chapman & Hall, London (1954).
3. Gordon Pask, "Physical Analogues to the Growth of a Concept," *Symposium on the Mechanization of Thought Processes.* H.M.S.O., London. (In press.)
4. Stafford Beer, "The Organization of Operational Research," *Research,* 9 (5) (1956).
5. William Morris, *The Rationalization of Industrial Decision Processes.* Ohio State University, Columbus, U.S.A. (1957).
6. Stafford Beer, *The Scope for Operational Research in Industry.* Institution of Production Engineers, London (1957).
7. Stafford Beer, "The Irrelevance of Automation," *Transactions of the Second International Congress on Cybernetics.* Namur, Belgium. (In press.)
8. Stafford Beer, "A Technical Consideration of the Cybernetic Analogue for Planning and Programming," *Process Control and Automation,* 3 (8), (9).
9. Ross Ashby, "The Mechanism of Habituation," *Symposium on the Mechanization of Thought Processes.* H.M.S.O., London. (In press.)
10. Stafford Beer, "Operational Research and Cybernetics," *Transactions of the First International Congress on Cybernetics.* Namur, Belgium (1959).

BIBLIOGRAPHY

1. Anshen, Melvin, "The Manager and the Black Box," *Harvard Business Review*, November–December, 1960.
2. Ashby, W. R., *Introduction to Cybernetics*, John Wiley and Sons, 1956.
3. Beer, Stafford, *Cybernetics and Management*, Science Editions, 1964.
4. Bell, D. A., *Intelligent Machines—An Introduction to Cybernetics*, Blaisdell Publishing Co., 1962.
5. Bellman, R., "Control Theory," *Scientific American*, September, 1964.
6. Eisenhart, C., "Cybernetics: A New Discipline," *Science*, April, 1949.
7. George, F. H., *Automation, Cybernetics and Society*, Philosophical Library, 1959.
8. Guilbaud, G. T., *What Is Cybernetics?*, Criterion Books, 1959.
9. Kemeny, J. G., "Man Viewed as a Machine," *Scientific American*, April, 1955.
10. Matthias, S. C., "Message of Cybernetics," *National Association of Accountancy Bulletin*, February, 1965.
11. Michael, D. N., *Cybernation: The Silent Conquest*, Center for the Study of Democratic Institutions, 1962.
12. Sinaiko, H. W. (ed.), *Selected Papers on Human Factors in the Design and Use of Control Systems*, Dover Publications, 1961.
13. Smith, O. J. M., *Feedback Control Systems*, McGraw-Hill Book Co., 1958.
14. Theobald, R., "The Cybernated Era," *Vital Speeches*, August, 1964.
15. Taube, M., *Computers and Common Sense: The Myth of Thinking Machines*, Columbia University Press, 1961.
16. Wiener, N., *Cybernetics*, John Wiley and Sons, 1948.

Part IX.   Electronic Computers

No single tool has had the impact on business operations as had the computer. Its almost blanket acceptance by the business world has raised it to the pinnacle, an awesome deity that has mesmerized many a neophyte in its spotless temples. To assert that computers have revolutionized business is but to acknowledge a fact of life. In our day they are engaged "shoulder to shoulder" with management personnel in the making of decisions. There is hardly a company nowadays that has not in some way or other been affected by the presence of the computer or data processor.

When speaking of computers we are referring to the electronic devices for the processing, transfer, and storage of data. Computers are capable of performing arithmetical operations at fantastic speeds, and it was for this reason that they were first employed, thus reducing data processing costs. In those instances where they were properly employed they were generally successful. Because of the computer's large memory storage capacity and because of its ability to make logical comparisons and thus render routine decisions, it has great potential in the business world, where it is inundated with enormous waves of analyzable data. The computer can present management with greater speed and accuracy in the processing of such data, with more timely reporting, and with the predicted results of choosing alternative courses of action.

In spite of the obvious advantages of computers, they somehow have not lived up to their expectations. It is interesting to note here that some authorities attribute this failure to management and not to any inherent defects or shortcomings of the hardware. As with other novel techniques that have invaded the managerial field, computers too have often been looked upon as a panacea for all of management's problems, and when they have not been proven such, their failure was duly noted. While some companies have been able to justify the use of computers on the basis of clerical savings alone, others, lacking imagination and initiative in utilizing them in the areas where they possess their greatest potential, have found it hard to justify their continued use. Moravec, in a previous selection (Chapter 13), expressed the belief that present-day data processing systems are grinding out far more data than any manager can possibly assimilate. Others have seen the organizational structure as the villain blocking the proper utilization of the computer for information technology. Because of the similarity to punched-card accounting equipment, the responsibility for the data processing equipment was often "logically" assigned to the assistant controller who typically lacked the creative ability to optimize the computer's potential and who further lacked the authority, status, and the entrepreneur's viewpoint of the company as a whole.

Another possible factor to be considered in connection with business's failure to utilize the computer's full potential may be the opposition exhibited by middle management, the familiar line-staff conflict. Their lack of participation in the initial planning stages may be due to an apparent threat (as they see it) to their traditional authority on the part of the computer personnel, "the high priests of the new cult."

In the McKinsey & Company's survey of 27 large corporations it was found that only one-third of the companies had achieved outstanding success with their computer systems.[1] In the companies considered successful, the greatest single cause of this success was attributed to top management's assessment of computer potential. Top management indicated a positive attitude toward the computer and as such gave continuing direction and guidance. In the less successful companies, top management viewed the computer as a glorified accounting machine which could best be left to the care of specialists.

Brabb and Hutchins are much concerned with the place of the electronic computer in the organizational structure. In the first selection they remind the reader of the surprisingly rapid adoption of the computer by industry since its initial introduction in 1954. Yet despite its eager acceptance, for some the computer has been a bitter disappointment. Generally the blame is laid on the men who use and sell computers. Specifically, failure has been attributed to inadequate organizational planning and to the lack of clear delineation of authority and responsibility. Because of the serious nature of these charges the authors are intent on examining the various facets of the problem. They discuss four at length: (1) the internal organization of the computer department; (2) the location of the data processing department in the corporation; (3) the status of the computer personnel; and (4) the impact of the computer on middle management and on other departments.

History, of course, has had something to do with the internal organization of computer departments. Originally computers were introduced in order to reduce clerical costs, put in charge of the controller, and used for routine accounting. No wonder computers failed at times to turn in a profit.

[1] John Garrity, "Top Management and Computer Profits," *Harvard Business Review*, July–August, 1963.

However, they did enable the personnel to acquire valuable computer experience and to get an inkling of its real potential. Since then a different view, fortunately, has prevailed. The computer is no longer looked upon as a mere clerical replacement but as the core element in an effective information system. As such it should not be viewed as the exclusive property of one department but should be made to contribute to the common good of the entire company.

Because of this change in outlook computer departments are generally and most naturally taken up with tasks such as systems analysis, computer programming, and computer operation. Each of these functions is sufficiently specialized to be best carried out by specialized groups. But with the assigning of functions goes the shouldering of responsibility. Neuschel believes that breaking up the responsibility and spreading it out over all the departments involved is conducive to little good. No one is really being held responsible. Nor should a department head be invested with the charge of a specific function unless in actual practice he does have such a function. Otherwise special difficulties could easily arise. Work priority could become a divisive issue and the head could be asked to perform services normally outside his role. In principle then the computer personnel should be held accountable to top management. In this way interdepartmental objectives can more systematically be integrated and their implementation assured.

Computer programming and computer operation are two distinct functions to be performed by distinct groups. Because of their rather specialized knowledge and experience the programmers should be in position to advise when certain work, e.g., exception routines, ought not to be programmed into the system and when valuable computer time could be saved by revising existing programs. Such revision, some believe, can best be left to a special set of programmers, and this for sound reasons. In any event the management of computer programming should be distinct from that of operations. Computer operations typically involve an input unit and a console operating unit.

Brabb and Hutchins believe it is better to teach a programmer something about accounting, etc., than to teach an accountant something about programming. The latter approach tends to isolate departments and to encourage work duplication.

The second point discussed is the physical and sociological location of the data processing department in the corporation. The physical location should be determined by the nature of the information required. Whether there should be centralized or decentralized facilities, though the former are normally more economical, will have to be decided by the geographical scope of the business and the bulk of its operations. Because of the changes effected by the computer in the clerical section, these groups may have to be physically relocated or centralized for better operation.

For successful electronic data processing (EDP) it is not enough to have good programmers and efficient operators; top management must participate in a positive manner in the computer venture. Too much is at stake in both time and money. EDP systems are responsible for the largest single indirect costs of business operations. Too often in the past top management has relinquished its responsibility by allowing the EDP group to determine its own objectives, set up its own standards, and to measure its own performance. This is management by default.

Furthermore, top executives should see to it that the data processing department should not be located either physically or sociologically in a major department of the business, for this would eventually turn that major department into a servicing unit for other departments or necessitate similarly expensive facilities in other major departments. Besides, the surrender of authority by department heads to the head of the major department with EDP would

certainly be resented. It is best if the EDP group is constituted an independent major department that reports to a "neutral" executive who himself is not a direct user of the equipment. This department would accept input data from all other departments and produce all required information but it alone would be responsible for the intermediate processing.

The status of the EDP personnel must be clearly defined by top management. The systems analysts, programmers, and the rest should be given both the authority and the responsibility to execute their respective tasks. This may necessitate extensive changes in the organizational structure if a piecemeal approach to EDP is to be avoided. For a realistic total systems approach, the data processing director should be constituted an independent member of the top management team. That this may give rise to intensely felt human problems elsewhere can easily be understood but these problems must be faced and solved satisfactorily by top management.

As for the fourth and final point, the specific impact of the computer on middle management, the authors acknowledge that the question is not yet settled. They admit that the computer has made a substantial impact on all of business management but just how it will affect middle management they do not know. We have already considered this particular point in a previous section. There we saw that some believe that the computer will take over many lower and middle management functions and will consequently cause these groups to diminish both in number and in function. The top management staff, on the other hand, will grow in size and handle more of the decision-making. Other authors, however, see very little change. Anschen and Bach, for instance, believe that the management situation in 1985 "will not be startlingly different than what it is today." When all is said and done, the limiting factor of computer application to the problems of management may well be not engineering know-how but the willingness to use and the art of applying the computer to these problems.

In the selection by Virgil Blank the focus is on EDP and its relationship to an integrated management system. The major emphasis nowadays is on the systems approach to management and tied to this approach is the computer which helps make it possible. However, computer utilization is not to be identified with the systems approach. Blank feels that many of the smaller companies are not exploiting computer potential simply because they lack the systems approach. His "engineered approach" is apparently a cybernetic systems approach which he holds is essentially a frame of mind. Its objective is the optimization of performance by the proper interrelationship of parts to be accomplished by suitable management control based on proper, accurate, and timely information.

In order to develop a realistic integrated system in a company one must be familiar with the available EDP equipment, its limitations and its assets. The better to evaluate the equipment he first outlines the six basic operations involved in all data processing (classifying, sorting, calculating, summarizing, recording, and communicating) and contrasts the characteristic features of the electronic and non-electronic equipment.

In the non-electronic field the highest degree of sophistication is represented by the punched-card equipment. In the electronic field it is the computer that holds this distinction. The various types of computer input and output devices, storage, and processing units are explained.

In all of this discussion the means (EDP devices) are explained in order to show how they can enable one to attain the end (top quality managerial control through information). Information may often turn out to be the crux of an integrated managerial system. Top-level management still uses a good deal of intuition precisely because it lacks suitable information. The quality of management control is determined not only by the skill of the managers

but also by the quality of the information presented to them.

The creation of an integrated system will be for management a means of solving problems but it will also create some—problems like the decision to undertake the organizational changes necessary, the decision to invest substantial amounts of capital for EDP equipment, and the decision to relocate and retrain personnel.

Robert McFarland, a psychologist, treats an aspect of the computer problem that has hardly been touched upon in the literature. In "Electronic Power Grab" he poses an unusual question, "Is it possible for an individual or for several individuals working in collusion by computer facilities manipulation to take over control of a firm with regard to the key operating and policy decisions without the company executives and stockholders being aware of it?" However, before tackling the issue directly, he first reviews other aspects that have a bearing on the problem.

One of the perennially perplexing tasks of management has been how to keep from being overwhelmed by floods of irrelevant, useless, and perhaps unreliable reports. At present this problem is even more acute. For the earlier man-made machines (engines and generators) there were clearly set limits to the amount of abuse and misuse they would tolerate before breaking down, but for the computer there are unfortunately no such limits. Asked a stupid question it will not break down but will grind out answers in kind for the fool. And the fool will unquestionably proceed to act upon the given oracle. Hence today with so much information being processed by computers there is an even greater need to check the output for relevance, utility, reliability, and validity.

Another problem arises with the need to increase EDP capitalization and computer operating staff. The supervisor, typically with an accounting background, who originally was responsible for computer applications in the firm, continues to favor the accountancy-oriented applications and either sidetracks or delays other worthwhile computer projects. And when newer computer facilities are to be acquired a power struggle is apt to ensue at the top management level as to who should control the computer.

A third problem, involving effective computer use by several operating divisions, arises when lower echelon groups control the computer facilities. Unless top management is actively involved in the problem, the middle management group controlling the computer staff will assign too low a priority for interdivisional applications.

In view of all this, McFarland subscribes to the opinion voiced by Philip Thurston and by John Garrity in the McKinsey report that top management must direct, manage, and lead and must not abdicate control to the computer personnel or to much lower echelon managers.

The McKinsey report proposed an examination of conscience for the chief executive, the items of which McFarland reproduces. His aim is not to endorse the technique but simply to stress the chief executive's part in the control system. Since executives are human, methodologies developed in other behavioral science fields would appear applicable also to them. So rather than formulate answers to the five soul-searching questions in the McKinsey report, top-level managers would find more useful methodologies concerned with identifying the relevant controllable variables in a given company situation.

The final portion of the selection deals with the concept of effective "computermanship" in terms of "How to steal a company without anyone ever catching on." In explaining the method he breaks it down to three fundamental techniques.

The first of these concerns how one goes about eliminating potential competition. McFarland presumes, of course and rightly too, that the individual interested in effective "computermanship" is bright, capable, and aggressive and is willing to master enough computer technology and other allied activities in order to forge ahead. With those potential competitors 40 or more years of age one should ostensibly agree in season and out of season that the old tried ways are the best and that these newfangled ideas besides being ineffective are costly in terms of money and effort. One could also reinforce the competitor's fears that these newfangled ideas are far too technical and besides not worthwhile. The months and years spent in mastering the new technology would be wasted for in that time the field would have advanced so far that one would still be hopelessly behind.

The other two techniques are concerned with one's competitors who are presumably also young, energetic, and aggressive, and willing to master the necessary computer technology. With this group different techniques will undoubtedly be necessary. Since these men will also be maneuvering for power, the all-important detail to be attended to is: Am I now ready for the power play, for the coup d'etat, for the showdown?

If the answer is in the negative, then technique No. 2 concerning how one goes about slowing down or delaying the showdown should go into effect. If one is on the computer staff a wise move would be to discourage as much as possible other company divisions from getting involved with the computer. If, however, they unfortunately are already involved one could repeatedly slow down their programs by making relevant suggestions, thus engaging them in endless rewriting and debugging of programs. One could also discourage the use of the larger computer installation by encouraging them to get their own smaller computers, never once letting on that such things as Shared Time and Data Phone transmission ever existed.

If the answer is in the affirmative, then technique No. 3 concerning how one goes about forcing a showdown should be employed. Of course, one should be reasonably sure that he will win the upper hand. The evident thing to do is to insist that if one were given complete managerial responsibility he could make the computer installation a profitable enterprise by employing systems approaches and other operational research techniques. One must be sure that the chief executive to whom the claim is made actually manages these company operations; otherwise those who do will not fail to withhold the support so necessary for validating one's claim.

Other non-interpersonal ploys could also be used. Organizing information flow so that the actual decision-making functions bypass the operating managers and pass over to the computer is one that is illus-trated with two true-to-life examples. Also deliberately withholding technical or analytical skills by an elite group as a form of job insurance is another way. The main point that McFarland makes here is that the aspiring electronic power-grabber by identifying the relevant controllable variables as suggested by control systems theory could innocuously program the data along with the mass of traditional input data and by occasionally checking the key data would be able to establish a reputation as a remarkably accurate forecaster, or, better, he could covertly make use of this valuable information for his own private advantage.

30. ELECTRONIC COMPUTERS AND MANAGEMENT ORGANIZATION

GEORGE J. BRABB * AND EARL B. HUTCHINS †

Electronic data processing has made significant contributions to improved operations in many businesses since the first introduction of a commercially produced large-scale computer in 1954. By fall of 1957, over 450 electronic digital computer systems were actively processing business data in industry and government.[1] By March of 1961, nearly 5,000 electronic data-processing systems (including 540 in government) had been delivered and an additional 6,500 were on order.[2] Machines in current use are produced by twenty different manufacturers and include about forty models varying widely in size, capacity, and speed. Computers are effecting an "information handling revolution" and now handle a major share of the recording and reporting of most routine business transactions of major industrial firms. In addition, they have made possible the application of many new managerial skills.

The revolution now in progress, like all revolutions, is not progressing smoothly and without problems. There have been reports of disappointment and disillusionment and even, in some instances, of withdrawal of computers. The situations have more often been attributable to those who use and those who sell rather than to the equipment itself.

The reasons and combinations of reasons for these negative results are numerous. Many such failures can be attributed, however, primarily to inadequate organizational planning, including lack of a clear delineation of authority and responsibility.[3]

The importance of appropriate and effective organization and direction of the data-processing function is further emphasized by the dramatic change from viewing the computer as a "clerical replacement" in existing data-processing systems to viewing the computer as providing the cornerstone for an effective management-information system. The original need and commonly envisioned purpose of a business-data processor was to reduce or curb the growth of large clerical forces required to handle the burgeoning paperwork burden. It soon became evident, however, that the proper role of business-data processing should be to process from source generation all basic business data and to produce selected information as required to operate the business. To successfully exploit the potential capability of the enormously powerful and versatile equipment presently available in "automated information factories," a competent personnel force is required to design, program, and operate the complete information system. The placement of this force in the corporate structure, its own internal organization, and the support extended to its activities by top management will obviously determine how successfully it accomplishes its objectives. The National Industrial Conference Board's report covering a study of the experiences of 124 companies concluded that the deterrents to data-processing progress include "poor planning, weak organization, and lack of internal support." [4]

This paper will be devoted to a consideration of the four facets of the subject which deserve particular attention:

• Internal organization of the computer department.
• Location of the data-processing department in the corporation.
• Status of computer personnel management.
• Impact of the computer on the organiza-

SOURCE: *California Management Review* (Fall, 1963), pp. 33–42.
* Associate Professor of Business Statistics University of Washington.
† General Electric Company.

tion of other departments of the company with particular reference to its effects on middle management personnel.[5]

We will attempt to determine the major outline of an effective organizational structuring of the data-processing function, based on interpretations of experience and understanding of the problems as these have been reported through formal studies, by management consultants, and by individuals engaged in data-processing work. A brief initial section will examine the current organizational status as background for this task.

There is, of course, no necessarily optimum organization of the electronic data-processing (EDP) function or best single definition and scope of EDP functional responsibilities. Also, other factors important to the success or failure of an EDP installation are recognized but will not be specifically discussed in this paper. A suggested list of such factors would include selection of the proper equipment, correct economic decisions on computer applications, and competence of the various EDP staff groups.

Throughout this paper reference is to a general purpose rather than a special purpose computer. Scientific and engineering applications, while not specifically discussed, could comprise part of the working load of the centralized computer.

The subjects of location in the corporate structure and effective internal organization of the data-processing function are discussed from the standpoint of a major manufacturing organization. The computer has made substantial contributions to the handling of business data for many other types of businesses, such as insurance companies, banks, utilities, and major retail establishments, but manufacturing firms generally present more diversified potential applications for computers, offer a relatively similar organizational pattern as a common framework for discussing optimum structuring, and comprise the largest sector of the civilian economy.

FIRST INTEREST

The first interest of industrial firms in conducting a computer feasibility study and acquiring an electronic data processor usually has been to reduce clerical costs. Consequently, two results are common: operation of the computer is placed within the controller's department and accounting routines, normally little changed from the manner in which they were previously performed, are the first jobs placed on the computer. Following the payroll and a few other accounting activities, machine applications are developed for inventory control, production scheduling, sales and market analysis, and personnel analysis. The machines may also be used in the solution of scientific, engineering, and operations-research problems.

Generally the routine handling of "programmed" work has been successfully accomplished, but limited progress has been made toward "integrated" and "automated" processing of total business data. Also, returns to date have not been in terms of financial gain, but rather in computer experience and in awakening to a clearer understanding of the potential of computers as the foundation of a total business information system.

With two to six years of EDP experience behind them, most large manufacturing companies are looking for the answers to some important questions. Have the original computer acquisition objectives been met; if not, are they still valid? What are the opportunities ahead for improving the business, and how can the data-processing function help to realize these? How can computer capabilities be more fully and profitably exploited? Should we develop an integrated business information system and, if so, how is this done?

Several administrative questions are being asked at this point. Who should operate and control the scheduling of the computer(s)? Who should be responsible for developing new applications, and what should be the criteria for their implementation? What should be the relationship among the groups directly associated with the computer and between the computer operation and its "customers," the operating departments?

The primary administrative responsibility of the manager of data processing can be defined as the organization of the EDP department to more effectively contribute to the over-all objectives of the company. He must possess a command of current data-processing technology sufficient to realize top management expectations from electronic data processing. He, therefore, has the important continuing responsibilities of evaluating the efficiency and progress of the department and of the specific employees, as well as of managers in operating components of the department.

The most natural and conventional subdivisions of the functional work associated with the computer department are:

- Systems analysis.
- Computer programming.
- Computer operation.

"Systems analysis is an orderly study of the detailed procedure for collecting, organizing, and evaluating information within an organization, with the objectives of improving control of the operations of the organization." [6] When used to describe a work function this term usually is understood to include also "systems design," which is the creative phase of devising a new system.

Programming, as applied to computers, is the technique for completely specifying to the data-processing equipment all the possible operations which might occur in the solution of a problem.[7]

Computer operations pertain to the actual day-to-day functioning of the centralized data-processing equipment, i.e., machine scheduling, operation, and maintenance. This component usually provides key-punching service, machine processing of established and developmental application programs, and preparation of output in usable form.

Each of the three computer department functions is of sufficient complexity and magnitude to warrant separate specialization and management. Some companies have believed that the ideal organization has a single group of employees providing all three functions for computer applications. However, "this has generally been found to be impractical. The functions are therefore carried out by specialized units. . . ." [8]

The reasons offered by proponents of separate sections within the EDP department, as opposed to combining at least two of the functions are:

1. Each operation is a distinctly different kind of work and requires different knowledge and skill.

2. Performance of each major function by a separate staff helps to avoid compromises in the new system or in machine-programming or operation.[9]

The study and analysis of business information requirements are vital steps in bringing a potential machine application into reality. The systems analysis group designs a system or set of procedures and thus tends to establish specifications for the auxiliary equipment required to implement the system. This group recommends, or decides in cooperation with the components having operating responsibility, the new methods and procedures to establish, the files to set up or eliminate, the equipment to obtain or discard, and the organizational changes to make. This group also reviews the economic aspects of proposed changes.

Neuschel [10] has covered the subject of where in the organizational structure the responsibility for interdepartmental systems and procedures should be placed. He points out (p. 48) three alternatives: assignment of the responsibility to all departments; assignment to the head of a major function, typically the comptroller; retention of the responsibility by top management.

His primary conclusions are:

1. When responsibility for interdepartmental procedures is broken up and distributed among all departments, accountability for completeness of the program is wholly lost. No position can be held responsible for observing needs or crystallizing objectives. Nor can there be any assurance that the most promising opportunities are being exploited . . . (p. 56).

2. It may be stated as a general principle, therefore, that responsibility for investigation, analysis, and recommendation regarding interdepartmental procedures should not be assigned to a functional executive unless, in actual practice as well as in the minds of the other division heads, he operates in the capacity of "chief of staff" on this kind of work for the principal executive (pp. 60–61).

3. In principle, staff personnel engaged in interdepartmental procedures studies should report to the chief executive of a relatively self-contained operating unit—that is, either to the president, executive or administrative vice-president, or general manager of a company . . . (p. 62).

In addition, the common result of procedures developed within each department (1 above) is that the resulting systems become data-processing "islands" because they are usually only loosely connected to adjacent areas. The work tends to be viewed out of perspective with the organization as a whole; as a result, integration and over-all economy are seldom obtained.

TWO PROBLEMS

Two of the main problems which arise when consolidated systems analysis is assigned to a particular functional department (2 above) are that the priority of work usually becomes a major issue and the manager of the department is asked to provide many services which are outside the normal scope of his particular function. Finally, systems integration cutting across departmental lines must have the direct support of top management if the objectives desired are to be achieved.

The computer-programming function poses fewer controversial alternatives as to its optimum organization. Only a few companies believe that once the system has been designed its complete implementation should be the function of a single staff.[11] The argument is that employees with equipment knowledge are best qualified to develop the program of machine instructions and that the intimate knowledge of machine operations will reveal the best refinements for programming. They further reason that the manager of the computer operation should be responsible not only for meeting the due dates of a new application but also for the quality and efficiency of the programming, which has a close relationship to best utilization of the computer.

Experienced programmers often can make significant contributions also to the design of an application through recognition that there is a definite point at which it becomes uneconomical and unwise to include work within the computer system. For example, the cost of programming and operating many exception routines usually makes it more economical to process these phases of the work manually.

Revisions to existing EDP programs are an important part of the programming function. Virtually every company which has used electronic computers for several years has programs which, if revised, would release valuable machine time, speed up overall processing time, and permit a greater input-output flexibility for the particular application.

A Controllers Institute research study advocates a separate program-revision group in preference to programmers handling both new and revised programs. Reasons for this preference center around the freedom to do a more thorough job; to reduce "set-up" time and conflicts with deadlines on new work; and to take advantage of the "natural" divisions in

personality, technical ability, and new work versus improvement work preferences of programmers.[12] The programming activity should, however, be managed separately from the computer-operation functions. Reasons for this are the importance and complexity of the work, difficulty of recruitment and training, and the volume of work in installations of the size considered in this paper. In actual practice, separate management of the programming group is the most commonly used organizational arrangement.

Occasional variations in the normal structuring of the computer-operation section include separate management of the input function, operation of a separate punched card department, and use of an "open shop" computer center.

The "typical (and ultimate) EDP organization"[13] usually consists of an input manager in addition to a programming manager and an operations manager. The usual input unit would consist of key punch supervisors and operators and a control section responsible for proofing, batching, and other activities necessary to input and output operations. The operations unit would have the usual console and machine operators, tape handlers, and perhaps a supporting punched card operation. A separate input unit can develop conflicts with the computer operating unit.

Companies usually have not merged conventional punched card departments with the EDP operation if EDP utilizes large-scale computers.[14] This tends to support the viewpoint that both types of data-processing equipment have particular areas in which they can best serve. (In companies using small or medium scale computers, operations commonly have been combined with those of the conventional tabulating department.)

The final alternative approach to computer operations is to provide data-processing hardware and limited technical assistance but generally to expect using components to provide their own systems design, programming, and operators. This technique has been successfully tried in engineering departments using smaller computers but should not be regarded as an acceptable alternative for operation of a large-scale, multiple-usage computer. The National Industrial Conference Board found this to be a costly method in comparison with the conventional approach of providing a full line of technical assistance.[15] More important, it tends to delay the development of an integrated information system since it encourages departmental isolation and duplication of processing activities among departments.

Current developments in computer-programming languages have led some persons to believe that it is easier to teach the subject-matter expert (accountant, economist, etc.) how to program than to teach the programmer something about the subject matter (accounting, economics, etc.). Even if this approach were completely feasible, which it is not,[16] the basic point remains, this approach cannot be expected to lead to the development of an integrated information system for the organization. Rather, it tends to encourage departmental isolation and duplication of processing activity.

The location of the data-processing function must correspond to the dynamics of the operations for which information is desired. The information requirements are important determinants of both the locations and organization of data-processing facilities. Thus, the question of centralized versus decentralized computer facilities will have to be answered within the operational and geographical scope of the particular business. Operations that are concentrated at only one location pose less problem as to physical location, but still contain problems concerning organizational location and relationships. Normally, centralized processing of all operations offers some economies of scale through the use of larger-scale equipment. Alternatively, problems of communication and scheduling may offset some of these advantages. Finally, a variety of operations usually can be handled more economically on a centralized large-scale computer. Actually, the use of electronics has tended to force many companies toward centralization of data processing, although decentralization is taking place in manufacturing, engineering, and marketing operations.

Geographically dispersed operations present problems of both physical location and organizational structure. A centralized processing unit is valuable for dealing with numerous, undispersed operations and is probably mandatory for highly centralized management control. On the other hand, divisional data-processing facilities may often be justified by the nature and volume of divisional activity and degree of local autonomy. Current developments in telecommunications equipment at least make centralized processing easier to accomplish. Centralization of data processing, however, does not preclude stages or phases of data processing at the divisional level.

LOCATING EDP

In addition to the more vital issue of where to locate the EDP function, it should be noted that another type of organizational impact is often associated with successful computer applications. Because of extensive change in the procedures of clerical sections which prepare and receive machine-processed data, these groups are or should often be transferred or centralized for more logical or economical operation. There is in such instances a twofold need. First, it must be determined to what extent consolidation of work units or (perhaps) more fundamental changes will be needed. Second, the likelihood that these organization changes or shifts in responsibility will, in fact, be made must be evaluated.[17]

The degree of success of an EDP installation depends to a large extent upon the understanding and cooperation received from top management and from the key individuals throughout the company who are affected by the new methods of electronic data processing. Good work by the EDP group in the technical aspects is not enough. Positive participation by top management is essential to successful cooperation between two or more components with diverse interests.

As pointed out in the National Industrial Conference Board study,

Failures arose from such conditions as poor systems, inaccurate source information, and lack of adequate top-management support. Companies have also found that the more advanced the equipment and its proposed use, the more serious internal obstacles become.[18]

Top management should be periodically satisfied in at least five areas concerning the data-processing function: objectives, applications, hardware, organization, and economics.[19]

If for no other reason, executive management must act in accordance with the recognition that data processing is one of the largest single indirect costs of business operation. Members of top management cannot in the long run divorce themselves from direct participation in decisions pertaining to expenditures of time and money on the scale required by the typical

EDP system. The cost of failure or inefficiency can be substantial because of the investments involved. Top management must also recognize that poor execution can often prevent a good decision from being fully effective.

Milton Stone states the case as follows:

The time would seem to have arrived for management to pay some attention to the management of its data-processing tools, to measure performance, to judge results.

Far from exercising control over the more ambitious systems, management treats this complex, hard-to-understand child of technology with the kid gloves and indecision of the modern parent. In many organizations, lack of understanding by top management allows the data-processing activity to determine its own objectives, set its own standards, and measure its own performance against those standards.[20]

In its broadest scope, the job of administrative organization is to marshall and use the limited resources of business to achieve specific objectives. Organization defines the lines of authority and the responsibility of individuals and coordinates individual efforts for harmonious attainment of the predetermined objectives.[21] These points of predetermined objectives, definite authority and responsibility, and harmonious relationship are the principal missing ingredients in much of present administration of the data-processing function.

With the possible exception of a limited introductory period, the alternative of placing the computer installation within a major department is not satisfactory for a complete manufacturing business. As soon as other major departments require a large amount of EDP work, a decision must be made to adopt one of the two alternatives: operation as a servicing unit or installation of similar "captive" facilities in each major department. A major objection to the second alternative is that an equivalent amount of money spent to operate multiple data-processing centers will not buy as much computing ability as will a single installation. More important, the computer applications become "islands" of data processing instead of being integrated into a complete business information system.

There are several operating variations of the service center which is located within a major department. These variations include having a charter which stresses its interdepartmental

nature, having each department do its own developmental work, including machine programming, and reserving particular shifts for each department.

Such a service center is not intended to interfere with existing departmental structures; however, as reported in the Controllers Institute research study,

When a center is responsible to another major departmental user, many department heads feel they have lost some of their former authority and responsibility. This reaction can become fairly strong . . . the broader the scope of the application, the greater the reluctance appears to be to turn over a major part of a function to a machine center supervised by another department. This reluctance does not appear to be as great when the EDP group reports to a "general" or "neutral" executive who himself is not a direct user of the equipment.[22]

Typically, computers have been the administrative responsibility of a company's financial group. While this can be an appropriate organizational location, there are conditions under which this arrangement impedes rather than facilitates effective exploitation of the computer's potential. These conditions usually involve the personality, interest, and company status of the controller or financial officer and the nature of the applications chosen for computer processing. When the controller is accounting-oriented, rather than general management-oriented, experience to date indicates that chances are good that the computer will not be used to its best advantage.[23] Also, if feasible applications include many engineering problems or manufacturing activities in addition to accounting work, there is a strong possibility that a computer system including those activities will be slow to develop.

THIRD ALTERNATIVE

The third alternative, establishing the EDP component as an independent major department whose responsibility is to process data from source acquisition to final report form appears to be most likely to lead to the development of an efficient, integrated data-processing system. The EDP department accepts input data as approved by each department and produces all required information. The originating department has responsibility for approving and initiating the source data and, within limits, prescribing the final data, but the intermediate processing is not its concern. It should be emphasized that only the programmed data-processing activities and not the important decision-making or control responsibilities are assumed by the EDP servicing center.

Much of EDP's value lies in its capacity for consolidating separate information files and for preparing interrelated series of operations without manual intervention. Management of the EDP facility should be assigned authority to effectively exploit the information potential of basic raw data. This does not imply that EDP would usurp the primary responsibilities of the other major departments. Rather, the EDP facility would operate as a production center serving all traditional major functions of the business.

Responsibility of the director of data processing should in general include the following:

1. Planning, supervision, and control of the electronic data-processing program.

2. Continuous study of interdepartmental systems and procedures.

3. Determination of acceptability of new machine applications.

4. Continuous review of current applications, including appropriateness, degree of integration, usefulness, etc.

5. Appraisal and evaluation of new EDP equipment.

6. Conducting a formal program to teach managers how to use data-processing advantageously.

7. Development of competent staffs for systems analysis, machine programming, and machine operation.

8. Establishment of processing priorities.

9. Prescribing of forms and methods for input procedures.

10. Limited authority over the form, content, and scheduling of records and reports output.

Vesting authority in the director of data processing to decide matters which closely affect departments over which he has no line authority naturally leads to occasional conflicts which must be solved by persuasion or appeal to higher authority. In actual experience, the most sensitive areas involving questions of authority are the following:

- Systems definitions.
- The dates for input data to be available.
- Priorities for various applications.
- Acceptance and servicing of new applications.

To attain maximum effectiveness of the EDP installation, the organizational role of the data-processing operation must be defined by top management. The entire organization must be made aware of management's interest and involvement. It must be made to understand the desirability for a computer operation involving systems analysts who will have a voice in the internal operations of individual departments. Finally, the central data-processing group must feel it has both the authority and the responsibility to execute the tasks before it.

In order to put computer capabilities to work more rapidly, the piecemeal approach to EDP should be abandoned in favor of the more efficient total systems development. A management-control system must be "designed" complete with all specifications necessary to make required decisions. Necessarily, "the constraints of the existing organization must be ignored." [24] Operating executives at the highest management levels must be induced to cooperate fully in making the changes necessary to accomplish these goals. That such cooperation is not extended to an executive of lower rank or to the manager of a "computing" operating department is not surprising. These considerations dictate that the director of data processing be an independent member of the top management team.

Since first recognition that digital computers could be successfully used for processing business data, there has been a continuously mounting tide of conjectural discussion and speculation as to the computer's ultimate effect on managerial responsibilities and business organization. There is no disagreement on the inevitability of very extensive and substantial impact on the role of all business management. Rather, most controversy centers around the technical capacity of computers to duplicate and surpass human activities including thinking, the degree to which decision-making can be assumed by the computer, and the extent to which present managerial functions will be taken over by computers.

Predictions of the impact of computers on business management have consistently emphasized the same two basic points: computers being programmed to make middle-management level decisions, and necessary organizational changes.

Without going into the arguments of whether computers can be designed to think creatively and hence to perform virtually all managerial functions including policy determination, we can safely assert that currently available computer technology greatly exceeds the present usual role of computers in business decision-making and problem-solving.

Daniel's assessment is:

To date, largely because of the routineness of most applications, this impact on organizational structure has not been felt, except in a few companies which have made substantial innovations. These efforts usually involve establishment of a separate business information department which assumes responsibility for the paperwork processing activities of the major functional departments.[25]

Recent advances in information technology lead to emphasis on quantification and the explicit definition of assumptions and judgments involved in specific decision processes. In addition, the use of computers improves information technology because more data can be considered, a greater range of alternatives can be explored, and a more comprehensive evaluation of a given decision's impact is possible.

These developments would seem to indicate that the staff of top management can be expected to increase sharply as these new decision-making processes become more important. There may well be fewer lower and middle management jobs handling the routine technically-oriented operating decisions which can be handled best by the computer. Human beings will be needed, however, to control the machines, handle the non-routine problems, and supervise employees. The pressures on top managers will undoubtedly increase. The advances in information technology now under way will tend to integrate decision-making and move it higher in the organization. At the same time, it will provide additional information which will make possible a detailed check on the success of individual management decisions.[26]

Although there is no positive way to forecast accurately the overall future effect of computer-based information systems on business management, it appears reasonable to conclude that the extent and speed of advances in information technology will be determined by personal and economic rather than technical considerations. Some of the content of management jobs will change, information available for decision-making will be greatly increased, and the computer will become a vital tool in the overall improvement of management abilities.

We can agree with Postley that "it seems likely that the art of applying digital computers to problems, and not the art of engineering the machines to do the jobs assigned to them, will (continue to) be the limiting factor in digital computer use."[27]

Most people, including business managers, resist changes which they believe will deeply affect their established responsibilities, duties, and routines. Intensely human problems arise. The apparent loss of prestige and authority by operating executives is probably the major cause of management difficulties in the transition to the computer as a business information system.

UNCEASING CHALLENGE

In spite of the unceasing challenge to the status quo in the years ahead, extension of the role of the computer in business management will be at the most only "dynamically evolutionary" because of inherent institutional and individual inertia. Irrespective of the pressure exerted by rapid technological advancement, it would be unrealistic to expect rapid and radical changes in organizational structure and functions of managers.

Dean Simon, who is one of the optimistic prognosticators of the eventual capabilities of computers, has stated:

The conclusion I draw—is that the automation of decision making, irrespective of how far it goes and in what directions it proceeds, is unlikely to obliterate the basically hierarchial structure of organizations. The decision making process will still call for departmentalization and subdepartmentalization of responsibilities.[28]

A symposium discussion on this topic concluded that the management situation in 1985 "will not be startlingly different from what we see today."[29]

The most critically necessary element for

more rapid development of integrated information systems is the increased interest of top management. Top management has generally failed to devote sufficient attention to data processing, particularly the development of information systems. Marion Harper, Jr., expresses this need aptly in stating that "to manage a business well is to manage its future; and to manage the future is to manage information." [30]

One of the keys to successful computer innovation and improvement therefore becomes that of reorienting the thinking of those most closely involved in order to overcome human resistance. As Arnold Keller has so succinctly observed, "It seems to me that we have a much greater need for 'integrated management' than we do for integrated data processing." [31] Or, as Blank has written of the proposition, "What all this probably implies is that, in addition to needing management-oriented systems personnel, there is a real need for systems-oriented management personnel." [32]

REFERENCES

1. Peggy Courtney, ed., *Business Electronics Reference Guide* (Controllership Foundation, Inc., New York, 1958), pp. 273–274.
2. "Computer Census," *Data Processing,* April 1961, p. 32. These data on number of computer systems delivered are also supported by the John Diebold and Associates computer census at the end of 1960 as reported in their *Automated Data Processing Newsletter* of January 23, 1961.
3. See Richard F. Neuschel, *Management by Systems* (McGraw-Hill Book Company, Inc., New York, 1960), p. 40; James D. Gallagher, "Organization of the Data Processing Function," Chapter II-B, *Management Control Systems,* Donald G. Malcolm and Alan J. Rowe, eds. (John Wiley and Sons, New York, 1960); and Carl G. Baumes, *Administration of Electronic Data Processing,* Studies in Business Policy, No. 98 (The National Industrial Conference Board, New York, 1961).
4. Baumes, *Administration of EDP,* p. 4.
5. Adapted from D. Ronald Daniel, "Measure Your EDP Progress: A '5,000-Mile Checkup' for Computer Installation," *The Management Review,* March, 1961, pp. 75ff.
6. Robert H. Gregory and Richard L. Van Horn, *Automatic Data Processing Systems—Principles and Procedures* (Wadsworth Publishing Co., Belmont, Calif., 1960), p. 378.
7. John A. Postley, *Computers and People* (Mc-

Graw-Hill Book Company, Inc., New York, 1960), p. 24.
8. Baumes, *Administration of EDP,* p. 57.
9. *Ibid.* See also Daniel, "Measure Your EDP Progress," esp. p. 76.
10. Neuschel, *Management by Systems.*
11. Baumes, *Administration of EDP,* p. 59.
12. J. Gibbons Conway and D. Watts, *Business Experience and Electronic Computers, a Synthesis of What Has Been Learned from Electronic Data Processing Installations* (Controllers Institute Research Foundation, Inc., New York, 1959), p. 80.
13. Conway, *et al., Business Experience,* p. 80.
14. Baumes, *Administration of EDP,* p. 59.
15. *Ibid.*
16. For two expositions which indicate that programming languages still have a way to go before they reach their full potential, see "The Rand Symposium: 1962," *Datamation,* October, 1962, pp. 25–32, and Harry N. Cantrell, "Where Are Compiler Languages Going?" *Datamation,* August, 1962, pp. 25–28. That programmers are still much in demand and considered to be, in part, "born" rather than "made," is maintained by Olaf Engelsen in "A Pressing Problem: Trained Programming Personnel," *Data Processing Digest,* October, 1962, pp. 17–20.
17. Neuschel, *Management by Systems,* p. 269.
18. Baumes, *Administration of EDP,* p. 8. See also Neuschel, *Management by Systems,* p. 23. John S. Sinclair in the foreword to the National Industrial Conference Board study suggests possible reasons for the neglect in direction and guidance. "First of all, management may be so impressed with the great power and versatility of electronic computers that they may be led to think it possible to achieve savings despite weak planning, lack of sound organization, and the inertia or resistance of their employees. For another thing, many managements are not aware of the degree of coordination and integration that is needed to make electronic data-processing really pay off."
19. Daniel, "Measure Your EDP Progress," p. 23.
20. Milton M. Stone, "Data Processing and the Management Information System," *Data Processing Today: A Progress Report,* Albert Newgarden, ed. (American Management Association, New York, 1960).
21. William P. Leonard, "The Management Audit," Chapter 5, p. 94. See also, Edward McSweeney, "How to Organize Your Business for More Effective Management." Section 3, pp. 116–117; *J. K. Lasser's Business Management Handbook,* Sydney Perau, ed., 2nd ed. (McGraw-Hill Book Company, New York, 1960).

22. Conway, *et al., Business Experience,* pp. 146–147.

23. Daniel, "Measure Your EDP Progress," p. 76.

24. D. G. Malcolm and A. J. Rowe, "An Approach to Computer-Based Management Control Systems," *California Management Review,* Spring, 1961, as summarized in *Data Processing Digest,* August, 1961, p. 18. See also, Virgil Blank, "The Management Concept in Electronic Systems," *The Journal of Accountancy,* January, 1961, p. 59, and "Editorial," *Data Processing,* May, 1961, p. 50.

25. Daniel, "Measure Your EDP Progress," p. 76; see also, Baumes, *Administration of EDP.*

26. George P. Shultz and Thomas L. Whisler, eds., *Management Organization and the Computer* (The Free Press of Glencoe, Illinois, 1960), pp. 18–19.

27. Postley, *Computers and People,* p. 19.

28. Herbert A. Simon, *The New Science of Management Decision* (Harper and Brothers, New York, 1960), p. 42. Simon's comments on another occasion are summarized in Melvin Anshen and George Bach, eds., *Management and Corporations, 1985* (McGraw-Hill Book Company, New York, 1960), p. 207.

29. Anshen and Bach, *Management, 1985,* pp. 207–208. See also Anshen, "The Manager and the Black Box," *Harvard Business Review,* November–December, 1960.

30. Marion Harper, Jr., "Business Needs an Intelligence Director," *Management and Business Automation,* March, 1961, p. 20; see also, Wallace, *Management Influence on the Design of Data Processing Systems, A Case Study* (Harvard Business School, Division of Research, Cambridge, Mass., 1961).

31. "Effects of Business Automation in the Sixties," Round Table, Part 2, *Management and Business Automation,* February, 1961, p. 28.

32. Blank, "Management Concept," p. 66.

31. THE MANAGEMENT CONCEPT
IN ELECTRONIC SYSTEMS

Virgil F. Blank *

Today there is a major emphasis within the business community on systems and procedures development. Why is this? Principally because of three factors: (1) increased clerical activity and its associated costs; (2) management's interest in more effective control reports; (3) availability of powerful data processing equipment. If we were to examine closely most of the installed electronic data processing systems, however, we would gain the impression that they were installed for one or more of the following purposes:

1. To take over functions already performed by punched card equipment, thus making a superspeed punched card system.

2. To do some large-volume accounting job which offers possibilities of net cost reduction.

3. To acquire a special purpose machine to do a particularly difficult "problem area" job. (This usually results in a crisis in another area which needs a different machine for its solution.)

4. To experiment with a small system on a selected application with the intention of expanding the system to larger equipment later, if the initial equipment is successful.

Each of these approaches to the use of electronic equipment constitutes a patchwork solution to the over-all data processing problem. Furthermore, most of these approaches involve fairly large companies which can afford medium or large-scale equipment, even though used on a partial solution basis.

This present use of EDP equipment has been misleading in that system development thinking has tended to be weighted heavily by it. The tremendous potential for utilization of EDP by

SOURCE: *Journal of Accountancy* (January, 1961), pp. 59–66. Reprinted by permission of the *Journal of Accountancy*.

* CPA, Haskin & Sells.

smaller companies is yet to be realized. It will only be realized when EDP systems are developed under an engineered approach.

THE ENGINEERED APPROACH

An engineered approach to system development is based on a frame of mind. It is a frame of mind which accepts the business enterprise as a high order system composed of interdependent parts. These parts are people and their methods and procedures of sales, production, purchasing, accounting, etc., working toward a common goal. These parts are usually separated into departments for organizational reasons, but not for data processing reasons. In systems development, then, the organizational structure must give way to the data-flow structure.

The business system, being interdependent, acts like any servo-mechanical system. Just as a thermostat and a gas furnace operate as a balanced servo-mechanism sensitive to temperature, so does a business system represent a structure of people sensitive to various economic and commercial forces. There is a balance of relative effectiveness of each part within the enterprise acting in relationship with every other part to produce the performance of the whole system. As a matter of fact, strengthening one part of a business system may put stress on other parts so as to lessen over-all performance.

DESIRED OBJECTIVES OF
SYSTEM DEVELOPMENT

It is easy to picture the effect on the production department of a suddenly successful sales campaign of which the production manager had no knowledge, or the effect of extreme overproduction in one department on all other production departments on a processing line.

These would be examples of system imbalance resulting from patchwork "improvement" within a system.

The objective, therefore, of the engineered approach to system development is to optimize performance within the enterprise through achievement of proper relationships between the parts of the business system. How is this accomplished? Usually, it is accomplished by exercise of management control based on timely, proper, and accurate data.

As we learn more about EDP we realize that here for the first time is a machine system powerful enough to assist management in this control. So our question now is not, "How can I use this shiny new gadget?" but rather, "What is this particular enterprise all about and what does it take to manage it?" Perhaps the answers will include some use of electronic equipment.

Generally, there are two principal levels of management. At the top level, decisions are based on external as well as internal conditions; while at the lower level of management, concern is principally for control of conditions within the enterprise. Top management uses market analyses, projections, and predictions, while lower management uses operating reports.

Much of the decision making of top management is now based upon intuition. A great deal of the necessity for this is due to lack of the proper data available on a timely basis. Jay Forrester's recent paper on "Industrial Dynamics" (*Harvard Business Review*, July–August 1958) described some of the research now being devoted to the development of a more professional approach to management through the use of scientific analysis and electronic computers. This paper suggested certain ways of thinking about management that should be helpful to systems and procedures personnel as well as to executives in working on inventory control, production scheduling, advertising, sales, and other related problems. Formal research on the subject of principles of scientific management is now included in the programs of many of our universities and large corporations.

One of the basic aims of systems work in this field is the establishment of standards. These, in effect, are pre-decisions of what conditions should be. Exceptions to these conditions are subject to computer analysis for reporting to top management.

CONTROL OF A BUSINESS SYSTEM

Let us look more closely at the data-flow structure and see what we mean by a business system and its control by management. Chart I presents a generalized representation of an information system within a manufacturing enterprise.

The decisions as to production control and other operating matters are based upon reports prepared as a result of the entry of orders into the production cycle. In a business such as this, there are relatively few key factors which are needed to supply management's informational needs. These might include: (1) competitive product styling; (2) effective marketing; (3) lowest possible production costs.

Factors of this type are fundamental in that their control should result in success for the business. Once the control measures matching these key factors are known, we are well on our way toward understanding the interdependence of the parts of a business system.

What are control measures?

Let us again examine our information system design. We have said that it acts like a servomechanism. By this we mean that a business is controlled by information fed back in a manner similar to the way that a missile is controlled by its radiated impulses acting within a guidance system. Inventory information af-

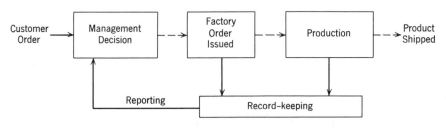

CHART I.

fected by manufacturing and sales data can be fed back to management through reporting so that the minimum amount of capital will be required to be invested in inventories.

In a business it is not alone the skill of management which determines the quality of management control. Good control depends also upon what information executives use and for what they use it. Management intuition must be fortified with proper, timely information if costly errors are to be avoided.

A proper goal in EDP system design work should be *profit improvement*—not *cost cutting*. This implies that the system analyst be management-oriented in his thinking so that he can visualize the business as an over-all operation and not as a set of separate parts requiring cost reduction through mechanization.

So the first important consideration in applying systems and procedures techniques to electronic data processing is a matter of attitude. It is a matter of adopting a frame of mind equivalent to the viewpoint of management. It is only in this way that the eventual potential of EDP will be realized. The broad-scope objectives of achievement now possible must become the concern of top corporate personnel since technical knowledge alone is not enough. It must be fortified with management abilities.

CAPABILITIES OF ELECTRONIC EQUIPMENT

Now that the atmosphere has been established for working in the field of EDP, let us inquire as to *why* we are directing our attention so forcefully to the utilization of electronic data processing equipment. What are the unique capabilities of these machine systems that make them more powerful than former equipment? Perhaps it would be possible to determine this by first reviewing some of the points of difference from other business machines and then by giving some thought to the meaning of system integration. A working knowledge of these matters should be part of management's background.

As we examine the basic characteristics of non-electronic business equipment, we come to the realization that in most cases its use has required a change from normal manual data processing procedures. Without going too far back into fundamentals, we might divide all data processing into six operational steps. These are: classifying, sorting, calculating,

summarizing, recording, and communicating. In the human performance of one or more of these six basic steps, there is usually the completion of all necessary work on one document before proceeding with the next. Hence, manual recording is of a continuous process nature.

With the departmentalization caused by business growth, there has been a splintering of the recording functions into many segregations of specialized duties. Single purpose machines have been developed to handle limited portions of these duties where there were similar operational steps in sufficient volume to justify the equipment cost.

PUNCHED CARD EQUIPMENT VERSUS EDP SYSTEMS

The highest degree of development in this regard has been punched card equipment. For this reason we might review some of the characteristics of this equipment so as to be able to make comparisons later with electronic systems. The principal features of punched card equipment may be stated as follows:

1. Data is stored on a punched card which is capable of both human and machine reading. Card capacity is limited to 80 or 90 character records but the record can be extended over more than one card.

2. To a certain extent, each machine in the system is a single-purpose one, usually performing just one of the six basic data processing operations.

3. There is a limited amount of automatic control within the system. This is accomplished to a large extent by control panel wiring.

4. A high ratio of human participation is necessary—especially in moving the card records between the various special-purpose machines.

5. The recording machines have a speed limitation of approximately 150 records a minute.

6. A certain amount of system integration has been possible through the development of peripheral equipment capable of capturing data in a mechanized form at the time of original recording of a transaction.

The combination of these and other minor features of punched card equipment has permitted a rather high degree of mechanization within selected portions of business data processing systems. However, this equipment is customarily utilized within a limited scope of operations and has usually been adopted for use in the handling of high-volume transactions.

Let us turn our examination to some of the characteristics of electronic data processing systems and learn how these characteristics permit a higher level of mechanization than was previously feasible with punched card machines. Some features for comparison might be the following:

1. Data is stored within the machine elements or within machine-accessible elements. Record lengths are not limited, although, in some equipment, certain record lengths are more economical to use.

2. All control instructions for complete processing of sets of data are stored within the machine system and can be modified automatically to suit special processing conditions.

3. Storage, control, and processing machine elements all operate on compatible electronic principles which permit their inter-coupling into a completely automatic system.

4. No human manipulation of data is necessary during processing.

5. Logical decisions can be made within the equipment based on predetermined rules. Completely on its own, the EDP system can select data or choose alternate procedures.

These characteristics of electronic data processing systems are the principal factors which widen the scope for more extensive system development. Uninterrupted data processing is extremely fast and internal program control is extremely versatile.

DESIGN FEATURES

Up to this point, the general characteristics of electronic and other systems have been considered. Of particular interest, however, is how the design features of electronic equipment affect the problems of system and procedure installation. What are the points of difference that should be known with respect to how the electronic system does things? To acquire this background consideration must be given to the equipment itself.

In the design of electronic systems there are certain limiting factors—just as there are in the design of a new system or procedure on any equipment. However, these factors differ somewhat in electronic data processing and are usually somewhat more difficult to ascertain. Therefore, let us first look at some of these.

Capacity to Handle Work Volume. The approach to system design with respect to volume limitations has certain features under EDP not found in other methods.

The usual approach when installing bookkeeping machines or tabulating equipment is to order enough machines to handle the work volume. This is not a recommended approach with EDP equipment since there are available complete systems within various ranges of capacities, each capable of handling certain work volumes.

Once work volumes are determined, it is necessary to give attention to equipment features of the various systems so as to select the range of electronic machine systems which would be capable of performing the entire work load.

Just a word of caution on accumulating work load data: In EDP one of the most important features to consider when calculating equipment capacities is the time-demand curve of input. Most EDP systems will have a heavy daily work load. Accordingly, the time-demand for each hour of the day should be studied so as to provide machine capacity for the maximum hourly load necessary to be processed. Weekly, monthly, and annual volume fluctuations in the data flow should also be considered in establishing timing limitations.

There are also some unique features of EDP equipment which bear upon the matter of capacity. Some systems provide for overlapping of the input of data, internal processing, and the output of data. Where equipment does not perform in this manner, the input, processing, and output timing must be totaled.

This equipment is also capable of utilizing a variety of input and output devices. Usually, many possible combinations of these devices must be considered in order to obtain the optimum operating condition for the system.

Capacity to Handle Working Files. Most data processing consists of applying certain information from files to the daily transactions in order to prepare an output report. For example, the order from a customer may not contain standard shipping instructions, adequate product descriptions, credit terms, item cost, discounts, or allowances. This information must be supplied from files. In EDP systems, the simplest approach to processing is to store these files internally, that is, within the machine components.

There are many design problems relating to these files. Perhaps the most confining problem at this time is the size of file necessary. Even relatively simple business applications require vast files of data for their accomplishment. Data file storage is relatively costly in electronic equipment, especially when there is usually low reference frequency to approximately 80% of the file content. This would be in accordance with the 80-20 rule where 80% of the activity falls within 20% of the items.

Another design consideration with respect to working files is whether reference thereto can be on a sequential basis or whether it must be random. Since the sequential files have greater capacity and are less costly than random files, it is important to weigh these advantages against the disadvantages of sequencing all transaction data before processing can commence.

Relative Complexity of Process. Because of the versatility of EDP equipment, the scope of applications possible, and the detailed information necessary, this type of systems work is the most difficult to perform. There is a superior challenge here that constitutes a barrier to acceptance due to lack of highly trained personnel. This has been a material factor in limiting the more extensive use of computers in smaller industries.

Cost. Electronic data processing systems represent the most costly office equipment yet offered for business use. Although there has always been a certain readiness to install expensive production equipment in the factory, extensive mechanization of the office is still a relatively new idea and meets with a certain amount of managerial resistance.

These matters of work volume and file capacity, processing complexity, and high cost are some of the systems and procedures design problems inherent in EDP work. The solving of problems of this type requires a high level of ability plus a good collection of procedural techniques.

In addition to a knowledge of how to accomplish an electronic data processing installation, it is necessary for the installer to acquire a rather broad knowledge of all typical equipment available in this new field. He must also learn how this equipment works before he can start the application of his problems to it.

EDP EQUIPMENT FEATURES

In a short paper such as this, it is possible only to point out various features of electronic equipment so as to indicate some of the system capabilities that make it so powerful. To do this, we might scan the typical system components for input, storage, processing, and output.

In order to start processing business information within an electronic system, it is necessary to present the data to the equipment in a form of language readable by it. Although most equipment in use today requires a conversion of data from the business document to some other form, recently developed special-purpose machines are capable of reading directly from the original document.

Currently, the most widely used input method is punched cards. This is due to relatively low preparation cost, ease of verification, and development of fast card readers. Where extremely high input speeds are needed, the card may be transcribed to magnetic tape and this tape used for data entry into the system. There is some use of punched paper tape and direct key-board entry. This latter is confined to the smaller types of systems. All of these methods are customarily accomplished by a transcription of the original document, although in some instances the cards or paper tape are by-products of other recording processes.

Recently, most of the equipment manufacturers introduced electronic systems capable of reading directly from documents printed with magnetic ink. These systems are special-purpose inasmuch as they have been designed for banking operations.

Just as there are a variety of input devices and related speeds, so also are there a variety of internal electronic circuits in the processing equipment, each with its ranges of speeds. Older types of equipment utilized mechanical relays as well as vacuum tubes. Most of the newer designs incorporate diodes, transistors, or ferractors—all of which lend themselves to miniaturization. Additionally, the recently developed systems incorporate circuit elements which permit extremely fast access to all data being processed within the equipment.

One circuit element which is critical in the system design is storage. Here there is a wide range of capacities, speeds, and costs from which to choose. Some of the older systems utilized mercury-delay lines and electrostatic tubes. However, most current systems use magnetic cores, magnetic drums, tape reels, and, in some instances, magnetic disks or tape bins. Of these, the magnetic cores are the most rapid in operation and offer the greatest potential for future development. Presently, the high cost of core storage makes use of other devices economically desirable, especially where speed is not a prime factor.

After data has been processed, there are certain system design considerations which are related to the available output devices. Generally, there are advantages in using a combination of two or more of the types of available output methods. Some of the system output is usually in the form of updated records for future processing and is not meaningful in terms of the primary report requirements. Such records may be retained on tape or cards and only printed out in readable format at periodic intervals. Other data must be obtained in readable format as rapidly as possible.

Because of the system demands for a choice of output media, there are available, in most systems, magnetic tape, punched cards, paper tape, and a printer. Additionally, most systems provide for auxiliary equipment to handle output of the EDP equipment for purposes of preparing printed reports outside of the electronic system. This is termed "off-line" operation.

All of these electronic components have been combined in a variety of ways by the equipment manufacturers so as to offer machine systems which presently cover a wide scope of versatility and cost. Additionally, there are available many pieces of recording equipment designed to function as parts of the completely mechanized system. These recording machines act as links between the manual system and the machine system so as to permit a high degree of integration within the entire system.

INTEGRATED DATA PROCESSING

Integrated data processing is not a new concept. To a limited extent we have always had some forms of integration in our recording systems. However, these recent developments of electronic data processing machines have stimulated the parallel development of other machines designed as integrating devices.

Since integration of data processing is an important concept in the design of an EDP system, it might be well to review the meaning of this term.

As used in our work, integration has two facets: (1) unification of the system and (2) interconnection of the equipment. System unification has as its objective a design which includes on source documents sufficient information to permit use of these data wherever they are needed within the entire business structure. Interconnection of equipment encompasses the objectives of early recording of source data in machine media and the use of this machine media subsequently for all data processing. To put it more simply—the ultimate objective of integrated data processing is to have one manual recording of a transaction at its inception and to accomplish all future recordings mechanically. However, we rarely achieve more than a partial success in approaching this objective.

POTENTIAL ADVANTAGES

The decision to integrate a particular portion of a system must be based on certain advantages. What are these? They should be lower cost, increased speed, and reduction of errors. As we consider machine components, we must keep these desired advantages in mind so as not to get lost in the fascinating hardware of the many ingenious gadgets for integration. It is often not feasible to push the application of integration techniques all the way back to the primary source of data.

Just as design features of electronic equipment were said to affect the problems of EDP installations, so do available designs of recording machines and recording media affect system integration. For this reason, we should approach this part of our work by becoming acquainted with the machine components and learning how these components can be modified to meet our particular methods problem.

Although punched cards are probably the most used medium for system integration, there is also extensive use of punched paper tape. Paper tape is especially useful where there are distance problems in communication between machines. Magnetic tape is rarely used for initial data capturing because of cost, but it is the principal recording medium within the electronic machines. Magnetic ink, either in coded form or in printed characters, is still in limited use. However, magnetic character sensing seems to have passed through the experimental stage and now offers the systems technician a new field of exploration for use in integrating systems.

There is a large family of machines from which to choose in this field of EDP. Practically every type office machine can now be inter-coupled to a card or tape punch. Flexowriters, add-punches, teletype equipment, cash registers, and ink imprinters are all machines capable of translating document language into machine language. Once translated, the machine language can be re-translated for use in other equipment where direct use is not possible or practicable. For this purpose there are card-to-tape, tape-to-card, and even tape-to-tape machines. There are presently few limits to machine compatibility. However, this matter of compatibility must be considered carefully by the analysts if minimum cost and maximum advantages are to be achieved.

NEW PROBLEMS FOR MANAGEMENT

We have mentioned some of the objectives which should be sought after in the development of electronic data processing systems and we have mentioned also the capabilities of the electronic and associated equipment. Because of the magnitude of the task of achieving these objectives with this equipment, many new problems have been created for the managers of the business enterprise. They are management problems because they require decisions to make major organizational changes, use large amounts of capital, and retrain and relocate many of the personnel.

However, these are not exclusively management problems inasmuch as the systems man is usually a key figure in their solution. For this reason, the systems man must understand the implications of his work in terms of the related management decisions necessary for the accomplishment of the systems job. Accordingly, we should examine some of the decision areas so as to understand better the role of the systems man.

Generally, the systems and procedures activity within the organizational structure is relocated when it encompasses the installation of an integrated electronic data processing system. Although data processing has customarily been assigned to the controller's department, the EDP systems group should be the responsibility of top management. It

would be preferable to locate this group close to the executive vice president or someone of similar stature.

The reason for requiring a direct line to top-level authority is founded on the necessity for disregarding the formal organizational structure in the new system design. It is at this top level that the choice must be made as to how far away to go from a patchwork systems approach and to what extent an engineered approach can be embraced. There is always a less immediate financial risk in the patchwork approach. A more visionary approach requires both understanding and sanction by management.

PERSONNEL SELECTION AND TRAINING

One of the most difficult problems involved in installing an EDP system lies in the selection and training of high caliber systems personnel. The success of the new system is dependent to a great degree on the quality of the systems work and programing accomplished. Therefore, the program should be staffed with a blend of trained EDP specialists and experienced company personnel. The staff should be fortified with persons experienced in mechanized data processing, even though this may mean going outside the organization for such talent. A study of this size should be a team effort, and it is desirable to include in active participation an outside consultant specializing in this field as well as selected representatives from company management.

Top management must supply sufficient funds for preliminary study and installation. The budget for these phases must be prepared by the EDP group leader, so he must be acquainted with management policy in this regard and also must be adept at long-range planning.

It is not sufficient, though, for management to supply financial aid only. Top management must become genuinely interested in and give active support to the entire concept of EDP. This drive must carry middle management by influence and be extended to operational levels by education. Management must join in solving the problems of how to get information about the systems and their dynamics. If electronic systems are to be used for decision making, only management can contribute the bases for those decisions.

MANAGEMENT PARTICIPATION

Now, how can management participation be encouraged? One device which has proven successful in practice is to schedule an EDP meeting at regular intervals. This may be every week or every second week. These meetings should start at the inception of the EDP program and should continue, at least, until the new system design has been tried successfully on the equipment. Participating in the meeting should be the key system personnel, top management (especially the officer responsible for the EDP system function), outside consultant, and representatives of the electronic equipment manufacturing company. Whenever system analysis work is being done in a certain area, department heads from that area should attend the current meeting. By using a device such as this, there is an opportunity for exchange of ideas and for management to be fully informed at all times as to the status of the EDP project.

There are other problems which require different devices for their solution. One of these is personnel relations. The start of an electronic system survey is usually no secret within an organization. Knowledge of this impending change gives rise to fear of loss of job by many of the clerical personnel. From the start of the project there should be a definite program for informing the personnel of what is being done. They should understand that all persons who might be required to do different work under the new system will have ample time to retrain. Usually, normal attrition within the work staff solves the problem of reduced personnel requirements.

In addition to allaying the fears of relocation, there should be positive attempts to inform all personnel of the nature of the contemplated change. This can usually be done at a group meeting, or series of meetings, where, after a short description of what is being done, one of the sound film strips or movies available from the equipment manufacturer can be shown. Continuing information can be furnished through the company bulletin or by the department heads.

All management, down through the level of department heads, should attend executive-type courses so as to become acquainted with the equipment and how it works. This will permit them to do a better job when they sit in on the system meetings or participate in the design of a portion of the new EDP system.

A most difficult problem is that of the technical upgrading of key management personnel. In order to do a better job of management and utilize the electronic equipment to its greatest potential, it is necessary that each person give a high degree of attention to the problems of data processing. To become qualified in this regard demands special effort on the part of the individual. This effort could be minimized through the adoption of a positive policy by management of seeking out beneficial seminars and courses at colleges and universities or programs sponsored by organizations such as the American Management Association.

SUMMARY

What all of this probably implies is that, in addition to needing management-oriented systems personnel, there is a real need for systems-oriented management personnel. It is evident, therefore, that these two groups come very close together at the higher levels of system development such as in the installation of an EDP system.

However, future progress in the area of scientific management will depend to a large extent upon the enlightened contributions of top management. Managers of our expanding business complex of men and machines will need solutions to their problems by methods based upon the exception principle. This principle provides for the sifting of vast quantities of day-to-day business data to bring out for management attention only those matters requiring action. Electronic equipment is the tool for accomplishing this rapid appraisal in an effective manner. To be able to use electronic equipment, managers must become informed. They must become informed not only of the equipment capabilities but of the vast unexplored areas of professional management techniques. In short, system development, especially where EDP equipment is involved, should be the concern of top management.

32. ELECTRONIC POWER GRAB

Robert L. McFarland *

Is it possible to "steal" a company in such a subtle way that few of the company officials and certainly none of the stockholders would be aware of it? "Stealing" here would mean actually making the key operating and policy decisions without the chief executive and top management being aware that they themselves were not truly in control of the overall operation. Could someone gain control over the relevant informational inputs of a centralized company computer facility, and specify the nature of the output of such an information gathering system without the awareness of top management? Could such an informational system be so manipulated that control could come to reside in one individual or several individuals working together? These questions imply, of course, that the theft would accrue to the great benefit of an individual or a given ingroup. In addition, it is assumed here that the individual's or ingroup's ability to remain hidden, but in complete control of the company, would be desirable for a considerable period of months or years.

Practically no discussion of these questions appears in the professional literature of operations research or of computer sciences. Nor have there been popular novels in the style of the famous "Executive Suite" referring to power plays centering around a company's computer. This lack of published scientific or fictional literature led the author to pull together his own observations and the observations of other people actively involved in the area of concern. Discussions were held with persons from top management groups of organizations possessing large central EDP facil-

ities, from regional sales managers of several major computer manufacturing concerns, from members of the teaching staffs of certain commercial companies manufacturing computers who provide computer orientation and training for top management, and, finally, from a series of research consultants who function in the area of operations research and computer management. In general, the people interviewed maintained that they had not been involved in any power struggles revolving around a company computer, yet each seemed most anxious to discuss the issue.

As background to a discussion of this problem, we should recognize that as of 1964, over 21,000 computers were in use throughout the world and apparently over 7,000 additional computers are currently on order. These computer facilities vary in price from 12 thousand dollars to over seven million dollars. The United States Government alone spends close to one billion dollars per year on computer facilities and employs over 45,000 people in connection with its data processing activities. The Government, in the last decade, moved from possessing ten such facilities to over 1,200 in use today. Over half of the computer facilities in Government are employed in the Department of Defense.

Apparently over 500 different business and scientific usages of computers are now available for private industry. Among the industries with high computer budgets it is not infrequent that 10 to 12 percent of the *annual* capital expenditure is devoted to investing in additional new facilities in the EDP area. Such commitment of annual capital to computer expenditures represents the investment of huge sums of money by some of the shrewdest business minds in the world. Marshall K. Evans and Lou R. Hague in their article "Master Planning for Information Systems," which appeared in the *Harvard Business Review*, January–February 1962, provide a clue as to

SOURCE: *Business Automation* (February, 1965), pp. 30–39. Reprinted by permission of *Business Automation*, Copyright Business Publications International, Division of OA Business Publication, Inc.

* President, Human Systems Institute, and Assistant Professor of Psychiatry and Neurology, Northwestern University.

why these companies are engaged in such heavy capital expenditures. They say ". . . in U.S. industry today, the gathering, storing, manipulating and organizing of information for managing enterprises cost as much or more than does direct factory labor." The indications are that the relative proportion of company costs for information gathering, data processing and decision making in the years ahead will increase as automation further reduces manufacturing cost.

An article in the February 24, 1964, issue of *U.S. News and World Report*, entitled, "Is the Computer Running Wild?" expressed great concern over the possibility of EDP facilities and technology getting beyond the control of our society. A computer expert was quoted in that article as saying the "computer craze" could end as a nightmare for the modern executive. He envisions an office of the near future with computers grinding out a flood of statistics and draws this picture for a poorly planned system:

There was a sales executive crushed under four tons of sales reports. There was a production engineer being strangled by punch tape. There was the president of the company, his office piled from floor to ceiling with reports, figures, indexes, computations, and permutations . . . his office stuffed, and he, emaciated and bug-eyed, reading his way through reports at a rate slower than reports were being produced.

ASK A STUPID QUESTION . . .

This nightmare would be the appropriate "living hell" for executives of any company who would permit themselves to operate under such impossible circumstances. Long before the advent of the computer, it was entirely possible for any executive to permit himself to be flooded by much irrelevant and extraneous material. Successful executives have long been aware of the necessity of guarding against such flooding or overloading.

Other experts were quoted in the same article as indicating much more appreciation for some of the truly perplexing problems confronting management and computer facilities supervisors. For example, Professor Elting E. Morrison of M.I.T. says that earlier machines developed by man—engines and generators—

set clear limits as to how much misuse they would tolerate before resisting. He points out:

Over-loaded, abused, they stopped working, stalled, broke down, blew up; and there was the end of it. Thus they set clear limits to men's ineptitudes.

For the computer, I believe, the limits are not so obvious. Used with ignorance or stupidity, asked a foolish question, it does not collapse, it goes on to answer a fool according to his folly. And the questioner, being a fool, will go on to act upon the reply.

Thus one of the dangers of the computer technology is clearly indicated in Professor Morrison's remarks, insofar as man's intellect must determine what is to be put into a computer, how it is to be programed or processed, and how the information derived is going to be checked for its reliability, validity and usefulness.

As large companies with sizeable computer facilities have reached the point where the extremely heavy start-up costs and extremely long periods of writing and debugging the programs become relatively less pressing, certain new problems are beginning to emerge (in these companies). Philip Thurston, writing in the *Harvard Business Review*, January 1963, in an article entitled, "Who Should Control Information Systems?" says, "I consider that in the past decade a significant characteristic of information systems work has been to place a great degree of control in the hands of specialists. This situation has developed in part through the failure of top management to place controlling responsibility with operating managers."

STAYING ON THE TOP AT THE TOP

In personal interviews held in the Chicago area, nearly half of the people interviewed referred to the McKinsey report, which was authored by John Garrity and published in 1963 under the title "Getting the Most Out of Your Computer," as being the most pertinent single reference about appropriate top management control of computer facilities. In this widely distributed booklet, the McKinsey team provided certain bench marks for evaluating computer effectiveness. They felt that constructive, clear cut and positive answers to the following questions must be present if one is to predict a company's success in this area:

1. Is the computer systems effort, currently and cumulatively, on a self-sustaining basis?

2. Is the computer systems producing intangible benefits in the form of better operating information, reduced manufacturing cycles, improved customer service and the like?

3. Is the computer systems effort addressed to the key profit determinants of the business? Is it making itself felt in all major divisions and functions?

Here in brief summary is what these management consultants attempted to do. They studied 27 companies, nine of whom they indicated were highly successful in their computer applications. They then compared these nine companies with the remaining 18, whose computer applications seemed to be of average or inferior quality. Garrity, in summarizing the findings, pointed to the central issue involved in successful management of computer facilities when he said, "In the lead companies, as their actions indicated and the results show, each one of the top managements has correctly assessed the computer's potential and has given it the continuing management direction and guidance it so badly needs and so much deserves. . . . The computer's challenge to top management is that it (management) must direct, manage, and lead, if profits are to result."

The eleven major differences between the lead and average companies studied in the McKinsey evaluation which led to Garrity's remark can be stated precisely as follows: (1) Top management devotes time to the computer systems effort in proportion to its cost and potential; (2) Top management reviews, plans and follows up on computer systems results; (3) Computer applications are selected on the basis of careful feasibility studies; (4) Project plans are developed and progress reports planned; (5) Operating management participates in project selection and planning; (6) Operating management plays a significant role in project manning; (7) Operating management takes responsibility for progress and results; (8) The systems staff has a broad range and depth of technical skill; (9) Some management sciences people are located under the computer systems manager, although larger OR operations may be conducted in parallel to this operation; (10) The computer systems effort is organized on a divisional basis which conforms to the company's normal organizational pattern; (11) The corporate staff monitors progress and appraises results.

In general, conflict begins to develop in companies where real time computer capabilities become as badly needed as high speed batch processing. Such issues are very difficult problems for top management to solve, particularly when both types of applications are more than amply justified by each of the separate operating divisions.

ON THE COATTAILS OF THE COMPUTER

Another type of problem occurs as the result of simply increasing capitalization and size of the staff necessarily involved in operating the computer effectively. The middle management supervisor who had a hand in making the initial computer application to the first routine business problems, and who successfully carried through this application, tends to be promoted both salary-wise and echelonwise. Thus the original "company parent" tends to rise in the company along with progressing sophistication of computer applications. This man typically tends to be a person with fiscal or accounting background, and his superiors in turn gain increasing say within the top management group as to what would be the appropriate use of the facilities. Quite naturally they tend to favor applications in areas in which they could depend upon "their boy" to deliver for them as he had quite obviously done in the past. This creates a situation in which many other worthwhile projects proposed by the other operating vice presidents get side-tracked or put on a very slow time scale.

When the time comes for either the direct computer facility supervisor or his immediate superiors to begin considering the purchase of the second generation or third generation computer facility, they quite naturally want to maintain their unilateral control over the new equipment. However, by that time, successful applications have been demonstrated in two or more additional divisions, and therefore the stage is set at the top management level for a showdown as to who should control the computer.

If the chief executive of the company has

not grown in this period of time in his own sophistication as to the computer applications, he very frequently will leave these kinds of arguments to be thrashed out two or three echelons below his direct perusal. Therefore, he avoids committing himself to one operating division or another of his company. However, those chief executives who stay with the developing computer facilities and who attempt to maintain direct managerial control over the process, soon delegate the direct operating responsibility for this facility to one of their immediate subordinates and place the computer facilities supervisor not more than two or three levels down below their own offices. A vice president of a steel company, in charge of the computer facilities, told me that such a decision is warranted if for no other reason than the fact that they were spending nine percent of their total annual capital in this area.

A NEED FOR LOYALTY

In many different companies effective use of the computer across several operating divisions becomes extremely difficult, if not impossible, if the computer facility and its staff are controlled primarily through lower echelon staff groups. In such instances, the technical staff may be highly competent, and attempt to initiate highly appropriate applications in a variety of divisions, but they are not in a position to secure sufficient loyalty and continuing attention to their program applications by the operating middle management group. Unless the top management group in each such division plays an active part in such activities, the operating middle management group will give such applications too low a priority for their monitoring and expediting.

Without firm, continuing direction by the chief executive, power struggles for control of these facilities then develop in the middle management area, or at a level approximately three steps down from the chief executive's office. In one printing industry, a fiscal accounting head found himself in a position where he really wanted a larger computer facility, but he also found that he would have to permit a drastic reorganization of this facility with a high probability that control of this larger facility would be placed considerably beyond his own control. He viewed himself as being not quite powerful enough, nor viewed favorably enough by top management, to insure that job assignment for himself, and

consequently at this point he actually blocked further consideration of this larger facility, even though the original recommendation was his. Thus in the upper "never-never land" of middle management groups, computer control becomes quite involved and yet it tends to slow the computer program development and tends to insulate department by department. This is a situation in which the research group and the fiscal accounting group, in particular, often resolve the conflict by seeking geographical separation of their computer facilities. This resolution also occurs with fiscal groups and manufacturing groups, when the latter are attempting to use computer facilities for on-line control of automated equipment.

. . . AND A RELEVANT CONCEPT

Up to this point in the discussion, some of the relevant literature has been reviewed and some of the anecdotes which were collected in preparing this article have been presented. In general, these observations confirm what was found in the McKinsey report and urged by Thurston. But, the McKinsey report seems to suggest to the chief executive certain procedures which, while pointing to successful operations, are based largely on empirical day-to-day experience. These practical findings are not presented within an explicit theoretical framework. Looking at the systems and considering possible theoretical frameworks to be employed, the concept of the unified information flow system appears relevant. This concept is expressed by Joseph Redding in an unpublished manuscript, entitled "The Unified Information Flow Concept for the Organization of an Information Processing and Computing System," prepared for Standard Oil Company (Indiana) in February 1964. Redding bases this system on separating the output requirements from the information inputs by means of an information file or storage. He proposes that there should be only one file for all purposes, entering just a single recording of a given event and from which all reports are prepared. Separate programs would be used for updating of files, analysis of data, and preparation of reports.

ASK YOURSELF A QUESTION

Beyond Redding's concept, control systems theory applications seem to provide a method of synthesis which might be even more appropriate for consideration. For the present, however, I would like to discuss a theoretical matrix in which practical decisions must be made by top management, and point out some clues as to the nature of the concepts needed in this area. First, there are several questions which the McKinsey group recommended the chief executive ask of himself. Now, I am frank to say I do not know when the executive should ask these questions. Possibly he might do so while shaving in the morning. The McKinsey report lists them as follows:

1. Do I devote to the computer systems effort the time and attention that its cost and potential warrant, or have I backed away from my role by delegating the responsibility to the technical people three or four levels down?

2. Do I see that the computer is used for more than just routine record keeping, i.e., that we are also using this new resource to find new and better ways of running the business?

3. Have I insisted on carefully pricing out all proposed computer applications and do I follow up to insure that we have earned a significant tangible return?

Now, if the executive hasn't slit his throat in despair and utter frustration by this time, the McKinsey report continues by recommending further self-punishment by asking these final two questions:

4. Have I clearly indicated to operating managers that I hold them accountable for seeing that they get the most out of computer systems in running their divisions?

5. Have I provided the company with the kind of computer systems manager needed to get the job done; and have I given him the support, stature and staff he needs?

While I have been somewhat facetious in listing these remarks, I do think they reflect kinds of questions that imply control system ideology.

Control systems theory in a formal sense apparently has not been directly applied to the chief executive as he functions in his job world, and yet the critical elements for an effective control system are displayed quite consistently by the successful chief executive as portrayed in the McKinsey report. A successful executive must continually collect information from the subordinate parts of his over-all operation, and participate in the formulation of company policies, such as planning for future development, maintaining reasonable profit levels, and establishing good community and public relations. These considerations can be regarded as two separate types of input to his internal control system. Thus, the executive must acquire input information about the company internally as well as its relation to the larger environment. These data are regularly compared with the goals imbedded in the policies of the company which serve as the second form of input. His own activities in the formulation of lower-level policies are appropriately regarded as his means of attempting to reduce the discrepancies between the inputs from the environment external to himself and his internally perceived policy goals. His corrective actions (his output) consists of his own policy formulations which are intended to influence the lower echelon decision making of the company in a corrective manner.

What has impeded our looking at the executive himself as a feedback control system is the fact that such behavior occurs on an extremely slow time scale unlike the ultra-fast time scales found when we make control theory applications to electronic gear. The executive may have a conference on Monday regarding policy formulation, and he may take several days to compare the information that he has from additional company informational sources before he has arrived at a decision, say late Friday, to fire one of the operating managers. This slow time scale, however, should not be an impossible barrier to either behavioral sciences or physical sciences, because many phenomena studied in both scientific fields have similarly slow time scale characteristics. However, because of the time scale it is very, very easy to look at the chief executive and categorize his behavior as of a given hour or as of a given act. Such behavior then is viewed as separate autonomous units that might be related to his other activities in an empirical or a correlational sense. Thus, on a day by day basis it is extremely difficult to view the executive's behavior as a continuous control system. But all of his control system's inputs and outputs can be related simultaneously on the appropriately slowed time scale. Once this is done conceptually, one can see that the chief executive must direct his attention to a series of *identifiable controlled variables*. In this instance, I am using the concept of variable in the physical science sense, and I am further suggesting that the concept of

Ten Point Program For Success

Top management devotes time to the computer systems effort in proportion to its cost and potential.

Computer applications are selected on the basis of careful feasibility studies.

The corporate staff monitors progress and appraises results.

The systems staff has a broad range and depth of technical skill.

Operating management takes responsibility for progress and results.

Top management reviews and plans and follows up on computer systems results.

Operating management participates in project selection and planning.

Some management sciences people are located under the computer systems manager, although larger OR operations may be conducted in parallel to this operation.

The computer systems effort is organized on a divisional basis which conforms to the company's *normal* organization pattern.

Operating management plays a significant role in project manning.

---

controlled variable is an extremely useful one. We can distinguish between controllable variables and uncontrollable variables both in a physical system and a living system.

THE COMPLEX INDIVIDUAL

The research of the immediate years ahead lies in identifying which variables effective, successful managers actually do control. In our research in the mental health field, we have developed some paper and pencil test procedures, as well as some laboratory tests, in which it can be demonstrated that individuals do function as complex control systems monitoring clearly identifiable controlled variables. These methodologies developed in the mental health area seemed to warrant application to studies of the behavior of chief executives—not because the executives are mentally ill but rather because they are human! Our theoretical system then permits one to estimate the appropriate working procedures for the top executive and probably would enable him to move away from simply asking questions so artificially formulated in the five recommendations previously discussed. The top management group as a whole probably has arrived in its position of authority by identifying, more or less intuitively, the relevant controllable variables for their given company situation. Further research in a more rigorous

control systems framework would permit a shift from the correlative approach to measuring these phenomena in a much more direct physical science type manner.

Finally, it is important to discuss briefly some of the strategies of conflict that would be involved in effective "computermanship." This section of this article is related to the concept of "How to steal a company without anyone ever catching on!" I would like to discuss this topic in terms of three problems. The first is (1) "How does one go about eliminating one's potential competition?" I will assume that the reader is bright, capable, aggressive and wishes to master sufficient computer technology, operations management and other human science activities to equip him to move ahead. However, one must eliminate competition by whatever means available if one is to "ever succeed in business by really trying!" So one should first consider those competitors who are 40 or more years of age. In general, one should repeatedly say to these men that the old ways are the best and these new-fangled ideas are just costing the company a great deal of time and effort, and will certainly not be as effective as standard time-tested techniques. One should also slightly reinforce the competitor's fears in the direction that maybe this stuff is just too technical for him, that he would have to study too many months or years to try to catch up, and even if he did the field would have then taken another dramatic leap forward and he would still be left behind. If one is also sadistically inclined, one might well suggest that his learning capacities are being impaired by his increasing age.

A TIME FOR THE SHOWDOWN

For the successful budding executive to move ahead he must make some decisions as to when the showdown, or the confrontation, or the pure power play is to occur. Any good young Machiavellian knows that the time for the coup d'etat must be chosen with care. So consider for a moment (2) "How does one go about slowing down or delaying the showdown?" If one is in the computer facility proper, one should very seriously try to discourage many different divisions of the company from getting involved in using the computer facility. Of course, outright refusal to do such work is not a very wise strategy to follow. Rather, it would be much more desirable to slow down such applications by continually changing the program with *relevant* (not irrelevant) suggestions. In this way one can keep the other group in the writing and debugging stages for endless periods. In this situation, one should also encourage the development of small or medium size computer applications in different parts of the company, and one should pretend to have no awareness of Data Phone transmission or any technology which would suggest that the large computer installations could ever be a centralized phenomenon. One would also in this instance encourage great geographical separation between the various medium size computers.

SUPPORT BEGETS SUCCESS

Finally, then (3) "How does the young Machiavellian force a showdown?" If he feels he is ready for the showdown, there is a certain battle cry here which should facilitate it. Of course, the young man in question should be reasonably sure that he will end up either the technical director of the computer facility, or the executive who is charged with the operational responsibilities of this facility, before he starts the countdown. The battle cry for the showdown would be the insistence

that he would demonstrate that the computer facility can produce tangible profits and maintain itself on a pay-as-you-go basis if he is given complete management responsibility. By now, this claim can undoubtedly be demonstrated in companies having had computer facilities for five years or longer, providing the management orientation McKinsey described exists in that company. The young man should bet that his management of the information flow systems could be carried out effectively by utilizing the systems approach and many of the operational research technologies.

Crucial to this ploy is the idea that his chief executive truly manages this part of the company's operations as he does other parts. The young Machiavellian would find himself out on his ear in eighteen months should he make such a battle cry his rallying point and should his chief executive fail to provide him with unqualified and continuing support. As in all power struggles, one takes a calculated risk in terms of either delaying or facilitating the showdown. But as our understanding of the empirical results in other companies grows, and we begin to articulate much more explicit management theory expressed particularly in a control systems framework, the chances of success and moving for the showdown will grow more favorable and this trend will continue into the future.

The ploys suggested thus far are more or less overt interpersonal actions. But such ploys, or similar ones, could be combined with sound operations research and programing competency. The young Machiavellian has now suddenly new dimensions in which to carry out the old power struggles. What if he organizes the informational flow of data so that actual decision making functions pass from the operating managers to the computer without their knowledge? This is often consciously and deliberately done by operating managers to facilitate administrative chores at the lowest management levels. But it can be done inadvertently.

For example, such an event nearly came to pass recently in a midwestern telephone company. Throughout most of the telephone system, the Traffic Management Division assigns telephone numbers to subscribers and assigns most equipment lines. These basic activities are crucial if economical and efficient use of telephone equipment is to be maintained. In this particular instance, a senior staff officer proposed in a meeting that number and line assignments are logically so simple that such items could be programed for continuous control by their computer (which is operated by another division). The staff immediately objected violently. They saw that these two activities, plus what is called "loading and balancing" procedures, constitute the basic operations that justify Traffic Management departments today. In former years their *raison d'être* was management of the large staff of local telephone operators, but this function has gradually been reduced as operators have been replaced by automatic dial equipment. Thus, a decision to program number and line assignments into a computer system would eliminate a major function of their entire division. Their few remaining functions, from a top management viewpoint, could be readily assigned to other divisions. Whether that fate will come to pass or not is not our concern here. Rather this incident illustrates how easy it is to "lose" control (power) by transferring forms of decision-making to the computer. In this instance, the senior staff man was proposing to serve as his own executioner. A less bright executive could be conned into a similar ploy by a clever "thief."

A second example, concerning the same company division, focuses on the second major functional area of "loading and balancing." Over 100 separate report forms were received by and processed in and through their basic data unit. A significant bulk of this mass of data was relevant to "loading and balancing," but very few men in this division could effectively read this data and take action to avert undesirable conditions from developing. One or two "pundits" high in the division had such skills and were accorded much honor, salary, etc., for their knowledge. However, these experts seemingly could not impart their skills to the younger men who would ultimately succeed them. In this instance, it did not appear that they were deliberately withholding their knowledge; they performed their activities in an intuitive manner. While they could logically justify their decisions after-the-fact, they simply could not specify the sequence of analysis they actually employed, and, consequently, they could not train their subordinates.

IT'S WHAT'S UP TOP THAT COUNTS

In contrast to this, technical or analytical skills are sometimes deliberately and consciously withheld as job insurance by a minority of older workers. The story is told of a Marine sergeant in charge of plumbing and sanitation at an East coast base who carefully memorized the blueprints of all water lines and hydrants and then burned them! Presumably he kept his job at that base until he retired because "the only set of blueprints left was in his head." This example can serve to remind us that the young Machiavellian might, by diligent effort, identify the company's relevant controllable variables as suggested by control system theory. Once he determined these variables he could program the data regarding them into the mass of other data typically associated with them. He need only check the key data occasionally to be able to prognosticate with amazing accuracy, should he wish rapid overt advancement. However, he or a group of associates might wish to use this information covertly. Such a circumstance could occur when that old dream (pre-SEC) of manipulating the company's public stock issue might appear to be "controllable." Here it would be assumed that neither the company officers nor the SEC could readily discern these manipulations. This then could be an instance where young Machiavellians would pass up a promotion to steal a company and thereby gain a fortune, and the manipulations might even prove to be legal.

THERE'S MORE TO COME

It should be clear now that from my viewpoint a company could be stolen without top management knowing it. Such a steal could be achieved through clever use of the company's centralized computer. The input information needed for effective predictions about the company's short term future operations could be buried among other traditional input information and could be easily overlooked by top management. It should be clear, too, that many more overt power struggles will occur in the years immediately ahead, and they will center around the control and use of computer facilities.

One can predict such struggles if for no other reason than that computer costs are approaching the ten percent level of available annual capital in many companies. Also, human nature being what it is, executive power struggles will continue even though the means to do so, and the objectives sought, are undergoing rapid technological change. "Who controls the computer controls the company," ceases to be a science fiction adage and becomes increasingly valid in the present industrial world.

Perhaps the most interesting in-fighting of the next five to ten years will occur when two highly effective executive vice presidents—each of whom has had considerable computer system training, operations research training, plus detailed knowledge of the operation of one or two of the company's major divisions—begin to struggle for ultimate control of computer facilities. That will truly be "a fight of the century."

BIBLIOGRAPHY

1. Anshen, M., "The Manager and the Black Box," *Harvard Business Review*, November–December, 1960.
2. Baumes, C. G., *Administration of Electronic Data Processing*, Studies in Business Policy, No. 98, The National Industrial Conference Board, 1961.
3. Blank, V. F., "Management Concept in Electronic Systems," *The Journal of Accountancy*, January, 1961.
4. Brabb, G. J., and E. B. Hutchins, "Electronic Computers and Management Organizations," *California Management Review*, Fall, 1963.
5. Bright, J. R., *Automation and Management*, Harvard University, Graduate School of Business Administration, 1958.
6. Burck, G., "The Boundless Age of the Computer," Parts I, IV, V, VI, *Fortune*, March, June, August, October, 1964.
7. Burlingame, J. F., "Information Technology and Decentralization," *Harvard Business Review*, November–December, 1961.
8. Conway, J. G., and D. Watts, *Business Experience and Electronic Computers, A Synthesis of What Has Been Learned from Electronic Data Processing Installations*, Controllers Institute Research Foundation, Inc., 1959.
9. Daniel, D. R., "Measure Your EDP Progress: A '5,000-Mile Checkup' for Computer Installation," *The Management Review*, March, 1961.
10. Dunlop, J. T., *Automation and Technological Change*, The American Assembly, Columbia University, Prentice-Hall, Inc., 1962.
11. "Effects of Business Automation in the Sixties," Round Table, Part 2, *Management and Business Automation*, February, 1961.
12. Emery, J. C., "The Impact of Information Technology on Organization," Proceedings of the 24th Annual Meeting, Academy of Management, 1964.
13. Greenburger, M. (ed.), *Management and the Computer of the Future*, M.I.T. Press and John Wiley and Sons, Inc., 1962.
14. Jacobson, H. B., and J. S. Roucek (eds.), *Automation and Society*, Philosophical Library, Inc., 1959.
15. Jasinski, F. J., "Adapting Organizations to New Technology," *Harvard Business Review*, January–February, 1959.
16. Johnson, R. A., *Employers—Automation—Management*, University of Washington, Bureau of Business Research, 1961.
17. Kozmetsky, G., and P. Kircher, *Electronic Computers and Management Control*, McGraw-Hill, 1956.
18. Krout, A. J., "How EDP Is Affecting Workers and Organizations," *Personnel*, July, 1962.
19. Leaver, E. W., "How Automatic Can We Get?" *Keeping Pace With Automation*, American Management Association, Special Report 7, 1956.
20. Lipstreu, O., "Automation and Morale," *California Management Review*, Summer, 1964.
21. McCraken, D. D., "The Human Side of Computing," *Datamation*, January, 1961.
22. Malcolm, D. G., and A. J. Rowe (eds.), *Management Control Systems*, John Wiley and Sons, 1960.
23. Neuschel, R. F., *Management by Systems*, McGraw-Hill, 1960.
24. Newgarden, A., and E. R. Bailey, *Data Processing Today: A Progress Report*, No. 46, American Management Association, 1960.
25. Postley, J. A., *Computers and People*, McGraw-Hill, 1960.
26. Schwitter, J. P., "Computer Effect Upon Managerial Jobs," *Academy of Management Journal*, September, 1965.
27. Shultz, G. P., and T. L. Whisler (eds.), *Management Organization and the Computer*, The Free Press, 1960.
28. Simon, H. A., *The New Science of Management Decision*, Harper and Bros., 1960.
29. Taube, M., *Computers and Common Sense: The Myth of Thinking Machines*, Columbia University Press, 1961.
30. Whisler, T. L., *Executives and Their Jobs: The Changing Organization Structure*, Graduate School of Business, University of Chicago, Selected Papers, No. 9.

Part X.   Models and Simulation

One of the features of any system may be said to be pattern maintenance. If a system is to remain what it is, for instance, an operable efficient communications system, it is evident that it must somehow manage to retain and renew the mechanisms and patterns integral to the system as a whole. Because every system is in some state of dynamic adaptation to its environment, here understood as everything outside the system boundaries, there will always be problems to be solved. And as long as the recurrent problems are of approximately the same nature, their solution presents no special difficulty, but when the problems are substantially different, new solutions may be called for. This is where the use of abstract system models proves advantageous.

No problem is ever solved without some kind of a model.[1] When the dependent and independent variables of significance for the solution of the problem are few and their interrelationships rather simple, a model of the situation as it exists in the mind of the problem solver may be all that is required in the way of explicit model construction. But when the number of significant variables becomes very large and their interrelationships complex, then the eventual problem solver may not be able to contain the model in his head and may be forced to use pencil and paper to elaborate his design. But in essence there is no difference, for in either case the model is but an abstract representation of what supposedly is the real world situation.

The model generally used for the solution of systems problems is a mathematical one. Once the significant variables involved in the problem are identified, the problem is then posed in mathematical terms and solved by available mathematical techniques. There is, however, no simple way to do this. The identification of the variables that ought to be considered in the solution may be anything but easy, and the interrelationships of these variables extremely complex. A realistic model of the problem can involve knowledge and skills beyond the possession of the model builders. Take, for example, the problem of smog in urban areas.

A complete understanding of the problem involves knowledge of climate, the molecular behavior of gases, the chemistry of the automobile engine whose exhaust helps create smog, the number of automobiles, the geographic layout of the city, including the location of the homes, work places, and highway arteries, the availability of alternate means of transportation, the speed of traffic and the timing of traffic lights, the incomes of the population, the chemistry and biology of the lungs and blood stream, problems of microbes and virus growth under the chemical, light, and temperature conditions produced by smog —among many other problems.[2]

Once the components of the problem have been isolated and described in terms of mathematical symbols and the appropriate mathematical techniques employed

[1] Stafford Beer, "What Has Cybernetics to Do with Operational Research?" *Operational Research Quarterly*, March 1959.

[2] Alfred Kuhn, *The Study of Society: A Unified Approach* (Homewood, Ill.: Richard D. Irwin and The Dorsey Press, 1963), p. 4f.

(here the electronic computer can be most efficiently used), there still remains the all-important step of translating the mathematical solution into the real-world solution. After all, the solution arrived at through logical reasoning was that applied to a mathematical model, not to the problems of the real world. As such it is an abstraction. The original process must therefore now be reversed. The mathematical symbols employed in the solution must be applied to the component variables and their interrelationships as they exist in the original problem. No matter how sophisticated the solution may appear, since it is based on a model which is itself but an abstraction of concrete events from the real world, its usefulness will be proportional to the goodness of fit between the model and the events abstracted. The bread-and-butter test of any model involves the use of data from the real world. Without this data mathematical model building would be just another pastime, another form of mathematical recreation. Without this data there could be no valid test of the model and hence no real scientific progress. Hard-headed data and speculative mathematical models must go hand in hand!

In the business world there has been an increased utilization of models in the form of simulation exercises (management games). These simulation exercises, currently used in many industrial, educational, and government organizations for the training and development of managers, are based on mathematical models of the business world which in many cases are highly realistic. Such models consisting of a group of cause and effect formulas enable one to determine the outcome of input decisions made by the participants. For complex games electronic computers are employed to rapidly process the results.

Most simulation exercises concentrate on general management principles such as decision making and planning; however, others are specifically oriented to developing particular skills and techniques. One of the chief benefits of these exercises is the overall orientation to the interacting dimensions of the company, i.e., the participants are made aware of the impact of their decisions on the whole company and not merely on their own functional entity. As with all models, some aspects of reality are omitted and, although in many cases such omissions do not impugn the utility of the model, in others the abstraction of reality makes it more of an analytical tool than a learning device. Simulation of not only business problems but of complex management and industrial engineering problems may someday provide a breakthrough in management education.

Irwin Bross's selection on models, though published in the 50's, still serves as a good introduction to the subject. After mentioning briefly the various linguistic uses of models, he treats of physical models, abstract (verbal) models, symbolic models, and, finally, of mathematical models, all the while exemplifying his treatment with down-to-earth illustrations. Models have various advantages, among which he lists their remarkable record of predictions in the past history of mankind, their use as a frame of reference on which to "hang the problem," their usefulness (even when a failure) for suggesting fruitful avenues of research, their simplification of the problem by employing only the significant attributes abstracted from the real world, their use of symbolic language for both manipulation of the model and for purposes of easy communication, and finally their economical approach to the costs of prediction. Among the disadvantages he notes the usual reversals of the coin: the tendency toward oversimplification, the limitations of the symbolic language used, etc. He also points out for special treatment the all-too-human tendency of model builders to reify their brain children, to look upon their models not as representations of the real world but as being identified with it. Scientific model building however, because it is not divorced from data, will always bring its creator, after his jaunt into the symbolic world, face-to-face with the stark world of reality. When his model does not fit the facts of the real world, it is the model that must give way, and not the other way around.

Models are neither true nor false; they are either useful or not useful for making predictions in certain situations. A knowledge of this will eliminate several apparent paradoxes that may otherwise prove a problem.

In his admirably lucid explanation of the role of the model Bross compares and contrasts the model with a work of art, with an artistic painting. In all of this he stresses the important relationship that should hold between real-world data and the hypothetical model and illustrates it with examples from the world of physics. The pendulum example is an especially happy one, for it also serves well to illustrate the nature of the statistical (probability) model.

In his selection, Karl Deutsch looks upon a model as "a structure of symbols and operating rules which is supposed to match a set of relevant points in an existing structure or process" and which can perform four more or less distinct functions (organizing, heuristic, predictive, and mensurative). The organizing function is the ability of a model to meaningfully order apparently unrelated data and to reveal previously unnoticed relationships; the heuristic function leads to discoveries of new facts and methods, even though these (predictions) cannot be verified by presently available techniques. The predictive function enables one to obtain predictions verifiable by physical operations. The predictive spectrum, however, admits of many degrees, from the yes-no at one end to the quantitative at the other end. The mensurative function becomes identical in a way with the predictive in its extreme quantitative dimension.

Evaluation of a model consists of examining its performance with regard to each of these four functions. To these considerations should be added three additional ones: originality, simplicity, and realism.

For truly scientific progress we need more than sophisticated mathematical models and techniques. The assumptions underlying these models must be relevant, not naive; the constants in the equations real, not arbitrary. Examples of pseudo-models in the social sciences are cited, notably Rashevsky's, Zipf's, and Richardson's. Mathematical disguises are no substitute for genuine intuitive insight.

Joel Kibbee's article illustrates management's use of models and deals exclusively with the type of simulation that management is currently concerned with—computer simulation.

After briefly noting the various usages of the term "simulation," he identifies it with what is sometimes known as "computer simulation," "analytic simulation," and "symbolic system simulation." Symbolic System Simulation (SSS), often represented by the now-famous Black Box with its many dials and meters, is illustrated by an example and a variety of its applications noted.

Nowadays simulation is extensively used as a training technique and the form generally used is that of the "business game." Since their inception many of these games have been devised, some for training purposes only, others for research and teaching, some simple, some rather complex. Among the more notable games are AMA Executive Decision Making Simulation, SMART for systems and procedures management, and STEPS for computer programmer management. Among the more complex and ambitious business games so far designed for research are the UCLA Game and the Carnegie Tech Management Game, both of which are described in the text. However, the AMA General Management Simulation (GMS) Game is the one singled out for most attention since this is the game used as the basis of the "Management in Action" course of the American Management Association. The objective of this particular game is training in general principles of organization theory, control, and human relations. As such it is designed to teach management principles and not business principles: stress is on management and human relations, not on costs and profits.

Human System Simulation (man *and* the Black Box) uses business games as a laboratory for research into management control principles and thus bears a striking resemblance to the type of sociological research now generally known as Small Group research. Instead of using human beings in the study of human behavior the AMA GMS uses computerized models of such behavior. Such models are useful, even though not all types of sociologically significant behavior can be programmed.

Kibbee then proposes for consideration a preliminary model for research on management control systems. His Black Box is made up of three smaller black boxes, one each for control, operations, and environment. The details needed for each will depend upon what is being researched. The management control subsystem is singled out for special study together with the experimental variables that are to be manipulated, viz., the organizational structure, the information flow network and the decision rules. Decision making is definitely not a unitary process. It can be broken down into operations decisions and into the more complicated procedural decisions.

The author concludes the discussion with a few considerations on modeling. He points out that simplicity in the details is absolutely essential if the model is ever to be successfully programmed and run on the computer, that complicated questions need not require complicated models, that randomized factors may not be required by a truly workable model, and that the basic time interval used is crucial to the study.

33. MODELS

Irwin D. J. Bross *

THE SYMBOLIC WORLD

. . . I want to devote some attention to the broad concept of a *model*. Models are vitally important in scientific work and, in my opinion, in any intellectual endeavor. An understanding of the nature and role of a model is prerequisite to clear thinking.

In ordinary language the word "model" is used in various ways. It covers such diverse subjects as the dolls with which little girls play and also the photogenic "dolls" who occupy the attention of mature men. I shall be concerned here with model in the sense of replica (as in a model airplane).

PHYSICAL MODELS

There are several kinds of model aircraft. Solid scale models resemble the actual planes in general appearance (shape, markings, etc.). The flying model aircraft not only resemble the originals in appearance but, to some extent, in *function* as well (i.e., they are capable of free flight). Some very elaborate models are essentially simplified versions of real aircraft; they have gasoline engines, operable controls, and may even have radio-control mechanisms which allow the plane to be directed from the ground.

A boy who is interested in aviation can learn about the subject from the construction and operation of such flying models. In much the same way a scientist who has constructed a model of some natural phenomenon may learn about this phenomenon from a study of his model.

The model aircraft is easier to study than a full-sized aircraft for various reasons. It is more convenient to handle and manipulate. It is also simpler than the original, and principles of operation may be more apparent. There is some danger of over-simplification, of course, and some characteristics of a real aircraft would be overlooked if all attention were focused on the model.

As a matter of fact, adult scientists use model aircraft to learn about the performance of full-sized aircraft. They build carefully scaled replicas and test these models in wind tunnels. This is a much more economical process than to build a full-sized airplane and then to test *it* in a wind tunnel (a mammoth wind tunnel is a fabulously expensive piece of equipment). This type of argument by analogy has proved quite successful and is used all the time by aircraft engineers.

I do want to emphasize that the aircraft engineers do not trust the method entirely, that they carefully test the full-sized aircraft as well as the model. In other words, it does not follow that one can *automatically* obtain useful information about the original phenomena from the study of a model. Whether a model will be useful or not will have to be learned from experience, by comparing the performances of the original phenomenon and the replica.

The model represents a process of abstraction. The real aircraft has many properties or attributes such as shape, weight, and so on. Only a few of these properties are duplicated in the model. The wind tunnel model, for example, duplicates only the shape. However, the aerodynamic performance depends largely on this one characteristic; the other properties are more or less irrelevant.

This is an example of an effective process of abstraction. It allows us to focus our attention on a much simpler phenomenon without much loss from the fact that many details have been neglected.

This particular type of abstraction, the construction of a physical model, is used in various branches of science, engineering, and industry.

SOURCE: *Design for Decision,* Macmillan Company, 1953, pp. 161–182. Reprinted by permission of the Macmillan Company from *Design for Decision,* by Irwin D. J. Bross, © 1953.

* Statistical Consultant, Cornell University, Medical College.

Models are used to design ocean liners, bridges, water supply systems, and all sorts of products from automobiles to stage scenery. Not all models involve a change in size. In aircraft construction, for example, a full-sized model of a part of a plane is sometimes constructed out of wood in order to insure that an absent-minded designer does not put components in places which cannot be reached for repairs. In this situation the relevant factor is size, and the mock-up (as it is commonly called) eliminates other factors such as weight, function, and so on.

ABSTRACT MODELS

In the scientific world physical models are occasionally used for instructional purposes. In a planetarium you will generally find a model —little spheres which revolve on wire arms around a big sphere—which presents a picture of the astronomer's conception of the solar system. This sort of model is often used to demonstrate a phenomenon such as an eclipse. A rather similar physical model is sometimes employed to explain the atom to the general public. The solar model and the atom model illustrate one striking and sometimes confusing characteristic of models; two very diverse phenomena can sometimes be represented by similar models.

The solar model which you can see in a planetarium has had a very interesting history. Nowadays we think of the sun as a giant globe with a large family of little spheres circling around it. We locate ourselves on the third little sphere (counting out from the sun), and this notion does not cause us any mental anguish. In earlier days the picture was quite different and the earth was regarded as the center of the system. Of course if we go back still further there are all sorts of fabulous models which involve giants, turtles, and sea serpents. The history of astronomy is the story of the evolution of a model.

Did you notice that in describing the solar model I was actually taking a further step in abstraction? I was going from a physical model to a *verbal* model. The little balls were replaced by their symbols, the words "little balls."

All of us are accustomed to using verbal models in our thinking processes and we do it intuitively. Verbal models have played an important role in science, especially in the preliminary exploration of a topic and presentation of results. Verbal models are subject to a variety of difficulties, some of which I have discussed earlier, and most scientific fields have advanced (or are trying to advance) to the next stage—symbolic models of a mathematical nature. Astronomy was one of the first subjects to make this transition to the symbolic model. It should be noted that *until* this stage was reached there was really no reason to prefer a model with the sun as a center to a model with the earth as a center.

SYMBOLIC MODELS

In a symbolic model the balls and wire arms of the physical model of the solar system are replaced by mathematical concepts. Geometrical points are substituted for the balls. The next problem is to replace the wire arms which hold the balls in place. Now the wire arms have fixed lengths, and these lengths can be stated numerically. If all of the little balls revolve in the same plane, only one additional number is needed to locate the geometrical point. This number would be the angle between the wire arm and a stationary arm which would serve as a reference point.

Hence two numbers—the radius (length of arm) and an angle—will fix the location of the geometrical point just as effectively as the wire arm fixes the location of the little sphere in the physical model. Actually the astronomer's model is much more complicated than the symbolic model which I have described, but the general principle of construction is the same.

Now suppose that the astronomer wants to use his model to predict eclipses. He will have to take observations to obtain specific numbers to use for the radius and angle. These empirically determined quantities are substituted in the mathematical model and, after various manipulations, the astronomer announces: "There will be an eclipse of the moon visible in the northeastern part of North America on such-and-such a date and at so-and-so time."

It is at this point that a comparison of alternative models can be made. If the predictions are borne out, the successful model can be used for future predictions. If, on the other hand, the eclipse does not occur at the specified time, the scientist must begin looking for another model.

The Ptolemaic astronomers set up a mathematical model of the solar system with the earth as a center. They first considered that the other astronomical bodies moved in circles. When this picture did not lead to adequate predictions the Ptolemaic astronomers decided the paths of the heavenly bodies were epicycles. If you would like to visualize an epicycle, imagine two gears, one large and standing still and the other small and rolling around the rim of the large one. An epicycle is the path of a tooth of the small gear.

This complication led to a little improvement in prediction, but the forecasts were still quite unsatisfactory so the model was complicated still further. This time the astronomers postulated that the paths of the heavenly bodies were epicycles *on* epicycles, literally a "gears within gears" situation.

If you think that this is getting too complicated consider the sad plight of the astronomers. *They* had to make the calculations which go along with this model of the solar system. Nonetheless it was many years before the simpler model with the sun at the center of the solar system was widely accepted.

There is a moral in this epicycle story. Scientists occasionally become attached to a model even though it does not give adequate prediction. They try to use the model by cutting off a piece here or adding a piece there. This patchwork can go on for many years, and the resulting crazy quilt may prevent the development of new and more efficient models. After all, when it takes a scientist ten years to master a complex model, he has a vested interest in it, and he sometimes is hostile to labor-saving devices which may deprive him of his job. "Epicyclitis" is a symptom of senility in a scientific field.

MATHEMATICAL MODELS

It might be puzzling to understand why the astronomers should go from a nice simple physical model with little spheres on wire arms to a symbolic model with all sorts of queer mathematical signs when, if sufficient care were taken in the construction of the physical model, it would be possible to use it directly in order to predict eclipses. The astronomer's choice is a matter of taste. From the astronomer's point of view it is the mathematical model which is the *simple* one and the physical model with balls and wire which is complex. Since the physical model is made out of metal it not only has attributes which are intended to

simulate the solar system, but it also has a lot of attributes which depend on the materials used in its construction and the way in which it is made. Thus the wire arms can be geared to rotate at an appropriate speed but the mounting and drive arrangements of the model are attributes of the model and *not* attributes of the solar system which it is supposed to represent.

Even though great care is lavished on the construction of the physical model the predictions which would come out of it would depend on friction, vibration, and other characteristics of the *model*. Hence the prediction would be rendered inaccurate by the entrance of attributes other than the ones which were deliberately built into the model to simulate the solar system.

In a *mathematical* model, on the other hand, the material of the model itself—in this case the symbolic language—does not ordinarily contribute such extraneous and undesirable attributes. If we want friction in the mathematical model we can put it in symbolically, but otherwise this friction will not appear in the model and hence cannot disturb our predictions. In the physical model the process of abstraction tends to introduce new and irrelevant details, while in the mathematical model the process of abstraction does not.

In this sense, therefore, a mathematical model is simple whereas a physical model is complex. It may strike you as curious that I should say that Einstein is working with an extremely simple model in his theory of relativity, while a schoolboy is working with an extremely complex model when he builds an airplane. If you think it over carefully, however, you may see the justice of the statement.

Now and then a mathematical model gets beyond the resources of the mathematicians who construct it, so a physical model is substituted to obtain an answer. This is done in the Monte Carlo method, a device for solving mathematical problems by having one of the giant brain computers play gambling games with itself. However, such devices are used for computational convenience rather than conceptual simplicity.

The construction of symbolic models is an important part of the job of the scientist, and the great advances in science are those in which a useful new model is introduced. In physics the powerful model devised by Isaac Newton is one landmark, the relativity model of Einstein is another, and the quantum models are a third landmark. In chemistry the gas laws, the mass action laws, and the periodic table are all the end results of successful models of atomic and molecular processes. In biology the evolutionary model of Charles Darwin (a verbal model) has been developed into a mathematical model by R. A. Fisher and Sewell Wright. Another important biological model is the one which describes genetic inheritance. In medicine the models are mainly verbal, but they are of great importance. Harvey's model of the circulatory system, and the various models of the reaction of the human body to invading organisms have influenced the development of the modern treatment of diseases.

Effective verbal models which describe the transmission of disease have been useful in the eradication of many of the epidemic diseases which used to terrorize humanity. Efforts are currently in progress to translate these verbal models into mathematical ones (epidemic theory), but the earlier models have been so successful that a modern investigator is often hard put to find enough data to test his new mathematical models!

Currently, there is research under way which is attempting to devise mathematical models for sociological phenomena, such as the growth of cities, and for psychological phenomena. Norbert Wiener in *Cybernetics* [1] deals with the mathematical model associated with the operation of the human brain.

One of the key steps in the progress of a field of knowledge toward scientific maturity is the fabrication of models which enable successful prediction in that field. A tremendous amount of imagination and insight is needed for the creation of new models, but they are only half of the story. The mere creation of models is not enough; the models must survive exacting tests, they must meet the pragmatic criterion, they must work.

This brings us back to data. The test of the model involves data from the real world. Without adequate data the construction of models is a mathematical pastime. Purely speculative mathematical models may be as useless as purely speculative verbal models. For example, I might construct a very fancy mathematical model to describe the mechanism of transmission of some virus disease. No good

[1] Wiener, N., *Cybernetics*, John Wiley & Sons, New York, 1948.

diagnostic test may be known for the disease, and consequently the available data may be quite unreliable. If a doctor comes along with a quick, cheap, and effective skin test for this disease, it may then be possible to get adequate data to test my fancy model. Until this happens my model is just another mathematical game. After the development of the skin test, the model may turn out to be useful in the understanding and control of the disease or, as is more likely, it may turn out to be a complete waste of time.

Progress in science is based on this constant interplay between model and data. Sometimes there is a tremendous amount of observational data available but no satisfactory model, so that little progress is made. This was the situation in astronomy before the heliocentric model and it also has occurred repeatedly in the biological sciences. At other times there are elaborate models but little adequate data. Something resembling this situation occurred in economics where an elaborate mathematical theory was developed which did rather poorly when tested with actual data.

Occasionally a scientist not only works out the model but also obtains the data. Darwin and Galileo accomplished this feat. More often one man, such as Brahé, gathers good data and another man, such as Kepler, supplies the model. When this division of labor occurs it is rather pointless to say that the model-maker is a greater scientist than the data-grubber, for the advance depends on teamwork.

ADVANTAGES

Why should a model be used? The real answer to this question is that this procedure has been followed in the development of the most successful predicting systems so far produced, the predicting systems used in science. It is simply a matter of going along with a winner.

Some of the advantages of model-making might, however, deserve a separate statement. A big advantage of a model is that it provides a frame of reference for consideration of the problem. This is often an advantage even if the preliminary model does not lead to successful prediction. The model may suggest informational gaps which are not immediately apparent and consequently may suggest fruitful lines for action. When the model is tested the character of the failure may sometimes provide a clue to the deficiencies of the model. Some of the greatest scientific advances have been produced by *failure* of a model! Einstein's work was the outgrowth of the Michelson-Morley experiment in which the aether model led to unsuccessful prediction.

Another advantage of model-making is that it brings into the open the problem of abstraction. The real world is a very complex environment indeed. An ordinary apple, for example, has a great many properties—size, shape, color, chemical composition, taste, weight, ad infinitum. In making a decision about the apple, such as whether to eat it or not, only a few of these characteristics are considered. Some degree of abstraction is necessary for decision.

The model-maker must, therefore, decide which real world attributes will be incorporated in the model. He may decide that the size of the apple rather than shape is important to decision. He may, if he is setting up an inspection plan, concentrate on the number of worm holes. If he is interested in the velocity of a falling apple, on the other hand, he may include only the weight of the apple in his model.

By making this process of abstraction deliberate, the use of a model may bring such questions to light. Moreover, it may suggest preliminary experiments to determine which characteristics are relevant to the particular decision problem under consideration.

Once the problem is expressed in symbolic language there is the advantage of the manipulative facility of that language. The symbolic language also offers advantages in communication. It allows a concise statement of the problem which can be published. Moreover, it is more easily integrated with the other scientific work which is also in symbolic language.

Another advantage of mathematical models is that they often provide the *cheapest* way to accomplish prediction. Sometimes it is possible to reach the same results by the sheer mass of data—by a "brute force" attack on the problem—but the mathematical route is generally more economical.

One reason for this is that a newly-minted Ph.D. in mathematics can be hired (alas) for a salary which could not entice a good plumber. A Ph.D., a pencil, and some paper may be all the equipment necessary to handle the symbolic manipulations of the model. Only

a very small proportion of the millions currently spent for research goes into model-making. Even when the scientists are well paid, most of the money goes into the process of collecting data.

DISADVANTAGES

The use of models also has some drawbacks. The model is subject to the usual dangers inherent in abstraction. A mathematically feasible model may require gross oversimplifications. There is no guarantee that an investment of time and effort in constructing the model will pay dividends in the form of satisfactory prediction. No process, however, can provide such a guarantee.

The symbolic language is also subject to limitations. It may be beyond the ability of a mathematician to manipulate the symbolic language so as to obtain useful results. In such cases it may be more efficient to use direct methods. In gambling-game problems, such as the game of solitaire, it may be easier to play a large number of solitaire games and determine the probabilities by the Direct System than to embark on a mathematical analysis of the probabilities.

There is another very grave danger in the use of models. After a scientist plays for a long time with a given model he may become attached to it, just as a child may become, in the course of time, very attached to a doll (which is also a model). A child may become so devoted to the doll that she insists that her doll is a real baby, and some scientists become so devoted to their model (especially if it is a brain child) that they will insist that this model *is* the real world.

The same sort of thing happens with verbal models, as the semanticists point out, when a word and its counterpart in the real world are regarded as the same thing. This identification in the world of words has led to unhappy results which are reflected in the real world. The behavior of individuals who are unable to distinguish between words and the real world may become so bizarre as to lead to the classification "insane."

Now things are not this bad at the scientific level largely because of the self-corrective features of the sequential process of model-making which provide a periodic return to the real world after each excursion into the symbolic world. The test of the model acknowledges, as it were, the supremacy of the real world. If the model fails to predict what will happen in the real world, it is the model that must give way. This is the standard of scientific sanity.

When this standard is not admitted, a conflict between a model's predictions and happenings in the real world will sometimes lead instead to the rejection of the real world. This course is the prelude to disaster. To guard against such disasters it is well to remember the following rule for working with models: A model is neither true nor false.

The standard for comparing models is utility, i.e., successful prediction. The evaluation of a model is therefore dependent on the situation in which it is to be used; it is not *intrinsic* (i.e., dependent only on the model itself). If this point is understood several apparent paradoxes in science disappear.

One such paradox is the simultaneous use of two contradictory models. An example of this paradox occurs in the field of physics in which a *wave* and a *photon model* for light are both accepted. Wave theories are used when *they* provide successful prediction, and in other situations the photon theory is employed. Hence the paradox arises only if the models are identified with the real world.

Another paradox is the occurrence of scientific revolutions which (unlike political revolutions) do not interrupt the orderly development of the area. If models are not identified with the real world, the revolution is merely the substitution of a refined model for a cruder earlier model. Most of the time the older theory continues to be useful in the original applications; it is only in extended applications that the newer theory gives better prediction. The older theory is often a special case of the new theory. This explains why, despite the revolutionary work of Einstein, the older Newtonian physics is still used. In designing a dam or bridge, for example, both models would lead to essentially the same predictions (or in other words, the predictions are indistinguishable at the practical level).

One class of scientific workers does not worry about the testing of its models. They are the mathematicians. Their only interest (as long as they are functioning as mathematicians) lies in symbolic derivations from the models. Their business is to provide models in which the symbolic implications are worked out—anyone who wants to use the model for real world

predictions will have to test it first. Nevertheless, the mathematicians serve a useful purpose in society (though a pure mathematician would strenuously deny it) by providing the scientists with ready-worked models. Often the models created by mathematicians are not used for years, or even centuries, but the literature of mathematics is a sort of Sears-Roebuck catalogue of models which may be consulted whenever a special type of model is needed. Unfortunately it takes some mathematical sophistication in order to use this catalogue.

As long as the model is completely divorced from the real world the criterion of utility cannot be used. Instead the mathematicians employ an *intrinsic* standard, *consistency*. Various attempts have been made, all unsuccessful, to extend this standard to the real world. The only result which these attempts have accomplished is to confuse matters and cause an identification of models and the real world.

ROLE OF THE MODEL

The disadvantages inherent in the use of models can be avoided to a large extent by a judicious balancing of the two processes, model-making and data collection. The relationship between these two aspects of Scientific Method deserves careful consideration; it provides one of the main keys to scientific success, and it also involves several notions which can be carried over into our thinking about everyday problems. The relationship can be represented diagrammatically by Figure 1.

The model itself should be regarded as arbitrary; it represents an act of creation like a painting or a symphony. The model can be anything its creator desires it to be. In practice, of course, it is generally stimulated (and therefore affected) by data from the real world (which is labeled "Original data" in Figure 1). Artistic creations also use sensory data. Even in abstract canvases there is some influence from the original data (sensory experience). If the modern artist paints the portrait of a woman, it may not look like a human being to me. But presumably the dabs of paint have some relationship to the woman, though it may require an expert to understand this relationship. Similarly, a physicist's mathematical model of the atom may be far removed from any material substance; again only an expert can appreciate it.

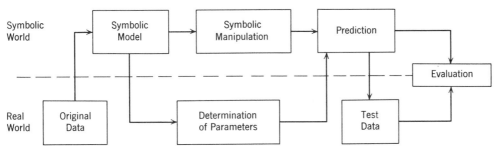

FIG. 1.

In many cases the symbolic representation used in the model is chosen because it was successfully used in previous models, because it seems plausible to the creator, or because it is convenient. However, some very useful models are based on assumptions which are not evident from common sense or—as in the quantum model—are actually repugnant to common sense.

I would not consider it very plausible to be seated at a desk in Los Angeles and then suddenly to find myself at a desk in Baltimore. It is even less sensible for this jump to have been accomplished in no time at all and without passing through any intermediate point in the process. Yet electrons jump around in this remarkable manner in the quantum theories of physics. Models which embody this curious behavior lead to successful prediction.

Scientists are generally pictured as coldly logical creatures with no disposition to embark on wild flights of fancy. But the geniuses of science have at least as much imagination as any other creative artist. In some respects the symbolic language of science allows greater freedom for expression than the printed word, musical notation, or oil paint.

There is one very important respect in which the scientist differs from the artist, however. The model itself may be arbitrary, but once it is constructed it must meet exacting and carefully specified tests before it is acclaimed as a masterpiece. In the artistic world the criteria for judging the finished product are vague and unsystematic.

There is a second respect in which science and art differ. In art the portrait is the end of the job; in science it is just the beginning. Once the model has been created there are two lines of development—one in the symbolic world and the other in the real world.

In the symbolic world the implications of the model are pursued by manipulations of the symbolic language. If I am interested in the behavior of a pendulum I can set up a mathematical model in which the bob of the pendulum is replaced by a geometrical point. The cord or arm of the pendulum is replaced by a symbol, L, which can be interpreted as the length of the cord. The Newtonian laws may be applied to this model and, by manipulations of the symbolic language, I may derive as a consequence of my model a relatively simple relation between the period (the length of time it takes to complete a full swing) and the length, L. All of this takes place in the symbolic language.

In the real world the numerical value for the length must be obtained. This quantity, L, is often called a "parameter." The word "parameter" is merely mathematical jargon for a symbolic quantity, such as L, which may be associated with some measurable quantity in the real world. The process of measuring the length of the cord would therefore be called the "determination of the parameter." In most problems there will be more than one parameter involved.

The two paths from the model now join again when the numerical value from the real world is substituted in the formula (derived by symbolic manipulation) in order to obtain the period. The period is found, mathematically, to be proportional to the square root of the length, L. If my pendulum is 4 feet long it is easy to calculate that the period will be about 2.2 seconds. This statement is made as a prediction.

In order to test this prediction it is necessary to return once again to the real world. I set up my pendulum and time the swings. I find that the period as determined experimentally is about 2.2 seconds. Perhaps I go ahead and

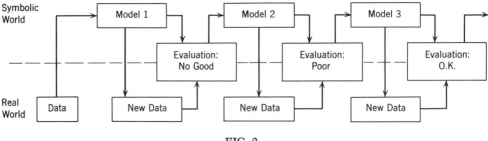

FIG. 2.

try a whole series of different lengths and the agreement between prediction and experiment seems to be good.

As a consequence of this agreement, I am encouraged to use my mathematical model for prediction purposes and also in the design of clocks or other equipment which utilizes a simple pendulum.

The reader may find it worth while to consider another example, such as the astronomical model of the solar system, and trace through the steps in Figure 1 in order to clarify his own ideas on the role of the model.

One striking characteristic of the relationship between the model and the data is the periodic return to the real world which is indicated in Figure 1. It should be noted that the original data used in the construction of the model may be quite useless for the determination of parameters or testing the model. Hence the return to the real world may not mean merely the collection of additional data, but it may require collection of data of a completely different *type* from the original data.

Now a reader who has forgotten his elementary physics may have wondered why I did not include the weight of the bob as well as the length of the cord in the model of the pendulum. An interesting feature of the mathematical model of the pendulum is that if this additional factor, weight, is included in the symbolic structure, it will cancel out in the manipulations. In other words, the model implies that the period of the pendulum does not depend on the weight of the bob, i.e., the weight is irrelevant in this particular problem. The same thing happens if other factors, such as the way in which the pendulum is set into motion, are included in the model. Thus the symbolic model has served the useful purpose of focusing our attention on the length of the cord. It has therefore suggested an efficient way of experimenting on the pendulum; the

model has told us what *data* need to be collected.

The little story about the pendulum had a happy ending, for the model was satisfactory. However, few scientists are so fortunate or clever as to devise a useful model on the first attempt. If prediction from the first model turns out very badly the scientist will have to start over again. The way in which the predictions break down sometimes provides valuable information which can be used to construct a second model.

The role of the model as given by Figure 1 is therefore only a part of a larger sequential process. This sequential role is indicated by Figure 2.

The evolution of a successful model generally follows the above pattern. The first shots are often very wide of the mark, but by gradual stages the scientist zeroes in on his target. There is really no end to the sequence. Even after a model has years of successful usage (i.e., Newtonian models in physics), a situation may come along which will not be adequately predicted by the model. A new model must then be developed.

Some readers may find this viewpoint rather unpleasant because they would like this sequence to stop somewhere (i.e., at the truth). Nowhere in the scientific world has this stopping place been attained, although now and then the models have survived for many years. The attitude that the truth had been attained was often a barrier to progress.

A MODEL FOR DATA

The mathematical model for the solar system or for a pendulum can be used for prediction and then tested against actual data. In this test it is not expected that the data and prediction will agree *exactly*. In the pendulum example the predicted period of a 4-foot pendulum is

2.2 seconds. If a 4-foot pendulum is constructed and the period is measured with a stopwatch or other timing device, the periods so measured will be about 2.2 seconds, but there may be some departure from this figure.

Note that these departures of the data from the predicted value have received no allowance in the mathematical model for the pendulum. In order to *evaluate* the model, however, this behavior of the data must be taken into consideration. This may be done intuitively by an argument such as "the departures from the predicted value are very small and quite negligible for practical purposes." A more sophisticated approach is to set up a second model, a model to deal with the measurement data.

Such a model would be a *statistical* model; it would characterize the measurement process itself in mathematical terms. One parameter of this model might be interpreted as the *precision* or repeatability of the method of measurement and this might be estimated from new data collected for this purpose. Many scientific measurements are given in the following form: 2.22 ± 0.10 seconds. The number after the plus-and-minus sign relates to the precision of the measurement. Thus 2.22 might be the average period calculated from a series of measurements on the period of the pendulum. The 0.10 second might indicate that the average is only reliable to $\frac{1}{10}$ of a second. We would not be very surprised, therefore, if we had gotten 2.32 or 2.12 seconds as our average period. Consequently, there is no reason to feel that the data contradict our predicted value of 2.2 seconds. If, on the other hand, we had found the average period to be 3.22 ± 0.10 seconds, we would feel that something was wrong either with the model or with the data.

When we set about constructing a mathematical model which will describe data we immediately are confronted with the problem of including, in the mathematical formulation, the well-known inadequacies of data. Thus the inadequacies of the measuring instrument must appear in the model: it must include such things as sensory lapses of the human measuring instrument; various errors introduced by the inanimate instruments as microscopes, telescopes, or clocks; and, in biological work, where an animal is used in the measurement process, all sorts of additional sources of variation due to the animal.

Then there will be incompleteness of the data due to the various steps in abstraction. Some of the data may be irrelevant; some of the relevant factors may have been neglected. Also, only part of the available data may have been collected and only part of this data actually used. In short, any real data will be inadequate and incomplete, and these deficiencies must be included in the model.

It would be hopeless to try to catalogue all the things which might go sour in the process of collecting and utilizing the data, to analyze all of the factors which might operate to influence the experimental results. About all that is possible is to consider broad categories of deficiencies and to include these broad categories in the model.

Now how can these inadequacies, and the resulting uncertainties, be handled mathematically? As you might suspect, this is accomplished by the introduction of the concept of probability into the model. In fact, the notion of probability can be regarded as the distinguishing feature which sets statistical models apart from other mathematical models.

STATISTICAL MODELS

The role of a statistical model is in many respects quite similar to that of any other mathematical model. The diagrammatic representation is indicated in Figure 3. . . .

. . . Occasionally a simple model of this type can be applied to situations in everyday experience. Suppose that I am interested in the proportion of male babies in 10,000 records of live births. There are two outcomes possible when a baby is born (just as in a coin flip)— the baby can be a boy or a girl. I might therefore think of sex determination as analogous to the process of flipping a coin.

One distinction between the coin toss and sex determination is that while the mechanism for determining heads and tails on a coin is fairly well understood, the corresponding mechanism for fixing the sex of a baby is not well understood. Consequently it would be specious to argue that each sex was equally likely. There is, in fact, a large amount of data to show that this is not the case. Hence if a symbol, p, is used in the mathematical model to indicate the probability that a baby will be male, it may not be assumed that $p = \frac{1}{2}$.

Consequently, one of the things that will have to be done in order to use the model is to

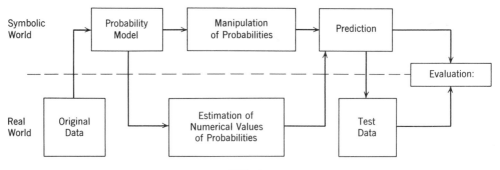

FIG. 3.

obtain data which will enable us to estimate the value of this parameter, p. Perhaps a number such as $p = 0.52$ will be determined from this excursion into the real world.

A second chain of reasoning stays in the symbolic world. Taking the probability as p that a live baby will be a boy, we must answer the question: What will happen in 10,000 births? I will not burden you with the manipulations of probabilities required to answer this question. The mathematics involved in calculating the probabilities for each of the 10,001 possible outcomes becomes too tedious, even for a statistician, and in practice a mathematical approximation which yields useful results with little effort is employed.

With the aid of this device, and substituting the value $p = 0.52$, we can obtain a prediction of the following form: The probability that there will be between 5,100 and 5,300 male births in the sample of 10,000 is equal to about 0.95. In other words, if I am convinced that the model is a good one and that my value of $p = 0.52$ is also reliable, I would be very confident that the actual data should show between 5,100 and 5,300 live male births.

This particular model has taken into consideration only one source of variability in the data on live birth—the variation due to sampling. Now in practice there are a number of other inadequacies of the data which might very well cause trouble. The reporting procedures may introduce difficulties. In a well-run department of vital statistics in the West-

ern World the tabulation of births may be done rather carefully. On the other hand, if my 10,000 live births were reported by tribal chieftains in a colonial administrative district there might well be a tendency to forget female children.

The problem of *evaluation* of the statistical model is a tricky one. If I found 4,957 boys in the sample of 10,000, I could not say that this result was *impossible* insofar as my model was concerned. The model itself allows a very small chance of this sort of sample.

To a large extent the users of nonstatistical mathematical models can dodge the problem of evaluation by making the evaluation intuitive and simply stating that the agreement of prediction and data is either satisfactory or unsatisfactory. In statistical models one must come to grips with the problem. . . . A major part of a statistician's job lies in the no-man's-land between the symbolic world and the real world, and in particular he must evaluate the predictions of models relative to actual data.

SUMMARY

The key role played by models in scientific thinking is illustrated by several examples. The notion of a model for data is introduced and leads to the concept of a statistical model. The advantages and disadvantages of models are considered. Special stress is laid on the distinction between models of the real world and the real world itself.

34. THE EVALUATION OF MODELS

KARL W. DEUTSCH [*]

In recent years, increasing attention has been paid to both the use of symbols in the process of thinking, and to the problems that arise when symbols are combined into larger configurations or models—particularly when these models are then used as an aid in investigating or forecasting events that occur in the world outside the thinking system. One important use of such models is in describing the behavior of social organizations.

The organizations to be described may be informal groups, they may be political units or agencies of government, or they may be industrial or business organizations. Each of these organizations is composed of parts which communicate with each other by means of messages; it receives further messages from the outside world; it stores information derived from messages in certain facilities of memory; and all these functions together may involve a configuration of processes, and perhaps of message flow, that goes clearly beyond any single element within the system. Whenever we are discussing the past or future behavior of such an organization, we must use a model for it, and much of the effectiveness of our discussion may depend upon the degree of similarity or dissimilarity between the model and the thing supposedly modeled.

Investigation of such models, therefore, is more than a mere play upon some fine points in the theory of knowledge. We are using models, willingly or not, whenever we are trying to think systematically about anything at all. The results of our thinking in each case will depend upon what elements we put into our model, what rules and structure we imposed on those elements, and upon what actual use we made of the ensemble of possibilities which this particular model offered.

SOURCE: *The Public Opinion Quarterly* (Fall, 1952), pp. 356–367. Reprinted by permission of *The Public Opinion Quarterly*.

[*] Professor of Political Science, Yale University.

In one sense the study of models, and the theory of organizations that could be derived from it, cuts across many of the traditional divisions between the natural and social sciences, as well as between the particular social sciences themselves. In all these fields, symbols are used to describe the accumulation and preservation of patterns from the past and their arrangement into more or less self-maintaining, self-destroying, or self-transforming systems. The resulting models are then used to describe further the impact of outside events upon such systems and the responses which each system makes to them. In this manner we use models in describing the behavior of a social group, or of a state, or of a nation, or of the memories and preferences that make up an individual personality. In a similar way, we use models in describing a system of logic, or in suggesting a theory of games, or in describing the behavior of an array of communications machinery.

SOME EARLIER WORK ON MODELS

By a model is meant a structure of symbols and operating rules which is supposed to match a set of relevant points in an existing structure or process. Models of this kind are indispensable for the understanding of more complex processes. The only alternative to their use would be an attempt to "grasp directly" the structure or process to be understood; that is to say, to match it completely point for point. This is manifestly impossible. We use maps or anatomical atlases precisely because we cannot carry complete countries or complete human bodies in our heads.

Each model implies a theory asserting a structural correspondence between the model and certain aspects of the thing supposed to be modeled. It also implies judgments of relevance; it suggests that the particular aspects to which it corresponds are in fact the important aspects of the thing for the purposes of the model makers or users. Furthermore, a model, if it is operational, implies predictions which can be verified by physical tests. A rough survey of major models used in human thinking in the course of history suggests that there has been a change in the character of the models that predominated in each period, and that it has been a gradual change from pictures to full-fledged models in the modern sense.

THE EVALUATION OF MODELS

We may think of models as serving, more or less imperfectly, four distinct functions: the organizing, the heuristic, the predictive, and the measuring (or mensurative).

By the *organizing* function is meant the ability of a model to order and relate disjointed data, and to show similarities or connections between them which had previously remained unperceived. To make isolated pieces of information fall suddenly into a meaningful pattern is to furnish an esthetic experience; Professor Paul Lazarsfeld once described it as the "Aha!-experience" familiar to psychologists.[1] Such organization may facilitate its storage in memory, and perhaps even more its recall.

If the new model organizes information about unfamiliar processes in terms of images borrowed from familiar events, we call it an explanation. The operational function of an explanation is that of a training or teaching device which facilitates the transfer of learned habits from a familiar to an unfamiliar environment. If it actually does help us to transfer some familiar behavior pattern to a new problem, we may feel that the explanation is "satisfactory," or even that it "satisfies our curiosity," at least for a time. Such an explanation might be subjectively satisfying without being predictive; it would satisfy some persons but not others, depending on each person's memories and habits, and since it yields no predictions that can be tested by physical operations, it would be rejected by some scientists as a "mere explanation" which would be operationally meaningless.[2]

[1] Paul Lazarsfeld at a meeting of the Columbia University Seminar on Methods in the Social Sciences, March 12, 1951.

[2] Conant, James B., *On Understanding Science*, New Haven: Yale University Press, 1947; cf. also

Certainly, such "mere explanations" are models of a very low order. It seems, however, that explanations almost invariably imply some predictions; even if these predictions cannot be verified by techniques practicable at the present time, they may yet serve as *heuristic* devices leading to the discovery of new facts and new methods.[3]

The heuristic function of a model may be independent to a considerable degree from its orderliness or organizing power, as well as from its predictive and mensurative performance.

Little has to be said about the *predictive* function of a model, beyond the well known requirement of verifiability by physical operations. There are different kinds of prediction, however, which form something of a spectrum. At one extreme we find simple yes-or-no predictions; at higher degrees of specificity we get qualitative predictions of similarity or matching, where the result is predicted to be of this kind or of that kind, or of this particular delicate shade; and at the other extreme we find completely quantitative predictions which may give us elaborate time series which may answer the questions of when and how much.[4]

Bridgman, P. W., *The Logic of Modern Physics*, New York: Macmillan, 1927.

[3] For the concept of heuristics, see Polya, George, *How to Solve It*, Princeton: Princeton University Press, 1944.

[4] For the relationship of prediction to time series, cf. Wiener, Norbert, *Extrapolation, Interpolation, and Smoothing of Stationary Time Series*, Cambridge: Massachusetts Institute of Technology Press, 1949.

In the natural sciences a yes-or-no prediction might answer a question like this: Will this paper burn or not? A qualitative prediction might answer the question: Will it burn with a bright yellow flame? A quantitative prediction might answer the question: In how many seconds will it heat the contents of a test tube to 400° Fahrenheit?

In economics or politics, yes-or-no questions might be: Will the Jones Corporation build a new plant? Will the Blank party put on a political drive? Qualitative questions might be: Will the Jones Corporation build a large and modern plant? Will the Blank party put on a drive for clean government? Quantitative questions might be: How large a plant will they have built by what date? How many meetings, poster, radio appeals will the Blank party use before next November, and when will the drive reach its climax? It should be re-

At this extreme, models become related to measurement. If the model is related to the thing modeled by laws which are not clearly understood, the data it yields may serve as indicants. If it is connected to the thing modeled by processes clearly understood, we may call the data obtained with its help a *measure*—and measures again may range all the way from simple rank orderings, to full-fledged ratio scales.[5]

A dimension of evaluation corresponds to each of these four functions of a model. How great is a model's generality or organizing power? What is its fruitfulness or heuristic value? How important or strategic are the verifiable predictions which it yields? And how accurate are the operations of measurement that can be developed with its aid? If we collect the answers to these four questions under the heading of the "performance" of a model, we may then evaluate the model still further in terms of the three additional considerations of originality, simplicity and realism.

By the *originality* of a model, or of any other intellectual contribution, we mean its improbability. Any idea, scheme or model may be thought of as the product of the recombination of previously existing elements, and perhaps of a subsequent process of abstraction omitting some of the traces of its combinatorial origin. The greater the probability, or obviousness or triteness, of a model, the more frequent is this particular recombination in the ensemble of combinatorial possibilities at the immediately preceding stage. Originality or improbability is the reverse of this value.

A structure of symbols may be highly original but useless. Or a model may be original and perform well but require such a large share of the available means and efforts as to impair the pursuit of other work. Models are therefore evaluated for their *simplicity* or economy of means. But it turns out that the concept of simplicity is not completely simple. Francis Bacon declared in the controversy between Ptolemaic and Copernican Astronomy that, in the absence of conclusive data from observation, he would choose the simpler of

the two hypotheses; he then duly chose the Ptolemaic system on the grounds that it required fewer readjustments of his everyday experience.[6] Clearly, all notions of simplicity involve some sort of minimization problem, but what is to be minimized? Is it the number of unverified assumptions or distinctions, as William of Occam seems to have taught? Or is it a number of calculating steps, as Copernicus suggested in praise of his system? Or is it the number of readjustments of acquired habits, as in Lord Chancellor Bacon's reasoning? If we could succeed in reducing the number of logical or calculating steps required in a model by introducing a large number of suitable fictions, have we simplified the model, or have we increased the complexity of its assumptions? Would we not have simplified it according to Copernicus, but made it more complex according to Occam?

Perhaps the concept of simplicity itself is operational, and could be considered to resemble the concept of efficiency in engineering and in economics. Efficiency in economics denotes the attainment of a given result with the greatest economy in the employment of those means which are shortest in supply at each particular time, place, or situation. Since such supply conditions are historical, simplicity, like efficiency, would then be a historical concept. (If there is merit in this approach, we might wonder about the effect of the availability of cheap calculating aids and electronic calculators on the traditional stress on elegance in mathematics.)

If simplicity is measured by the economy of means in critical supply, then claims to simplicity on behalf of rival models or theories can be evaluated more objectively. We might also be able to predict cross-cultural disagreements about standards of simplicity, as well as changes in accepted standards of simplicity over time. Some of these considerations of simplicity could also be applied to the evaluation of research programs as well as to the measurement of organizational behavior.

The last consideration for evaluating a model or a conceptual scheme is its *realism:* that is, the degree of reliance which we may place on its representing some approximation to physical reality. According to P. W. Bridg-

membered that the spectrum formed by these different kinds of questions might well be continuous.

[5] Cf. Stevens, S. S., "Mathematics, Measurement and Psychophysics" in Stevens, ed., *Handbook of Experimental Psychology*, New York: John Wiley, 1951, pp. 1–48.

[6] Frank, Phillip, *Modern Science and Its Philosophy*, Cambridge: Harvard University Press, 1949, pp. 209–10.

man, we may impute "physical reality" to a construct or model if it leads to predictions which are verified by at least two different, mutually independent physical operations. If we put this somewhat more formally, we may say that the statement "X is real" implies the prediction that "Predictions based on the assumption of X will be confirmed by $(2 + N)$ mutually independent physical operations, where N is any number larger than one." The larger N—the number of independent confirmatory operations—actually turns out to be, the greater the degree of reality, or content of reality, we may impute to X. If N approaches infinity, we may be justified in treating X as real, though by no means necessarily as exhaustive. This approach implies the assumption that every real object or process is in principle knowable but may be inexhaustible. It may seem farfetched to define the concept of reality as a prediction about a series of other predictions, but it is a definition that can be tested, and I believe, applied to the evaluation of models, or of statements about the inferred inner structure of organizations.

GENUINE VERSUS PSEUDO-MODELS

Mathematical models in the social sciences may lose much of their usefulness through starting from too naive assumptions, or through the introduction of pseudo-constants: that is, magnitudes represented as constants in the mathematical equations, but incapable of being checked by independent and impersonal operations.

An example of sophisticated mathematical techniques prevented from becoming useful by regrettably naive assumptions is found in Professor Nicholas Rashevsky's discussion of changing levels of activity in social groups and of the "interaction of nations," in his *Mathematical Theory of Human Relations.*[7] Professor Rashevsky assumes that members of the politically and economically "active population" differ from the "passive population" by hereditary constitution, and that the relative proportions of "active" and "passive" population then develop according to certain

patterns of genetics and natural selection, depending largely on the numbers and density of total population. To what extent Professor Rashevsky's mathematical techniques could be applied to more realistic social and economic assumptions, and particularly to processes of social learning, in contrast to mere heredity, only the future can show.

A far more striking combination of relatively sophisticated mathematics with utter naïveté in social science can be found in the work of the late George Kingsley Zipf.[8] According to Zipf the size of communities in terms of their number of inhabitants should approximate a harmonic series for each country, if its cities were ranked in the decreasing order of size of population. The closeness of the actual distribution found to the theoretical harmonic series was then naively taken as an indicator of social stability. Thus, Zipf found that Austria between the two world wars had too large a capital city and too few cities of middle size, and that the aggregate series of cities in Germany and Austria after Austria's annexation by the Nazis approximated a harmonic series more closely than before. From this he concluded that the German annexations of Austria and the Sudetenland in 1938 had increased the stability of Germany and the social and economic balance of her "Lebensraum."[9] This "mathematical" conclusion completely overlooked the fact that before 1938 Germany had already been a food-deficit area, dependent on exports for part of her living, and that Austria as well as the Sudetenland had similarly been areas of food deficits, export dependence, and unemployment. What the Nazi annexations of 1938 had produced had been a merger of three deficits. The "greater Germany" of 1939 was more dependent on food imports and on export drives to pay for them than its component parts; the pooled threats of unemployment in all three territories were met by an armament drive, and food supplies and exports were sought by imperial expansion. What Professor Zipf has described as a harmonic series on paper, was in reality a situation of

[7] Rashevsky, N., *Mathematical Theory of Human Relations: An Approach to a Mathematical Biology of Social Phenomena*, Bloomington, Indiana: Principia Press, 1947, pp. 127–48 and esp. pp. 148–49.

[8] Zipf, George Kingsley, *National Unity and Disunity: The Nation as a Biosocial Organism*, Bloomington, Indiana: Principia Press, 1941; and *Human Behavior and the Principle of Least Effort*, Cambridge: Addison-Wesley, 1949.

[9] *National Unity and Disunity*, pp. 196–197 and figure 18.

extreme unbalance and disharmony, which led within a year to a violent explosion in the German invasion of Poland and the unfolding of the Second World War.

Perhaps it is too much to expect at this stage that individuals should undergo the highly specialized training of the advanced professional mathematician and at the same time, the at least equally intense training of the experienced social scientist. The difference in the intellectual techniques in these two fields should not obscure the fact that both approaches represent full-time intellectual jobs. The main task of the mathematician is perhaps to concentrate on the single-minded pursuit of long trains of symbolic operations. He may start out on these from any set of given initial conditions, without caring overmuch, as a rule, why just these conditions or assumptions and no others were selected.

Much of the training of the historian and social scientist is just the opposite. He must become familiar with a very wide range of social and economic situations at different places and times. The outcome of this part of his training is at best a sense of relevance, an experience in judging which factors in a situation must be taken into account and which ones may be neglected without much risk of error. To be sure, the social scientist can only benefit from analytic training. He does and should study economic, political and psychological theory, and to an increasing extent mathematics and symbolic logic. Yet all analytic work in the social sciences is primarily tied to judgments of relevance, to evaluating the realism of assumptions and the appropriateness of models. This ability is not easily acquired by mathematicians in their periods of rest between or after their more arduous professional labors. And the advice to younger social scientists to study more mathematics should be tempered with the insistence that they will have to judge the relevance of their models against their fund of factual knowledge as social scientists; no amount of mathematical knowledge or advice can take this task from their shoulders.

The most hopeful answer to this problem at the present time lies perhaps in the development of teamwork between men who are primarily social scientists but who have had enough analytical training to put their problems into a form where mathematicians can go to work on them, and mathematicians who have had enough of a solid training in the social sciences to understand what the social scientists need from them, and how to select lines of mathematical treatment which will lead more closely toward reality rather than away from it.

Another source of trouble with mathematical models in the social sciences stems from the tendency to put arbitrary constants or coefficients into equations so as to make their results fit a known series of numbers or their extrapolations. Thus, Lewis F. Richardson's "Generalized Foreign Politics" attempts to predict the armaments expenditures of two rival countries by equations which contain numerical coefficients for the "grievances" and the "submissiveness" of each country vis-à-vis the other.[10]

It is well known that any finite series of numbers can be fitted by more than one equation, and, on the other hand, that any result can be attained in an equation by introducing a sufficiently large number of arbitrary constants or coefficients. There is all the difference in the world between such arbitrary coefficients and a constant in physics, such as Planck's quantum constant h. Genuine constants in physics can be verified by impersonal physical operations of measurement, or by impersonally verifiable inferences from measurement. Such constants are the same for all physicists regardless of their sympathies or political beliefs, and they would be confirmed, in principle, by impersonal recording and measuring devices. The use of such operationally independent and verifiable concepts in models, such as in Bohr's model of the atom, is therefore quite legitimate. As long as social scientists cannot specify an impersonal set of operations for producing a numerical measure of "grievance" or "submissiveness," there will remain a grave suspicion that coefficients based on arbitrary estimates in such matters are

[10] Richardson, Lewis F., "Generalized Foreign Politics; A Study in Group Psychology," *British Journal of Psychology*, Monograph Supplement No. 23, London: Cambridge University Press, 1939; cf. also the summaries in Quincy Wright, *A Study of War*, Vol. II, appendix 42, pp. 1482–83; Kenneth J. Arrow, "Mathematical Models in the Social Sciences," in Daniel Lerner and Harold D. Lasswell, eds., *The Policy Sciences: Recent Developments in Scope and Method*, Palo Alto: Stanford University Press, 1951, p. 137.

somewhat akin to the "variable constants" familiar from the folklore of undergraduate humor.

To be sure, there may be cases where such mathematical pseudo-models may describe, however inadequately, some genuine intuitive insight of their author. It would be folly to suggest that only that is real which is measurable by present-day methods; the perception of *Gestalt* or the structural vision of a previously unrecognized configuration of phenomena all have their places among our sources of knowledge. In all such cases, however, it is the qualitative insights that are relevant, and not the mathematical disguises which they have prematurely donned.

35. MANAGEMENT CONTROL SIMULATION

JOEL M. KIBBEE *

INTRODUCTION

Simulation is one technique for the study of management control systems, whether of their design and evaluation or in the search for fundamental principles. That aspect of the general research approach with which we shall be concerned here is the simulation model. We shall begin with some comments on the type of simulation to be undertaken, shall describe certain "business games" which are related to such simulation, and conclude with a proposal for a preliminary model.

The term "simulation" has been applied to a variety of situations: a model of an airplane in a wind tunnel, a pilot in a Link Trainer, the simulated environment and inputs used in the SAGE System Training Program, research into the design of a bus terminal by the Port of New York Authority. Some authors have used the word "simulation" as a synonym for the Monte Carlo method. In its broadest sense any construction of a model, physical or symbolic, might be called simulation. Let us introduce the term "symbolic system simulation" for the type of experimentation to be discussed here. This has also been referred to as "analytic simulation," "computer simulation," and just "simulation."

SYMBOLIC SYSTEM SIMULATION

Symbolic System Simulation can be best illustrated by an example. Consider a retail store which handles one product, sells it daily to customers, and carries an inventory which may be replenished by orders placed at a factory. At the beginning of any day there is a particular quantity of stock on hand; during

the day this is increased by deliveries from the factory and decreased by sales. When the stock is not sufficient to meet the customer demand there are stockouts, and the sales are less than the demand.

We may build a mathematical model of the above system: the inputs are the customer demand and the deliveries from the factory, the output is the number of sales, and the state of the system at the end of any day is the quantity of stock on hand. Suppose we are given the state of the system on day 1, i.e., the stock on hand, as well as the customer demand and the factory deliveries for each day for one month and that we want to know the total sales, the total stockouts, and the state of the system on day 30. If we knew that the inventory had always been sufficiently large to meet demand, and thus that there were no stockouts, the stock on hand on day 30 would be simply the stock on hand on day 1 plus the total deliveries minus the total demand. But in general there is no simple analytic expression relating the state of the system on day 30 to the state on day 1, nor for computing the total sales, and it is necessary to perform thirty computations, albeit simple ones, representing a day by day stepping through of the model.

Symbol System Simulation is thus characterized by the construction of a mathematical model of a real system—mathematical, meaning to include both logical and algebraic operations—and the "running" of it through a sequence of time intervals. Building mathematical models of real systems is a fairly common technique, and the behavior of such models is often investigated by analytic techniques. It becomes simulation, at least in our sense here, when the current state can be computed from the initial state only by stepping through all intermediate states.

Symbolic System Simulation is exemplified by such studies as United Air Lines Airport Model, the Port of New York Authority's Bus

SOURCE: *Management Control Systems*, John Wiley and Sons, 1960, pp. 300–320. Reprinted by permission of John Wiley & Sons, Inc., from *Management Control Systems*, edited by Donald G. Malcolm and Alan J. Rowe, © 1962.

* Systems Development Corporation.

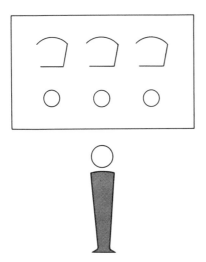

FIG. VI-C-1. A man and a model.

Terminal Model, and General Electric's Job Shop Scheduling Model. The mathematical model is nearly always programmed for a computer, the usual reason being that computations are generally too lengthy to be done by hand. However, worthwhile simulations have been performed without using a computer. Most real systems which one is likely to study will contain stochastic elements but stochastic elements are not necessarily a part of every simulation. In job shop scheduling if one begins with a known set of orders, rather than a sequence of random ones, there still may be difficult combinatorial problems, and such problems have been attacked through simulation.

Symbolic System Simulation has a variety of applications. As a research tool to search for optimal procedures, simulation of petroleum refineries has been particularly successful, and this is now a generally accepted technique. Other applications have been in such areas as production planning and control, distribution, transportation, and more recently in marketing and finance. It can be used as a management aid, helping a manager to select among several alternative decisions. When computers are placed "on-line" one can imagine operating decisions being quickly tried out, through simulation, before their implementation.

Symbolic System Simulation can be used in the design and evaluation of systems. It can be used for testing out a system before implementation, with the mildly paradoxical situation of modeling a "real" system before it

exists. It can also be used as a research tool for discovering general principles of system design.

It is conceptually useful to think of a Symbolic System Simulation as a black box with certain dials and meters. For the moment let us place a man in front of the box. (Figure VI-C-1.) He sets the dials, the box purrs, and results appear on the meters. He observes the results, perhaps records them, sets the dials to new positions, and the cycle repeats. Normally the procedure would be carried out by a separate program within the computer, instead of by the man. This program would cause the model to be stepped through a sequence of time intervals, with relevant data being printed out, and then certain changes would be made in the parameters, and the model would again be stepped through a sequence of time intervals, etc.

Let us return to the man in front of the black box; perhaps a research worker is interested in studying the man's behavior. The human subject moves the dials, reads the meters, etc., and the research worker observes this through the usual one-way glass windows. For the research worker the model is no longer just the black box, it is the man and black box. When humans are included in the model we shall use the term "Human System Simulation." With several human subjects and several black boxes we have the type of simulation of the SAGE System Training Program, and also of the RAND Logistics Simulation Laboratory, though this is an oversimplified description: the black box is a bit more fuzzy, beginning to surround the man, and there are questions about simulating the environment.

Let us now assume that we construct some sort of mathematical model of the human subject himself. The model of the man is added to the other model inside of the black box, and the research worker is now twisting the dials on this new box attempting to learn something about the man-machine behavior without using a real man. Let us ignore for now the question as to whether we can usefully construct an adequate model to the man. What we have done is return to a Symbolic System Simulation. Most models used in Symbolic System Simulation do contain factors associated with human behavior. For example, in studying business problems one may introduce price-demand curves, as an aggregate model of customer behavior, instead of using human sub-

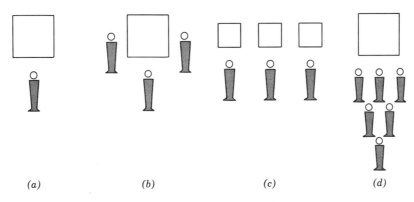

FIG. VI-C-2. Various system simulation.

jects who, provided with the various prices, feed back to the model their decisions to buy or not.

Let us turn now to Figure VI-C-2. In (a) we have one man experimenting with a model. In (b) we have several men experimenting with the same model and in competitive interaction with one another. This is perhaps a model of several salesmen competing for a common customer. In (c) we also have a competitive situation, but without interaction between the men. This would be a case in which the men faced identical tasks and compared their performance. The first type of competition, characterized by interaction, is analogous to tennis; the second type is analogous to golf. Instead of one man, we might have a group of men, as in (d), each with their own dials to set, but working towards a common goal. And of course in (b) and (c) we could also replace each man by a team of men. In order to study management control systems one would be most interested in the situation represented by (d). To study a business management situation it would be necessary to include the concept of intercompany competition, but most likely one would do this through mathematical models within the box rather than by adding additional teams.

BUSINESS GAMES

Simulation has extensive use today as a training technique, and in particular there has been considerable publicity about its use in what are usually called "business games" or "management games," or, in order to avoid certain unfavorable misinterpretations of the word "game," are frequently called "simulation exercises." A business game involves humans using Symbolic System Simulation, in one of the forms illustrated in Figure VI-C-2; the model is of a business, or some part of a business, and the objective is training.

The first business game was introduced by the American Management Association, being initially demonstrated in December, 1956, in Los Angeles. This game is usually referred to as the AMA Game, though it would be more properly called the AMA Executive Decision Making Simulation, as AMA has since constructed, and has in use, several other games. UCLA, IBM, The Pillsbury Company, and many other organizations are using quite similar games. This particular set of games is characterized by several companies competing in a common market, each manufacturing and selling one product, and with decisions being concerned mainly with selling price, advertising, production level, and the purchase of capital equipment. However games, like automobiles, undergo frequent model changes, and a variety of other business elements such as credit, dividends, stocks, the ability to purchase information about the economy or one's competitors and to engage in market research are now fairly common. Games may be modeled after a complete business, or after some particular component such as production planning and control. They also may be specialized to a particular type of organization such as banking, public utilities, supermarkets, or the detergent industry. We have recently seen such specialized games as SMART, for systems and procedures management, and STEPS, for computer programmer management.

The pedagogical intent of the various games may differ greatly: practicing decising making, improving analytic ability, learning to learn from experience, gaining an appreciation for particular business problems. Of more importance to our present discussion is their use in exemplifying certain general management principles in the areas of organization theory, planning, communications, control, and human relations. It is possible that certain management principles could be evidenced by having the participants play football. Perhaps going out for the team should be a requisite in business administration colleges: as English leaders are developed on the playing fields of Eton, corporation presidents would be developed on the playing fields of Harvard Business School. There are, however, some fairly obvious advantages in providing a business model for business executives.

There are some important relationships between business games and Symbolic System Simulation. Executives playing a business game provide a ready-made laboratory for studying management problems, though very little work has so far been done along this line. Existing games can, at least, offer guidance to the research worker. Modeling techniques are quite similar whether one is interested in training or research. Furthermore, a few Symbolic System Simulations undertaken for problem-solving purposes have been models of a complete business organization, and certain business games now existing can serve as a preliminary step— one is tempted to speak of a model of a model.

Any business game could be used for some form of research; the obverse of the coin is that any simulation could be used for training. This has actually been done in several cases, such as in job shop scheduling, where, though the model was primarily designed to search for and evaluate decision rules, it can also provide training for operating production people. A simulation, used as a game, can serve as an orientation device. One can perhaps more easily evoke critical feedback by allowing someone to play with the model than by having him listen to an exposition about it.

USE OF SIMULATION FOR RESEARCH

In order to do research on management control systems one would want a simulation represented by item (d) in Figure VI-C-2. Until recently, most business games, while perhaps complex in concept, were at least simple in the playing details; optimum size teams were usu-

ally five or less. One could obviously have allowed ten people to work as a sort of executive committee—such large teams have been used—but this represented a type of cooperative decision making and the individuals did not each have detailed tasks to perform. If one is interested in a management system, as distinct from the behavior of one manager, then one must provide for quite a few tasks and quite a few decisions, so that an organization structure is a necessity, and so that information networks must be established, authority delegated, and so forth. In most organizations it is not a question of whether the chief executive wants to make all of the decisions, or whether he is capable of making the best decisions, but that it is impossible for him to make all of the decisions that have to be made.

There are games today which do have an increased complexity—complexity from the standpoint of the number of details that have to be considered by the participants rather than by the extent of the sophistication of any one element. We shall consider three of these games here: The TASK Manufacturing Corporation, a new game under development at UCLA; the Carnegie Tech Management Game, for which complete details have been published; and the AMA General Management Simulation, which will be discussed more fully below.

The new UCLA game is an extremely ambitious project. The model will comprise a great amount of detail, but also considerable flexibility. One type of flexibility is the possibility of having certain operations controlled by computerized decision rules or policies, or, instead, the possibility of breaking into the system, as it were, and allowing human beings to take various managerial roles. The model is being designed as a tool for both research and training. The model will certainly be able to accommodate quite a few human managers and as such can be used for studies on management control system problems. In addition, because of its modular structure, control system research can be performed completely within the computer through changes in interconnections between the modules, changes in decision rules, and so forth.

The Carnegie Tech Management Game was also an ambitious undertaking. It was designed to allow participants to exercise habits of thought and analysis rather than to give practice in rapid decision making. It is very complex and can accommodate, typically, a team of say nine participants, and each would be kept adequately busy. The model is patterned after the detergent industry, has extensive sub-models of the production, marketing, and financial functions, allows for introduction of new products and for removing them from the market if they prove unsuccessful. The model is designed so that it can accommodate either several teams acting as separate companies and competing in a common market, or one team, still in a competitive market, but with competitors programmed in the computer. Part of the research plan is to attempt to replicate—i.e., mathematically model—some of the decision processes of the participants. One would expect research results in the general area of management control systems as well as in other areas.

THE USE OF SIMULATION
FOR TRAINING

The General Management Simulation, henceforth referred to as GMS, is currently being used as the basis of the fourth week—called "Management in Action"—of the four-week management course conducted by the American Management Association. This particular unit of the course was introduced in January, 1959, and since then has been given a little more often than once a month, with, on the average about sixty business executives participating. The unit is held at the AMA Academy at Saranac Lake, New York, and the IBM 650 installed there is utilized for the computations. GMS was expressly designed to exemplify certain general principles in the areas of organization theory, communications, control, and human relations. It was designed to teach management principles rather than business principles. Considerable design effort was directed, in fact, towards the de-emphasis of such things as the relationship between price and demand, and other quantitative factors. The task is one of running a business represented by the mathematical model within the computer, but the emphasis is not on the task as such, not on the profit attained, but on the management problems associated with the task, and on the human interrelations that result.

The simulation takes place in quarters, with decisions being made at the beginning of quarters, and operating reports, prepared by the computer, distributed at the end of quarters. A history of the company is provided to the participants before they arrive at the Academy, together with the most current quarterly reports. A typical history states how the company started—in a Circleville, Ohio, garage in 1935—and how it grew, expanded to new areas, improved its products, and so forth. Today the hypothetical company manufactures and markets a "Gopher" and a "Midgit," and may develop additional products. Some reality is given to these products with regard to their general nature, but they are not identified with any particular industry.

The model is somewhat intermediate in size between the first generation aggregated games and the more complex UCLA and Carnegie Tech games. The simulated company has plants, sales regions, and a home office. It markets several products, some of which may be developed during the play through a research and development program. There are the usual problems of production scheduling, marketing policies (i.e., pricing, advertising, the number of salesmen to employ and what to pay them), purchasing, shipping, finance, and so forth. Altogether there are about seventy decisions which can be made for each quarter.

USE OF THE GMS IN
ORGANIZATIONAL TRAINING

The accounting system has been specially designed to allow for a flexibility in the management organization structure. An average costing system of inventory evaluation is used, and all manufacturing costs, raw material costs, and corporate overhead costs find their way out to the sales regions so that individual profit and loss statements can be prepared for any product or any region. As such it permits a company to organize by product line, or by geographic location, or by function, or by any combination.

The GMS requires about fifteen participants to adequately operate one company—the complexity of the model and the pace of the decision periods were designed for about this level of participation. Many companies can be in operation simultaneously, each facing similar problems. There is no interaction between them. On the average, one year is simulated in a couple of hours, many "years" of operations taking place during the week. A method of job rotation has been introduced and each participant gets the opportunity to fill various positions.

It would be pleasant to discourse at length on the various non-computer aspects of the week at AMA; however, from the standpoint of training, the mathematical model (which was the author's primary responsibility when with the American Management Association) is of somewhat minor importance. The model without its environment is like an outboard motor without a boat. Briefings, planning sessions, critiques, and so forth are all of considerable importance, and the manner in which they are being handled is most impressive. There are also many projects or incidents completely unassociated with the profit and loss aspects of the model. The emphasis is always on humans, not on mathematics.

In order to allow additional feedback on less quantifiable aspects of performance, an "observer" role has been created. The physical setup includes one-way glass observation booths with earphones connected to microphones in the various company offices. In addition to verbal reporting at critique sessions, the observers could influence the profit and loss directly by feeding their judgments to the computer, based on the observation of non-quantifiable elements of company performance such as stated personnel policy, which in turn can directly affect, within the computer, such items as worker or salesman effectiveness.

The GMS model seems well suited to its needs. Discussions in critique sessions, which are usually not directed by the staff, center more often around management problems and management principles than around pricing or production policies. GMS is being used solely as an aid in management training. It does provide an example of the type of laboratory that one could use for studying management control systems. A footnote to this is that GMS has been used in the AMA Systems and Procedures Course, where the participants operate the company for a few years, then engage in a project session where procedures and controls are designed, and are then implemented in an additional few years of company operations.

Most business games are run in a somewhat similar manner. The participants represent new management taking over a going concern. The first problems they face are ones of organization, planning, and setting of policies. They have to decide on particular organization structure, assign individuals to specific positions, and designate the lines of authority. This is not just a question of drawing an organization chart—there are decisions to be made and individuals have to be designated to make them. There is a need for coordination, for controls, for communications. It is gratifying that in most games disorganization leads to poor performance, even to chaos. The pedagogical objective is to give practice in the application of organization principles, not to try to demonstrate the efficiency of a particular organizational scheme.

The organization chart that does emerge will usually be of some conventional hierarchical form. There will usually be a president and vice presidents, sales manager and plant manager, manager of research and development, of personnel and purchasing, controller, and so forth. One of the principles soon apparent is that the particular organization established must be suited to the task to be performed, and not merely something that looks good when drawn up by the company's art department. There is not much use in having a manager of research and development if the model does not include research and development. This is not a failing in the model, but a reinforcement of the realization that people organize to do something, not just to be organized. Thus an executive leaves his real-life company, replete with traditions, and its own way of doing things, and is faced with a new real-life-like situation. It is an exercise in the design of a management control system.

We should note again that the majority of games being used do not require very large teams and are not as useful for demonstrating organization principles as the second generation games discussed. All games do, however, produce a variety of problems in coordination and control, an example being the conflict between sales and production. There are problems of pricing, of scheduling, etc. There is a need to coordinate the hiring and training of manpower with company long-range objectives. There is the ever-present problem of cash flow. In every decision that is made there is a need for coordination and control.

Most games produce a large quantity of information in the form of reports and there are questions as to who gets what reports. In the newer games the information content can be as perplexing as in real life, and thus can be used to exercise the participants' system design abilities. Furthermore the games are dynamic, with new situations arising, perhaps the introduction of new products; and from time to time—just as in real life—management may decide to reorganize, or to overhaul the system.

We have then, in present-day business games, laboratories which could be used for research into management control principles. A great amount of data has been generated; however, nearly all games are being used almost exclusively for training purposes, and no research has been published. This situation will no doubt be altered for the Carnegie Tech and UCLA games.

MANAGEMENT CONTROL SYSTEM SIMULATION

Using business games as a laboratory for research into management control principles would be an example of what has previously been called Human System Simulation. This is also related to the type of work that has been done, or is being done, by such people as Bavelas, Guetzkow, Christie, Ackoff, and others through the observation of small task performing groups. In such work the groups are usually small, the tasks simple, and the experimental conditions well controlled—even here experimental design is a severe challenge. Controlled experimentation using business games with ten to twenty participants poses formidable problems. The amount of data to be collected and analyzed is in itself staggering.

The advantages and disadvantages of using human beings in the study of human behavior have often been discussed. An alternate approach is the construction of a completely computerized model. Experimenting with numbers inside a computer rather than human subjects inside a room offers many inducements, such as ease of control, reproducibility of results, and above all, the immense increase in speed. In the AMA GMS, a typical decision cycle would be about thirty minutes, with about twenty minutes spent on making decisions, and about ten minutes spent on processing them. Of this ten minutes only about two minutes are devoted to internal processing within the computer, the total ten minutes representing the interval from collection of decisions to distribution of reports. Thus, even with the comparatively slow speed of an IBM 650, the computer could run through several simulated years of operations while the humans are planning their decisions for just one quarter.

The primary challenge to a Symbolic System Simulation is the inclusion into the computer of certain aspects of human behavior. However, to study organization, communications, and control problems, one is not interested in individual behavior in its idiosyncratic sense, but in over-all sociological behavior. Certain individual characteristics can be included—e.g., the rate at which decisions can be made—and one might even develop managerial types, analogous to social types; but one would ignore the particular image—syndromes, neurotic or otherwise—and the myriad of interpersonal relationships which we know greatly affect real-life situations. It is hoped that there are fundamental management principles which are independent, except in unusual circumstances, of the particular personalities involved.

The social sciences offer a sufficient number of abstractions and generalizations that have been drawn in spite of the variety of the individual man. The search for general principles to guide the design of management control systems is too important to be put aside simply because of the difficulty of computerizing those aspects of the system that arise from human behavior. Furthermore, as machines continue their invasion into the field of decision making, the value of such an approach will increase.

A PRELIMINARY MODEL

As a first approach to the design of a Symbolic System Simulation to be used for research on management control systems it is helpful to make some arbitrary separations within the over-all model. We begin (see Figure VI-C-3) by assuming that within the total black box there are three smaller black boxes, which we shall label "control," "operations," and "environment." Each of these is a subsystem of the total system.

The operations subsystem is essentially a physical mechanism for performing a task. It could consist of business, military, or government organizations. As an example, let us think of a manufacturing organization. The operations subsystem would represent the flow of material, men, and money, which we might generalize here by the single term "material flow." The task is to take raw material, capital equipment, men, and money and to produce products and distribute them to the customers. It would be something similar to the UCLA, Carnegie Tech and AMA second generation game models already discussed.

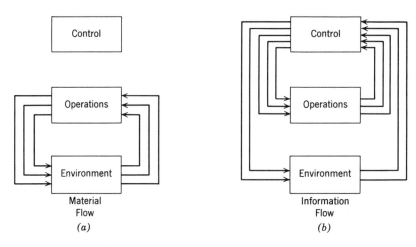

FIG. VI-C-3. Separation within the total model.

The control subsystem is the management control function, being made up primarily of decision making and information flow. We shall describe this subsystem in more detail in the next section. The environment represents those items external to the manufacturing company, such as the vendors of raw material, the customers, and the competitors, as well as the government, the over-all economy, the sources of funds, and so forth.

In Figure VI-C-3, we show first of all the separation of the over-all model into its three subsystems. We have further separated the material flow and the information flow. In item (a) we see the material—using the term in a very general sense to include such non-material items as financial credit and purchasing by consumers as well as such obvious items as raw material and labor supply—originating within the environment, being processed by the operations subsystem, and returned as products, as well, perhaps, as several less obvious items, to the environment. In item (b) we see information originating in the environment, such as raw material costs and general economic indices, together with information originating in the operations, such as stock reports and production costs; these are communicated to the management control subsystem, which in turn uses this information to arrive at certain decisions such as level of production, as well as certain information which may be thought of as being supplied to the environment, such as the sales price, which are communicated to the operations subsystem.

Before examining the inside structure of the various boxes shown in Figure VI-C-3 it is necessary to point out that in any model there can be various levels of detail, or of aggregation. As an example, consider customer demand. For certain questions it is adequate to provide, as input, random customer demands generated within the computer. In other cases one might wish to tie the demand to the company policies through somewhat aggregated functions, such as a price-demand curve, an advertising-demand curve, and so forth; this is essentially the method used in the AMA's General Management Simulation. In certain competitive-type business games an individual company's demands are dependent on the behavior of the other competing companies. In the UCLA TASK Manufacturing Company, detailed models—such as the "customer image" —have been constructed. If one is mainly interested in marketing problems then perhaps one has need for more details in the models of customers and competitors. If one is interested in inventory control, a simple aggregated demand function should prove adequate. The most desirable procedure is a modular one, where at the outset certain aggregated submodels are used, but when the need arises, they can be replaced by more detailed models.

In looking at management control systems, at least in those aspects which are mainly associated with the internal flow of information, and with internal controls, one would want the control subsystem to be quite detailed, the operations subsystem only moderately detailed, and the environment least detailed. This suggestion is predicated on certain types of research questions. If the main problem in the control system is one of coordinating the needs of the marketing and production functions, in such things as setting and implementing an inventory control policy, then a quite aggregated model of the national economy is adequate. If the control system is mainly concerned with pricing, long-range capital investment, or research and development, the model of the national economy would have to be more detailed. The same is true of the operations subsystem. It needs to be sufficiently complex to provide the control subsystem with realistic control problems, but it need not be so detailed as would be necessary, for instance, if one were studying job shop scheduling problems.

In a preliminary model the environment would provide merely some over-all economic factor which, coupled with a set of curves for price, advertising, and perhaps research and development, would yield a customer demand for each product. A price-demand curve implies both the behavior of the consumers and the existence of competitors; the curve can also change with time, representing, for example, price changes on the part of the competitors. The environment would also supply such items as the cost of raw material, the size of the labor market, etc.

An adequate operations subsystem might be that shown in Figure VI-C-4. This represents a manufacturing organization which produces and markets several products. In the particular model there would be one plant, and several sales regions. The products would require several raw materials, some of them shared by more than one product. The vendors would be represented by a very aggregated model (not shown in Figure VI-C-4) which would give merely the cost of the raw material, the maximum possible supply, and the time from placing an order to delivery of the material. This delivery time would be represented by a probability distribution.

The plant would have a raw material warehouse, a finished goods warehouse, and possibly, depending on the production mechanism used, one or more in-process warehouses. There is considerable variety in the type of production process that could be modeled. A simple scheme would have several production lines, each capable of handling only one product at a time, and each with its own flow rates, and so forth. Including a limited capacity, and production set-up time, the management control system would be faced with production scheduling problem. The plant would also have a work force, but perhaps only one class of workers. However, for costing purposes there could be provision for both direct and indirect labor costs, as well as supervision and management costs. Again we have an analogy here with several business games; on the other hand,

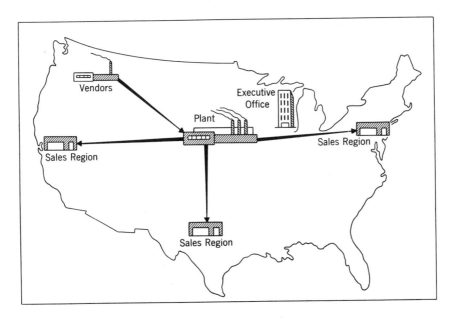

FIG. VI-C-4. An operations subsystem.

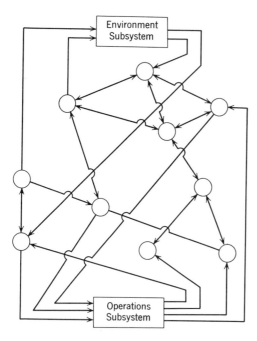

FIG. VI-C-5. The management control subsystem and a typical information flow.

THE MANAGEMENT CONTROL SUBSYSTEM

In Figure VI-C-5 we take a look inside the management control subsystem. The operations and environment subsystems are shown as black boxes, the remaining structure in the figure represents the inside of the box previously shown as the control subsystem. At the outset it is necessary to distinguish between the experimental variables, which represent those inputs provided by the staff research worker, and those inputs which are outputs from the other subsystems. The variables which are to be manipulated are primarily the organizational structure, the information flow network, and the decision rules. Figure VI-C-5 illustrates one possible information network with a particular set of rules. The management control subsystem takes information from the other subsystems, such as customer demands, stock status, and costs, and by means of decision rules provides the operations subsystem with such information as a production schedule, shipping orders, and sales price.

Within the other subsystems, there are also parameters which can be varied, such as costs, general economic condition, etc. The experimental plan is to study a particular management control system, observe its effect on over-all system performance, of which there are many measures in addition to the most common one of profit and loss, and to also test the sensitivity of the management control system to variations in the parameters within the other subsystems. One can then experiment with some other management control system. The schematic plan shown in Figure VI-C-5 is then merely one experimental setup. The model would allow complete flexibility in the choice of an information network.

For want of a better word, the circles shown in Figure VI-C-5 will be called "nodes." A node is any point at which information is received, processed, and transmitted. A node may be a man, a machine, or it could be a group of men acting as a committee. Although many straightforward data-processing tasks are now performed by computers, it is helpful in discussing this model to take an anthropomorphic view and assume that each node represents one human being.

From the internal structure of the model, as it would be programmed on a computer, there

the new UCLA game permits a distinct image for each individual worker, not only his capabilities, but also his desires.

Finished goods would be shipped directly from the finished goods warehouse at the plant to the warehouses in the sales regions. One would provide for perhaps a normal and expedited method of shipment; otherwise the transportation aspects of the model would be kept simple. Even the most simple model engenders adequate problems for the control system, there being the fundamental problem of inventory control as affected by warehouse costs, expected demand, and so forth.

In the sales regions one would have a certain number of salesmen, perhaps problems about the level of compensation, together with the usual marketing questions of price and advertising. There could be both local and national advertising; there could be local or national pricing. These are the types of problems that the management control system would face—there is not only a question of what price to set, which of course is very much tied to the environment model, but also the question of who is to set the price, when, on what basis, and how it is to be implemented.

is a great similarity between what might be called data processing on the one hand and decision making on the other. We may, at least in this preliminary model, think of a decision maker as a man who takes certain information, such as customer demands and stock on hand, and, by the use of a decision rule, arrives at what might be called new information—such as the production level—it is information to the person who is informed of the decision. Structurally this is the same as a clerk or a computer adding up a column of numbers and arriving at a total. There are, of course, some important differences between decision making and data processing; two of these, as pointed out by Roger Sisson, are the difficulty of formulating the decision rules and the search for optimum ones. But if one is provided with a set of decision rules, then, within the model, the node acts like a data processor. This is obviously true for such decision rules as an inventory reordering rule; it becomes more questionable as one looks at what might be called higher order decisions.

DECISION MAKING AND INFORMATION FLOW

In a preliminary model one might provide the management control subsystem with only those decisions which are necessary for the operations subsystem directly, such as how many units of raw material to purchase, what production level to set, and so forth. One might call these, "operations decisions." At the next higher level of complication one might allow the management control system to make decisions affecting its own operations directly, such as the decision rule at one node changing the decision rule at another node, or automatically changing the information flow network: we might call these, "procedural decisions." As one examines the types of decisions made in the real world it is obvious that the operations decisions are only a small subset of all possible ones.

If one is interested in the decision maker *qua* decision maker a great amount of research and effort would have to go into the attempt to model him. However, certain questions about the management control system might be investigated with even a quite simplified model of the decision-making process. For this preliminary model let us assume that only

operations decisions will be made by the management control subsystem.

Each node will have a certain amount of internal structure. A node will have several tasks to perform, be they simple data processing or decision making. Each of these tasks will take time and certain queuing problems will arise. In addition there will be various random tasks facing each node. The node will be able to communicate with other nodes, receiving and sending information, either in the form of reports, or as specific requests. In any particular scheme the nodes will take on the names of typical blocks in the organizational structure, as the plant manager, the president, the shipping clerk, the controller, the regional sales manager. The experimental scheme will consist in the assignment of tasks—just where do shipping orders originate and how are they implemented: perhaps the regional sales manager, based on his information as to stock status and past sales, sends an order directly to the shipping clerk, who immediately fills the order; perhaps the orders have to be cleared through a materials manager; perhaps the market research manager first supplies the regional manager with a sales forecast, or vice versa. The myriad problems of coordination, planning, and control are fairly obvious.

Associated with every information channel there would be time delays, costs, and random noise. There would be a choice of sending a report by a slower and cheaper medium, or a faster but more costly medium. The number of messages sent on a particular channel could be counted. As mentioned previously, the computer plays two roles: one part of the program is the model itself; another part monitors the operations and prints out that information which the staff wishes to analyze.

SOME MODELING CONSIDERATIONS

It should be noted that the simplified picture of the management control subsystem is a generalized one. In computer terminology it is somewhat analogous to a program compiler. Given a particular management organization—real or hypothetical—with its decision rules and information pattern, one manipulates the various parameters so as to achieve the applicable model.

Simplicity is not a too-well-defined word: an algebraic expression might be simple to look at, but complex to solve, and vice versa. A simulation model may be conceptually complex, but, as most people who have worked in the field continually stress, simplicity in the details is essential. Computers work fast, but not instantaneously. In designing models one is constantly faced with the problem: what to leave in and what to leave out. If the model is ever to be successfully programmed and run on a computer it is essential that it be kept simple. Fortunately, quite complicated behavior can result from the interaction of many simple elements.

There is no *a priori* reason to assume that complicated questions can only be answered using a complicated model, as is evidenced by much research that has been done in the physical sciences. There are a variety of techniques for combining initial simplicity with flexibility for expansion. For example, one can program for a polynomial function but begin by using only the linear terms, later, as part of sensitivity studies, introducing quadratic and higher order terms. A business game that used a linear price-demand curve exhibited quite real behavior. Thus one need not be delayed because of difficulties, such as the precise shape of a demand curve, in representing reality. One might expect to find certain management control principles which are independent of the shape of a particular curve; one might also be able to at least demonstrate those situations in which more precise knowledge is necessary.

Similar remarks can be made about random factors. While some stochastic elements are certainly essential, this does not mean that every factor in the model need be randomized. In one business game all random effects were eliminated, but, as one participant said, "Sales still seem damn random to me." Jigsaw puzzles can be tough even when one has all of the pieces at the outset. Since computer capacity and speed are always limited one should only introduce random factors when there is a clear understanding of their relationship to the activity being studied.

Symbolic System Simulation always requires the use of some basic time interval. The choice of that time interval presents problems: if it is small it might require too much computer time to cover an adequate total period and if it is large it might mask certain of the factors in which one is interested. Consider a manufacturing organization: Does one want to use simulated hours, days, weeks, months, or years?

The answer of course depends on the questions to be asked. The same model cannot be used for all problems. In the preliminary model discussed here it seems fruitful to allow the operations subsystem to run in days—that is, all sales for a particular day are aggregated—and to allow the management control system, by means of a clock arrangement attached to each node, to proceed in minutes. In this latter case it does not mean that one would cycle through several hundred minutes each day, but that task times would be given in minutes, and that the clock would then indicate whether a particular node was free for its next task.

If the operations subsystem is carried forward in days then it is obvious that certain types of problems cannot be examined with this model, problems relating to long-range planning, to capital investment, to financing. The preliminary model would then be used to examine day-to-day type problems associated mainly with the flow of material through the system. One would use a different model, in which certain quantities were now aggregated, to examine the behavior of the control system under conditions of new product introduction, long-range economic factors, and so forth. One could use one over-all model in which, through parameter changes, certain components would be aggregated or not, though this is conceptually similar to having two models. A somewhat different approach would be to allow for two types of time intervals, a short and a long, and to use the short one to perform a sort of sampling experiment for the latter. That is, the model would proceed in detail for one month, then extrapolate the results for the remainder of the year. The next year conditions may have changed—perhaps a new product has been introduced—and again a month of operations is sampled. In the approach first mentioned, one has to supply the program with separate functions, those for short time intervals and those for long; in the second approach the computer, through simulation, arrives at its own functions for the larger time interval run.

CONCLUSION

Management control problems can be studied by means of simulation, either of the Human System type, which is similar to doing research on executives playing business games, or of the Symbolic System type, for which a preliminary model has been discussed here.

The Symbolic model presents many design problems, but it does avoid the complications inherent in experimentation with human subjects, and, above all, it offers the speed of modern computers.

Some scientific advances are made by starting with a particular hypothesis and designing an experiment to test it, but this is not the only approach. The existence of an adequate simulation model will help formulate the problems to be investigated, and the modeling process itself can lead to new insights. We can best conclude with a quotation from an article by Chapman, Kennedy, Newell, and Biel in the April, 1959, issue of *Management Science:* "A scientific investigation is not the cold-blooded, straight-forward, logical process that texts proclaim. It's an adventure. Sheer scientific excitement arises from the unexpected event, from the obvious assumption that's very wrong, from the hunch that pans out, from the sudden insight, and from the invention that covers the unanticipated procedural gap. The fact is that as organizations took form before our eyes, their struggle determined ours."

BIBLIOGRAPHY

1. Buffa, E. S., *Models for Production and Operations Management,* John Wiley and Sons, 1963.
2. Buzzell, R. D., *Mathematical Models and Marketing Management,* Division of Research, Graduate School of Business Administration, Harvard University, 1964.
3. Charnes, A., and W. Cooper, *Management Models and Industrial Applications of Linear Programming,* John Wiley and Sons, 1961.
4. Churchman, C. W., R. L. Ackoff, and E. L. Arnoff, *Introduction to Operations Research,* John Wiley and Sons, 1957.
5. Fetter, R. B., and W. C. Dalleck, *Decision Models for Inventory Management,* Richard D. Irwin, 1961.
6. Hesse, M. B., *Models and Analogies in Science,* Sheed and Ward, 1963.
7. Langhoff, P. (ed.), *Models, Measurement and Marketing,* Prentice-Hall, Inc., 1965.
8. McMillan, C., and R. F. Gonzalez, *Systems Analysis—A Computer Approach to Decision Models,* Richard D. Irwin, 1965.
9. Malcolm, D. G., A. J. Rowe, and L. F. McConnell (eds.), *Management Control Systems,* John Wiley and Sons, 1960.
10. "Models Make Blueprint Reading Easy for Management," *Business Week,* November, 1952.
11. Optner, S. L., *Systems Analysis for Business and Industrial Problem Solving,* Prentice-Hall, Inc., 1965.
12. Reisman, A., and E. S. Buffa, "A General Model for Investment Policy," *Management Science,* April, 1962.

Part XI.   Measurement

In the history of science there are two converging avenues along which flows the potential of progress: the avenue of ideas and the avenue of techniques. It is the confluence of these that has made possible the marvels of modern civilization.

Though ideas precede in time the appearance of any tool or technique (even these are born of previous concepts), it is the latter that can effect the implementation of the former. Ideas constitute, as it were, the threads with which the fabric of progress is spun, while the tools and techniques are the instruments employed in the spinning process.

Of all the basic techniques perhaps none is more fundamental than that of measurement. From the days of primitive man to our own space age, measurement has been a constant companion of progress. It is indeed a long way from the tally stick to the computer, from traditional Taylorism to scientific systems approach but the progress made along the way is attributable in part to refinements in measuring techniques. Recent years especially have witnessed increased interest in measurement philosophy and measurement standards. In the physical sciences units of length and of time have had to be redefined by the Bureau of Standards, so great was the need in this day and age for new standards. The behavioral scientists too have devoted much time and thought to measurement techniques applicable to as wide a field as possible.

Some of the confusion enveloping the field of measurement may be attributable either to the lack of fundamental probing for its basic assumptions and constitutive elements or to the identification of the measurement process with something else— with measure as a number or with definition. Measurement can perhaps be looked upon as an *operation*, a process involving an observer and some form of (measuring) apparatus, while measure is the *number* that emerges as a result of such an operation.[1] Operation(al)ism, popularized by P. W. Bridgman, identified the physical entity with the set of operations by which it was being measured, thus spreading even further the confusion already enveloping the concept of measurement by identifying definition with measurement.

In the selections that follow, chief consideration is given to the fundamentals of the measurement process since these seem most in need of critical examination. For too long they have lain shrouded in the dust of uncertainty and it is only in recent years that philosophers, scientists, and operation researchers have busied themselves clearing away the accumulated dust of the ages. Selections with a management approach have been preferred to mathematical treatises that may have appealed to the budding scientist or the frustrated mathematician.

At times it may be helpful to take a long and hard look at those things that we take for granted. This is exactly what Paul Kircher does in his selection when he singles out for critical examination the field of measurement and discusses its funda-

[1] Peter Caws, "Definition and Measurement in Physics," in C. West Churchman and Philburn Ratoosh (eds.), *Measurement: Definitions and Theories* (New York: John Wiley & Sons, 1959), p. 4.

357

mentals. This is especially appropriate since management is at present intent on upgrading its own admittedly inadequate measurement tools. Since measurement provides information and information provides a logical basis for decision making, the quality of decision making will ultimately be dependent upon the quality of measurement.

The measurement process can in no wise be viewed as a simple one. It can be broken down into a number of basic elements, the number depending upon the refinement of the analysis desired. Many standard analyses offer for consideration only a very few elements. Kircher here pinpoints seven distinct elements which he explains and relates to the world of business management. Each of these seven ingredients can involve considerable difficulty in the practical realm. These elements are: (1) definition of the objective, (2) determination of the factors relevant for attainment of the objective, (3) selection of the measurable key aspects of these factors, (4) choice of measuring method and unit, (5) application of the measuring unit, (6) analysis of the measurement, and (7) evaluation of the measurement's effectiveness.

The choice of a business executive to fill a vacancy well illustrates the difficulties attendant upon mensuration. What are exactly the objectives toward which a would-be executive is to work? What relevant factors ought to be considered in choosing such an executive? What quantifiable aspects of these factors are the important ones? What will be the unit of measurement? etc. It becomes immediately apparent that even at this late date much still remains to be done in this special area.

The operational researcher, R. W. Shephard, views measurement as an essential in ensuring confidence and maintaining objectivity in decision making. The basis for this view is the set of assumptions that concern the nature of operations research itself. Operational research, which is concerned with systems that include human beings, is essentially objective decision

making and as such is oriented toward the improvement of confidence in these decisions. As was pointed out in an earlier selection by Stafford Beer, operations research is not a science but a technique, a method of science. Correct decisions can indeed be reached by methods other than operations research; the main difference between them and it is the degree of confidence that can be reposed in the results acquired by the various methods.

One of the problems that engages Shephard's attention is the measurement of the human factors involved in operations research. Since the degree of confidence in a decision reached by operations research methods depends upon all relevant factors being included and measured correctly, it follows that as much attention must be paid to measuring the psychological and sociological factors as to measuring the physical factors in the system under study. Unfortunately the measurement of these human factors is still at a rather primitive level, comparatively speaking, and a way to understand the problems involved would be to examine some of the problems of measurement in the physical sciences.

After commenting briefly on the traditional types of measurement scale and on basic and derived, direct and indirect measurement, he points out that the physical sciences need a form of measurement applicable to many diverse systems. Psycho-physical measurements, characterized by human variability, use a scale that generally represents the mean reaction of the population as a whole. This then serves as a norm. For at least some psycho-physical magnitudes ratio scales may be used.

Shephard concludes his article with a few observations concerning measurement in operational research.

C. West Churchman's selection looks at the problem of measurement from a decision-making viewpoint. He believes that the problems inherent in measurement are very difficult to solve, so much so that even now approximate solutions are unavailable. Yet somehow they must be solved if we do not want to pay the heavy penalties for our failure to do so.

Churchman arrives at his particular viewpoint in this way. Why is it considered better to measure than not to measure? Is it because measurement assigns numbers to objects? If so, why is the assignment of numbers better than non-assignment? Is it because it makes information precise? If so, then precise for what? Certainly not precise for precision's sake! Thus he is led to the function of measurement as the development of methods for generating a class of information applicable in a wide variety of contexts and problems. But there are many ways in which the objectives of measurement can be accomplished. Generally used are these two: the one that qualitatively assigns objects to classes, and the one that assigns numbers to objects. Which is better? This line of reasoning cannot but lead to the idea that measurement is essentially a decision-making activity to be evaluated by decision-making criteria.

From the functional point of view then there are at least four aspects of measurement that present decision-making problems: (1) language, (2) specification, (3) standardization, and (4) accuracy and control.

What language will the measurer use to express his results? The more precise the language the less generally will it be understood, yet the purpose of language is to communicate to as many potential users as possible. Thus the language of measurement is seen to involve a decision problem.

To what objects and in what environments will the measurements apply? Specification thus is seen to pertain to the scope of application of the measurements in terms of time, place, and items. It was seen that one of the aims of measurement is to develop information applicable to as many situations as possible, if possible, to all things at all times and all places. Yet the more general the information, the more useless it becomes to any specific context, also the more expensive to acquire. So here too there is a decision-making problem to be resolved.

How can measurements be used? Standardization is that aspect of measurement that allows us to use information in a wide variety of situations. The decision problem here springs from two rather conflicting needs: one wants to find a method of measurement such that a minimum amount of adjustment is required when times, places, and peoples change, and one wants to find a method for differentiating various aspects of the world we live in (precision). The greater the needed adjustment of the data to a standard, the less precise the information.

Accuracy concerns the degree to which a given measurement deviates from the "truth" while control provides the guarantee that the measurements can be used in a wide variety of contexts. The problem of accuracy is to develop measures that enable the user to evaluate in a meaningful way the information contained in the measurements. The problem concerning control lies in the amount and kind that should be had. Thus it is not economical to check every measurement against a standard nor is it economical to use measurements without any check.

The problems inherent in measurement are indeed formidable.

36. FUNDAMENTALS OF MEASUREMENT [1]

PAUL KIRCHER [2]

Measurement has always been an important factor in providing information to serve as the basis for solving business problems. But as business management has become more and more interested in using scientific tools to aid in making decisions, it has become increasingly evident that present methods of measurement in the business field frequently are inadequate.

For this reason the Management Sciences Research Project at UCLA (sponsored by the Office of Naval Research) has undertaken a research study of the general problem of measurement.

Preliminary analysis has shown that the fundamentals of measurement, as such, have never been clearly defined, even by scientists. Each discipline or science has developed its own techniques and methods, with few attempts at coordination with others. This is true in spite of the fact that it is difficult to evaluate the effectiveness of any system of measurement, or of any other logical activity, from criteria which are part of the system itself. If the system can be viewed from "outside," from a more fundamental point of view, it often is easier to correct mistakes and to obtain insights which lead to new and better methods.

There is a limit to this search for fundamentals, it must be admitted. One of the interesting aspects of modern mathematics is the discovery that as yet we cannot prove that the ultimate logical structure of mathematics is consistent. The most ambitious attempt to do this, by Hilbert, was shown by Godel to have the form of a proposition which could neither be proved nor disproved. It merely could be accepted, if one chose to do so.

There are many aspects of business logic which rest on indefinable terms or unprovable propositions. In the past these assumptions have been so numerous and so important that business has been characterized as an art. There have been few precepts of general significance—each problem the manager encountered was seen as being a brand new one, at least in some respects. As Vatter has said, "Business is an experiment."

Whereas, we can expect that much of this indefinability will continue, nevertheless there are many relationships which can be measured in business. Especially in situations where methods such as linear programming have proven useful, businessmen are coming to recognize that decision-making can be moved to a higher plane. In these situations, it can be seen that when certain objectives are clearly defined, and the factors of the situation are objectively measured, then decisions are already made. Scheduling the operations becomes mechanical—it can be done on an electronic computer.

As a simple example, suppose a manager makes the decision that he will choose the course which earns the highest profit. He has three courses open to him (such as shipping routes). If he can measure the profitability of each of the three routes, then the policy decision in effect makes the operating decision.

We are still a long way from being able to put policy-making on a scientific basis. Policies are always set in an atmosphere of much uncertainty. Indeed, a major difference between the human brain and the so-called "electronic computer brain" is that the former can operate with partial information. A computer must have a complete program, or it will stop or give inaccurate results.

However, policy-making can be improved with experience, since certain situations do tend to repeat themselves. But lessons can be learned only if the important factors in each situation are measured, so they can be com-

[1] SOURCE: *Advanced Management* (October, 1955), pp. 5–8. Reprinted by permission of *Advanced Management.*

[2] Associate Professor of Accounting in the School of Business Administration, University of California at Los Angeles.

pared and correlated with the results of the decisions.

THE STRUCTURE OF THE MEASUREMENT PROCESS

The major effort of the present research study is directed toward the attempt to establish the basic structure of the measurement process. It is hoped that by dividing the process into important elements, each of these may be studied with more precision, and the relationships between them can be seen more clearly.

As indicated in the paper presented by the author to the 1955 national meeting of the Operations Research Society of America,[3] the following elements of the measurement process have been identified:

1. Determination of the objective of the business entity, the purpose which is to be served in a particular situation.

2. Determination of the types of factors which might serve to attain the objective.

3. Selection of the key aspects of the factors, the aspects which are to be measured.

4. Choice of (a) a measuring method, (b) a measuring unit.

5. Application of the measuring unit to the object to be measured—the central action of measurement.

6. Analysis of the measurement—relating it to other measurements (other in time or in kind).

7. Evaluating the effectiveness of the measurement by determining the extent to which it assisted in the attainment of the objective.

Each of these needs investigation and is being studied in some detail. Since it is impossible to describe all the various considerations within the scope of a single article, an attempt will be made to indicate something of the direction and purpose of the research by relating each of the above elements to a few specific problems. Examples will be given from:

a. highly developed and effective systems, such as the measurement of length,

b. highly developed but less effective systems, such as accounting,

c. moderately developed systems, such as job evaluation, and

d. areas where systems hardly exist, as yet, such as selection and evaluation of executives.

The first and most obvious step is to define the objective. Obvious as it is, however, it is not always easy to do.

Executives have struggled with the problem of objectives ever since companies grew from the single proprietor stage. Now that social consequences are a major consideration, many executives spend a great deal of their time attempting to establish policies which exhibit business statesmanship, and which will lead to stability and continuation of earnings, as well as immediate gains.

Unless these problems are solved, it is not possible to develop the objectives in terms that will be susceptible of some sort of quantification. In other words, it is necessary to set the stage for measurement.

Without a clear understanding of the purposes which a to-be-hired executive is to serve, it is difficult to establish standards by which to select him, and later, to judge his performance.

DETERMINATION OF RELEVANT FACTORS

The second step is to determine which factors may be employed to attain the objective.

In physical problems this step is often clearly definable. When it is, the measurement process may become relatively easy, unless certain factors are physically inaccessible, or unless methods have not been sufficiently developed to handle the particular type of problem. For example, if the purpose is to provide a means of travel across a river at minimum cost, certain obvious alternatives are present— a bridge, a ferry, or a tunnel. (Of course, every such problem also presents an opportunity for the "genius" who can by-pass the problem, e.g., by finding a better route that does not go near the river, or by using helicopters.) Excepting the unusual solutions, the problem then becomes one of measuring the expected flow of traffic, measuring the cost of construction and operation of the various alternatives, and expressing the costs and capacities in comparable terms.

With a problem such as the selection of an executive the "factor" choice is considerably

[3] Held in Los Angeles, California, August 15–17, 1955.

more difficult. In the first place, though the company organization chart may appear to offer a "slot" which is to be filled, it is not possible with present knowledge to describe the position in terms comparable to those which can be used to describe the quantity of traffic flow—such as the expected weights of the vehicles.

Even if it were possible to define the job narrowly, at the executive level the individual capabilities of the manager chosen will soon start reshaping the responsibilities and activities concerned.

Moreover, it is at least theoretically desirable that each vacancy should be the occasion for a re-examination of the company organization to see whether the position should be redefined, or perhaps even eliminated. Such considerations add considerably to the difficulty of the measurement problem.

SELECTION OF KEY ASPECTS

Once it has been determined what the purpose is, and the objects to be measured, it is necessary to select those aspects, which can and should be measured. These are the aspects which are themselves quantifiable, and are related in some way to the quantifiable aspects of the purpose or objective of the entity involved.

An example can be drawn from accounting. Various types of assets and liabilities are measured in order to obtain information concerning the revenue and expense flows, and the financial position of the firm. These are indicative of the degree of attainment of the profit-making objectives of the business.

The illustration from accounting is especially interesting since accountants have deliberately chosen to restrict their activities to those measurements which they believe can be made within a certain standard of accuracy. This means that certain other items, vital to the well-being of the firm, are resolutely omitted. For example, the company's investments in advertising its products, or in developing its executives, are not considered to be assets, but are written off in the period of expenditures, as a rule. Goodwill as such has almost disappeared from company statements.

In certain types of job evaluation, it is possible to quantify some of the key aspects. For example, a stenographer should be able to take shorthand at so many words per minute and type at a given rate, in order to perform the duties of a given job. Other important attributes, however, such as the ability to get along with others, are harder to quantify.

In choosing an executive the problem is much more difficult. There is little knowledge as to the particular abilities which are required for a manager to act successfully in a specific situation. Even where certain abilities have been ascertained as desirable, it is seldom that they can be expressed in terms which are quantifiable. They are seldom established on the basis of what the man can *do;* rather they are usually expressed in terms of what he *is*— e.g., sincere, capable, loyal, patient, trained, experienced, etc. These attributes are difficult to express quantitatively, and thus are difficult to relate to later performance, however measured.

CHOICE OF MEASURING METHOD AND UNIT

The act of choosing a measuring method and a measuring unit has been given considerable attention throughout history, but so far not much of the theoretical work is helpful to businessmen. Mathematics, "the Queen of the Sciences," is a logical process whose object, in the words of Comte, is "the indirect measurement of magnitudes," and "it constantly proposes to determine certain magnitudes from others by means of the precise relations existing between them."

Most of the theoretical mathematical work, however, has deliberately avoided the problems of application, especially to anything so "crass" as business problems. The essence of mathematics is deductive reasoning from explicitly stated assumptions. Only since World War II have many mathematicians discovered, much to the surprise of most of them, that business problems are difficult, challenging, and can be as intellectually interesting as the act of contemplating abstract "Number."

In recent years, however, activity in the application field has increased tremendously. In addition to increased activities in this field in many societies nationwide, three societies have been formed—"The Institute of Management Sciences," "The Operations Research Society of America," and the "Society for Industrial and Applied Mathematics," whose objectives express this interest.

DEVELOPMENT OF SCALES

Perhaps the most advanced work in the field of measurement of a type useful for choosing executives has been done by the applied psychologists. In their attempts to measure such things as intelligence, men like Thurstone have had to develop scales where zero could not be fixed, nor could absolute intervals be specified. In several works Stevens has shown how various types of scales are possible depending upon the type of manipulation which can be performed on the measurements—the nominal, ordinal, interval and ratio scales.

Further developments have been hampered, however, by lack of clear-cut definitions of the relationship between the concepts we call "qualitative" and those we call "quantitative." Following the mathematicians, most writers appear to treat "quantity" as referring to an abstraction which somehow has almost a physical significance of its own.

It would appear to be more useful to firmly establish the concept that quantities are measurements of qualities. For example, the quality "length" occurs in various physical objects. By choosing some standard unit, and determining the number of repetitions of the unit in the object, the length can be expressed as a quantity. Then, following Stevens, the manipulations of arithmetic—addition, etc.—can be attempted to see what type of scale is involved.

In this process of measurement the problem for the observer is to identify certain characteristics in the object to be measured, characteristics which appear similar to those in the measuring unit, and which also have some identifiable relationship to the purpose of the measurement. These characteristics should be invariant, in the sense that they can be identified and seen to persist. Basically, of course, every object and every event in the universe is unique, and it is constantly changing through time. To find invariant characteristics, then, requires the human process of abstraction.

In measuring an executive, for example, the objective desired may be the organization of a research program. It is necessary to determine which types of ability are required for this, then to find a means of measuring these types of ability in the alternative men available. Each type of ability must be defined in such a way that it can be seen as a distinct part of a complicated personality. It must also be comparable to a part of the complicated personalities of the other candidates.

We are far behind the physical sciences in our ability to accomplish this. So far behind, in fact, that many people consider any effort in this direction to be useless. However, it does appear to offer the best hope for eventual improvement over present intuitive methods, so research in this direction probably will continue.

The importance of invariance can be seen in the difficulties which arise when the measuring unit chosen has varying characteristics. The dollar, the measuring unit of accounting, is an example. Changes in purchasing power not only create difficulties of evaluation, but can lead to serious inequities. An appreciable part of the "income" taxed by our government in recent years is really the result of the diminished value of the dollar unit.

APPLICATION OF THE MEASURING UNIT

The simplest method of measurement is to identify the unit characteristics in the object to be measured, and then merely to count the recurrences. Almost equally simple are the cases where the unit can be directly compared, as in measurement of length or weight. More advanced measurements, such as in astronomy, require the construction of chains of relationships.

Most business measurements involve quantity of performance in given time periods, since business is a dynamic process. The time factor introduces many complications.

Another major factor in business measurements is the force of custom. Even when systems are demonstrably weak, the difficulties of retraining and reeducating the users of data, to say nothing of the problem of development of a better system, frequently operate to hinder improvements.

On the other hand, custom does offer some advantages. Most businessmen are familiar with the major elements of the accounting system, and so can interpret results even when these are not as precise as one might wish.

In newer fields, such as measurement of executive abilities, there are several systems in use. They exhibit few attributes in common. The result is that acceptance of the systems is correspondingly more difficult to achieve.

ANALYSIS OF THE MEASUREMENTS

The area of analysis of measurements in business has seen startling advances in recent years, and there is reason to hope that even greater improvements can be achieved. Primary interest has centered on attempts to relate various measurements into integrated systems that reflect the business operations. These attempts usually involve the construction of mathematical models of the operations.

Developments in linear programming, game theory, communication theory, etc., have shown that complicated situations can be resolved by the use of models if the relevant data can be obtained, and if the relationships are of certain types. While the use of some of these models requires advanced training in mathematics, others are simpler and yet very effective. Examples are the method for studying investment decisions (developed by Markowitz, see article by Weston and Beranek in the *Analysts Journal,* May, 1955) or for forecasting working capital needs (article by Rothschild and Kircher, *Journal of Accountancy,* September, 1955), or inventory control in production (Vazsonyi, *Management Science,* June, 1955).

One of the pioneers in the field of management improvement is General Electric. In a speech to the Controllers Institute, M. L. Hurni of General Electric's Management Consultation Services Division, gave a summary of the management problem which indicates how measurements are used and evaluated.

The examination of an operation, or a situation within an operation, as a problem in logic consists in doing fundamental research upon the operation itself. It is not providing quick isolated solutions to current problems as they arise on the basis of readily available means.

First, it consists of systematic examination of the environment in which the business exists for such things as the possible structure, range, and probability of specific demands upon the business, the recurrence or lack of recurrence of particular aspects of the environment, the drift in the environment from a given known position.

Such examination includes not only a qualitative examination of characteristics of this type, but also application to them of strict methods well known in other disciplines, for the purpose of determining units of measure through which such phenomena or characteristics may be increasingly quantified or expressed in numbers.

Second, it includes the systematic examination of the resources of the business for the purpose of determining quantitatively the identifying characteristics of such resources— for example, characteristics of performance, or probable malfunctioning, and the balances, limitations and restraints that may exist within the resources.

Lastly, it includes the development and testing of models of action that give a description of the relation between the environment and the resources and which will define needs for performance and contribution, the information which must be communicated to make such performance or contribution possible, units of measure of the resultant performance, and the statement of possible risks that will result from a range of probable courses of action.

In short, the purpose of the problem in logic is not the taking of specific action but the attainment of more complete understanding so that increasingly purposeful action may be taken with greater assurance.[4]

CONCLUSIONS

The material given in this article may serve to indicate that the problems of measurement in business are increasingly being investigated, and also that some progress is being achieved.

However, much more remains to be accomplished. The author would hesitate to present such limited results if it were not for the fact that this affords an opportunity to let people know of the research and to contribute criticisms and suggestions.

It does seem certain that progress in the directions indicated can be no more rapid than is permitted by our methods of measurement. This is a field in which business can carry on a great deal of basic research and discussion with some assurance that the payoff can be considerable.

[4] M. L. Hurni, "Planning, Managing and Measuring the Business," Part 6, *Future Horizons in Business Management,* Controllership Foundation, Inc., New York City, Jan., 1955.

37. WHY MEASURE?

C. West Churchman [*]

INTRODUCTION

"Measurement" is one of those terms which has attained a social prestige. Apparently—all other things being equal—it is better to measure than not to measure. Some people think that the social sciences do not—or cannot—measure; and one implication of the thought is "less power to them!"

Why should measuring have this preferential status? What is it that measuring accomplishes that nonmeasuring does not? These are the questions to be dealt with in this paper.

At the outset one can suggest a rather obvious answer to this question, namely, that measurement assigns numbers to objects. But this suggestion can scarcely be adequate to explain why measurement is to be preferred to nonmeasurement in some contexts. Why is number assignment a good idea? Whatever it is that number assignment accomplishes may give us a clue to the meaning of measurement. The contrast between quantitative and nonquantitative information seems to imply a contrast between "precise" and "vague" information. Precise information is information that enables one to distinguish objects and their properties to some arbitrarily assigned degree of refinement.

We are thus driven to a first formulation of the function of measurement which will suffice to define the problem area of this paper. There is no reason to be precise for precision's sake, of course. But the reason that precision is useful is that precise information can be used in a wide variety of problems. We know that we can measure the lengths of some objects very

SOURCE: *Measurement: Definitions and Theories*, John Wiley and Sons, pp. 83–94. Reprinted by permission of John Wiley and Sons, Inc., from *Measurement: Definitions and Theories*, © 1959. Edited by C. W. Churchman and P. Ratoosh.

[*] Professor of Business Administration, University of California, Berkeley.

precisely. This means that, in the various situations where we want information about length, we can obtain the information we want. Sometimes we do not need to make a fine distinction between objects, and sometimes we do. But whatever our needs, length measurements can be found to satisfy them—within bounds, of course. Beyond the bounds there are still problems of length measurement which have not been solved—the very fine and the very far.

Suppose, then, we propose that the function of measurement is to develop a method for generating a class of information that will be useful in a wide variety of problems and situations. This proposal is very tentative. It needs defending in terms of the historical usage of the term "measurement" and the practice of measurement. It needs clarification, since "wide variety" may include time, place, persons, problem type, and many other properties of breadth and depth.

Instead of considering these important questions, I want to continue the theme with which I started. Suppose we acted as though we knew what the proposal meant to a sufficient extent to enable us to develop the problems entailed in such a functional definition.

We can begin by noting one rather striking consequence of the proposal. The objective of measurement can be accomplished in a number of ways, as this volume of papers clearly shows. The qualitative assignment of objects to classes and the assignment of numbers to objects are two means at the disposal of the measurer for generating broadly applicable information. But which means is better? The striking consequence of the proposal is that measurement is a decision making activity, and, as such, is to be evaluated by decision making criteria.

In this sense, i.e., measurement taken as a decision making activity designed to accomplish an objective, we have as yet no theory of measurement. We do not know why we do what we do. We do not even know why we measure at all. It is costly to obtain measurements. Is the effort worth the cost?

I have no intention of developing a functional theory of measurement here. Instead, I want to reconsider some of the well-known aspects of measurement in the light of the tentative proposal given above. In each case, I want to ask what alternative decisions the measurer has, and to what extent he has guides which enable him to select the best alternative. The topics selected for discussion do not necessarily represent the best way of organizing measurement activities; I have selected them because they have each received considerable attention in the literature on measurement. In each case, it will be found that the measurer is caught between at least two desirable aims, and the more he attempts to emphasize one aim, the more he must sacrifice another—which is the typical problem setting of the decision maker.

The topics to be considered are: (1) the selection of a *language;* (2) *specification* of the items and their properties; (3) *standardization* of the information to permit adjustment to various times and places; and (4) *accuracy* and *control* of the measurement process.

Any "scheme" of measurement does violence both to reality and to the functional meaning since there are many methods of accomplishing a goal. I do not intend to imply, therefore, that these topics must occupy the attention of the measurer in this order. But it is safe to assume that every measurer must decide:

1. In what language he will express his results (*language*).

2. To what objects and in what environments his results will apply (*specification*).

3. How his results can be used (*standardization*).

4. How one can evaluate the use of the results (*accuracy* and *control*).

There is a distortion which I will have to introduce in order to discuss these topics. The method of deciding how to handle any one of the problems does eventually involve consideration of all the rest. But the main point here is to show that a true decision problem does occur in the case of each of the four topics, rather than to suggest how the decision problem is to be solved.

LANGUAGE

The measurer must develop a language which adequately communicates to another person what the user must do to utilize the information contained in the measurement. The emphasis here is on the language of communication.

One aim of the language of measurement is to communicate to as many potential users as possible since this will increase the scope of utilization. Another aim is to enable the user to employ the information when there is need for fine distinctions since this also will increase the scope of utilization. These two aims are apparently in conflict—the more common the language the more difficult it is to use the language for portraying fine distinctions.

One way out of a dilemma is to escape through the horns. This I think has been the solution proposed by advocates of "fundamental" measurements. Suppose there are some operations which can be described in unequivocal language so that virtually every intelligent person will understand what is meant, or can be trained to understand. Suppose, too, we can find a process by which other operations can be understood in terms of these more elementary ones, and that these operations permit greater and greater refinement. If this were so, then we could accomplish *both* a wide scope of communication and a great depth of utilization of measurement. One example of a simple operation might be the comparison of straight rods: by successive steps we go from the "simple" language of comparison to the more complicated language of measuring the distances between the planets. Another example of a "simple" operation is the preference comparison of commodities: we may try to go from the "simple" language of preferences to the more complicated language of utilities.

In recent years there has been considerable study of the various ways in which the process of going from the "simple" language and "simple" operations can take place. These studies have resulted in formalizations of measurement language which are undoubtedly important in the development of the theory of measurement. For example, the symbol "$<$" can be made to denote an operation of comparison of two objects (e.g., "shorter than," or "is preferred to"). Sometimes the comparisons obey some simple rules like transitivity ($a < b$ and $b < c$ implies $a < c$), which enable us to introduce into the language the concept of ordering. But we can only introduce the concept if the comparisons obey the rules; i.e., we cannot enrich the language unless certain rules are upheld. The measurer is faced with a decision making problem when the rules fail. He may look about for another comparison operation with which he is satisfied and for which the rules hold, or he may abandon the rule itself and look for other rules to enrich the language. In any case, it seems to be confusing to say, for example, that "transitivity" fails over the class of preference comparisons. Such statements hide the fact that the measurer may always select another meaning for "preference" (there are clearly very many possible meanings) rather than let the rule fail *if* this seems economically advisable.

The language of measurement may be enriched in many ways. In each case the measurer has to decide whether the formalization is advisable. An enrichment of the language often makes the measurements more useful as items of information. But additional rules must be satisfied, often at the expense of a great deal of research time.

The process of developing a measurement language which I have been discussing has the following character. A formal system is constructed which includes terms, and relations between the terms. Some of the terms and at least one of the relations are taken to be "primitive" in the formal sense: the terms and relations are not explicitly defined. These terms and relations are also taken to be semantically primitive: the things and the comparisons which they denote are supposed to be simple to understand or to perform. This method of constructing the language of measurement is neither the only one nor necessarily the best one available to the measurer. A language without semantic primitives has many obvious advantages, besides more realistically reflecting the actual operations of measurement (where nothing is simple to understand or to perform). But the techniques of developing such a language have not yet been explored. Further discussion of this point would take the present discussion too far from its central purpose.

Finally, the amount of complexity that one should permit in a measurement language is also a problem of considerable importance. The more complicated a language, no matter how it is developed, the fewer the number of people who will understand it. In some cases, this restriction on communications seems clearly desirable. In other cases, e.g., in inspection work, one tries to develop a language that will be widely understood although it may not be very precise.

In sum, the language of measurement does entail a decision problem. The more precise a language the less broadly is it understood. To put it otherwise—if one wanted to be cute about it—the clearer a language the more confusing it is to most people. Precise languages narrow the class of users but increase the degree of refinement that any user can attain. The proper balance between breadth and depth is the linguistic decision problem of measurement.

SPECIFICATION

The problem of the specification of measurement is the problem of deciding what objects are being described and under what circumstances. This is simply the problem of deciding on the scope of application of the measurements in terms of time, place, and individuated items. This is not a decision about how the application is to be made, which will be considered under another head.

A conflict of aims is clear in this instance as well. It would be very fine if we could develop information that could be used in connection with all our problems, i.e., on all things at all times and places. But the more general information becomes the more expensive it becomes to acquire, or, else, the more useless it becomes in any specific context.

Perhaps one illustration will suffice to clarify the issues. In the theory of detonation, we would like to measure the sensitivity of various compounds. It would be a nice thing if we could measure how sensitive a piece of mercury fulminate is wherever the piece may be, no matter what its size, and no matter what is happening to it. But we do not do this at all. The term "sensitive" applies only to compounds which have a specific kind of shape and which exist in a specific class of environments. We restrict the term to these items and environments because we feel it would be entirely too costly to try to extend the scope beyond them, relative to the gains made from the more extensive information. Generalizing:

each measurer is involved in the economic problems of balancing the "costs" of extending the application of measurement and the "returns."

STANDARDIZATION

We turn now to the aspect of measurement that enables us to utilize information in a wide variety of contexts. In searching for a suitable title under which this topic could be discussed, I could find no better one than "standards." Standards of measurement are designed to provide a basis for adjusting experience in widely different contexts. Although the term is usually used in a narrower sense than the one adopted here, the purpose of standards so exactly corresponds to the notion of "wide applicability" that the extension of meaning seems legitimate.

It is strange that in philosophical discussions of measurement, the problem of standards is often neglected. This may be because it is often assumed that the problem is trivial, or not nearly as important as setting up an adequate language. Yet even a casual inspection of the process of measurement shows how very intricate and delicate is the operation of standardizing measurement readings.

The necessity for standards of measurement is based, in part, on an almost obvious observation that not all human experience takes place at the same time or in the same circumstance. Even if there were but one mind in all the world, such a castaway would need to compare the experience of one moment and place with that of another moment and place. He would have to communicate with his own past. The devices that men have used to make these comparisons are many indeed. One of the most direct methods consists of reconstructing each experience into an experience of a given moment and a given time, i.e., the present experience is "adjusted" into the experience that would have taken place under some standard set of conditions. This is not the only way in which experiences of various moments can be communicated, but it is a very powerful device for communication. Robinson Crusoe cannot bring along his hut as he searches for a flagstone for his hearth. But he does need to compare an experience on the beach with a past experience in his hut. He does this (say) by the use of a piece of string. He argues that

if the string length fits the flagstone, the flagstone will fit the hearth. What he is really saying is that each experience—of the hearth and the flagstone—can be adjusted to a comparison with the string under "standard" conditions.

The general purpose of standards can now be made clear. One wants to be able to assert that x has property y under conditions z at time t in such a manner that the information contained in the assertion can be used in a wide number of other conditions and times to enable many different kinds of people to make decisions. The assertion that company x had a net income of y dollars in the U.S.A. during 1919 means nothing at all unless there is some way in which this property can be compared with a net income in 1956, say, or in England. Hence, the need for a "standard" dollar. Even the standard dollar does not accomplish the desired result of transmitting meaningful information if the circumstances in which the company operated (e.g., postwar economy) were different from the circumstances of today (cold-war economy). We require richer standardization to enable us to make meaningful comparisons of such a company's activities.

The decision problem of standards arises because of two rather obvious needs. First of all, one wants to find a method of measurement such that a minimum amount of adjustment is required when times, places, and people change. This desire for simplification is so strong that many thinkers have believed that certain simple sensations have this very desirable property: reports about such sensations can be understood intelligibly by a wide number of people in a wide variety of circumstances. A witness of an accident can report which car was going faster, a laboratory technician can report the color of litmus paper, a stock clerk can report the number of items in a bin; in each case the report is supposed to be reliable, no matter how the surrounding conditions vary.

The other need that standards are supposed to supply is precision. This is the need to differentiate aspects of the world we live in. The planning of a large meeting only demands a rough notion of the size of the crowd, say, between 2000 and 3000, in order to select a meeting hall economically; but the planning of a dinner meeting requires much greater precision. The decisions about instrument readings, highly refined products, bridges, and the like, all demand extreme precision.

It requires little reflection to see that the aim of minimizing the effort to adjust data usually conflicts with the aim of precision. In effect, the "cost" of adjusting data rises as more precision is attained, just as the cost of the absence of precision goes up as we attempt to find "simpler" data. Experience has shown that it is possible to be naive with respect to precision in an attempt to be simple in procedures. All of the supposedly "simple" instances mentioned above—a report of a witness, of a laboratory technician, of a stock clerk—are not simple at all if the decision on which they are based has any importance. There are countless instances in which such reports have been shown to be faulty, and these instances have pointed to the need for "checking" the accuracy of the data. Such checks amount to setting up standards to which the data can be adjusted. For example, what is meant by saying that one car was seen to be speeding more rapidly than another? As a first approximation: the witness who saw this was "reliable." What does "reliable" mean? As a second approximation: had any other normal person been at the scene, he would have made the same report. What does "normal person" mean? As a third approximation: a person with an intelligence quotient in a certain range, with emotional factors below a certain level of intensity, with vision in a certain range, etc.

This "normal" is the standard of measurement for a "witness" report. It may be noted that defense attorneys often argue that the witness's report is *not* adjustable to this standard, e.g., that the witness is excitable, or known to exaggerate, etc. Usually, when the witness is shown to have a property significantly different from the standard, his report is rejected. In this case, we can say that the "adjustment" has been a rejection. This terminology will enable us to emphasize the economic gains that occur when "unreliable" reports can be adjusted to reliable ones, rather than rejected. If we knew, for example, that a witness was normal on all counts except an emotional instability of a certain type, then we might be able to adjust his report to the report that would have occurred if a completely normal person had been at the scene of the accident. We could do this if we could estab-

lish a law relating visual reports in various circumstances to the degree of a specific emotional disturbance. This kind of thing Bessel accomplished in his study of observer reaction times. It is not necessary to discard the readings of a "slow" observer if we can find a method of adjusting his readings, e.g., by adding a constant to each one.

Thus, we see three "levels" of standardization of data. The first tries to restrict itself to data reports that are virtually certain to remain invariant with time and place so that zero adjustment is required. This level minimizes the cost of adjustment, but the data themselves have little precision and, consequently, little value where refined distinctions are needed. The second level consists of rejecting data not collected under standard conditions. The method of adjustment is simple, but the waste of information may be considerable. The third level consists of adjusting data to standards by means of "laws" that enable one to say: *if* report R_1 was made at time t_1 in circumstance z_1 by a person having properties w_{11}, w_{12}, etc., then report R_0 would have been made at time t_0 in circumstance z_0 by a person having properties w_{01}, w_{02}, etc. The "standards" are specified in terms of circumstance, observer, and observer actions.

It seems natural enough to ask why reports should be adjusted to a standard report. If laws exist that enable one to adjust in the manner stated above, why not adjust directly from one circumstance to the problem context without going through the medium of a standard?

The reason for standardized data is easy enough to give. Without standards, one would have to report all the relevant information about the time, place, persons, etc., in addition to the data report itself. Otherwise, no one would know what values to assign to the variables in the laws that enable one to use the report in other circumstances. But once a standard has been given, then all data reports can be adjusted to the standard, and all that is needed is the data report itself. Thus, the standard conditions constitute a data processing device that simplifies the amount of reporting required. But the construction of an optimal standard is a very complicated problem, as anyone knows who has followed the literature on the selection of a standard of length. Indeed, the whole problem of standards has received a great deal of attention by various professional societies. But as far as I know, the philosophers of measurement, i.e., those interested in tying together the whole structure and function of measurement, have tended to ignore this work.

ACCURACY AND CONTROL

There are two other aspects of measurement —each fully as important as those just discussed. These are concerned with the accuracy of the measurements and with the control of the measuring process.

Accuracy is itself a measurement—the measurement of the degree to which a given measurement may deviate from the truth. No procedure can claim the name of measurement unless it includes methods of estimating accuracy.

"Deviation from the truth" must be defined in terms of the uses to which the measurement is put. This remark has the awkward consequence that accuracy is a highly relative term, the meaning of which depends on the individual decision maker. But measurements are pieces of information applicable in a wide variety of contexts and problems. This means that it must be possible to find accuracy measurements which are applicable in a wide variety of contexts and problems. It must be admitted that, at present, we tend to adopt a rather naive solution to the problem of measuring accuracy by using one overall figure such as the probable error or standard deviation of the mean. For example, in statistical literature, accuracy is sometimes defined in terms of a "confidence interval." In so far as this computed interval has any meaning, it tells us that a certain range of numbers constructed out of observations has a specific probability of including the "true" measurement. Each set of observations is the basis for forming a net to "catch" the truth, and the confidence interval tells us the probability of a successful catch. But it is almost always difficult to determine how the information supposedly contained in a confidence interval can be used; i.e., what difference would it make if the confidence interval were twice as large, or half as large? Most statisticians seem to prefer to negotiate this tricky question by urging the decision maker to set his own size of confidence interval. Since most decision makers honestly do not see the purpose of the interval in the first place, the interval is set "arbitrarily," i.e., pointlessly.

Now the problem of accuracy is to develop measures that enable the measurement user to evaluate the information contained in the measurements. It seems clear that to date we have overemphasized one aim and underemphasized another. We have tried to develop general measures of accuracy at the cost of their meaningfulness in specific contexts. The decision problem of accuracy, therefore, has not been adequately solved, except possibly for some industrial processes where there is repetition of data and cost functions can be obtained.

Control is the long-run aspect of accuracy. It provides the guarantee that measurements can be used in a wide variety of contexts. In other words, a control system for measurement provides optimal information about the legitimate use of measurements under varying circumstances. The economics of control are extremely difficult to work out. It is certainly not economical to check measurements at every feasible instant, nor is it economical to use measurements without any check. What the proper amount of control should be and what its structure should be are in general unsolved problems.

It may be noted that control is, in effect, the test of a good standard. If adjustments can satisfactorily be made to a standard in accordance with the criteria of control, then the standards have been sufficiently specified. If not, then either the laws of adjustment must be changed or, else, additional specifications must be added to the standard.

SCIENCE AND DECISION MAKING

Enough has been said to establish the point that measurement involves highly complicated —and as yet unsolved—decision problems. It is important, I think, to point out that I realize that many people feel that decision making models cannot be applied to scientific work. They arrive at the feeling in various ways. Some feel that formal decision models applied to scientific decisions would stifle the creative powers of the scientist. Others feel that the "costs" and "returns" of the scientific input and output are intangibles. These feelings may be right, but at least we owe it to ourselves as scientists to determine whether they are right, and this means a frank statement of our decision problems, which is what I have started to do in this paper. My argument is not with people who feel this way.

But others may feel that science is immortal, and what is not solved today will be solved sometime. Existing decision making models implicitly or explicitly assume a penalty for delays. Perhaps to an immortal mind no such penalty is relevant. Thus, we can investigate some aspects of our measurements now, and let the next generation solve some more. People with this attitude are serious opponents of the endeavor of this paper. However, they cannot be right. Science may be immortal and I hope it is—but this does not imply a zero penalty for delay. It is ridiculous (I feel) to think that science is a gradual accretion of bits of knowledge. Instead, we ought to think that, as time goes on, scientists will feel that the distance between what they know and what they could know is greater and greater. Hence, the penalties for wrong steps become magnified, not diminished, the longer the life of the institution. Therefore, the decision making problems of science are terribly important ones, and decision making models that penalize for delay, i.e., for overemphasis or underemphasis of some kind of activity, can be appropriately applied to science today.

SUMMARY

The decision making problems of any of the aspects of measurement are enormously difficult, and even an approximation to their solution still escapes us. Everything that has been said here about measurements is applicable to a broader class called "information" and "data." A rather significant portion of our resources is devoted to generating and processing data. However, it is apparent that no one knows how the data should be expressed (the decision problem of data *language* is now unsolved), what data are needed (the decision problem of data *specification* is unsolved), how the data are to be used in various contexts (the decision problem of *standardization* is unsolved), and how the data are to be evaluated (the decision problem of *accuracy* and control is unsolved).

38. AN APPRAISAL OF SOME OF THE PROBLEMS OF MEASUREMENT IN OPERATIONAL RESEARCH *

R. W. Shephard †

Operational research is invariably concerned with the examination of systems which include human beings. Since the degree of confidence in a decision reached by operational research methods depends upon all relevant factors being included and measured correctly, it follows that as much attention must be paid by operational research workers to measurement in the fields of psychology and sociology, for example, as to measurement of physical quantities. Unless this is done, confidence will be reduced, and the whole purpose of operational research (which is to give confidence in decisions) defeated.

INTRODUCTION

There are advantages to be gained by surveying from time to time the progress operational research has made as a science; it is then possible logically to decide in which areas more emphasis should be given if advancement is to continue soundly in the future.

The choice of subject for this paper followed from taking stock in this manner. It was impossible not to be struck by the preoccupation there seems to be in operational research circles with methods (elegant or otherwise) for manipulating measurements, and, on the other hand, by the small amount of attention that appears to be given to the problems of making these measurements. There seem to be very few articles in operational research books or journals which even touch on the problem of how the factors under consideration are to be measured in practice.

This paper, therefore, expresses some personal opinions on this subject. The aim primarily has been to be provocative and to stimulate thought that may improve the situation.

SOURCE: *Operational Research Quarterly* (September, 1961), pp. 161–166. Reprinted by permission of the *Operational Research Society*.

* Based on a talk given to the Operational Research Society, London, on January 2, 1961.

† Ministry of Defence, Defence Operational Analysis Establishment, United Kingdom.

BACKGROUND

The following three statements provide the basis on which the rest of the paper is built:

(a) *Operational research is objective decision making.* Two comments must be made in this context. Firstly, operational research is not necessarily merely advisory, but is a scientific method by which decisions can be taken; it is only advisory if the people who use it are advisers. Secondly, since decision making is concerned essentially with future outcomes, the measurements that are necessary to keep operational research objective must often be essentially predictive in nature;

(b) *Operational research deals with systems.* These systems may be simple or complex, but in general they all contain human beings. To ignore these is to be guilty, often, of fatal sub-optimization;

(c) *Operational research is concerned with improving confidence in decisions.* A decision reached by operational research methods is not necessarily different from the decision that would be reached by other methods: a right decision is a right decision, irrespective of whether it is obtained by sticking a pin into a list of all the alternatives, or by a piece of operational research work. The basic difference is in the degree of confidence that can be placed on the correctness of the results.

373

It is worth while to digress for a moment on this question of confidence. In the physical sciences, facts from the real world are used as a basis on which to build hypotheses; predictions made from these hypotheses are in turn compared with other facts from the real world, and, if agreement is not complete, the hypothesis is rejected or modified. In operational research this approach is rarely possible: * an operational research model must be made and used for prediction before the "real life" situation occurs that enables a check to be made. Confidence in the model, therefore, often depends only on some intuitive assessment that it is realistic, backed up by confirmation that all relevant factors are included and measured correctly. Measurement is thus as essential in ensuring confidence as in maintaining objectivity—two of the most important requirements for any operational research study.

In this connection it is probably of value to stress the importance of following up a piece of operational research, and of checking upon the assumptions made and model used, in the light of subsequent knowledge. Only by this means can experience be gained and used to improve the quality of further research.

PROBLEMS OF MEASUREMENT

General

It has been pointed out that one of the main requirements for confidence in an operational research study is that all relevant factors should be included and measured; also that operational research is concerned essentially with systems that include human beings. It is clear, therefore, that it is important that as much attention should be given to measuring human factors (psychological and sociological) as to measuring physical factors in the system under examination.

Admittedly some progress has been made in this field; for example, quantitative methods of selection and training are becoming widely known, and the impact of ergonomics is beginning to be felt. But generally the measurement of human and subjective quantities is in a very elementary stage compared with physical measurement; factors such as goodwill, morale, motivation, and so on, tend to be treated as "imponderables" (that is, the opera-

* See, in particular, the article by W. J. Strauss in the *Journal of the Operational Research Society of America*.[1]

tional research worker ignores them) or, alternatively, they are in effect given some arbitrary value (a 1 in 20 chance of running out of stock is assumed reasonable as far as goodwill is concerned) and no attempt is made to include them on the balance sheet. Neither of these approaches is logical, reasonable or conducive to confidence.

There is, of course, no doubt that measurement becomes more difficult the more subjective matters are included. It would seem of value, therefore, to examine some of the problems of measurement in the physical sciences in an effort to understand what is involved, and then to determine how far the experience obtained is likely to be transferable to other fields.

Measurement in the Physical Sciences

It is pertinent, in the first place, to mention briefly the manner in which scales of measurement are usually classified.[2] Measurement can be defined as the assignment of numerals to events or objects according to rules, and the distinction between the various types of scales —nominal, ordinal, interval and ratio—is essentially on the basis of the mathematical transformations that leave the scale form invariant. In turn, these determine which statistical measures are appropriate. Table 1 summarizes the distinctions in convenient form, and provides a background for subsequent discussion.

In the physical sciences measurements may also be classified according to whether they are basic (lb, ft, etc.) or derived (lb/ft³, ft/sec). One very noticeable fact about the latter (secondary) quantities is that none is in present scientific use which does not satisfy the principle that its dimensional formula is composed of powers; that is, all are measured on ratio scales. The advantage is, of course, that the form of any mathematical expression in which these quantities are represented is independent of the precise units of measurement employed, and this flexibility has undoubtedly been responsible for the gradual elimination of measurements on scales weaker than the ratio scale.

It is also of interest to classify measurements according to the methods used to take them. These methods are either direct, as when an unknown length is measured by placing a foot rule immediately alongside, or indirect, as when a temperature, for instance, is measured in terms of the length of a column of mercury. The latter form of measurement generally im-

Table 1. Types of Scales of Measurement

Scale	Basic Empirical Operations	Allowable Mathematical Transformation	Example	Statistics	Remarks
Nominal	Determination of equality	Any one to one substitution	Numbering types or classes	Mode χ^2 test	
Ordinal	Determination of $>$ or $<$	$x' = f(x)$ where $f(x)$ is any monotonic increasing function	Street numbers	Median Percentiles Rank order correlation	
Interval	Determination of equality of intervals	$x' = ax + b$ $a > 0$	Temperature (°C or °F) Potential energy	Mean, s.d., t-test, F-test	Zero point by convention or for convenience
Ratio	Determination of equality of ratios	$x' = cx$ $c > 0$	Length Temperature (°K)	Geometric mean Harmonic mean	Actual zero point

NOTE: Each column is cumulative in the sense that any statement against a given scale not only applies to that scale but to all scales below it.

The third column shows the mathematical transformations that leave the scale form invariant.

plies that a quantitative relationship between the effect measured and the factor under examination is known; but this is not necessary. In fact it seems likely that in operational research indirect measurement will remain of extreme importance even if the connecting relationships are not known; the possibilities of measuring goodwill in terms of orders lost, or morale in terms of productivity are encouraging even though the causal connections are elusive.

One particular difficulty of measurement in the physical sciences is that, in general, it is desirable to have a form of measurement that can be applied to many different systems; only then can correlations between systems be expressed in a meaningful manner. Conversely, if measurements are to be applied to only one system they can be completely arbitrary; and this is the stage that has been reached in the majority of operational research problems— normally any system of measurement used is only invented for, and intended to apply to, the problem in hand. The desirability of eventually obtaining more universality is, however, obvious.

Psycho-physical and Subjective Measurement

It is now of interest to examine, against this background, the measurement of psycho-physical magnitudes, such as brightness, loudness, apparent length, and so on, and of other subjective magnitudes such as utility.

A noticeable difference between measurement in these fields and measurement in the field of the physical sciences is the intrusion of what may be called human variability; no two people react in exactly the same way to a given stimulus, and it is therefore obviously impossible to erect a single scale of values which can satisfactorily represent all their individual feelings. The most to be hoped for is that a scale can be chosen that will correspond to the mean reaction of the population as a whole. This scale can then be used as a basis on which to compare the effects of different stimuli, or as a "norm" against which individual idiosyncrasies may be measured.

Early work was carried out by Fechner who assumed that "just noticeable differences" corresponded to equal units of sensation; he was able to relate psychological magnitude, σ, to the magnitude of the stimulus, ϕ, by the well-known equation

$$\sigma = k \log \phi \qquad (1)$$

There is, however, some evidence that Fechner's assumption is not true for prothetic continua; that is, for magnitudes such as brightness or loudness in which excitement seems to be added to excitement as progress is made along the scale.[3] Just noticeable differences do not correspond to equal units of sensation in these continua, and, indeed, a relationship of the type

$$\sigma = k\phi^n \qquad (2)$$

will represent results at least as well, if not better, within the limits of experimental accuracy.

The implication is that a ratio scale (as distinct from the interval scale implied by Fechner's relationship) may be used for at least some psycho-physical magnitudes; since experience in the physical sciences has indicated the power of ratio scales there seems every advantage in pursuing this lead in the future.

A similar situation applies to the measurement of utility. There is an added difficulty here, of course; whereas the subjective response to, say, brightness can be tested out experimentally relatively easily, there is no method of asking for an estimate of the relative utility of £5 and £10 without mentioning the numbers 5 and 10, and this may well so bias the observer that his responses do not represent his real subjective feelings so much as a compromise between what he feels and what he thinks he ought to feel. The approach of von Neumann and Morgenstern is one attempt to overcome this problem; but the subject of an experiment on the lines they suggest is, in effect, asked not only to make assessments of utility but also of subjective probabilities, and the practical value is thus not really clear, in spite of the elegance of the approach. Other work, using more direct methods, has suggested that a ratio scale for utility may indeed be possible; [4] again, this would seem worth pursuing.

Other Aspects of Measurement in Operational Research

There are obviously many interesting implications of the above ideas, but these cannot be pursued here. In conclusion, however, it would seem pertinent to make the following three comments which refer particularly to measurement in operational research:

(a) The difficulty of combining measurements representing different aspects of a system (such as effectiveness and cost) into a single measure of overall value is well known, and is faced daily by operational research workers. The more aspects of a system that can be measured, the more difficult this combination is likely to be; and if all measurements use different types of scale, the problem will be aggravated still further. It is important not to lose sight of this when new scales are set up.

(b) Even if scales of measurement are available for all the aspects of a system in which an operational research worker is interested, there can still be an immense practical problem in obtaining data. The value of approximate methods, inequalities, taking limits, and so on, is therefore not likely to diminish in the future.

(c) There is a tendency in operational research always to examine a system in greater and greater detail, and this is often reflected in the scales of measurement that are set up. Great value has been obtained in the physical sciences, however, from building up overall measures of the system under examination; concepts of total energy, of conservation of mass, and of statistical mechanics, for example, are extremely powerful. Perhaps more use could be made of an analogous approach in operational research.

CONCLUSIONS

To sum up: Operational research is invariably concerned with the examination of systems which include human beings. Since the degree of confidence in a decision reached by operational research depends upon all relevant factors being included and measured correctly, it follows that as much attention must be paid by operational research workers to measurement in the fields of psychology and sociology, for example, as to measurement of physical qualities. Unless this is done, confidence will be reduced and the whole purpose of operational research (which is to give confidence in decisions) defeated.

REFERENCES

1. W. J. Strauss, "The nature and validity of operations-research studies, with emphasis on force composition," JORSA, 8, 675–693 (1960).
2. S. S. Stevens (ed.), Handbook of experimental psychology. John Wiley, New York.
3. S. S. Stevens, "On psychophysical law," Psycho. Rev., 64, 153–181 (1957).
4. C. W. Churchman and P. Ratoosh (eds.), Measurement: definitions and theories. John Wiley, New York.

BIBLIOGRAPHY

1. Ackoff, R. L., "The Concept and Exercise of Control in Operations Research," *Proceedings of the First International Conference on Operations Research,* Operations Research Society of America, 1957.
2. Bello, F., "How to Cope With Information," *Fortune,* September, 1960.
3. Bergmann, G., and K. W. Spence, "The Logic of Psychological Measurement," *Psychological Review,* 1944.
4. Churchman, C. W., "A Materialist Theory of Measurement," R. W. Sellers (ed.), *Philosophy for the Future,* The Macmillan Co., 1949.
5. Churchman, C. W., and P. Ratoosh (eds.), *Measurement: Definitions and Theories,* John Wiley and Sons, 1959.
6. Daniel, D. R., "Management Information Crisis," *Harvard Business Review,* September, 1961.
7. Dearden, J., "Can Management Information Be Automated?" *Harvard Business Review,* March, 1964.
8. Frisch, B. H., "Big Information Mess," *Science Digest,* September, 1965.
9. Kochen, M., *Some Problems in Information Science,* Scarecrow Press, 1965.
10. Littauer, S. B., and E. R. Bowerman, "Operations Engineering," *Management Science,* **2,** 1956.
11. Morse, G. E., "Pendulum of Management Control," *Harvard Business Review,* May, 1965.
12. Osgood, C. E., *Information Measurement,* Indiana University Press, 1965.
13. Quastler, H. (ed.), *Information Measurement,* Free Press of Glencoe, 1955.
14. Sullivan, A. M., "Management's Fight Against Technophobia," *Dun's Review,* April, 1961.
15. Thurston, P. H., "Who Should Control Information Systems?" *Harvard Business Review,* November, 1962.

Part XII.   PERT-PERT/COST

In the history of science and technology, the innovations that predominate are those involving minor adaptations and rearrangements of items from the cultural inventory. It is only rarely that something approaching a "revolution" appears on the scene. Yet when these drastic changes are carefully scrutinized, one generally finds that they too have had their roots sunk deep in the past achievements of many great minds. One would not be too rash to say that the remarkable discoveries and advances made in the field of atomic science have revolutionized the state of physics in the present century. Some do not hesitate to assert as much for PERT in the area of managerial science.

PERT is an acronym for Program Evaluation and Review Technique, a planning and control technique devised for large complex projects. Like other great "revolutionary" techniques it too had its predecessors. It is generally admitted that PERT owes much to the Critical Path Method and to the now famous Gantt Chart Method. However, as a refinement of previous methods it has effected significant changes in planning and control, so much so that some enthusiastic advocates look upon PERT as a panacea for all that ails management. A more sobering exposition would undoubtedly reveal that PERT was originally conceived not as a nostrum for management fevers but as a rationally based total system approach to the planning and control aspects of research and development projects currently in vogue.

PERT had its origins in the United States and developed in the wake of the rapid technological advances made after World War II. Weapon and support systems had by then reached such complex proportions that new techniques for managing their development, production, and installation were definitely needed. Because of the threatening aspect of international politics, the Cold War, etc., it was imperative that these systems be made operational in the shortest possible time.

Existing techniques proved unsuitable. Because of the interdependency of so many complex systems and subsystems, all surrounded by a great deal of uncertainty due to the unique nature of these never-before-attempted tasks, something new had to be developed consonant with the magnitude of the projects. That it was the Navy's Fleet Ballistic Missile program that occasioned the emergence of PERT in 1958 is a matter of historical record. Since then the proliferation of similar modified techniques has been truly phenomenal. From its original use in an astonishing Space Age project PERT has spread to many less exotic and more mundane tasks as book publishing, house building, theatrical production, marketing, and even making organizational changes.

Basically PERT is a managerial tool employing networks. The networks used are but "flow diagrams consisting of the activities and events which must be accomplished to reach the program objectives, showing their logical and planned sequences of accomplishment, interdependencies, and interrelationships."[1] The idea to be underscored is that the PERT net-

[1] PERT   FUNDAMENTALS   (Washington: PERT Orientation and Training Center, 1963), Vol. III, p. 16.

work depicts not only the many and varied components making up a system or sub-system, but also the all-important, intricate interrelationships that prevail among these. (The actual fundamentals of PERT network construction are outlined in one of the following selections.)

No doubt, the computer has had a hand in making PERT the success that it is. Although a PERT network with a hundred or so activities can be handled manually, it would be rather cumbersome and time-consuming to do so. A computer performs the same task with much greater speed and with a saving of human energy (and patience). Computers though are not essential in the use of PERT.

As this technique matures and as further experimentation and refinements occur, PERT will bring management an even more useful tool for planning and control of projects both large and small.

In the first selection David Boulanger presents a quick overall view of PERT with its network construction and network analysis. For illustrative purposes a hypothetical program, the Vehicle Armament System, is presented with its appropriate PERT network. Since the mechanics of PERT calculations are being stressed, each of the ingredients needed for network analysis, e.g., the determination of t_e, T_E, σ^2, slack time, etc., is explained briefly, its formula given, and then calculated. The real value of PERT for reevaluation and optimizing of resources is just barely touched on in the concluding section of the article.

That PERT/TIME has proved its usefulness as a planning and control device with respect to the time resource has been unmistakably shown in recent years. PERT/COST is presented by DeCoster in the second selection as a challenging new addition to management's repository of tools for optimizing project costs.

PERT/TIME was initially devised as a planning and control tool for the construction of complex weapons systems where time was of the essence. Its detailed network with the flow of activities and events all carefully mapped and with appropriate time schedules indicated represented a real breakthrough in management planning and control. With this technique various time-options can be selected for system simulation to ascertain which of the alternative options is best from the standpoint of time.

Of late a further refinement has been added to PERT/TIME. This is PERT/COST. When the optimum mix of time and cost is added to the alternative time-options, the manager can obtain time-cost totals for a realistic appraisal of the entire complex project. PERT/COST differs from conventional expense budgeting in several ways: (1) PERT/COST being activity-oriented cuts across organizational structures and accounting periods and focuses on the project work package. (2) PERT/COST uses activity time in place of volume as the variability factor.

DeCoster goes into much detail to show how a PERT/COST network can be constructed on the basic PERT/TIME framework. The project is broken down into successively smaller units, into subdivisions, work packages, tasks and subtasks, each with its dollar value, activity time, machine and personnel requirements. In all of this it is of paramount importance that the cost estimates be sound and consistent with company policy. To insure that the best cost estimates will be assigned, various approaches have been developed for this purpose: the single expected cost estimate, the combined expected cost estimate, the optimum time-cost curve, and the three separate cost estimates—each approach having its own advantages and limitations.

PERT/COST's merit lies not only in planning but also in control. Feedback data can be generated that will enable the project manager and others to compare continuously the actual cost expenditures with those previously estimated during the planning stage. And finally, though the basic problems of PERT/COST are many and formidable, still there is in it great potential to be exploited.

The article by Peter Schoderbek on PERT/COST takes up where the previous selection left off. After briefly enumerating the various values associated with PERT/COST in its planning and control phases, he confines most of his discussion to the limitations of the new technique. Among them he notes the following: (1) Padding which is related to the tendency "to play it safe." In order not to encounter a cost overrun the initial figures are inflated to take care of such a contingency. Steps, however, can be taken to discourage padding, a practice, of course, not unique to PERT/COST, and these steps are explained. (2) Changes in cost estimates made as the project develops. Either unforeseen technical difficulties arise or certain modifications are now seen as more feasible or desirable. These changes make it difficult to compare the accomplishment with the original plan since costs are for a "new" program. These changes are most liable to occur in cost-plus government contracts. (3) Initial difficulty of obtaining reliable cost estimates since PERT by its very nature deals with complex one-shot programs. (4) Cost allocations by departments for definite work packages which are often arbitrary and meaningless.

Though serious, these problems are not the only ones. Perhaps more significant is the basic problem of resistance to PERT that has lately been encountered. In the last selection Peter Schoderbek draws some sobering conclusions from a survey recently conducted to ascertain the characteristics of the PERT-using business community. He found that top management was partly to blame for the non-adoption of or resistance to this twentieth century managerial tool. Another major obstacle to PERT implementation was the lack of motivation and the quality of training of the PERT personnel. Over half of the companies using PERT indicated that this was *the* major problem. It seems that most formal training programs are structured toward an understanding of the technical aspects and neglect almost completely the development of appropriate interest and motivation.

No matter how good a tool is, its potential will never be realized unless it is used. Since for all practical purposes "resistance to change" is the one rather generalized incapacitating force standing in the way of either PERT adoption or full implementation, the author then reviews and illustrates with examples from his survey some of the findings of social scientists on this subject. No one should accept a simplistic unicausal explanation of this phenomenon. No single factor will infallibly and of itself always hinder change. There is an interplay of factors, a piling-up effect that will determine whether or not acceptance or rejection of change will be the rule of the day.

Four conditions affecting change are singled out for discussion. (1) Attitudes favorable or unfavorable to change. Though change, even rapid change, seems to be the dominating spirit of the times, especially of technological society, yet we tend to resist changes that appear to threaten basic securities, that we do not understand, and that we are coerced to accept. (2) Vested interests or differential outlook. One must not naively assume that the outlook of the innovators will necessarily be replicated in the rank-and-file. Members of different groups may find themselves threatened in different ways by the proposed change. (3) Felt-needs. Unless needs are felt, they remain merely speculative and will have little or no effect in motivating the individual to accept change. Men must be made to feel that they actually need PERT in their own work. Since the needs of different groups are different, different approaches in "selling" PERT will be needed. Managers must themselves be conversant with both the merits *and* limitations of PERT if they expect to do a good "selling" job. (4) Interests imply an even greater practical appreciation than do felt-needs. We are often aware of what we actually need, yet unless we are interested in doing something about it, the need will go unfulfilled. Creat-ing this interest is no easy task. However, there are techniques available. Self-involvement and participation in matters of concern can help to create interest. But in the last analysis the fate of PERT rests in the hands of management!

39. PROGRAM EVALUATION AND REVIEW TECHNIQUE [1]

DAVID G. BOULANGER [2]

Since the first management "principles" were introduced, most planning and control methods have been predicated on using historical data. Early shop practitioners sought the most efficient utilization of time by employing timestudy and task-setting methods based on stopwatch measurement of "past" processes that were physical and finite in character. Few useful techniques have been offered facilitating forward planning of management activities for which empirical information was not available.

Current industrial activities, however, can be summarized as heavily oriented toward research and development. A "one best way" of planning and pursuing R&D projects in terms of most efficient use of time presents some intangibles that cannot conveniently be measured. This growing condition, particularly in defense industries, has prompted the development of a prognostic management planning control method called Program Evaluation and Review Technique, or PERT.[3] This article intends to briefly present the idea of the PERT method in a manner permitting the reader to ascertain its potential usefulness. . . .

The PERT technique was developed as a method of planning and controlling the complex Polaris Fleet Ballistic Missile Program for Special Projects Office (SP) of Bureau of Ordnance, U.S. Navy. The team consisted of members from SP, the contractor organization, and Booz, Allen and Hamilton, Chicago.[4]

Over-all, PERT appears to be a manifestation of the program concept of management with emphasis on "management by exception," in that potentially troublesome areas in R&D programs can be spotted and action taken to prevent their occurrence.

PERT, as a dynamic program tool, uses linear programming and statistical probability concepts to plan and control series and parallel tasks which appear only remotely interrelated. Many tasks involve extensive research and development which itself is difficult to schedule, least of all to find a "one best way" of doing it. PERT's objective is to determine the optimum way by which to maximize the attainment, in time, of some predetermined objective that is preceded by a number of constraints—hence its linear programming feature. A measure of the degree of risk is predicted in probabilistic terms to foretell the reasonableness of accomplishment on scheduled time—hence its statistical probability feature.

PROGRAM NETWORK DEVELOPMENT

The bar chart, presumably derived from Gantt and still widely used, serves to plan the occurrence of entire phases of tasks in series and parallel groups over a time period. Figure 1 illustrates a sample.

An outgrowth of the simple bar chart, called a "milestone chart," indicates significant event accomplishments as illustrated in Figure 2.

Neither technique ties together interdependencies between tasks and significant events. Series and parallel paths should indicate the interrelationship constraints between events and tasks as shown by the arrows in Figure 3.

A network *event* describes a milestone, or checkpoint. An event does not symbolize the performance of work, but represents the point in time in which the event is accomplished. Each event is numbered for identification.

[1] From *Advanced Management* (July–August, 1961), pp. 8–12. Reprinted by permission of *Advanced Management Journal*.

[2] General Electric Company.

[3] Various acronyms are coined (*e.g.*, PEP, PET, etc.) to describe modifications from the PERT method described here.

[4] See Malcolm, D. G., J. H. Roseboom, C. E. Clark, and W. Fazar. "Application of a Technique for Research and Development Program Evaluation," *Journal of Operations Research*, Vol. 7, No. 5 (September–October, 1959), pp. 646–669.

Arrows connecting events are *activities,* and represent performance of work necessary to accomplish an event. No event is considered accomplished until all work represented by arrows leading to it has been completed. Further, no work can commence on a succeeding event until the preceding event is completed.

If we include in Figure 3 the estimated weeks to accomplish each activity, *e.g.,* $\xrightarrow{\quad 3 \quad}$, the earliest time objective Event 11 above can be accomplished is the sum of the longest path leading to it. This is the *critical path,* and is identified by the heavy lines connecting Events 2, 6, 10, and 11 totaling 17 weeks. The critical path contains the

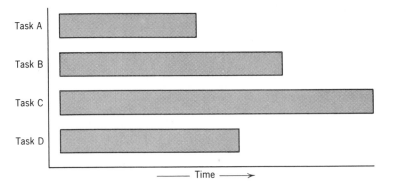

FIG. 1. Program bar chart.

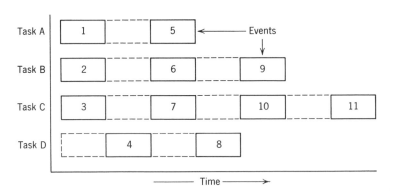

FIG. 2. Program milestone chart.

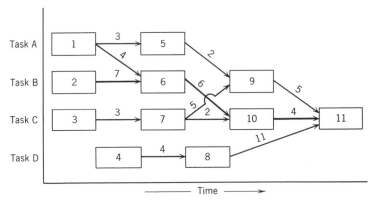

FIG. 3. PERT network.

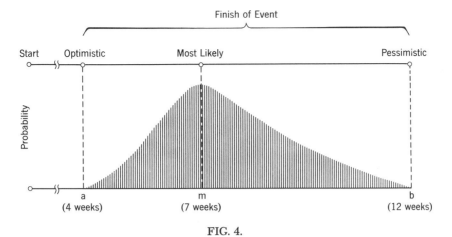

FIG. 4.

most significant *and* limiting events retarding program completion in less than 17 weeks.

But the time required to complete a future task is more realistically stated in terms of a likelihood rather than a positive assurance. To apply this likelihood in a probabilistic sense, three time estimates are stated as a future *range of time* in which an activity may be accomplished. The three time estimates are called *optimistic, most likely,* and *pessimistic.* They serve as points on a distribution curve whose mode is the most likely, and the extremes (optimistic and pessimistic) whose spread corresponds to the probability distribution of time involved to perform the activity. It is assumed there would be relatively little chance (*e.g.,* 1 out of 100) the activity would be accomplished *outside* the optimistic or pessimistic time estimate range. Figure 4 illustrates the estimating time distribution for completing an activity some time in the future.

From the three estimates (a, m, b above), a statistical elapsed time (t_e) can be derived by solving $t_e = \dfrac{a + 4(m) + b}{6}$ for each activity.[5] Following this, a statistical variance (σ^2) can be derived by solving $\sigma^2 = \left(\dfrac{b - a}{6}\right)^2$ for each activity.[6] Variance may be descriptive of uncertainty associated with the three time estimate interval. A large variance implies

[5] The elapsed time formula is based on the assumption that the probability density of the beta distribution $f(t) = K(t - a)\alpha(b - t)\gamma$ is an adequate model of the distribution of an activity time.

[6] The statistical variance formula assumes the standard deviation as $\frac{1}{6}(b - a)$.

greater uncertainty in an event's accomplishment and *vice versa,* depending on whether the optimistic and pessimistic estimates are wide or close together. This facilitates evaluating risks in a program network, and using trade-offs in time and resources to minimize risk and maximize more efficient use of "factors of production."

PROGRAM NETWORK ANALYSES

The analytical value derived from any PERT network depends on the configuration and content of the network. Every network should contain events which, to the program team's best knowledge, serve to significantly constrain the achievement of the end objective event. Next, events are interconnected with "activities" to illustrate their flow and interdependencies. After the network of events and activities is defined, three time estimates for each activity are made.

To illustrate network development and analyses, a hypothetical R&D program is assumed specifying contract completion 11 months (47 weeks) after order. Fixed resources are allocated to the program: *e.g.,* 40-hour work week, given personnel, budgeted money, *etc.* Management now is interested in:

1. What's the one best way of conducting effort toward completion?
2. What's the earliest expected time we can complete the program?
3. What are our chances of completing within the contract limitations of 47 weeks?

The network in Figure 5 is a simplified analogue of our plan to develop a "vehicle

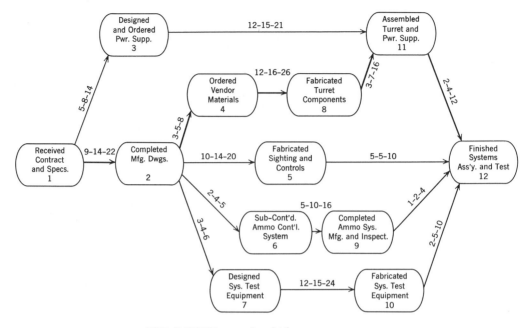

FIG. 5. PERT network vehicle armament system.

armament system." Events are described with a verb in the past tense to indicate their end accomplishment at a fixed point in time.

The analysis of the network is next performed and explained below.

Column A. Each event is listed beginning with objective event back to the start event.

Column B. The preceding event(s) is (are) listed beside each event. Hence, there is a succeeding and preceding event for each activity.

Column C. Statistical elapsed time (t_e) for each activity is found by substituting optimistic, most likely, pessimistic estimates for a, m, b and solving $t_e = \dfrac{a + 4(m) + b}{6}$.

Column D. Variance (σ^2) for each activity is found by substituting optimistic and pessimistic estimates for a and b and solving

$$\sigma^2 = \left(\frac{b - a}{6}\right)^2.$$

PERT Analyses

A Event	B Pre. Ev.	C t_e	D σ^2	E T_E	F T_L	G $T_L - T_E$	H T_S	I P_R	J $T_L - T_E$	K Event
12	11	5.0	2.78	49.5	49.5	0.0	47.0	.28	0.0	2
	5	5.8	.69						0.0	4
	9	2.2	.25						0.0	8
	10	5.3	1.78						0.0	11
11	8	7.8	4.70	44.5	44.5	0.0			0.0	12
	3	15.5	2.25							
8	4	17.0	5.44	36.7	36.7	0.0			9.5	7
4	2	5.2	.69	19.7	19.7	0.0			9.5	10
5	2	14.3	2.78	28.8	43.7	14.9			14.9	5
9	6	10.2	3.36	28.5	47.3	18.8			18.8	6
6	2	3.8	.25	18.3	37.1	18.8			18.8	9
10	7	16.0	4.00	34.7	44.2	9.5			20.5	3
7	2	4.2	.25	18.7	28.2	9.5				
3	1	8.5	2.25	8.5	29.0	20.5				
2	1	14.5	4.70	14.5	14.5	0.0				
1	—	—	—	—	—	—				

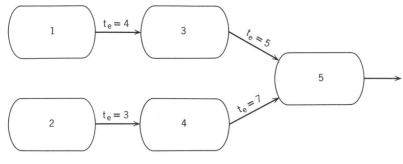

FIG. 6.

Column E. Earliest expected time (T_E) of accomplishment for each *event* is found by adding the elapsed time (t_e) of each activity to cumulative total elapsed times through the preceding event, staying within a single path working from "start to finish." When more than one activity leads to an event, that activity whose elapsed time (t_e) gives the greatest sum up to that event is chosen as the expected time for that event. For example, the earliest expected time to *accomplish* Event 5 below is 10 weeks. (See Figure 6.)

Column F. Latest Time (T_L) for each event is found by first fixing the earliest time of the objective event as its latest time. Next, the sum of the elapsed times (t_e) in Column C (*i.e.*, 5.0 weeks) for the activities lying between the given event and the objective event is subtracted from the earliest time of the objective event. When more than one activity leads from an event, the activity which gives the *least* sum through that event is selected.

Some events may be completed later than the expected time and have no effect on meeting the objective event. Knowledge of "slack" time in a network (*i.e.*, how much and where located) is of interest in determining program effects of "trade-offs" in resources from high-slack to low-slack areas.

Since linear programming theory says "negative slack" is not admissible (*i.e.*, not technically feasible at the objective event assuming fixed resources), we commence from an objective viewpoint to compute "positive" (or non-negative) slack. In spite of theory, a latest time derived from a fixed contractual date *less* than earliest expected time must be recognized to determine how much network "compression" is necessary to meet a scheduled date with reasonable assurance. The theory simply recognizes time is not reversible; therefore, to alle-

viate "negative" slack one must either extend contractual dates or employ added resources like overtime, more funds, personnel, *etc.* We assume in our analyses that resources are fixed at inception of program to maintain profit potentials.

Column G. Slack time for each event is found by subtracting Expected Time from Latest Time ($T_L - T_E$). The purpose is 1) to locate the critical path in the network designated here by events having zero slack and 2) to determine next-most-critical paths, as well as those events having substantial slack.

The critical path contains events most apt to be troublesome technically or administratively, and are danger points causing potential over-all schedule slippage. Next-most-critical path(s) is (are) found by substituting next higher slack event(s) into a second single path from start to finish. For example, the second-most-critical path is found by including Events 7 and 10 (whose slacks of 9.5 weeks are the next-higher slack event over the critical path events) to give a new critical path described as Events 1, 2, 7, 10, 12. Next-most-critical paths should be observed because their criticalness may be nearly as severe as the original critical path.

By locating events having substantial slack time, it becomes possible to effect trade-offs in resources to those events having little or zero slack. For example, Events 6 and 9 each have 18.8 weeks slack, meaning their expected time of completion could be intentionally delayed 18.8 weeks without causing slippage in over-all program schedule. A point of optimization in network development is approached when the greatest possible number of events have the smallest possible range in slack from the lowest to highest slack value.

Column H. Schedule Time (T_S) is the contractual date of completion. A scheduled time may also exist for major events within a network, which later facilitates evaluating the range of risks throughout a program plan.

Column I. Probability (P_R) of meeting a scheduled time is calculated to determine feasibility of program accomplishment under the constraints in the network. Generally, probability values between .25 and .60 indicate an acceptable range to proceed with a program as depicted in the network. Probability values less than .25 assume the schedule time, T_S, cannot reasonably be met with the given resources. Values higher than .60 may indicate excess resources "built in" the network, and may warrant consideration for their use elsewhere. Probabilities need not be computed where schedule time (T_S) and expected time (T_E) are equal, as this assumes .5 or 50 per cent probability of completing on schedule.

Probability of events is computed as follows:

1. Solve for each event which has a schedule time (in our example, the objective event):

$$\frac{T_S - T_E}{\sigma_{\Sigma\sigma^{2}*}} = \frac{47.0 - 49.5}{\sqrt{18.31}} = \frac{-2.5}{4.279} = -.584$$

2. Refer answer to Area Under the Normal Curve Table and compute probability P_R.

The value $-.584$ refers to $-.584$ standard deviations from the mean under a normal curve. Referring to a normal curve table, we find its corresponding per cent of area under the normal curve to be about $-.21904$. Thinking of area under the normal curve and probability as synonymous, we subtract $-.21904$ from .50000 (the mean of a normal curve) to derive a probability of .28096, or 28 per cent. Explained, there is a 28 per cent chance of meeting the schedule time of 47.0 weeks; hence it may be "acceptable" to proceed with the program under plans and resources factored in the network. Any standard of "acceptability" in probability terms should be flexible according to the importance of a program and the consequences if schedule time should not be

* Read as "standard deviation of the sum of the variances." In our example, this is solved by: 1) finding the sum of variances ($\Sigma\sigma^2$) for the events in the Critical Path, that is, $4.70 + .69 + 5.44 + 4.70 + 2.78 = 18.31$; 2) finding the square root of $18.31 = 4.279$. Probability for *any* event in a network can be computed if a T_S and T_E value is known, and by finding that event within a single network path.

met. Therefore, any probability value attached to a program plan should be viewed and used cautiously.

Diagrammatically, 28 per cent probability is roughly represented by the shaded area under the normal curve below (Figure 7).

Columns J and K. Under Column J is the ascending order of slack, and under Column K their corresponding event numbers. This brings out the Critical Path as 0.0 slack events, next-most critical path(s), and those events or paths with high slack from which resources and time may be deployed to events having zero or low slack. This facilitates locating the "one best way" of reaching the objective event in relation to time.

REEVALUATION AND OPTIMIZATION

A potential value from PERT at inception of an R&D program is the opportunity it affords to introduce revised constraints into the plan and then simulate its outcome. If repeated, the optimum network can be sought, its troublesome areas located, and various tasks set under optimum conditions before time, cost, and performance were expended. Computer programs are available to expedite this, but manual methods are economical for networks up to 200 events depending on complexity of event interrelationships. Various schedules and performance reporting formats can be developed from the analyses for team use and management analysis.

Two advantages from PERT are 1) the exacting communications it offers to participants in a program and 2) its use as a planning foundation to support bid proposals. Each participant can see his relative position and understand the timing and relationship of his responsibilities to other participants on the program team. Often the intangibles and assumptions that plague accurate bid proposals are brought out when supported with a PERT network and analyses.

USING PERT FOR RESOURCES PLANNING, COST ANALYSES [7]

Considerable study is reported with PERT applied to resources (manpower and facilities) planning. Introducing a second variable to

[7] Notes from American Management Association Meeting, Saranac Lake, New York, March 27–29, 1961.

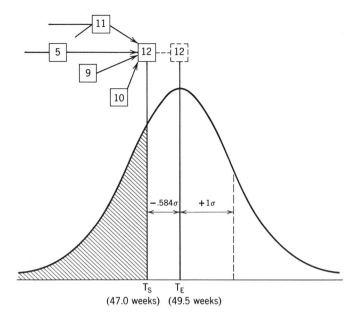

FIG. 7.

create a simultaneous two-dimensional model whose objective functions are to be optimized —while their preceding constraints are being manipulated (at the same time satisfying various restrictions placed on potential solution)— will be more difficult to perform, and probably involve more elaborate procedures.

Some work is reported with PERT applied to cost analyses of a program (presumably assuming a three- or N-dimensional model with variables of time, resources, cost, *et al.*). It appears the object would be something analogous to predetermining that point on an average total cost curve where marginal cost intersects marginal revenue—hence, maximization of profits. Some suggestions have been offered relative to the "assumed" linearity between time and cost, in the duration of a program, but this needs clarifying before concrete methods of planning costs by PERT can be formulated.

40. PERT/COST—THE CHALLENGE

Don T. DeCoster [*]

Each day that passes sees the growth of new management planning and control tools. Many of these new tools leave the accountant with the unhappy feeling that he should be participating in their use but that he lacks the orientation for active involvement. The desire of the accountant to become involved with these tools is evident from the growth of "management planning and control" chapters in textbooks and the numerous articles dealing with the managerial aspects of accounting output.

One of the newest tools, if evidenced by current publications, is Program Evaluation and Review Technique (PERT). Recently, there have been many discussions, publications, and applications of this technique. PERT's acceptance has been widespread. The accountant must become involved with PERT if he accepts the challenge of Norton Bedford that "the accounting profession has the potential to become one of the great professions if it will accept all phases of measurement and communication of economic data as within its province." [1]

The principal motivating factor in PERT development has been the growth of the concept of systems management within the military services. With programs of unprecedented size, complexity, and breadth, an integrating device has become mandatory. In addition, time is of the essence in weapons system design and development. PERT/Time has been a powerful tool in the kit of managers for planning, coordinating, and integrating these weapon systems.

The culmination of PERT/Time is the network. This network is a pictorial representation of the events and activities that lead to completion of the end objectives. The events represent the beginning and/or ending of activities. An *event* is a specific accomplishment, or milestone. The *activities* represent things that must be done in going from one event to another. The activity is the time-consuming task. The activities are related to their order of precedence in accomplishing the events. The end result is a network depicting a well-thought-out plan. After the flow of activities and events is mapped, schedule timing can be superimposed. When completion times are included on the activities, the critical path (longest time path) can be determined.

At this point the manager has a tool which needs no further justification. The network presents a clear picture of all the activities and events that must be accomplished before the end objective can be attained. The individuals with responsibility for accomplishment will have discussed all of the relationships, potential drawbacks, and completeness of the plan. When times are imposed upon the plan, the problems of a timely completion are apparent. The activities affecting a timely completion and the schedule's effect on workloads are laid bare for scrutiny. When actual times become available, the updated estimates provide a dynamic control tool to anticipate adverse results. There can be little question that PERT/Time is a tool which, when applied with common sense and vigor, represents a "breakthrough" in management planning and control of the valuable resource of time.

TIME-COST MIX

PERT/Cost is, in reality, an expansion of PERT/Time. With times indicated on the network, it becomes possible to consider alternative plans of action. As the network is being developed, time-options are presented which can be considered. Techniques of system simulation can be employed to ensure that the

SOURCE: *Management Services* (July–August, 1965), pp. 13–18. Reprinted by permission of *Management Services*.

[*] Associate Professor of Accounting, University of Washington.

[1] John L. Carey, *The Accounting Profession: Where Is It Headed?* (New York, American Institute of CPAs, 1962), p. 94.

activities and events will lead to the best climax. The next logical step, with time-options available, is to obtain the optimum mix of time and cost. This has led to the attempt to assign costs to the activities on the network. An additional advantage when costs have been assigned to the network for time-cost options is that they can be summed for total cost planning and control.

The development of a system for cost accumulation synchronized with the PERT/Time network must be founded upon objectives consistent with the responsibility of management. In program management, the manager is faced with a twofold job. He is charged with the financial planning and control of his firm's resources, while at the same time he is committed to delivery of the end items with a minimum of cost incurrence to the customer.

This was recognized by the developers of PERT/Cost, NASA and the Department of Defense, when they visualized it as a three-part system.[2] Basic PERT/Cost is intended to assist the project managers by assigning costs to the working levels in the detail needed for planning schedules and costs, evaluating schedule and cost performance, and predicting and controlling costs during the operating phase of the program. In addition, there are two supplemental procedures. The Time-Cost Option Procedure displays alternative Time-Cost plans for accomplishing project objectives. The Resource Allocation Procedure determines the lowest cost allocation of resources among individual project tasks to meet the specified project duration. The basic system is to provide total financial planning and control by functional responsibility, while the two supplements are to achieve minimum cost incurrence.

The concept of cost predetermination for planning and control is not new to the accountant. The entire function of budgeting is predicated upon predetermination. Comprehensive budgeting relates income budgets, covering revenues and expenses, to the financial goals of the firm. The expense budgets lead to financial planning and control via projected income, while at the same time the flexible budget and the expense forecasts serve as tools for decision making by relating costs to volume.

[2] *DOD and NASA Guide: PERT/Cost.* Published by the Office of the Secretary of Defense and the National Aeronautics and Space Administration, June 1962.

PERT/Cost estimates are a new way of looking at the expense budgets. If properly conceived, they can become an integral part of the comprehensive budget program. Yet they differ from conventional expense budgeting in certain respects. From the financial planning and control viewpoint, the PERT/Cost estimates are not concerned with accounting periods. PERT/Cost is activity oriented. There is a cutting across of organizational structures and time periods to define "things to be accomplished." The focal point of cost accumulation shifts from the department to the project work package. The annual budget is bypassed to encompass an end item accomplishment. From the detailed decision-making viewpoint, where the flexible budget normally uses volume as the factor of variability, PERT/Cost attempts to use activity time. These two differences will now be examined in more detail.

COST FRAMEWORK

The establishment of a PERT/Cost system begins by developing a framework for gathering cost data and preparing the schedule for all activity levels. The project is defined, then broken down into end item subdivisions, and then into work packages which are assignable to front-line supervision. The integration of the work packages is accomplished through the conventional PERT/Time network. When the interrelationships and time paths have been plotted, the responsible operating and managerial personnel develop cost estimates for each work package.

It is important that both cost and time be planned and controlled from a common framework. From such a framework, the managers can obtain an accurate picture of progress and at the same time appraise realistically the consequences of alternative courses of action. The PERT/Time network is this common framework. This imposes upon the network developers the responsibility of carefully defining the activities so that they can represent cost centers as well as the areas of work effort.

The identification of the project objectives in terms of end items is the starting point for network design to be used with PERT/Cost. By using a top-down approach in the development of the network, the total project is fully planned and all components of the plan are included. Standard units for the breakdown of

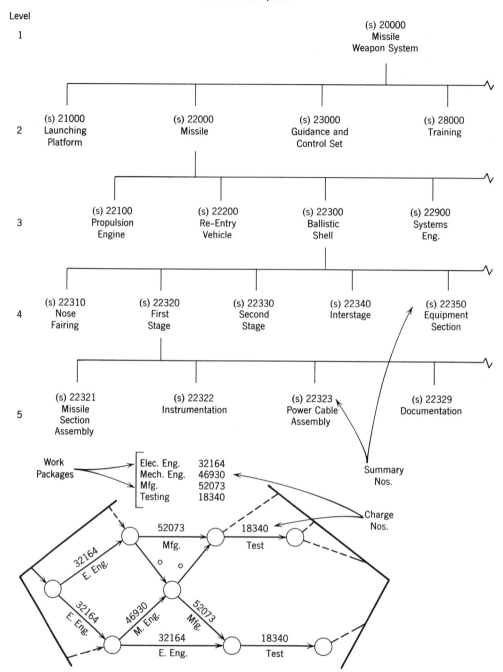

Simplified Example of a Work Breakdown Structure and Account Code Structure

work below the project level are system, sub-system, task, and subtasks. The work break-down continues to successively lower levels until the size, complexity, and dollar value of each level is a workable planning and control unit. These subdivisions are end item sub-divisions representing horizontal segments of the total project. The final step would be to divide each of these end item subdivisions into the tasks that must be done to complete them; i.e., design, manufacturing, testing, and so forth. This concept is demonstrated in the illustration [3] on this page. It is this project work breakdown that serves as the input data to the network.

[3] *Ibid.*, p. 28.

The theoretical optimum level of cost accumulation would be the functional level of each of the end item subdivisions. For example, a cost account would be established for mechanical engineering of the instrumentation, one for manufacturing, and one for testing. The PERT/Cost estimates would then be made for manpower, material, and overhead charges for each of these work packages. It is obvious that a cost accounting system broken down into such intricate detail would comprise numerous accounts. The pragmatic number of account subdivisions will naturally depend upon the detail needed for planning and control, the dollar value of the subdivisions, the activity time on the network, and the machine and personnel capacity available. A practical compromise is often necessary.

PERT/COST COST DEVELOPMENT

Once the network has been established, based upon the project work breakdown, costs can be estimated. If the breakdown has been made satisfactorily, it will serve as both an estimating and actual cost accumulation vehicle. The proper implementation of PERT/Cost, like budgeting, must rest upon active participation by the responsible executives. This was recognized by the NASA/DOD PERT/Cost Guide when it was recommended that the operating and management personnel develop the cost estimates for each work package.[4] As with budgeting, any accounting work during the estimation period would be of coordinating nature.

The development of the cost estimates must rest upon a sound philosophical basis consistent with management needs. Presently there are four approaches to developing the cost estimates:

1. A single cost estimate of expected actual cost

2. Three cost estimates combined by formula into expected cost

3. Optimum time-cost curves (used in construction industries and by NASA/DOD Resource Allocation Procedure Supplement)

4. Three separate cost estimates (used in the NASA/DOD Time-Cost Option Procedure Supplement)

Each of these theories of PERT/Cost estimating has as its goal the assigning of the

[4] *Ibid.*, pp. 109–113.

best cost estimates possible to the network. Yet each offers the manager separate, distinct planning capabilities.

A single cost estimate of expected actual cost is based upon the summation of the cost elements. These estimates are first made by determining the manpower, material, and other resources required to complete each work package. The estimates for the direct costs applicable to the network activities are expressed in terms of expected dollar expenditures. Indirect costs may then be allocated to the individual work package or added to the total cost of the project.

The three-cost-estimate approach has as its goal the determination of the "expected cost." The advantage of the three cost estimate over the single cost estimate is that the result is subject to probability analysis. The formula combines an optimistic, most likely, and pessimistic cost estimate. The mean cost for each activity is calculated by the formula:

$$C_e = \frac{C_P + 4C_L + C_O}{6}$$

where C_P is the pessimistic estimate, C_L is the most likely cost, and C_O the optimistic estimate. The standard deviation of the cost distribution can insert probability into the analysis. With this expected cost, the manager cannot necessarily assume that he has the optimum cost-time mix. However, if the cost estimates are realistic, the probabilities of achieving the expected cost can be used for project negotiations.

A third approach to cost estimates is the optimum time-cost curve concept. This is differential costing with time as the factor of variability. The intention of this approach is to optimize time and costs by using optimum estimated costs. It assumes there is a direct relationship between time and costs on any activity. This relationship can be expressed by a continuous curve. If a cost curve can be developed similar to Figure A, many insights can be gained. Network schedules can be modified to obtain the lowest cost commensurate with the customer's delivery desires. Other questions can also be anticipated—questions such as: How long will completion take with a fixed budget? What will the costs be to complete the project within a given time period? In theory this concept is undoubtedly superior to either the one or three formula estimates, but without complete his-

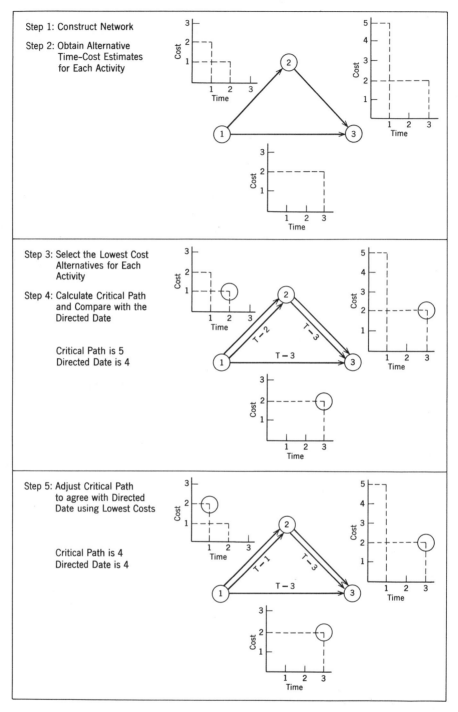

A Summary of the Resource Allocation Procedure. In the Resource Allocation Procedure, we can determine how to accomplish a project by a specified date at minimum
cost. The critical path here is the path from Event 1 to Event 2, and from Event 2 to
Event 3 since this will require five days at absolute minimum costs. But the Directed
Data for completing the project is four days from its beginning. Thus, from the time-
cost chart, we find that we can cut the time between Events 1 and 2 to one day, but
we double the cost of this activity. Since shortening the time of the second step in the
critical path would cost more, however, we choose to reduce time of the first step to
one day.

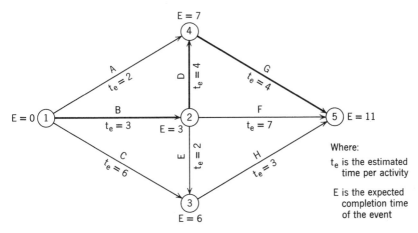

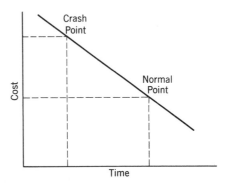

An Illustration of Normal-Crash Procedure. The critical path of this network is eleven days. To accelerate the program one day, activities B, G or D must be condensed one day. Based upon cost curves computed on a normal-crash basis, the table of costs on page 397 is available.

torical cost data the development of this curve is impractical.

Because the development of continuous time-cost curves for all activities is extremely difficult, if not practically impossible, the Resource Allocation Supplement to PERT/Cost was developed. This supplement is a variation of continuous time-cost curves which can be used in planning a small group of *significant* activities representing only a minor portion of the over-all project. This method is also based upon the concept that activities are subject to time-cost tradeoffs. The steps of this procedure are shown in the diagrams: "A Summary of the Resource Allocation Procedure."

Another alternate to overcome the practical problem of the continuous cost curve is a linear function based upon two time-cost relationships. The cost and time expenditures are forecast for two conditions: normal and crash.

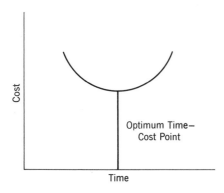

FIG. A.

FIG. B.

The normal point is the minimum activity cost and the corresponding time. The crash point is defined as the minimum possible time to perform the activity and the related cost. A linear function is assumed to exist between these points. Figure B shows this graphically. This method is similar to the high-low point method of fixed and variable cost determination and suffers from the same type of criticism.[5] The problems of realistic estimates, discretionary costs, stair-stepped cost functions, incorrect correlation between time and cost, and external factors are continually present. It is justifiable due to its relative simplicity when the element of nonpredictable error can be permitted. A simplified, but typical usage is shown in the illustration of normal-crash procedure.

[5] Glenn Welsch, *Budgeting: Profit Planning and Control* (Englewood Cliffs, N.J., Prentice-Hall, Inc., 1957), pp. 173–174.

The NASA/DOD PERT/Cost Guide presents a time-cost option (called the Time-Cost Option Procedure Supplement) based upon three time estimates. The single estimate of expected cost and the three-cost-estimate formula methods do not indicate whether there may be a substantially more efficient alternative plan. The continuous cost curve concept provides these data,[6] but requires considerable sophistication in cost analysis, or else, considerable supposition. The time-cost supplement recognizes that a single estimate will normally be used for contract proposals and that additional data are needed to provide information as to the amount of time that might be saved by spending more money or the amount of money that could be saved by extending the contract time. The three time estimates used are:

The Most Efficient Plan. This is the network plan that will meet the technical requirements of the project utilizing the most efficient use of present resources. This is the plan that would be chosen without budget and time constraints.

The Directed Date Plan. This is the network plan developed to meet the technical requirements of the project by the specified completion date.

The Shortest Time Plan. This is the network plan that will meet the technical requirements of the project in the shortest possible time.

Since the desired plan is the most efficient plan, any study should begin there. This most efficient plan must then be modified to achieve the project's objectives by the specified date. The most efficient plan when altered to attain the desired delivery date becomes the directed date plan. The directed date plan is then revised to obtain the shortest time plan. The work packages that have not changed in evolving the alternate plans will utilize cost estimates for the most efficient plan. New cost estimates will be necessary only on those work packages that are expected to increase or decrease because of the modifications. With three estimates on these work packages, the customer is apprised of the impact of his decisions during negotiations. Once the customer has made his decision, the appropriate cost estimate can be assigned to the network.

These cost estimating techniques represent the current approaches to computing forecasted

[6] See Figure A.

costs. When coupled with a sound approach to determining the project work breakdown, forward planning is definitely facilitated. To this point PERT/Cost is a planning tool, but the loop between planning and control is not closed. For control there must be comparisons of actual cost expenditures with those estimated during the planning stage. The accountant must play an active role when the loop is closed between the planning and control phases. The generation of feedback data consistent with the planning stage calls for a chart of accounts correlated to the PERT network.

THE PERT/COST CHALLENGE

The accountant is charged by management and society with providing financial information for all levels of decision making. If the accountant is to serve the managers effectively, he will have to broaden his influence beyond the confines of historical data to include all areas of the firm and the future. PERT/Cost offers him one challenge in this direction. It can be seen that if PERT/Cost can be coordinated with PERT/Time, the manager has an excellent tool for project planning and control. In addition to financial reporting both on the total cost level and the individual manager's level, it offers distinct opportunities for decision making during both the planning and control phases.

The discussions here might lead one to believe that PERT/Cost offers no problems. Unfortunately, this is not the case. Despite the potential there are basic problems. An enumeration of some of these problems would include:

1. PERT/Cost for decision making in optimizing costs requires a sophistication of cost analysis that is not possessed by some firms.

2. There is a lack of historical information for assigning costs to networks since the concept is new.

3. There is difficulty in making project costs compatible with fiscal practices.

4. The problems of overhead charges, joint costs, and incompatibility of the organizational cost flow with the functional flow are numerous.

5. There is a problem of reconciling the "jobs" that are using PERT/Cost with those that aren't for fiscal reporting.

Activity	Normal Days	Normal Cost	Crash Days	Crash Cost	Acceleration Cost per Day
A	2	80	1	130	50
B	3	70	1	190	60
C	6	110	5	135	25
D	4	60	3	100	40
E	2	90	1	100	10
F	7	85	6	115	30
G	4	105	3	175	70
H	3	50	2	70	20
Totals		650		1015	

Since Activity D costs $40 to accelerate whereas Activity G costs $70 and Activity B, $120, accelerating Activity D is least expensive. The total cost of completing the program in ten days is $690 ($650 + $40). By compressing the project one day, Activity F enters the critical path. To accelerate the program to nine days the following activities could be reduced: G and F at a total cost of $100 or B at a cost of $60. Therefore, for the reduction to nine days the cost would be $750 ($650 + $40 + $60).

6. The personnel and machine capabilities are not always available.

7. Cost accumulation for financial stewardship reports can conflict with the cost centers for PERT/Cost and can therefore create redundant systems.

8. The conversion of project oriented costs to mesh with annual budget concepts requires additional analysis.

If the problems associated with PERT/Cost can be resolved, PERT with COST could be considered a major breakthrough as was PERT with TIME. The majority of the potential problem areas with PERT/Cost lie in the controller's department. These difficulties present a very real challenge to the controller. PERT/Cost is putting the adaptability of the accountant to the test.

41. PERT/COST: ITS VALUES

AND LIMITATIONS

Peter P. Schoderbek *

WHAT PERT IS

PERT (Program Evaluation and Review Technique) is a method for planning, controlling, and monitoring the progress of complex projects. The emphasis is on time scheduling. A project is broken down into its component steps. These steps are represented graphically in the form of a network showing the dependencies among them. The times required to complete each step are estimated and potential bottleneck steps are identified. Then the planner is in a position to reassign manpower and resources to speed up the steps that might cause the project to fall behind schedule.

PERT, originated to coordinate the work of a large number of subcontractors engaged in the development of the Navy's Polaris missile, is credited with having cut two years off the time span of that project. Because PERT incorporates a method for estimating the time it will take to do something that has not been done before—and for which, therefore, no time standards exist—it is particularly useful in the scheduling of research and development projects. It has been widely applied in the space and defense industries.

PERT works this way:

All the individual tasks required to complete a given project must be identified and put down in a network. A network is composed of events and activities. An event represents a specific project accomplishment at a particular point in time. An activity represents the actions required to progress from one event to another.

Events and activities are sequenced on a network diagram. Activities are represented by

SOURCE: *Management Services* (January–February, 1966), pp. 29–34. Reprinted by permission of *Management Services*.

* Assistant Professor of Management, University of Iowa.

arrows connecting two events. The direction of the arrow shows which event must precede the other. For example, on the sample network shown on page 399, Events 2 and 3 both precede Event 4; Events 6, 7, 9, and 10 must precede Event 11; and Events 8, 11, and 12 must precede Event 13.

Sequencing must follow a rigorous set of rules. No successor event can be considered completed until all of its predecessor events have been completed. No "looping" is allowed; that is, no successor event can be a predecessor of one of its predecessors.

Time estimates are made for each activity on the network. Because completion times are assumed to be uncertain, three time estimates are sometimes made for each activity—optimistic, pessimistic, and most likely—and the expected time is calculated from these by means of a probability formula.

Once expected activity times are recorded on the network, it is easy to see the critical path (marked in color on the illustration). The critical path is the sequence of events that will require the greatest expected time to accomplish. Activities not on the critical path have slack time, which means that it would be safe to delay them somewhat by shifting resources from them to critical activities.

On a research project, for example, manpower can be shifted from Activities 1–3 and 3–4 to speed up Activities 1–2 and 2–4. Similar slack in Activities 5–7, 7–10, and 10–11 can be utilized to shorten the critical path 5–8, 8–12, and 12–13.

WHAT PERT/COST IS

PERT/Cost is an extension of PERT for planning, monitoring, and controlling the cost progress as well as the time progress of a project. Cost classifications are based upon project work breakdowns so that costs can be

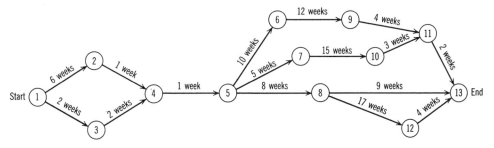

Sample PERT Network

identified with the activities on the PERT network. The breakdowns serve as vehicles for both estimating and accumulating costs. Thus the PERT network, with costs tied to its activities, can be used for planning and performance evaluation in terms of both costs and time.

In addition, PERT/Cost provides a method of comparing the costs of alternative courses of action. The cost penalty as well as the time benefit of transferring resources to the critical path can be determined. And the lowest-cost allocation of resources among individual activities can be determined—for comparison with the least-time allocation. PERT/Cost and its application were described in more detail in an earlier issue of *Management Services* (see *Management Services,* May–June, 1964, p. 13).

PERT, network diagraming, critical path scheduling, and similar planning and control techniques have proved highly useful in the scheduling and controlling of the time elements of large projects. Only recently, however, has a system been evolved to integrate both time and cost on a common framework.

The PERT/Cost system was developed in 1962 [1] for the specific purpose of integrating time data with the associated financial data of project accomplishment. Schedule slippages and the consequent cost overruns of many projects had made it necessary to add the resources dimension (manpower, materials, machines) to PERT/Time. Although PERT/Time provided the means of monitoring, coordinating, and controlling a project's time progress at various levels, it provided no means of measuring the project's financial status along with its physical accomplishment.

PERT/Cost is not yet old enough to have won a firmly established place in project management. Although it seems to have real potential as a means of cost control, it is more difficult to apply than PERT/Time. A number of problems have arisen in actual use. Some of them may disappear as users gain more experience with the technique and its application. Others may prove to be inherent limitations, however.

The use of PERT/Cost unquestionably has many advantages. It greatly facilitates the assessment of project status in relation to financial planning. It highlights the interrelationships of time and costs and the financial effects on the project of possible changes in resources and/or schedules. It permits evaluation of progress from multiple sources of information, and it provides a single set of reports for appraising both the financial and the physical status of a project.

OTHER VALUES

PERT/Cost also aids in conceptual planning by financially quantifying the project tasks to be performed and by assessing the adequacy of funding requirements for meeting total project costs. It provides a means for comparing time schedules and resource estimates of different departments or of different contractors. For example, with it the project manager can combine detailed information from engineering and manufacturing or fuse summary cost data from one contractor with in-house data and still have consistent program output information. Its outputs for network areas are useful even if one section is given in summary form and another in detailed network form.

By integrating PERT/Time and PERT/Cost one can determine whether the various-level managers are meeting their schedule commitments, cost estimates, and technical performance standards and, if not, decide how resources can be recombined so as to minimize costs.

In measuring the progress of a project, the sum of actual costs to date can be compared directly with funds authorized and the estimated cost of completion of the project. Such a comparison will reveal potential cost overruns and/or underruns and will pinpoint the segments of work that require cost control action.

LIMITATIONS

While PERT/Cost undoubtedly provides a substantial measure of cost control for large, complex projects, there are, nevertheless, shortcomings that somewhat limit its applicability.

Although the splintering up of large, unwieldy projects into smaller, more manageable units permits the sharing of exacting responsibility and the more precise delineation of multiple efforts, it also increases the overall problem of departmental coordination. Top management, of course, is concerned chiefly with summary reports. Much of the requisite on-the-spot control is delegated to departmental heads who have vested interests in the type and amount of information presented to top management. Just as time estimates in PERT/Time tend to be used for firm schedules (although they should not), so cost estimates in PERT/Cost eventually end up as budgets, and, despite the fact that cost estimates are subject to revision, there is a tendency to inflate the budget in the initial planning stage.

PADDING

This tendency to "pad" does not necessarily represent any willful attempt to convey fraudulent or erroneous information but rather that all too human desire to "play it safe." Since time and cost are directly related, and since engineers tend to be somewhat pessimistic about time estimates, there is concomitant hedging on the cost side as well.

No department head wants to encounter cost overruns, which would reflect adversely on his performance. As a result, he is naturally tempted to pad the cost estimates so as to compensate for any possible error in the time estimates.

This problem is by no means limited to PERT/Cost systems, of course. It is always a hazard in budget formulation, regardless of the control technique employed.

It is ordinarily impractical to have each cost estimate independently recalculated—or have its components independently verified—by someone outside the department responsible for preparing the estimate. However, several steps can be taken to discourage "fudging."

Complete work packages or specific activities within a work package can be selected at random for review and verification by the project manager. This review can be performed either during the planning stage of the project, in which case the validation is of time and cost estimates, or during the execution stage of the project, in which case actual times and costs may be available for comparison with estimates. These checks provide clues to estimator bias; they also act as psychological deterrents to fudging.

This review by the project manager is itself a kind of audit. However, it is also possible to have an internal audit by an accounting department or some other independent staff, performed randomly on work packages or at a summary level. On some government projects an external government agency routinely performs such an audit. An internal audit helps to provide control since it measures deviations from a standard; more important, however, the threat of an audit or close review "disciplines before it acts."

CHANGES IN ESTIMATES

Usually, as a project develops, changes are made in the product or system under design because unforeseen technical difficulties are encountered or because it becomes evident that certain modifications would increase the stability, reliability, or economy of the product or the system. Indeed, it has been suggested that out of thousands of government projects fewer than one per cent fail to undergo significant alterations.

Cost estimates, of course, change accordingly. Such changes are particularly characteristic of cost-plus government contracts, for under such contracts there is little or no penalty for underestimation of costs. Thus, contractors tend to understate costs in order to win the contracts and then make little effort to control costs.

COST-PLUS PSYCHOLOGY

This tendency to understate costs seems to be the rule rather than the exception. Reports of final incurred costs tend to play down or omit earlier cost estimates, thus making it difficult to verify the original estimates. Revisions partially absolve the individual responsible for the original estimates since the final costs are really for a new program, not for the one whose cost estimates he formulated. Furthermore, by the time the project is completed, it is usually impossible to demonstrate what the original program would have cost if it had not been altered.

On many projects the margins of error have been significant, even startling. Cost increases of 200 to 300 per cent and extensions of development time by one-third to one-half are not uncommon.[2] The degree of error in estimates depends to some extent on the type of program. Programs that incorporate many new technological innovations are particularly subject to large margins of error. For instance, on six missile projects in which The Rand Corporation played a major role, the actual cumulative costs ranged from 1.3 to 57.6 times the initial projected costs,[3] with a mean of 17.1; in other words, the final costs were on the average 17.1 times as great as the earliest available estimates.[4]

COST UNCERTAINTIES

Even if changes in cost estimates are not forced by external or project changes, they are likely to become necessary as a project moves along and estimating errors become apparent. Because PERT by its very nature deals so much with uncertainties, it is difficult to extrapolate from previous cost patterns. Nor do project costs always react in a linear fashion.

Thus, the assumption that a particular course of action will result in a least-cost situation may prove highly unrealistic. It is true that a computer can theoretically minimize costs and optimize resource allocation. In actual application, however, many of these costs are so difficult to estimate that the optimum allocation of resources remains a guess.

In the stage of project planning when entire networks are being visualized and computer programs are being prepared, it is often too early to subject cost patterns to precise mathematical determination. This is not to imply that costs are not predictable for discrete situations or that PERT/Cost does not provide a sound framework for cost control. But the difficulty of obtaining reliable cost estimates is certainly a limitation on the effectiveness of the technique.

ALLOCATIONS

Cost allocation is a major problem. Work packages are usually made up of activities involving several different departments. An engineering department, for example, is frequently involved in many aspects of a program, while the production department may be concerned with the major assemblies only. It is frequently difficult, if not impossible, to assign departmental expenses accurately among projects, and for control purposes an arbitrary allocation is about as useful as none.

Sometimes on large projects it is possible to break the work packages down in the planning stages in such a way that each department with a major contribution to make to the project can be assigned a specific criterion to be met, for example, $100,000 or three months' effort. The assumption implicit in this technique is that the necessary resources for the execution of the work packages are present and available.

So long as departments operate on tight budgets, however, the haphazard reporting of labor classifications is likely. Suppose, for example, that the engineering department has ten man-months allocated for one work package, and it actually requires only five man-months. If a second work package begins to show signs of slippage, then it is to be expected that engineering resources will be traded off accordingly. Department heads are often indifferent about which accounts their costs are charged to so long as they stay within their own overall budgets. Thus, the seeming definiteness associated with the PERT/Cost system may be only an apparent one, for there is always ample scope for flexibility and manipulation in the reporting of cost figures.

Whatever the reason for the misallocation of costs, there always remains the danger that these misleading figures will be used as a basis of estimating the costs of future work packages of similar nature. Obviously such forecasting, based on false or at best dubious premises, is likely to prove highly erroneous.

Actually, of course, these problems are not unique to PERT/Cost. They existed before it was developed, and they continue to plague project managers and controllers whatever the management and control techniques used. The particular problem with PERT/Cost is that it seems to be so scientific and its results seem so definitive that managers may be tempted to forget that no control technique is any better than the data upon which it rests.

EVOLUTION

PERT/Cost is not, after all, a complete departure from earlier techniques. Most of its elements existed before, often under other names. For example, the cost-to-complete estimates do not differ greatly from reports formerly titled future cost to be incurred, costs to terminate, or simply recosting. The organization status reports have been in use for years under the name of department work sheets or department budget reports. The manpower loading report goes back to the older manpower requirement report or the jobs skills form. Thus, most of the components of PERT/Cost are evolutionary rather than revolutionary; i.e., preexisting ideas of management and control have been refined and linked with the use of new data processing equipment and computers.

One of the chief advantages of this evolution is increased speed. However, although the PERT/Cost reporting system is relatively rapid, it still may not be fast enough to be really useful.

While it is relatively easy to gather historical costs, it is much more difficult to estimate the costs of physical progress for projects in various stages of completion. The rule that the value of work performed to date is measured by the actual costs, divided by the latest estimate to complete, times the budget to date is not an accurate guide for evaluation, especially if progress is not on target. By this formula, increasing the budget for a work package automatically increases the value of work performed—which is patently fallacious.

Thus, while PERT/Cost does aid in assessing the financial progress of activities, it is not an infallible guide. For many projects costs

can be accurately reported only after completion.

FUTURE

Despite these limitations, there is no doubt that PERT/Cost has added a new dimension to the field of operations control. It has brought management closer to the ultimate goal of total systems control. As PERT/Time provides timely information helpful in achieving goals more rapidly, so PERT/Cost provides information that facilitates achieving these goals not only promptly but also efficiently and economically.

Although it is premature to pass final judgment on the success or failure of PERT/Cost, most companies that use it feel that it provides true management control by focusing attention on significant deviations from set goals. Just as operating personnel are forced by PERT/Time to examine schedule dates and accomplishments in detail, so PERT/Cost forces personnel to be equally cognizant of resources. This awareness of direct labor hours, material costs, computer time, and the like in turn aids in setting objectives for departments and managers at various levels of management.

PERT/Time and PERT/Cost will not make decisions for the manager. They will, however, aid him by revealing schedule and cost segments of programs that require his special attention. They also will pinpoint "crash" areas where acceleration may be essential if the project is to be completed on the target date.

Like other control techniques, PERT/Cost is no panacea. Its usefulness is directly dependent upon the usefulness of the data fed into the system, and this in turn depends upon the efficiency of the operating personnel. If unreliable data are fed into the PERT/Cost program, then haphazard information will be received from the computer.

Many of the current efforts to improve the PERT/Cost system are aimed at alleviating the difficulties in cost estimating, at tying cost reports more closely to time schedules, and at introducing other mechanical devices to complement the system. More attention, however, should be devoted to increasing the capabilities of the operating personnel who are responsible for the day-to-day functioning of the PERT/Cost system. Technical problems will—and should—not be neglected, but the need to solve more of the problems of human engineering apparently far outweighs any of the mechanical deficiencies of PERT/Cost.

One promising area of further development of the PERT/Cost system is that of Time/Cost estimating procedures. It may soon be possible to place manpower needs and costs directly on the detailed project networks. This would facilitate the control function by enabling the operations manager to formulate a more realistic program initially instead of making continual readjustments. Although many time and cost schedule revisions result from changes in the program objectives and from unexpected contingencies involving resource availability and the like, a substantial number are due to misestimations by PERT personnel in the first place.

NOTES

1. Available at the present time are many manuals on PERT/Cost issued by private industries using PERT or by government agencies or departments. See especially U.S. Defense Department and National Aeronautics and Space Administration, *DOD and NASA Guide, PERT Cost, Systems Design,* U.S. Government Printing Office, Washington, D.C., 1962, and U.S. Department of the Navy, *An Introduction to the PERT/Cost System for Integrated Project Management,* Special Projects Office, Bureau of Naval Weapons, Washington, D.C., 1962. The following articles have also proved helpful: Richard E. Beckwith, "A Cost Control Extension of the PERT System," *IEEE Transactions of Engineering Management,* EM-9, December, 1962, pp. 147–149; Roderick W. Clarke, "Activity Costing—Key to Progress in Critical Path Analysis," *IRE Transactions on Engineering*

Management, EM-9, September, 1962, pp. 132–136; Roland Frambes "PERT and PERT/Cost in the RFP," *Aerospace Management,* V, May, 1962, pp. 24–26; J. Sterling Livingston, Willard Fazar, and J. Roland Fox, "PERT Gains New Dimensions," *Aerospace Management,* V, January, 1962, pp. 32–36; and Hillard W. Paige, "How PERT/Cost Helps the General Manager," *Harvard Business Review,* XLI, November–December, 1963, pp. 87–95.

2. A. W. Marshall and W. H. Meckling, *Predictability of the Costs, Time and Success of Development,* 2d ed., Rand Corporation, Santa Monica, Calif., 1959, p. 11.

3. *Ibid.* The above figures are unadjusted both for price level changes and, more importantly, for modifications that have been made since the initial cost estimates. For example, on the above-mentioned missile project where the latest cost estimate was 57.6 times the initial one, this would be reduced to 14.7 if adjusted for the above factors. Even this margin of error is highly significant, this writer feels.

4. In an effort to stimulate the profit motive and to cut costs for the government, "incentive" contracts have been made a policy for the Department of Defense since January, 1964. It is still too early to judge the effects of this policy. (See article in *The Wall Street Journal* which states that a "limited number of incentive contracts showed costs running about 50 per cent more than anticipated." See also "McNamara Cuts Costs, but Officials Wonder if Gain Is Exaggerated," *The Wall Street Journal,* June 11, 1964.) Some writers think that cost overruns will cease to be a problem with the advent of "incentive" contracts. However, while incentive contracts have undoubtedly reduced cost overruns in many instances, success has been far from complete; i.e., the controversial TFX project is currently expecting an overrun of about $.5 billion.

42. THE SOCIOLOGICAL PROBLEMS
OF PERT

Peter P. Schoderbek *

For the smooth functioning of modern complex industrial society new management planning and control techniques have recently been introduced, of which one of the better known, more useful, and now generally accepted is PERT (Program Evaluation and Review Technique).[1]

From its inception in 1958 PERT has not only aroused widespread interest in the business community but has also won acceptance by a growing segment of industry as an improved management planning and control technique. For years American industry has been seeking and has at last found a more realistic and more sophisticated approach to the conventional problems of management than those hitherto available. So successful in fact has PERT been in the United States that it has already moved up into Canada, crossed over into Great Britain and the European continent, and penetrated even behind the Iron Curtain.[2] Recently it has even been hailed as a *near panacea* for the planning and control of large, complex projects.[3]

Yet in spite of its remarkably rapid acceptance, certain problems remain to plague it in its application to the needs of the workaday world. The results of a recent survey indicate that one of the significant problems associated with PERT is due, not to the inadequacy of the technique itself, but rather to the failure of management to gain its acceptance.[4] Lacking often an appreciation of its benefits and an awareness of its limitations, top management has been less than eager in selling PERT to both the operational managers and to the

technical personnel. This is all the more damaging since the latter are often instrumental in the initial introduction and installation of the PERT program.

PERT management could then conceivably benefit from the specialized knowledge of sociologists, social psychologists, and of cultural anthropologists who in recent years have interested themselves not only in the problems of business and management, of power structures, informal work groups, etc., but also in the overall processes of social change. Their findings have some applicability to the problems associated with the survey and articulated in the personal interviews with PERT-users and their findings may well serve as guide lines for possible ameliorative action.[5]

The survey results also reveal that another major difficulty encountered in applying PERT was in the *motivation and training* of the PERT personnel. Over half of the companies using PERT indicated in their replies that motivation and education of personnel were *the* major problems in the application of PERT. Even companies with formal training programs in PERT admitted meeting with major resistance. This suggests that formal training programs as currently structured are concerned more with the technical aspects of the PERT approach than with developing in the personnel the felt-needs for and interests in the tool.[6] They are orientated almost exclusively to the *how* rather than to the *why*, to the mastering of the fundamentals of network construction, manpower levelling, and other basic operational aspects of the technique rather than to emphasizing in the first place the practical advantages and present and future rewards accruing to the men from the PERT system itself.

One major obstacle standing in the way both of initial adoption and of full utilization of the PERT system can be characterized as

SOURCE: Written specially for this book. A cursory treatment of some of the basic ideas can be found in Peter P. Schoderbek, "Overcoming Resistance to PERT," *Business Topics*, Michigan State University, Spring 1966, pp. 50–56.

* Assistant Professor of Management, University of Iowa.

"resistance to change." It is almost axiomatic that workers resist attempts by management to alter familiar work procedures and to modify existing work regulations.[7] The pages of history are replete with the activities of organizations that have fought tooth-and-nail against superior innovating practices. Somehow modern man often fails to notice that the problem of resistance to change has more than mere academic interest and that it too can assume a modern garb and appear in a twentieth-century managerial milieu.[8]

When considering resistance to change one must bear in mind that there is no single factor that will infallibly and of itself bring about or hinder change. There are many factors and any one can in a given situation outweigh another. It is the cumulative effect, therefore, of all the factors that will finally decide in which direction the scale will tilt—toward the acceptance of change or toward its rejection.[9]

"Management may look upon such resistances to change simply as obstructions in the path of progress, which should be swept brusquely aside. This is an exceedingly costly approach to the problem. Management may be able to make fairly close estimates of the dollars and cents costs in materials and labor used to install the new plan, but there will always and inevitably be costs or savings in the field of human relations that accompany such changes. They cannot be so closely estimated, but management can act with more intelligence and skill if these factors are taken into consideration." [10]

At this point it may be profitable to consider the conditions affecting change and to relate these to the social situation involving the PERT personnel.[11] For despite the many potential advantages inherent in the PERT system, these are ultimately downgraded when the system itself is repudiated.

ATTITUDE FAVORABLE TOWARD CHANGE

Like certain societies known to sociologists and anthropologists, some groups favor change more than others. A group that expects and favors change will change more readily than one that frowns upon it, that looks upon change as something undesirable or as a step backward, or even as something unthinkable. The anticipation itself of change favors change.

Now the contemporary American manager is not opposed to change *per se*. It is hardly convincing to affirm the opposite. For like the rest of us he lives in a world characterized by change. On all sides he is surrounded by it—from the political arena where strong currents of conservatism are altering the thought patterns and feeling tones of many of his fellow Americans to the domestic scene where time- and energy-saving devices are constantly being added to the repertoire of the busy yet unwearied housewife. He is in fact an integral part of the technological subsociety that places a high premium on both progress and efficiency, and any resistance to change, precisely because it is in such direct opposition to the prevailing cultural pattern or configuration, immediately becomes conspicuously evident. If the PERT system is not favorably received, this fact should not automatically be attributed (as is sometimes done) to any culturally conditioned tendency to oppose technological change as such.[12] All people tend to resist changes that appear to threaten basic securities; they tend to resist proposed changes they do not understand; they tend to resist being coerced to change.[13]

FACTIONALISM OR VESTED INTERESTS

Within a society one finds distinct interest groups, each with its own grievances, ambitions, and fears. If an innovation seems to advance the vested interests of the group, the group members will tend to accept and develop the innovation; if, however, it appears detrimental to their best interests, the group will resist the change.

PERT managers, as well as the would-be PERT personnel, are individuals with human emotions, hopes, and fears. Now fears thrive on lack of knowledge and are generated when men anticipate unknown changes that may affect them adversely.

Opposition to innovations decreases as the fears generating it are dissipated, i.e., explained away. But just because top management holds that the PERT system will advance the best interests of the corporation, one must not naively assume that this same opinion is shared by the individual employee. This fallacy is but a variation of the familiar theme, "What's good for General Motors is good for the country." This value would have to be demonstrated. One's fears to the contrary would have to be given serious consideration.

Managers too have fears. They fear lowering of status perhaps more than anything else. The fears employees generally experience concern loss of job, diminution of promotional advantage, reduction of wages, lowering of status position, and increase in hours or intensity of labor. All of these can be summed up in the rather inclusive term, *loss of security.*

No matter how irrational these fears may appear, they nevertheless loom large and real to those concerned and ought to be reckoned with. One department head, for example, who resisted all efforts to change over to PERT greatly feared that the staff personnel would encroach upon his own sphere of authority. He was afraid that he would thus lose status with those both above and below him in the organizational hierarchy. Another erroneously felt that there was something mystical or esoteric about this new technique and feared that he would never be able to understand, much less master it, thus lowering his position with respect to the younger men in the organization.[14]

Resistance to change that stems from fear of the unknown or from dread of the uncertain can in large measure be minimized by an effective communication system. Lack of reliable information on which to base a decision is one reason why men have at times impeded or delayed the introduction of a novel method. The men are not exactly sure how the change will affect them and therefore they balk, stalling for time, hoping the situation will eventually clarify itself. When initiating a change, sufficiently determinate information concerning not only *what* is going to happen but *why* it should ought to be provided. Once the reasons for the change become known, the men involved in the shift will probably begin assessing its impact upon their work and their status position. The longer they speculate in the absence of official facts about the effects consequent upon the change, the more entrenched their own dim views are likely to become. On the other hand, the more meaningful and relevant the information, the greater the likelihood of change. However, one must not naively assume that mere explanations will solve all problems.

In a somewhat different work situation,

Gardner conceived the resistance-to-change philosophy in a similar vein:

Now there are certain types of changes that always seem to meet resistance, and they can be roughly classified into three independent groups. First, we have those changes that *threaten to lower the status or prestige* of the group or of the individual. Thus we see concerted resistance to any attempt to move office workers to a low-status shop location. Such a move threatens their desire to be recognized as a superior group. . . .

Then we see the changes that *reduce the authority and scope of action and decision.* Thus giving the personnel department control over hiring and firing takes away some of the authority of the foreman and makes him feel reduced in importance. . . .

Finally, we see those changes that *disrupt the habitual routines.* A change in accounting procedures may meet with severe criticism primarily because it is a change, and the group reacts negatively to it, seeing all its faults and distrusting its virtues.[15]

FELT-NEEDS

A change will be most readily accepted if it is rewarding or if it at least promises to solve a problem or ease a tension. However, only *felt*-needs move individuals to adopt new ways, and a need that is felt is necessarily relevant to the culture of the group in question. At times the reward is self-evident and the felt-need only too obvious, in which case the innovation tends to be accepted without questioning. On the other hand, rewards that are not felt are no rewards at all. One does not, as a rule, buy something one does not feel he needs, especially if the object involves a great expense or risk, or calls for great personal sacrifice.[16]

The introduction of the PERT system must be effected in the light of the felt-needs. The men must be made to feel the need for the change. Many programs fail simply because the need was not established prior to the attempted introduction. In one of the companies surveyed by the author, for example, top management felt constrained by the press of time for filing its first PERT report to the Defense Department to hire "outside experts" who were then vested with the responsibility of implementing the PERT program in the corporation. This action on the part of top management in no way enhanced, rather it demeaned the prestige and status of the company's own middle managers and technical personnel, especially when in the haste and confusion surrounding the sudden introduction of the new system, top management failed to sell the organization on the need for and the advantages of PERT. An effective communication system is a must, even if only a beginning.[17]

Since needs are not experienced in the same way by all concerned, no one need-satisfying object will necessarily be acceptable to all. Motivation has its part to play in man's response to needs. Different motives will appeal to different individuals. Motives that appeal to top management may not appeal in the same way to operating personnel. Each official responsible for PERT implementation "must search out and identify those motives which would cause each of the groups to buy (accept and support) his ideas." [18]

INTEREST

It is not sufficient that the need for change be felt; an interest in the felt-need is also required. Felt-needs might be best looked upon as a *theoretical* appreciation, while interest implies a *practical* appreciation of the need that might be filled through the change. The lack of interest, for instance, in civil defense is due in no small measure to the fact that the rewards of the program, although theoretically appreciated, are too distant to get excited about. This explains too why sophisticated individuals in a highly civilized country like ours are relatively slow to accept preventives against poliomyelitis. It is not that they lack a theoretical appreciation of the value of polio shots or of the oral vaccine. They simply lack the necessary interest. And this explains why large-scale educational and promotional campaigns, rivalling those of political parties, are almost essential for a successful anti-polio drive in metropolitan areas.

This lack of interest can be an exasperating obstacle with which to cope. Too often, however, it is not even recognized for what it is—lack of interest. All of us have at one time or another come across individuals who in spite of the "overwhelming" evidence we presented in a discussion just would not be overwhelmed! "Why can't they understand what is so obvious? Why can't they see the light?" Our choicest words of wisdom (and our loudest thunder) fall on apparently deaf ears.

This mental blindness, this deafness may be accounted for in more than one way. Sometimes these individuals perceive the identical situation quite differently than we do. Their response to what they see is consequently also unlike ours. Because their definition of the situation is so dissimilar we find it difficult to communicate meaningfully with them. Unfortunately this may occur with managers who persistently thwart every effort to introduce or implement PERT. One manager, for instance, who was interviewed by the author confided: "I've been doing these things my own way long before the PERT staff specialists moved into this office. And besides, I don't care one whit *if* PERT is better. I'm still going to go on doing these reports the way I've always done them. And if worse comes to worst and I'm forced by the company to use PERT, I'll do it, but I'll still go on using my regular reports too!"

Fortunately for top management there is another explanation that has greater applicability. In many instances resistance to change may be due to a lack of interest, of practical appreciation of the need that might be filled by the change.

To create this interest may be no easy task. Any door-to-door salesman or classroom instructor can vouch for this difficulty. However, the obstacle is by no means insurmountable. To be effective the appeal must be made concrete, and not left dangling out of reach on a theoretical plane. To create such interest presupposes on the part of responsible management a more than superficial acquaintance with the PERT system and an intimate knowledge of the needs of the personnel.

One of the more effective techniques is to allow the individuals involved to share in the decision-making process. This involvement and participation in matters of vital concern to the men initiate powerful forces for change. One's own facts are always better understood, more emotionally acceptable, and more likely to be utilized than those of others, of some "outside experts." Group decision-making tends to commit each member of the group to carry out the decisions arrived at by the group.[19] It also helps to by-pass those resistances that arise from proceeding either too rapidly or too slowly. One PERT staff member stated unequivocally that in his experience PERT was uniformly accepted in those departments where the department head was personally involved in PERTing his own project. "Once we get them working for their own interests and advantage, PERT sells itself."

However, when using this approach management must be genuinely sincere, for any attempt to sell preconceived ideas can easily be aborted. Self-involvement must not be a gimmick to enforce adjustments but a tool to seek understanding and cooperation.

One cannot escape the conclusion that it is the task of management, and a not too simple one at that, to interest the would-be PERT personnel in the tangible advantages and present and future rewards flowing from the PERT system. Managers themselves must not only be sold on the system but must also be thoroughly conversant with it, with its many merits and its inherent limitations so as to be able to articulate the benefits of the system to others.[20]

The warning of Boverie is especially apropos. After identifying and discussing seven basic implementation and operation errors responsible for PERT failure, he concludes:

If the errors listed above can be avoided, then the chances of creating a successful PERT operation are increased. They may seem trivial to the individual who has been able to encounter PERT only on a theoretical plane, but they become painfully significant to the men who must encounter the practicalities of PERT.

It should be noted that no PERT implementation will be trouble-free since it combines the problems of a voluminous data processing system with the sometimes cool reactions of people who resist change for no justifiable reason. However, the benefits of a successful PERT operation cannot be overstressed:

The development of an intelligent, intelligible, and efficient plan.

The accurate measurement of progress against the plan.

The prognostication of task accomplishments and goal achievement.

The signalling of potential problem areas before they actually occur.

The capability to simulate and optimize plan changes and to determine impact upon program goals.

The capability to maximize the effective use of resources.

In order to gain these sorely required advantages, it is emphasized that the practical aspects of PERT need keen attention from the PERT implementer, and that every attempt should be made to avoid the described errors.[21]

The fate of PERT rests ultimately in the hands of management!

NOTES

1. Since PERT was introduced, some fifty or more variant forms have been developed. See U.S. Air Force Systems Command, *Glossary of Management Systems Terminology* (*Including Acronyms*) (Washington: PERT Orientation and Training Center, 1963).

2. "Shortcut for Project Planning," *Business Week*, July 7, 1962, p. 106.

3. Ivars Avots, "The Management Side of PERT," *California Management Review*, 4 (Winter 1962), pp. 16–27. In the past several years PERT has been used not only for complex industrial and defense projects but also for such varied tasks as book publishing, marketing, house building, theatrical production, new product introduction, preparation of legal briefs, organizational changes and many others. *PERT Fundamentals* (Washington: PERT Orientation and Training Center, 1963), Vol. I, p. 11.

4. An extensive survey of 200 of the 500 largest industrial corporations in the United States as listed in the *Fortune Directory* was conducted by the author in order to ascertain the characteristics of the PERT-using community. A response rate of 91 percent was obtained for the survey. This was then followed up by some one hundred personal interviews with government and company officials using PERT.

5. Homer G. Barnett, *Innovation: The Basis of Cultural Change* (New York: McGraw-Hill Book Co., 1953), pp. 39–180; John J. Honigman, *The World of Man* (New York: Harper & Brothers, 1959), pp. 200–232; Edward H. Spicer (ed.), *Human Problems in Technological Change* (New York: Russell Sage Foundation, 1952); Benjamin Paul (ed.), *Health, Culture and Community* (New York: Russell Sage Foundation, 1955). Some references to the periodical literature are given in footnote 8.

6. Formal PERT training was also one of the variables covered by the recent survey of Thomas V. Sobczak in "A Statistical Analysis

of the General Characteristics of a PERT Technician," *IEEE Transactions of Engineering Management*, EM-10 (March 1963), pp. 25–28.

7. For a good example of this type of resistance to change see the description by French and Coch of the long period required to get pieceworkers in a men's wear factory to adjust their output back to normal after minor changes were introduced by management. Lester Coch and John R. P. French, Jr., "Overcoming Resistance to Change," *Human Relations*, **1** (August 1948), pp. 512–532.

8. Besides the instances of resistance to change detailed and analyzed in the casebooks edited by Edward H. Spicer, *op. cit.* and Benjamin Paul, *op. cit.*, the periodical literature abounds with numerous interesting and illuminating examples taken from nearly all areas of life. Only a few can be cited here: V. H. Whitney, "Resistance to Innovation: The Case of Atomic Power," *American Journal of Sociology*, **56** (November 1950), pp. 247–254; Elting E. Morison, "A Case Study of Innovation," in Edward Hutchings, Jr. (ed.), *Frontiers in Science* (New York: Basic Books, 1958), pp. 318–338; Bernard J. Stern, "Resistance to Medical Change," in *Society and Medical Progress* (Princeton: Princeton University Press, 1941), Ch. 9; *idem*, "Resistance to the Adoption of Technological Innovations," National Resources Committee, *Technological Trends and National Policy* (Washington: U.S. Government Printing Office, 1937), pp. 39–66; *idem*, "Frustration of Technology," *Science and Society*, **2** (Winter 1937), pp. 1–28; *idem*, "Restraints upon the Utilization of Inventions," *Annals of the American Academy of Political and Social Science*, **149** (November 1938), pp. 1–18.

9. See Alvin Zander, "Resistance to Change: Its Analysis and Prevention," *Advanced Management*, **15** (January 1950), pp. 9–11.

10. William Foote Whyte (ed.), *Industry and Society* (New York: McGraw-Hill Book Co., 1946), p. 193. Improved management techniques can be used to gain some of the benefits of scientific management without producing resistance to change. See esp. Leo Moore, "Too Much Management, Too Little Change," *Harvard Business Review*, **34** (January–February, 1956), pp. 41–48; Warren G. Bennis *et al.*, *The Planning of Change: A Challenge to Practitioners and Social Scientists* (New York: Holt, Rinehart and Winston, Inc., 1961).

11. Recent texts on human relations in industry contain much pertinent matter. See George Strauss and Leonard R. Sayles, *The Human Problems of Management* (Englewood Cliffs,

N.J.: Prentice-Hall, Inc., 1960), esp. pp. 263–283; Leonard R. Sayles, *Behavior of Industrial Work Groups* (New York: John Wiley and Sons, 1958); Charles Walker, *Modern Technology and Civilization* (New York: McGraw-Hill Book Co., 1962); Robert Dubin, *The World of Work* (Englewood Cliffs, N.J.: Prentice-Hall, Inc., 1963).

12. A fairly adequate amount of research has highlighted the fact that resistance to change is principally reaction to certain methods of carrying out change rather than an inherent human characteristic. See Alvin Zander, *op. cit.*

13. Spicer, *op. cit.*, p. 18.

14. Chester I. Barnard, "Functions and Pathologies of Status Systems in Formal Organizations," in William F. Whyte (ed.), *op. cit.*, points to the two sides of the incentive coin when he asserts (p. 78) that "the resistance to loss of status is in general stronger than the desire to achieve higher status." This essay is probably the best single analysis of status in work organizations.

15. Burleigh B. Gardner, "The Factory as a Social System," in William F. Whyte (ed.), *op. cit.*, pp. 15–16. (Italics mine.)

16. In one company personal interviewing revealed that the employees in order to comply with government regulations were at times required to PERT a project even *after* its completion. Besides compiling their regular reports which they used for the task at hand, they were obliged *post factum* to go through the additional tedious and "useless" task of PERTing the completed project when no *felt*-need really existed for them.

17. See R. W. Peters, *Communication Within Industry* (New York: Harper & Brothers, 1949) for a general treatment of organizational communication. For a discussion on the informal channels of communication see Keith Davis, "Management Communication and the Grapevine," *Harvard Business Review*, **31** (September–October 1953), pp. 43–49; *idem*, "Making Constructive Use of the Office Grapevine," in *New Dimensions in Office Management* (New York: American Management Association, Office Management Series, No. 142), 1956, pp. 25–35.

18. Robert Blomstrom, "Selling a Personnel Program—A Positive Approach," *Personnel Journal*, **41**, 9 (1962), pp. 449–453. Blomstrom proposes four sets of motives for appealing to managers and personnel: (1) profit and economy, (2) comfort and convenience, (3) health and safety, and (4) pride and prestige, pp. 451–452. For a general treatment of motivation see Morris Viteles, *Motivation and Morale in Industry* (New York: W. W. Nor-

ton & Company, 1953) or Abraham Maslow, *Motivation and Personality* (New York: Harper and Row, 1954), esp. Chs. 4, 5, and 8. A short but down-to-earth consideration of motivation is given by Frank A. Busse, "E = mc^2" in Keith Davis and William G. Scott, *Readings in Human Relations* (New York: McGraw-Hill Book Co., 1959), pp. 69–76.

19. Kurt Lewin, "Studies in Group Decision," in Dorwin Cartwright and Alvin Zander (eds.), *Group Dynamics* (Evanston, Ill.: Row, Peterson, 1953), pp. 287–301. See also Floyd C. Mann, "Studying and Creating Change: A Means to Understanding Social Organization," in Conrad Arensberg *et al.* (eds.), *Research in Industrial Relations*, No. 17 (New York: Harper and Row, 1957), pp. 146–167; John R. P. French *et al.*, "Employee Participation in a Program of Industrial Change," *Personnel*, 35 (November–December 1958), pp. 16–29. Some examples of group participation are cited in N.F.R. Maier, *Psychology in Industry* (Boston: Houghton Mifflin Co., 1946) and the advantages of group participation summarized (pp. 95 ff.). For a discussion of the Scanlon Plan in which group decision plays a rather prominent part, see Frederick Lesieur (ed.), *The Scanlon Plan* (Cambridge, Mass.: Technological Press, MIT, and John Wiley and Sons, New York, 1958).

20. For the mathematical limitations of PERT see especially John E. Murray, "Considera-tion of PERT Assumptions," *IEEE Transactions on Engineering Management*, EM-10 (September 1963), pp. 94–99. For a more generalized overview see also John G. Barmby, "The Applicability of PERT as a Management Tool," *IRE Transactions on Engineering Management*, EM-9 (September 1962), pp. 130–131; C. W. Borklund, "Is PERT All That Good?" *Armed Forces Management*, January 9, 1963, p. 11; Philip Geddes, "How Good Is PERT?" *Aerospace Management*, 4 (September 1961), pp. 41–43; J. Sterling Livingston and Martin Paskman, "Is PERT What Management Needs?" *Aerospace Management*, 5 (October 1962), pp. 52–58; Walter Mayes, "What's Wrong with PERT?" *Aerospace Management*, 5 (April 1962), pp. 20–25; Bruce Mikesell, "Uncertainties of PERT," *Armed Forces Management*, 9 (January 1963), pp. 20–22; J. W. Pocock, "PERT As an Analytical Aid for Program Planning—Its Payoff and Problems," *Operations Research*, 10 (November 1962), pp. 893–903; Daniel D. Roman, "The PERT System: An Appraisal of Program Evaluation Review Technique," *Journal of the Academy of Management*, 5 (April 1962), pp. 57–65; V. Thompson, "PERT: Pro and Con About This Technique," *Data Processing*, 3 (October 1961), pp. 40–44.

21. Richard T. Boverie, "The Practicalities of PERT," *IEEE Transactions on Engineering Management*, EM-10 (March, 1963), pp. 3–5.

BIBLIOGRAPHY

1. Dooley, A. R., "Interpretations of PERT," *Harvard Business Review*, March–April, 1964.
2. Fazar, W., "Progress Reporting in the Special Projects Office," *Navy Management Review*, April, 1959.
3. Johnson, R., F. E. Kast, and J. E. Rosenzweig, *The Theory and Management of Systems*, McGraw-Hill Book Co., 1963.
4. Klass, P. J., "PERT/PEP Management Tool Use Grows," *Aviation Week*, November, 1960.
5. Levy, F. K., G. L. Thompson, and J. D. Wiest, "The ABCs of the Critical Path Method," *Harvard Business Review*, September, 1963.
6. Miller, R. W., "How to Plan and Control with PERT," *Harvard Business Review*, March, 1962.
7. Neuwirth, S. I., "An Introduction to PERT," *The Journal of Accountancy*, May, 1963.
8. "New Tool for Job Management," *Engineering News-Record*, January, 1962.
9. *PERT Summary Report, Phase I*, Department of the Navy, Bureau of Naval Weapons, Special Projects Office, 1958.
10. *PERT Fundamentals*, Washington: PERT Orientation and Training Center, 1963.
11. Phelps, H. S., "What Your Key People Should Know About PERT," *Management Review*, October, 1962.
12. Roman, D. D., "The PERT System: An Appraisal of Program Evaluation Review Technique," *The Journal of the Academy of Management*, April, 1962.
13. Schoderbek, P. P., "PERT: Its Promises and Performance," *Michigan Business Review*, January, 1965.
14. Thompson, V., "PERT: Pro and Con About This Technique," *Data Processing*, October, 1961.
15. U.S. Air Force Systems Command, *USAF PERT COST System Description Manual*, AFSC PERT Control Board, March–December, 1963.
16. U.S. Air Force Systems Command, *USAF PERT Time System Description Manual*, Government Printing Office, 1963.

Part XIII.   Real Time Systems

In a previous section concerned with the design of information systems it was pointed out that one of the important elements of such a system was the feedback component. There it was stated that for information to be useful it must decrease the degree of uncertainty surrounding decision making. Such information, if timely, concise, and meaningful, could provide managers with nearly all the decision-making tools necessary to · run the company. While present-day computer systems cannot quite live up to these expectations, such a goal may not be unrealistic within a decade. For with computer science feeling at ease in its seven-league boots, the ideal process of converting available business data into timely, concise, and meaningful information may be near at hand.

We have already seen that the new breed of manager is a systems man who is more of a problem-solver and less of a specialist than his former counterpart. Whereas his predecessor relied heavily on intuition and the "feel of the market" for correlating and integrating the many facets of the business concern, the manager of today utilizes the electronic computer to assess the ever-changing relationships of the variables involved. Besides supplying him with the historical accounting and financial data, it can also provide him with "real time" information—instantaneous information.

A real time system can be defined as one in which the results of the system are available in sufficient time to effect the decision-making process. It does this by being tied in to "live" operations. In some cases this will mean supplying the decision maker with data that truly reflects conditions as they are developing. In other situations the information generated need not be instantaneous; it suffices that the information be timely enough to be useful for decision making. A real time system thus classifies and integrates data from several different sources, and when called upon, can divert to managers the necessary information in a concise and meaningful form.

With computerized real time systems it is now possible to utilize simulation models to ascertain the impact of various alternative decisions before actually committing oneself (sometimes irrevocably) to a specific course of action. Dozens of possible situations or combinations of such can be simulated when management is provided with a continuous flow of real time information. With such computerized business operations at his disposal, the manager of today will surely become a manager of "situations."

While most of the some 15,000 computer installations are still oriented to the processing of routine data and clerical operations, there is a growing realization among the new breed of managers of the vast potential available with real time systems. The demonstrated success of the widely heralded SAGE and SABRE programs has caused many an organization to strike out in new directions the better to get the advantage over its competitors.

Knowledge is power and control—provided it is timely. This is the theme of H. C. Hartmann's selection. As National Accounts Manager for IBM he is well aware that management information and control is the main objective of real time systems.

413

The old-fashioned, one-man industry, with all the facts in his head and all the printed data in a small box before him, was in real time all the time. But with the growth of business, with greater and more complex demands made upon the firm, with live competition, the need to again obtain control as close as possible to the one-man business control is quite apparent. How this was done with IBM is briefly recounted. That the results were immediate and impressive cannot be doubted. The use of full-scale simulation by IBM in effect resulted in a management information and control system.

Hartmann concludes his article with a few predictions. Among the more exciting predictions regarding the management information and control system of the future are the ones concerning the storage, retrieval and alteration of engineering drawings, the automatically updated whereused files and the updated standard costs recalculation for realistic price estimates.

That the traditional computer-based information system has many shortcomings preventing management from communicating with it in an easy, timely, and meaningful way has been stated over and over again by many a critic. We have encountered this in previous readings. However, because these shortcomings (communication difficulties, time delays, excessive costs, irrelevant volume) are not necessarily inherent in the system they are not insuperable and corrections can be applied. Some changes though will have to be introduced: a more flexible programming, a more familiar and richer computer-user language, and on-the-spot visual display mechanisms. In his article "Management in Real Time," Sherman Blumenthal seems to favor the role of visual displays in a total, functionally integrated, advanced management system.

After outlining three major functions of a management information system, the author shows how information on a 10 percent production deficit could be grossly mishandled in non-real time systems. A moderate and perhaps temporary deviation could easily be mistaken by management as indicative of a persistent trend, and changes introduced to correct it would only give rise to sustained and ever amplifying oscillations instead of the dampening effect intended. Well designed information displays could invaluably assist managers in their decision-making tasks. Managers could well use their time interrogating the various business information files in their search for relevant answers instead of spending most of it absorbed in perusing the customary periodic reports.

In many instances an alternate method of meeting the problems posed by the traditional information system has been decentralization, but decentralization can easily lead to abdication rather than to delegation of responsibilities. To ensure that delegated powers are not abdicated, one must have a way of evaluating the handling of these delegated responsibilities. Also decentralization must not lead to a loss of focus of the needs and objectives of the whole company. Too easily the needs and goals of each administrator is all that is in clear focus while those of the total organization are in the fuzzy background. Nor is centralization an automatic alternative solution to these problems. Centralization can lead to chaos rather than to order. It is this chaos that has been graphically portrayed in popular presentations: sales executives crushed under tons of sales reports, a production engineer strangled by punch tape, etc. Rather, the objective of a central information system, as Blumenthal aptly phrases it, is to minimize the volume and to maximize the communication.

One must not be led to think, however, that the introduction of a management information processing and display system will automatically do away with creative decision making. This error, Blumenthal believes, is due to the failure to distinguish between what he calls analytic and synthetic decision making. The former, no matter how complex, because it is subject to sets of rules can be programmed; the latter, which deals with peculiarities and unknown parameters of the problem, cannot. Intuition and "feel" still have a part to play in these decisions.

A typical solution to the control problem is to leave strategy and long-range planning to the men at the top while the day-by-day operations are in the hands of those in the lower echelons. However, the information that flows to the top of the power structure is a distillate of voluminous raw data that have been carefully analyzed, sifted, and summarized many times over. This distillation takes time and sometimes valuable time, and this is precisely where management information systems with visual displays can cut down on the time lag.

The author then describes the characteristics and peculiarities of a total, functionally integrated, advanced management system. By its very nature it is a real time system. It incorporates a real time computer system and not merely a batch processing computer system. It is horizontally and vertically integrated. It is an integral part of an ongoing real world activity and is temporally responsive to the ongoing requirements of the real world activity.

In his concluding section, Blumenthal considers under design problems the advantages and disadvantages of visual display, time sharing by many users at remote stations, ease of use, flexibility, man-machine symbiosis, and especially the structuring of files for easy access and for visual display purposes.

Norman Ream's selection deals with the problems involved in implementing real time management information systems and the problems that he considers concern hardware, systems design and programming, and management use of these systems.

Although converting an integrated information system based on batch processing to one based on real time would be an exceedingly difficult task, real time systems have actually been set up. Perhaps the first in the world of business were those that controlled machine tools in manufacturing operations and those that controlled chemical process operations. Following these were military command and control systems. However, all of these, strictly speaking, are not real time management *information* systems since the information generated is treated as a by-product, not as the primary product as in a true management information system.

The importance of a real time management information system is predicated on the accelerating pace of technological progress, shorter product life spans, and rapidly changing marketing conditions. Consequently managers can no longer rely on their periodic reports or historical data compilations. They need real time information if they are to survive.

Ream proceeds to parcel out and define the field of real time systems and he does this rather inclusively. He distinguishes a real time control system, a real time communication system, and finally a real time management information system. It is with the last of these systems that he is particularly concerned. Planning, control, and operating reports are essentials of such a system.

Real time systems components include input and output devices, a communication network, and a central computer. Though all are important it is with the central computer and the various configurations in which it can occur that the rest of the article deals. Each of these configurations has its own advantages and disadvantages, system-wise and cost-wise. The seven configurations that Ream considers basic and which he describes in some detail are: the simplex system, the simplex system with I/O multiplexor, duplex system with I/O and file multiplexors, master/slave system, shared file system, duplex or dual system, and multiprocessing system.

The duplex configuration mentioned by Ream is best illustrated by the SABRE system next discussed in the selection by

R. W. Parker. This is American Airlines' real time passenger reservations system. Besides giving some general idea of what the system does, Parker details the three major elements of the system: the input/output devices used at reservation and ticket sales desks, the electronic reservations center with its two IBM 7090 computers, and the communication network consisting of more than 31,000 miles of leased facilities and about 50 terminal interchanges. The development and implementation of this very complex system with regard to the hardware, software, and personnel involved is interestingly depicted and the discussion of the practical difficulties encountered that follows is both frank and illuminating.

In his selection, "The Myth of Real-Time Management Information," John Dearden not only seriously questions the utility of a real-time *information* system for top management and the practicality of a real time management *control* system but he raises grave doubts about the worth of a real-time system in other areas of concern for top managers. His estimate of the real-time system is succinctly expressed in the concluding sentence of his introduction, ". . . of all the ridiculous things . . . foisted on the long-suffering executive in the name of science and progress, the real-time management information system is the silliest."

Dearden launches into the battle by first attacking the semantic confusion and vagueness that too often appears in the literature when real-time information systems are cursorily defined. That this is not something unique to real-time information systems is nowhere intimated. He fails to mention that the same situation holds for the very concept of systems as such or, for that matter, for the concept and definition of cybernetics, automation, etc., and for some of the behavioral sciences themselves, like sociology, social psychology, and perhaps for business management too.

He then proceeds to identify the "real-time system" with a computer system possessing certain definite characteristics: a computer that can be interrogated from remote terminals and with "on-line" data that will be updated as events occur. What these "events" are he does not specify. He further limits the application of the concept to data stored either in the computer memory itself or at least in random access files, thus specifically excluding all data stored on magnetic tapes. The reason for this is not any intrinsic characteristic of real-time systems but the increasingly less expensive new generation of computers now available, together with the latest advances made in data transmission equipment and techniques.

He further limits the subject under discussion by restricting "top management" to the "president and executive vice president in centralized companies, plus divisional managers in decentralized companies." The entire discussion that follows is thus predicated upon these initial definitions and delimitations of "real-time systems for top management." One must keep these definitions in mind when perusing the article.

One cannot, of course, question Dearden's right to define these terms the way he does. Definitions, after all, are but the basic assumptions from which one wishes to begin a discussion. But to be optimally meaningful and useful to others, a definition should be neither too broadly nor too narrowly conceived. This is but in keeping with the cardinal rules of logic pertinent to definitions. One can therefore level the same indictment against him that he leveled at the authors of the definitions that he himself deplored. Theirs were too broad; his are too narrow!

In the subsequent sections Dearden considers the general functional categories of top management and their applicability to real-time systems. Six categories are singled out: management control, strategic planning, personnel planning, coordination, operating control, and personal appearances. The last of these could well be equated with *social functioning,* since it involves such things as entertaining visiting dignitaries, giving out 25-year watches, etc. Only the first five categories are assumed to have any bearing on real-time management information systems, and each is in turn measured against the yardstick of real-time practicality and found wanting.

As for management control involving, as it must, an objective, a system of evaluating performance, and an "early warning" system, Dearden not only cannot see how a real-time information system can be used but also rejects the belief that any attempted use would enhance control. Strategic long-range planning fares no better. A real-time information system will not appreciably help matters. The much-proclaimed use of models, of computer simulation, of interaction with the computer are all dismissed. Personnel planning, it is true, can be facilitated by the use of timely computer-spewed information, but whether it should be so employed, especially when visual displays are involved, is the big economic question. A real-time system, according to Dearden, is neither necessary nor useful for the solution of the coordination problems typically facing top management. Because most top executives spend only a modicum of their time on operating functions, it seems apparent that a real-time information system operating from their offices would be difficult to justify monetarily.

One must admit, that given the narrowly circumscribed definitions that Dearden outlines, these conclusions can logically be deduced. However, the wisdom of thus proceeding is questioned when one realizes that there is nothing in the nature of real-time systems that demands that expensive computer facilities be employed solely and directly for the president, vice president, and divisional managers. If one admits, as Dearden seems to, that staff specialists can well be entrusted with the task of developing models, of computer simulation, etc., not continuously but at particular moments

in time, and of reporting the results back to top executives, then decisions reached on the basis of these results must be considered related in a meaningful, albeit expensive way to model building, computer simulation, and the rest.

After carefully weighing the pros and cons of replacing the traditional published reports for management by console and display device manipulation by top executives to obtain desired information, Dearden discusses what he considers the three major fallacies upon which the desirability of real-time information systems rests: improved control, scientific management, and logistics similarity. The myth of improved control is grounded partly on the feeling of insecurity that managers often experience with regard to the imperfect type of control that they exert and partly on the glittering promise that knowing everything that happens when it is happening will help ameliorate the situation. Real-time systems will not eliminate this feeling of insecurity. The myth of scientific management is based upon the assumption that the only scientific way to manage is by using a computer. The fallacy of logistics similarity is founded on the belief that management control systems are but higher manifestations of logistics systems. Any real-time system is a logistics system in which rapidity in handling and transmitting a vast amount of data is an essential prerequisite. Such rapid processing and transmitting of voluminous amounts of data are not, in Dearden's view, a critical factor in management control systems.

With an eye to the near future, five to seven years distant, Dearden predicts that real-time information systems will be of little use in improving management control. As for the more distant future, some fifteen to twenty years hence, the question is quite different. Some experts believe that the new breed of manager will function in a peopleless, paperless office, with only his thoughts and his computer terminal and visual display devices. But since God alone can know with certainty what the next two decades will bring, one cannot say that these dreams of experts will not become a reality or that they will not remain what they now are—pipe dreams. Dearden rightly urges executives to use caution, to be open-minded to suggestions for improving management information systems but at the same time not to precipitously discard the tried and proven methods now in use. Over two centuries ago the famous poet and critic, Alexander Pope, gave somewhat similar sensible advice:

Be not the first by whom the new are tried,
Nor yet the last to lay the old aside.

43. MANAGEMENT CONTROL IN REAL TIME IS THE OBJECTIVE

H. C. HARTMANN *

In industry, knowledge is power and control —provided it is relevant, ample *and timely.* Delays in receipt of vital management information from anywhere within the manufacturing organization can adversely affect the objective of a sound Management Information and Control System, which is to deliver quality products to a customer, on time and at a profit.

INSTANT INFORMATION

Only a businessman who knows what is happening inside his company as soon as it happens can truly adjust his means to his aims. And only one who knows what is happening in the marketplace as soon as it happens can really make sound decisions about his aims.

Therefore, to insure the success of a modern management information system, it is essential that we shrink the management information cycle as much as possible. The solution to this problem is what is generally called "real time."

"Real time" can be a second, a minute, an hour or a week. It is the time element associated with the ability to obtain timely management data. Turned around, data must be timely enough to be of value to management.

It is illogical to think that all data requires the same real time element. Certainly, the receipt of an item of material that is already late should be recorded promptly in order to get the job started and to avoid the embarrassment of following a vendor on an item that is already on the receiving dock.

The old-fashioned, one-man industry, with all the factors in his head and all the data in a small box in front of him, was in real time all the time. He knew what orders he had in the

SOURCE: *Systems* (September, 1965), pp. 26–28. Reprinted by permission of *Systems.*

* National Accounts Manager, IBM Corp.

house, and he literally polled his customers and prospects to plan his medium- and long-range programs.

His ability to plan materials to meet his programs was a relatively easy matter—so long as his credit standing was good. His ability to plan his work load was also easy. He just worked more or less hours in order to meet his commitments to his customers. Intuitively, he knew the length of his manufacturing cycle.

GROWING PAINS

It was merely a matter of time, however, before the one-man business was incapable of supplying the demand for his product. His product line grew. The demands became more complex. Each new order received required additional engineering, tooling and equipment. Planning for materials presented more and more of a problem. It became necessary to hire more people in order to produce his products.

He soon found that he had competition where yesterday there had been no competition. To maintain his share of the market, it was necessary to meet competition head on—price-wise, delivery-wise and quality-wise. To produce a quality product, he had to engineer a little better. To reduce material costs, he had to shop a little better. To reduce labor costs, he had to plan his processes a little better. To reduce the elapsed time from receipt of customer order to delivery of the product to the customer, he had to establish areas of control to contract the total cycle time.

Area control proceeded to become a way of industrial life. It took the management problem and broke it down into more manageable elements. However, response time was not as good as it had been under the one-man business control. It took too long to evaluate accurately the effect of revised customer orders,

419

engineering changes, tool changes and vendor deficiencies. Each area of control did not operate from the same source data. Separate records were maintained in each area, creating excessive duplication of effort.

It became evident that it was necessary to attempt to bring the large industrial organization once again as close to the one-man business control as possible. So, a little over five years ago, the modern Management Information and Control System concept was born.

In IBM, we called it the Management Operating System. This system contained at least one central electronic file with multiple accessibility by Sales, Engineering, Quality Control, Industrial Engineering, Accounting and Manufacturing. Contained in this file were all the dynamic data required to run a business, such as sales demand, current inventories, master bills of materials and operations records, job costs, etc. This electronic file was updated daily with the transactions that affected these dynamic records.

IMMEDIATE AND IMPRESSIVE

The results were immediate—and impressive. Those who pioneered in this effort today have Management Information and Control Systems that have contracted the entire manufacturing cycle to produce goods for customers in less time and, in the majority of instances, at reduced cost.

NEVER ENOUGH PROGRESS

The more progress we make, the more progress we want to make.

Management soon realized that the ability to produce goods on time and at a profit meant that a better job of forecasting of end items, component parts and materials was required. No longer did management have the time or the people to poll customers and prospects on their need for the products manufactured.

Mathematical forecasting techniques brought forth one of industry's most valuable management tools—simulation.

The ability to schedule a final assembly line that will produce the end items consistent with predetermined production levels at the least total cost is another product of simulation.

In short, a full-scale simulator can be termed a Management Information and Control System, or we could say it the other way around —that a Management Information and Control System is a full-scale simulator for evaluating the effects of contemplated management decisions.

Without the advent of the computer, simulation to the degree to which we are referring would be an almost impossible task, even if we could afford all the personnel that would be required.

With current technology providing industry with the capability of processing data and placing it where and when it is needed, I would like to make a few predictions regarding the Management Information and Control System of the future.

Contained within the management information and control system could be a complete representation of all of a firm's existing engineering drawings. These drawings could be in either digital or image form and could be retrievable in a matter of seconds in either aperture card form or in hard copy. It would be a relatively simple matter to make changes to these drawings without redrafting the masters. Engineering drawing files as we know them today would be eliminated.

Bills of Material files will no longer be required. Customer specifications will be processed against data representing all possible variations from the basic product and as bills of material are required for material planning or any other purpose, they will be regenerated.

External Master Operation files will be eliminated wherever predetermined time standards are used. A simple alphanumeric code— an industrial engineering shorthand in effect —will enable the engineer to make changes in the manufacturing process with ease and in a fraction of the time it now takes to make the change and adjust the labor and material standards.

A where-used file will be an automatic by-a manufacturing engineer contemplated a product of the system. As an example, if change in an assembly tool, the computer would advise the part numbers of all assemblies this tool was used on. The same would hold true if there was the thought to change an item of material because of its improved machinability or reduced cost.

At a command, the computer would recalculate the standard costs of the end items affected by any change.

Because standard costs would always be up-to-date as of the latest change, quotations on new business of a highly competitive nature could be made with the satisfaction that the costs are truly representative of the current industrial process.

The internal master operation files would be able to regenerate a master operation record based upon a single inquiry for such a record.

These same internal files would be used as part of the Management Information and Control System to balance production lines in the industrial organization and to project space, equipment, tooling and manpower requirements for days, weeks, months and years in less time than it has taken me to write this paragraph.

And last—the Management Information System of the future will be economically available to the small industrial organization.

44. MANAGEMENT IN REAL TIME

SHERMAN C. BLUMENTHAL [*]

In traditional computer-based information systems, if management needed a new or changed type of report, a set of requirements had to be developed and submitted to the programming staff. Thereupon ensued a delay while the requirement was programmed, debugged, computer time scheduled for processing the necessary tapes, and the output finally printed, collated, bound and distributed. Management has found several shortcomings in this state of affairs.

1. Trouble in communicating the new requirements to the technical staff.
2. Delays in receiving requested information.
3. Cost of producing information, especially if it is only wanted on an infrequent or one-time basis.
4. Lack of proper emphasis or selectivity in information produced often resulting in voluminous printouts and reduced comprehensibility.

These barriers have proved so formidable that management has increasingly lost touch with the computer system through frustration and lack of understanding on the part of both the systems staff and the users of information.

It would then appear to be a major goal of an advanced, computer-based, information system to provide management with the ability to communicate easily and in a timely and readily understandable way with it. The achievement of these objectives requires three major innovations:

1. Programming that is flexible enough to permit the arbitrary structuring and output of processed data in a great variety of unanticipated arrangements and levels of detail.
2. A familiar and relatively rich language

SOURCE: *Data Processing Magazine* (August, 1965), pp. 18–23. Reprinted by permission of *Data Processing Magazine*.

[*] Contributing Editor, *Data Processing Magazine.*

with which the user can readily convey its requests for information to the system on-the-spot.
3. A mechanism that will *display* the information to the user or users on-the-spot, without the intermediation of people, devices, and procedures that tend to introduce delays, increase costs and lessen usefulness.

Recent developments in information display technology have made it possible to achieve these general goals. Specifically, an operator of a display interconnected to a management information system can today, after a short indoctrination, translate a user's verbal request through an information interface consisting of buttons, keyboards, light pencils, etc., into the desired display of information.

Major problems remain, however, in data base design and in devising a suitable set of languages with which manager-machine dialogues may be conducted.

MANAGEMENT REQUIREMENTS

In the planning and control of marketing, internal organization, facilities and finances, a management information system fulfills three major functions:

Continuously informing all levels of management of the corporate objectives as a whole as they affect each aspect of the business. Without this the company would disintegrate into very many small businesses operating independently of each other and in conflict with institutional goals.

Enabling each management echelon to ascertain how well delegated responsibilities are being carried out. Without this kind of information, management will have found that it has abdicated rather than delegated.

Providing the basis for strategic and tactical planning and decision making.

It is commonly understood that control comes into play after two basic requirements have been established and met:

A plan which reflects goals grouped according to individual responsibilities, and which is based on a rational assessment of organizational potential.

A means of accurately measuring and quickly reporting actual activity, so that deviations from the plan are highlighted and sources of problems can be pinpointed.

It is not untypical that a report may bring to top management's attention the fact, for example, that production in a certain product line is 10 per cent less than planned in a given month. Is this because of a drop in orders, excessive inventory, underutilization of plant and equipment, loss of efficiency, poor sales mix reflected in an overabundance of uneconomic production lot sizes, or combinations of these things?

The report of the gross variance is already after the fact if these deviations are reported only periodically. Moreover, with the inherent long delay in managerial response to these deviations, it is possible that local, nonoptimal corrective actions have been or are in process of being taken, whose dimensions are unknown to higher management. It is also possible that the deviations were isolated and not indicative of any persistent trend or fundamental shortcoming in the operational unit or units, and that the situation is correcting itself through the reassertion of long-term trends and pressures. Therefore, any inadequately informed or overly delayed control actions by management can have the opposite effect to that intended, creating sustained and ever amplifying oscillations, where only moderate and perhaps temporary deviations existed previously. This is typical of the management dilemmas which an intelligently used on-line information processing and display system can help solve.

Top management requires strategic, analytic and trend data. While a good deal of such data is not urgent, especially at the top management level, management cannot always predict ahead what information it wants, when it wants it, and how it wants it presented. This argues for providing the kind of flexibility achievable within the structure of an advanced management information system, that is, a management information facility on line to the management information system.

Since a major purpose of management information and display is to measure performance against a plan, well designed displays should suggest action, emphasize deviations from plan, direct thinking toward objectives, clearly indicate the present position relative to the desired goal, and indicate the probability of reaching the goal.

The form of presentation has a strong influence on the usefulness of display. Extraneous detailed data interfere with communication. Ancient history is a poor standard. Information must be selected critically to suit operating needs. Trends and indices are more useful than accounts and pennies. The degree of detail reported should correspond to the decision level where the information is used. Operating needs should be emphasized, rather than accounting interests.

POTENTIAL ROLE OF MANAGEMENT

If an organization provides means of interrogating a file (or better, several files) of business information, they may find their management becoming less report oriented and more event oriented. That is, management would tend to pay less attention to the traditional periodic reports to which it has become accustomed. Instead when a question arises, or a problem is forced upon management's attention by the information system, management would turn to querying the files, usually probing more and more deeply as the information system assists them in searching out relevant answers.

It must be recognized, however, that this is only one dimension of a management information system which also can and must affect all levels of management and control in an organization. A management information system to serve properly its objectives must aid in rationalizing, simplifying and coordinating all levels of control to achieve various institutional goals.

Frequently, these kinds of problems have been met through decentralization. If such decentralization is to mean delegation rather than abdication, then the delegating executive must have the means of evaluating how the delegated responsibilities are being handled. But, this is not the only requirement in a decentralized organization. The needs and objectives of the entire organization, not just the local goals of each administrator, must be made visible to the entire team. This type of management information is indispensible, if suboptimization at the expense of the whole organization is to be avoided.

Carried to the other extreme, an attempt to gather all possible information in one place and then use scientific methods to reduce it to a point where all decisions could be made centrally could result in chaos rather than order. Indiscriminate centralization of large enterprise would result in complete inundation of top management. The objective here is to minimize the volume and maximize the relevance of communication. The crucial information problem is the maintenance of relevant, consistent and valid context in each separate, disparate organization or headquarters. This is the central task of a management information system, the essence of managerial control.

When the rationale of installing computer systems is no longer merely clerical cost reduction, but is aimed at satisfying the information requirements of management, many companies find themselves perforce behaving more and more in a centralized fashion. With the information resources at hand, management is no longer happy with suboptimization at a product line or divisional level, but begins to look meaningfully at what is best from a total company point of view.

Management information processing and display systems are not characterized by the automation of creative decision making. There has been a good deal of confused thinking on this point in the past. What is important to a clearer understanding of this question is the difference between two essentially different kinds of decision making; viz., analytic and synthetic. In the present state of the art analytical decision making—no matter how seemingly complex—is subject to automation; while synthetic decision making—except perhaps at a very primitive level—is not. Analytic decisions are in a sense all made at once. That is, a set of rules or algorithm is established to make all choices that arise among a certain definable set of problems. Snythetic decisions arise where there is a one of a kind peculiarity of the problem, or all the parameters are either not known precisely or not subject to easy measurement, or the number of variables in the problem are too numerous for adequate rationalization, or as is usual, a combination of these things.

In fact, management information systems are important precisely because not all decisions can be "programmed" analytically. Hence, the need to combine the "known" from the information system with the "felt" in the manager's mind through a man-machine dialogue in such a way that as much "known" as is available is made as comprehensible as possible in a timely fashion.

The answer to some of the problems of control is usually to leave strategy and long range planning at the top, and the tactics and fast responses to the man on the spot. It will be useful to examine what this means in a little more detail.

The Stratification of Management

Level	"Pulse Rate"
Strategic (top mgt.)	monthly, annually
Tactical (plant or division mgt.)	weekly, monthly
Operating (dept. head)	daily, weekly
Supervisory (foreman or section head)	daily, "real time"

As one proceeds upward in this list, information increases in importance and in complexity. At the same time, comprehension time and immediacy decrease. In the process of reaching the top of this hierarchy, voluminous raw data is sifted, analyzed, selected, separated, combined, reduced and summarized many times, and interpretations of significance are made. This, of course, takes time, and is one source of the lengthening "pulse rate" that is observed as one moves upward.

Management information systems combined with information display have the potential ability to drastically affect this information delay. However, this in itself is not necessarily an absolute good. If the result of shortening the information delay were to enable top management to make the tactical or on-the-spot decisions that were previously the province of lower levels of management, that would be merely a displacement of function. One could very reasonably question whether the talents and experience of top management ought to be so employed, especially if it were at the expense of those decision-making functions which are characteristically and exclusively those of top management. Also, if the shortening of the information delay were to affect the strategic planning and decision-making cycle "pulse rate," there is always the danger that isolated or short-term variations—that would have ordinarily been submerged in the normal information cycle—might be seized upon by top management. Their consequent actions and decisions might have an effect opposite to that intended, causing a transient fluctuation to amplify into sustained and harmful oscillations. An organization requires time for changes in plans and policies to take effect.

Where operations have been increasingly centered on the computer, one typically finds the expanding data base handling orders, inventory, production scheduling, forecasting, purchasing and accounts payable and receivable as parts of one integral whole. Thus, important elements of the functions of sales, manufacturing, accounting, customer relations and even market analysis and forecasting are being centralized within a new systems synthesis. As this trend reaches its culmination, it is not too difficult to foresee the reduction and elimination in large measure of the human intermediary between the information base and direct management interaction with it through appropriate inquiry and display mechanisms.

The evidence indicates that while formal structural compartments within an organization may be retained for some time yet, the management and staff of the information systems department, reporting directly to the top of the corporate hierarchy, are assuming responsibility for more and more of the operations, tactical decision making, planning and finally, participation in strategic decisions.

It would seem reasonable, however, that the systems function in an organization will become different in a way that the production or marketing functions will not and cannot be. While decisions, policies and plans will continue to flow downward from level to level through the hierarchy at the respective "pulse rates" peculiar to each level and each type of decision (e.g., an annual plan will always be annual, but a new forecast may update it weekly or monthly—but certainly not at such a frequency that the revision does not have time to "sink in" and influence lower levels), information, however, will no longer flow upward. Rather information sensors at the operating level will feed data directly to the information system on-line in real time, where it will be processed and displayed in appropriately tailored form simultaneously to all levels and functional areas in the company according to the needs of each.

A SYSTEMS PERSPECTIVE

The confusion and inconsistency in the use of real time to describe information systems arise when the context is limited to the computer and its immediate logistical support. When the context is broadened to include information capture, processing, flow at all levels of the management hierarchy, and the functioning of the associated decision and action systems, the confusion disappears. A total, functionally integrated, advanced management information system is, *ipso facto*, a real time system. In fact, every management information system considered from this perspective is real time, whether computerized or not.

This conclusion is not reached by using the term "real time" in a trivially broad sense. The major differences, other than technological, between advanced and conventional management information systems are in terms of overall systems cost, effectiveness, and responsiveness. In the latter instance the increased responsiveness of advanced systems results from their ability to function in a highly selective way within much more highly restricted temporal constraints than before.

At the lowest level of the management hierarchy, say at the foreman level, the process of sensing raw information, deciding and acting upon it is a continuous one. This raw data is subsequently sifted, refined and summarized many times as it makes its way upward from supervisory to department head to plant or division management, and finally to company management. The tempo or "pulse rate" of the information flow is respectively from continuous to hourly and daily, to daily and weekly, to weekly and monthly, to monthly and annually. Such a regularized time discipline makes the information system real time when looked at from a total point of view.

A total, functionally integrated, advanced management information system is one that incorporates a real time computer system. A management information system benefits from being centered upon a real time computer system by not being burdened with the problem of accommodating its various tempos to the deficient capabilities of a batch processing computer.

For many reasons, most companies have in the past used their batch processors on a non-integrated, non-centralized basis. When real time equipment became available with massive and economic storages, and with capabilities for direct communication with remote input-output devices including displays, increasing numbers of companies decided to plan for total integrated data systems based on common sources of raw data. Integration is providing for a document such as an order to be entered into the system and to affect many functions in various departments all at the same level. An order in such a *horizontally* integrated system affects materials scheduling, finished inventory, production scheduling, dispatching, invoicing, accounting, sales commissions, etc. In implementing a total system, provision is also made for *vertical* integration—that is, the generation of management information at all levels of the hierarchy.

Inherent in the design approach must be a clear understanding of the special peculiarities and difficulties introduced by the requirement of an on-line real time operation. What are some of these peculiarities?

1. A management information system is an integral part of an on-going real world activity. This means that messages and transactions generated as a consequence of this activity must report and record events *as they occur,* and the information system must capture this data as it is recorded.

2. The management information system responds to the on-going requirements of the real world activity for processed data or information must be designed to fall within certain maximum acceptable limits. These time constraints vary widely, and only some of them are more or less instantaneous. The most severe time constraints in commercial applications (other than, for example, process control of a continuous manufacturing cycle like oil refining) are a matter of seconds or minutes, not milliseconds. However, these constraints do make the management information system *clock dependent,* and we are, therefore, justified in using the term "real time" in describing one of its dimensions.

DESIGN PROBLEMS

A major design problem centers around the particular advantages of display as opposed to normal hard copy output. In the latter case, the designer is concerned with volumes, formats, contents and periodicity of reports to be produced. In the case of display output the problem is considerably more complex, and these complexities are aggravated by management information requirements.

Let us look at these problems in light of some of the visual display's special characteristics from the user point of view.

The elimination or reduction of hard copy, while it is, of course, a consequence of the other features, does involve a problem for the systems designer. The user, for example, cannot take the display console home with him on the train like he can a piece of paper. Yet, if the hard copy document is not largely eliminated, much of the economic forcefulness of display as an alternative to conventional output will be lost. Perhaps facility for locally produced hard copy of the on-line displayed information in certain cases is the answer.

On-line access to stored information with randomized demand is a problem that has been thoroughly explored in other contexts. Time sharing by many users at remote locations is again a problem that has been attacked before: e.g., Project MAC, the SDC time-sharing system, DAC-1 at General Motors, KEYDATA, etc. Beyond the problem of dynamic user-system communications are others—principally the one concerned with time sharing. Obviously, the system will drive more than one display and, equally obviously, what is being displayed at each location will generally be different information. Therefore, the problem of multiple, simultaneous demands for service (on time sharing) is intrinsic to information display in a total, integrated, advanced business system. This problem has been solved a number of times, most successfully with a combination of software and hardware. Time-sharing software involves executive routines, core allocators, bulk storage control programs, I/O processors, error recovery, etc., features normally found in all real time systems with remote devices on line. Such time sharing, however, is difficult and costly to achieve without hardware features such as interrupts, relocation registers, memory protection and buffering.

The ease of use, flexibility in format and content, and the achievement of man-machine symbiosis are all related to the individual user; namely, ease of use (how much special preparation?), flexibility (can he get what he wants in the form he wants it?), symbiosis (can he hold a discourse with the machine—talk back to it in his language as he might with a particularly bright staff man—in developing problem solutions?).

Ease of use is related to language. Removing the imposition of communicating one's desires to the system in a highly formalized language foreign to the user is a must. The language may be artificial, of course, in the sense that an electronics designer wants to communicate in terms familiar to his universe of discourse. Similarly the manager wants to communicate in terms familiar to him. A high level language approach such as is familiar to COBOL programmers and report generator users is hardly conducive to meeting the requirement for easy on-the-spot dialogue between the technically untrained user and the system. However, other approaches may lend themselves to adequate solutions. Among these are information retrieval techniques involved in "browsing," decision trees, logic tables and others.

It is a fact of life that most organizations are getting only a residual benefit from their computer systems, impressive though this residue may be in itself. The computer spends a large part, if not most of its time dealing with the elaborate redundancies and formalities of input and output. One increasingly finds in consequence of this that separate units (or satellites) are often used to lessen this burden on the main processor. This problem is even more marked in the case of display systems.

Besides memory allocation, the executive programs have several other responsibilities: processing input and clock interrupts, handling all outputs and file writing, recording for off-line processing, etc.

Advanced real time programming systems are characterized by the ability to do automatic object time reassembly, dynamic storage allocation, allocation of input-output channels, handling asynchronous operation among modules of differently rated speeds, and the prevention of accidental interaction among concurrently operating programs simultaneously performing unrelated functions.

On the occurrence of an input or clock interrupt the executive program will govern the sequence of a complex chain of events. It will call on subprograms to update internally stored information, perform special computations, format output messages or displays, etc. Interrupt sequences can be designed such that

executives can control many demands on the system more or less concurrently through the collocation of the high speed internal processing with low speed external devices. Thus, on a shared basis displays can be generated, output queues processed, input messages accepted, bulk to core and core to bulk transfers made and internal processing take place.

The program structure must be related to the real time hardware facilities to result in a unifying approach permitting the maximum independent development of each part of the program and enabling a reasonably painless integration of the resulting complex.

Files are the heart of the system and crucial to its successful operation. Structuring files for most efficient access and processing is the most demanding systems design task, particularly where the systems users will be competing for the central processing unit to service their information requests in close to real time. Some displays (to say nothing of inputs) will require information to be assembled from several files. A file structured to permit this to be done efficiently may be poorly organized for output generation.

Typical problems in file design that will have to be dealt with include, for example, how to treat orders. If they are included in the customer file, how are they located without bringing into memory and searching all orders for the right one? If they are not so included, how are customers and orders related? If separate, is total on order data summarized in customer file, and how? There are good solutions to these problems, but each case has to be carefully studied on its own merits.

Some of the files in a total, integrated system might include:

> Customers
> Suppliers
> Raw materials
> Order and order status
> Finished inventory
> Tables of accounts
> Personnel records
> Tool records
> Facilities
> Cost and production standards
> Master schedules
> Etc.

These are no longer separate by function (i.e., payroll, inventory, etc.) in a fully integrated system, but are related to each other to the extent that common sources of input affect file data in many functionally separate areas.

The problem of display cannot be considered separately from the problem of the data base. In both cases various file records are being accessed concurrently. However, display does not change record content, nor does it involve restoring records to the file unless display is coupled with input functions. The user will not refer explicitly to a file or files and, in fact, should not even need to be aware of the structure or stratification of the information base.

A display request message, which may say something like "display all A's which are B's, if year and month is equal to $1\frac{2}{64}$, according to this picture which I have sketched," does not refer to any files explicitly. The picture is a pre-stored or newly devised display format sketched on the scope, and presumably will permit complete variability in presentation including information in graphic and tabular form. The display request message elements, which refer to items or sets of items of information, rather than to specific file records, must somehow be related to specific internal storage areas. These areas must then be accessed, undergo certain logical processes (in general), be formatted, and then output to display.

We may analyze the problem into its elements generally as follows, remembering that specific implementation may take quite a different approach:

1. Analyze display requirement (generated by external request or as a part of operation of internal program logic) into individual file referents.

2. Associate referents to appropriate file indices in core or fast storage.

3. Index file referent via associated parameters (date, account number, etc.) to a master file location in bulk storage.

4. Access bulk storage master file record(s).

5. Using format information in file index, select and rearrange fields according to logic specified by display generator program.

6. Perform logical and arithmetic operations on selected file information.

7. Place display in output area and return to executive which will queue display and output it during normal waiting line duty cycle.

45. ON-LINE MANAGEMENT INFORMATION

Norman J. Ream [*]

The past decade has seen the evolution of the use of electronic computers and the evolution and recognition of formal management information systems. The planning and formalization of these management information systems and the accompanying necessity of integrating them on a company-wide basis are a massive and difficult undertaking. The development of integrated information systems on a batch processing basis is difficult enough, but when we consider an attempt to place such systems on a true real-time basis, the problem becomes so large it staggers one's imagination.

Paralleling the evolution of more formalized business systems was the use of computers in process control, probably the first major use of computers in the real-time business environment. Examples are the introduction of numerically controlled machine tools into manufacturing operations and the development of computer controlled chemical process operations.

Closely associated with these latter developments was the development of military command and control systems that combined control of a process with the production of formally structured information. An example here is the SAGE system.

A real-time management information system may be defined as a system whose primary product is management information, as opposed to systems, such as process control and command and control, in which the production of such information is treated as a byproduct. This field is new although there are examples of limited applications of such systems. As in any new area there are many problems to be solved.

Management and the information system

within which they must operate are inseparably interdependent. The accelerating pace of technological advancement and the anticipated accompanying shorter product life-spans, together with the increasing rapidity of changes in marketing climates, mean that management reaction time to change in all areas must be speeded to the greatest degree possible. Consequently, we must recognize that management cannot continue to rely upon existing reporting cycles nor can they continue to place their dependence on historical information. Rather, management must have immediate access to the effect of changing conditions on their present management climate as well as a means of determining the effect of current conditions on planning strategy.

The problem facing management today is not what actions should be taken to meet present conditions, for those actions should have been taken yesterday; rather the problem is what action must they take today to meet future conditions and to insure corporate survival.

My intent here is to point out some problems involved in implementing real-time management information systems and to suggest some solutions to these problems. Basically the problems fall into three categories: hardware, systems design and programming, and management use of these systems.

WHAT IS A REAL-TIME MANAGEMENT INFORMATION SYSTEM?

A control system is a combination of a data processing system, a management information system, and a feedback system. If corrective action is taken while the process is still going on, we have a real-time control system. Further, there are three levels on which a real-time system may operate. First, if the system

SOURCE: *Datamation* (March, 1964), pp. 27–30. Reprinted by permission of *Datamation*.

[*] Director, Systems Planning, Lockheed Aircraft Co.

accepts input directly, processes it, compares it with predetermined parameters, and issues instructions to men and/or machines, we have a real-time control system. Second, the computer may inform affected parties of this information as it develops. This level may be termed real-time communications. Finally, suitable condensations of the information derived are prepared for higher levels of management. Here we have a real-time management information system.

Generally then, we may define real-time systems as those systems that keep pace with "live" operations, accept data directly without manual conversion, process these data and establish relationships among data of disparate types. Further, they output data, on demand or as a result of programmed logic, to men and/or machines in a *timely* and *digestible* form.

For purposes of this paper, however, a line must be drawn between command and control systems and real-time management information systems.

If a system exerts direct control over the physical environment from which it accepts data, I will classify it as a command and control system. Examples of these systems are the SAGE, BMEWS, and Mercury systems.

We can define a real-time management information system as one which monitors the physical environment but exerts control only indirectly by the production of management type reports or displays. Examples here include existing airlines real-time reservation systems, various savings bank systems, and Lockheed's Automatic Data Acquisition (ADA) system. These systems may have primary functions other than management reports. However, they all use the data gathered by the computer to provide management with structured information. This latter type of system will be the one which this paper will discuss.

WHY A REAL-TIME MANAGEMENT INFORMATION SYSTEM?

In order to answer this question we must first define the term "management information system."

Managers need communications systems or reports. These reports may be considered under the general headings of Planning, Control, and Operating reports. In order to exercise control, management also needs specifica-

tions of objectives, criteria for evaluation of performance, decision rules for corrective action, and a feedback system to evaluate the effectiveness of corrective action.

Planning reports evaluate the position of the company or industry as compared to other comparable business entities. These reports include alternate courses of action available under a series of predetermined premises.

Control reports inform top management of operating performance as compared to predetermined performance standards.

Operating reports inform functional management of the current performance of operations within a given function. Normally these documents include a comparative analysis of current operations and operations for a previous period, as well as current performance as compared to predetermined detailed standards.

In addition to these reports, a real-time management information system can develop byproduct data to produce new criteria for performance evaluation, particularly of a statistical nature, at virtually no additional cost.

For instance, tighter control of materials and more efficient production scheduling are being realized through the Lockheed Shop Order Location system. Reductions in clerical and data origination costs are being attained in many systems through the use of real-time recording of payroll and labor distribution transactions. An increase in sales may be brought about by real-time inventory control which allows management to make better use of available inventory.

In addition, the use of a real-time system can make more profitable use of computer time. Using the classic batch-processing techniques of file updating and reporting, approximately 40% of the computer time is spent in sorting. Additionally, about 20% is spent on set-up time. The random updating of files eliminates most sorting and set-up time.

We are finding that in today's complex corporate world, data origination is rapidly becoming prohibitively expensive. The high cost of recording, accumulating and converting operating data to machine sensible language, combined with the fact that batch processing techniques cannot supply "time current" information, has led to an increasing need for on-line, real-time systems.

Early real-time systems were usually quite large and even today most real-time systems being installed use large-scale computers as their central hardware. However, there have been real-time management information systems on a rather small scale.

As an example of one of these, an electric typewriter plant has installed a real-time quality control system centered around a small-scale random access computer. The system has proved very profitable to the manufacturing operation and yet the total machine rental is less than $5,000 a month.

REAL-TIME SYSTEM COMPONENTS

All real-time systems are composed of generally the same subsystems (Fig. 1).

There is always a number of data acquisition or input devices, a communication system including any necessary interfaces, a central computer, and an input and output system within the computer center. Usually the system will also include remote inquiry and output devices.

Input sensor devices usually allow the use of a coded badge or card together with a punched card and variable keyboard information. Needs in this area run to lower cost units of higher reliability and more flexible operation.

Output devices are generally of one of two types: the printing device such as the teletype page or strip printers and the flexowriter, or the newer CRT display devices. Requirements here again are the classical ones of lower cost and greater flexibility.

The communications network invariably plays a large part in the real-time system. Present networks commonly make use of multipart cable, standard telephone lines, radio or TV channels, or microwave links. Generally, capacity of these systems varies with the cost.

The central computers in a real-time network may occur in varying configurations and each of these configurations has its inherent advantages and disadvantages. The choice of a particular configuration depends in large part upon the system's requirements and in turn has a strong effect on the overall system performance.

Because the choice of a particular configuration is of such importance to the design of a system and to its eventual success, let us examine the seven basic hardware configurations.

The simplex system (Fig. 2) provides no standby equipment. Among its advantages are: It is the least expensive from a hardware standpoint and, therefore, tends to be easier and cheaper to program as there are no complex routines for switching between two or more computers. Significant savings can be realized through the use of a simplex system, providing one is willing, or able, to lower system performance standards in the area of back-up. The system must be off-line during maintenance, and recovery in the event of hardware unavailability must be manual. This, of course, requires that part of the savings in equipment and programming costs be rein-

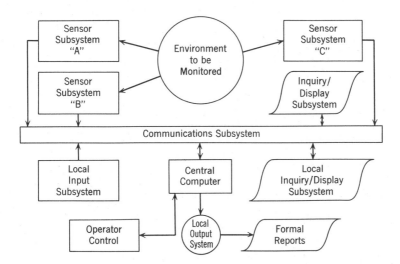

FIG. 1. Organization of a typical real-time management information system.

vested in an extensive manual back-up system.

If it is satisfactory, for instance, for the system to operate 16 hours a day rather than 24 and if it requires, say, 90%, rather than all of the transactions to be handled immediately, the simplex system may well be the best.

The next configuration is the simplex system with an input-output multiplexor (Fig. 3). The multiplexor is a simple stored program computer which acts as an interface between the communication terminals and the computer. It may be a simple buffer or may be more sophisticated to the point of accessing the main computer only when access to the files is necessary. The advantages of this configuration include added modularity—changes can be made in the multiplexor to effect different scan rates, changes in priority, etc., without disturbing the central processor programs. Also, the memory allocations within the central processing unit are simpler because input-output and queue functions are controlled within the multiplexor. The disadvantages of this system are higher equipment cost, program interface considerations, and more complex reliability considerations. In addition, program testing begins to get complicated.

In this configuration (Fig. 4) we have added a file multiplexor, which acts as an interface between the computer and the data files, to the previous system. Now the central computer is free of all specialized functions. The advantages and disadvantages are the same as for the previous system except that we have the added advantage of removing file access considerations from the central computer and the added disadvantages of programming for still another machine and of further complicating hardware reliability considerations and testing procedures. Incidentally, a new possibility is opened here of a direct route between the I/O and file multiplexors, by-passing the central computer altogether except when processing is necessary.

Here (Fig. 5) we have the first step in the configuration hierarchy that employs two computers. This system is well suited for any situation where a heavy load of internal computation exists. All housekeeping and scheduling functions are taken care of in the medium-scale master computer, leaving the slave, a powerful large-scale system, free to perform computations. Typically, the master receives data or information requests from the outside world and prepares all necessary tables, files, subroutines, etc. It then sends the entire package to the slave which in turn performs the calculations and sends the resultant data back to the master for formatting and output. The advantages of this configuration are more

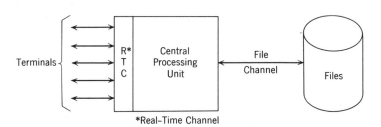

FIG. 2. Simplex system.

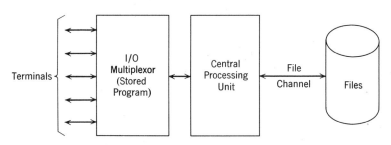

FIG. 3. Simplex system with input/output multiplexor.

computation capability per dollar, provided the medium-scale computer's cost can be justified, and automatic, one-direction back-up, i.e., the master can continue to receive, prepare, and batch input while the slave is unavailable. The disadvantages include high equipment cost and the complexity of the control programs.

The fifth configuration is called the shared-file system (Fig. 6). It is quite similar to the master-slave configuration and in fact the master-slave complex could use the shared-file concept. Here again the medium-scale processor is the scheduler and controller and the large-scale machine is the computation device. There is added flexibility here because

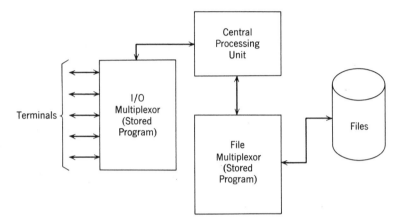

FIG. 4. Duplex system with input/output and file multiplexors.

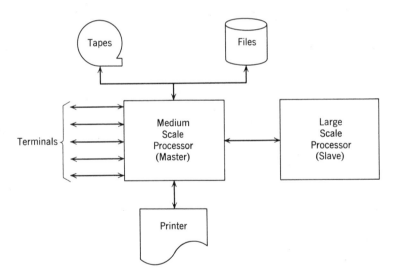

FIG. 5. Master/slave system.

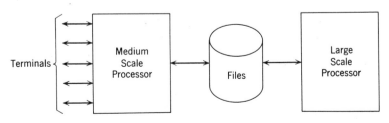

FIG. 6. Shared-file system.

the medium-scale computer can prepare jobs and place them on the file while the large system is busy. Both systems scan the file at intervals, the large system to pick up jobs and the medium-size computer to get the answers. As in the previous configuration, this system need not operate in real-time. The advantages and disadvantages here are the same as those for the master-slave system with the added disadvantage of having to develop programs to accomplish data transfer between the file and both of the CPU's.

Here we have the duplex or dual configuration (Fig. 7): two complete hardware systems, either of which is able to perform the total job.

In the duplex system the second machine is not on-line and must be switched over if the primary system fails or is taken off-line for any reason. The standby system, therefore, may be used for off-line batch processing, although it must have an interrupt built into its program monitor. In the dual concept both systems are on-line in parallel, performing the same functions except that output is generated by only one computer. Checking is carried on constantly, comparing the results obtained by the two systems. The dual system is generally

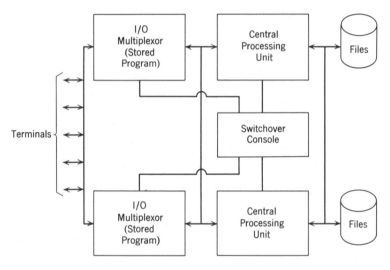

FIG. 7. Duplex or dual system.

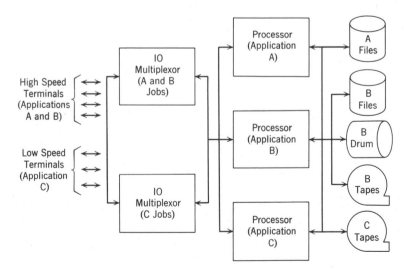

FIG. 8. Multiprocessing system.

considered the ultimate in reliability, but interestingly enough carries with it some fascinating problems, such as which machine is right when they are in disagreement? The dual system is, of course, more expensive than the duplex in terms of work accomplished, but also provides more reliability. Programming considerations are extremely important here as the complexity of control, monitor and switch-over programs may readily be seen. Most problems inherent in this type of system concern themselves with the transferring of information from one system to the other, the ability to update a system that has been off-line without interrupting the system that is functioning in real-time and the ability to preserve memory contents under an equipment failure. The general question here is "How far does the user go in search of reliability?" Project Mercury is a full dual system while SABRE, the American Airlines reservation system, is a duplex configuration.

Finally, in the multiprocessing system (Fig. 8) we have two or more computer systems each doing more than one job. Standby in this system is on a "degraded" basis. That is, when one system goes off the air another in the network may pick up the load. Because the computer picking up the load must also continue to perform its own tasks, a lengthened system response time usually results. Hence, the term, "degraded service." Depending on the configuration of the individual computers, any one may not be able to take over any other's task. These systems tend to be

geographically separated. When one center goes off the air, another temporarily takes over its duties. SAGE has this type of standby ability. However, in addition, each SAGE site is duplexed as well as being a multiprocessing system. The advantage of the multiprocessing system is standby reliability at a lower cost than for a duplex system. The disadvantages include a lower quality of service when one system is down, the difficulty of performing reliability analysis on the system because of the complex interdependency of the units, and the fact that the planning, development and testing of programs and specially of control programs is extremely difficult.

REFERENCES

1. "The Programming Gap in Real Time Systems" by R. V. Head, *Datamation,* February 1963, p. 39.
2. "Management Techniques for Real Time Computer Programming" by T. A. Holdiman, *Journal of the ACM,* July 1962.
3. "Real Time Systems Configurations" by R. V. Head, IBM Systems Research Institute paper, April 1963.
4. "Pitfalls and Safeguards in Real Time Digital Systems with Emphasis on Programming," by W. A. Hosier, *IRE Transactions on Engineering Management,* June 1961.
5. "The Need for Compact Management Intelligence," by Norman J. Ream, in Donald G. Malcolm, Alan J. Rowe, and L. F. McConnell (eds.), *Management Control Systems* (New York: John Wiley and Sons, 1960).

46. THE SABRE SYSTEM

R. W. Parker *

American Airlines' SABRE system is a large, real-time teleprocessing system designed to perform all the data collection and processing functions associated with the sale, confirmation and control of an airline reservation. Controlled through a computing center at Briarcliff Manor, N.Y., 30 miles north of New York City, it provides each American reservation sales agent with direct access to every available seat on any of the airline's flights. In addition, complete information on any passenger's reservation including name, itinerary, telephone number and related data is recorded on disc at Briarcliff and is, therefore, available to every agent in the system.

Access to the passenger name record makes it possible for any of American's sales agents immediately to confirm, alter or cancel all or part of a passenger's itinerary—no matter where or when the original reservation was made. Access in less than 3 seconds to the name record also provides authorization to the ticket agent to confirm the space and issue the passenger's ticket at an airport or city ticket office.

In addition to controlling seat inventory and maintaining passenger records, SABRE automatically:

—notifies agents when special action is required, such as calling a passenger to inform him of a change in flight status;
—maintains and quickly processes waiting lists of passengers desiring space on fully booked flights;
—sends Teletype messages to other airlines requesting space, follows up if no reply is received, and answers requests for space from other airlines;
—provides arrival and departure times for all the day's flights.

SOURCE: *Datamation* (September, 1965), pp. 49–52. Reprinted by permission of *Datamation*.
   * Director of SABRE Data Processing, American Airlines.

The system is made up of three major elements:

1. *Input/Output Devices.* At 1,008 reservations and ticket sales desks of American Airlines at 60 separate locations, these sets enable agents to communicate *directly* with the Briarcliff center. Teletype interface equipment, consisting of input communications adapters and output communications adapters, facilitates the handling of reservations traffic with other airlines.

2. *The Electronic Reservations Center.* At the heart of the system in Briarcliff Manor are two IBM 7090 computers, one of which is always on-line. The other 7090 acts as a standby and is used for other applications until it is required to take over the real-time job. Connected to the 7090's are six high-speed drums and 16 1301 disc files with a total capacity of over 700 million characters.

Information arriving at Briarcliff passes first through a duplex console which functions primarily as a switch to indicate which of the 7090's is on-line. From the duplex console, it passes to the real-time channel which formats serially transmitted messages into computer words and performs validity checks before passing data on to the 7090. The 90 is, of course, the logical controller and processor of the system. The most frequently used programs stay in the 90's core. Other programs, temporary storage and frequently accessed records reside on drums which have an access time of 11.25 milliseconds. Passenger name records and other records with a lower frequency of access are stored on discs which have an average access time of 115 msec.

3. *The Communications Network.* Agent sets are linked to the computer center by more than 31,000 miles of leased communications facilities. Also included in the network are 43 Terminal Interchanges which act as an interface between the I/O devices and the high-speed lines; one TI can handle 30 I/O devices.

436

In the field, agent sets and communications adapters are connected to a terminal interchange. The agent sets transmit pieces of customer transactions; the various parts of a customer's transaction with an agent are transmitted individually to the computer. The customer's name is transmitted as a message, his telephone number is a message, the flight number is a message. The communications adapters, on the other hand, transmit complete Teletype messages with longer messages broken into convenient "buffer loads."

Every input message will cause some kind of a response to be sent back to the input device which generated the message, and no device can transmit a second message until it has received a response relative to the first message.

The information entered into the terminal interchange from the I/O devices does not automatically pass out onto the high-speed line. The transmission of information from the TI is computer controlled from Briarcliff by a polling procedure. We have nine high-speed input/output line pairs; four or five TIs are attached to each of these pairs, and polling is carried out independently and simultaneously for each pair.

The situation with outputs from the computer is a little simpler. Output messages travel from the computer via a high-speed line to the terminal interchange and then without delay to the appropriate I/O device.

DEVELOPMENT AND IMPLEMENTATION

The development and implementation of a system as vast and complex as SABRE was not, needless to say, a simple undertaking. With our 20-20 hindsight, we can see many instances in which we could have saved ourselves some trouble by traveling an alternate path. Nonetheless if we had to do it all over again, we would do exactly what we did the first time in a vast majority of cases.

The decision to embark on the SABRE system was an outgrowth of several years of study and was American Airlines' answer to the growing complexity of our business. As air travel increased, it became more and more difficult for us to maintain records of all our passengers on all our flights with the accuracy and timeliness required to provide good service. Visualize, if you will, the difficulty of controlling manually the passenger name records and the inventory for 76,000 seats a day. The communications problems became horrendous, particularly when a passenger was involved in a multi-segment itinerary and each boardpoint had to be notified.

An agreement with IBM to produce SABRE came a year after the formulation of objectives by American in 1958. During the intervening year economic analysis satisfied American that a fully mechanized reservations system would, as traffic grew, increase in cost at a lesser rate

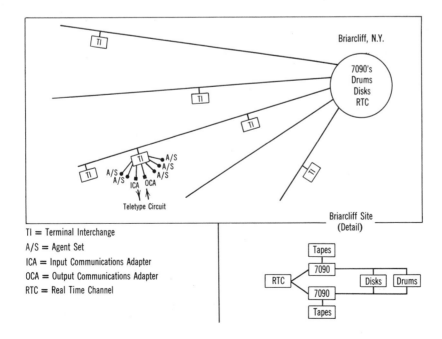

TI = Terminal Interchange
A/S = Agent Set
ICA = Input Communications Adapter
OCA = Output Communications Adapter
RTC = Real Time Channel

than the growth in business. On the other hand, it became apparent that the manual system when projected into the future, increased in cost at a rate equal to and, in some areas, greater than the growth of passenger volume. During this period, we also conducted the analysis necessary to make our choice of vendor. Perhaps the most significant factor in arriving at a vendor is the amount of backing and support we could expect.

THE AGENT SET

The design of the agent set was a joint IBM/American Airlines undertaking. Several man-years of experimentation went into the development of a device that was easy to learn, operate, and maintain. The most frequently performed actions are automated so the number of buttons to be depressed for a single action is minimized. Infrequent actions and variable data such as name, phone number, etc., are input through a typewriter keyboard.

The number of agent sets for the initial installation was determined by an application of queueing theory. American Airlines has a standard time within which incoming telephone calls must be answered. It was determined to provide enough sets so that this standard would be met in the peak hour of the average business day of a peak month when each set is manned. We had an accurate forecast of incoming telephone call volumes arrived at by applying statistical techniques to historical data and growth forecasts. The equation we used provided the number of manned positions (agent sets) when given the average number of phone calls and the average servicing time per call.

The determination of the number of terminal interchanges and the high-speed line configuration was performed on a somewhat more subjective basis. The number of TI's was determined by the maximum foreseeable number of input/output devices predicted during the life of the system. The placement of the TI's and, therefore, the lines was influenced by our desire to have the reservation offices protected against total lack of communication resulting from a failure on a single line. Therefore most major AA cities are serviced by more than one of our nine high-speed line pairs. A location serviced by two TI's, for example, has each TI hooked up to a different line. A further objective of the line configuration was line balance to

achieve equal traffic over all lines and TI's. This was deemed necessary in order that we achieve a response time—from input to answer back—of under 3 seconds.

The size of the file system was determined by forecasts of passenger transactions in number and size and by analysis of the "booking curve." A booking curve is essentially a table which tells what fraction of today's bookings applies to flights n days in the future. The curve varies with seasonal peaks in our business. Thus we determine how many records we would create, how long they would be in the files and hence what our maximum requirement would be for file space assuming that the files would be duplexed. We began operation with 24 disc modules and now are up to 32.

The original assumption on main frame hardware was that 7090's with a 32K memory would be adequate to handle all foreseeable volumes. However, in 1963 we discovered, after we had a number of cities already on the system, that we were saturating the computer with only 30% of our volume on the air. Therefore, we modified the 7090's to 65K to provide more core space for programs and thus eliminate the loss of computer time experienced by the necessity of waiting for programs. The system currently is capable of handling approximately 2,100 inputs per minute, and some 40,000 passenger name records in a day. The average passenger name record consists of 10 separate inputs to the computer.

DEVELOPING SOFTWARE

The general process by which the functional requirements of American Airlines were translated into operating computer programs has consisted of seven major steps.

1. Functional requirements were prepared by American Airlines people selected because of their thorough knowledge of reservations and sent to programming school to acquaint them with the capabilities and limitations (for as we all recognize, there are limitations) of data processors and, specifically, the 7090.

2. The functional requirements were translated by the programming staff into preliminary program specifications outlining in general and quite broadly how the programs would be designed to carry out these functions. This step revealed that in most instances what the airline-oriented people conceived of as a function re-

quired more than one program and, in a few instances, that one program could readily be used to carry out parts of several functions.

3. The preliminary program specifications were reviewed and discussed by the functional design group with the programming people and final program specifications were prepared.

4. From the final specifications, functional descriptions were written, translating the programs back into procedural language and describing, therefore, the manner in which the system would operate to carry out the reservations functions. The functional descriptions were then submitted to the people in the regular general office staff organization who were responsible for the operation of these functions in American Airlines. They were asked to sign off on these to indicate they were satisfied that the functions in which they were concerned would be carried out properly by the system.

5. We were faced with the problem of training some 1,500 people in 100 locations in the use of SABRE, so we developed a training section which was responsible for the maintenance of training materials and for the instruction of instructors. We had a small training facility at the SABRE processing site to which we brought from each of our 37 cities those people who were responsible for training all of the others. We gave them a thorough two-week course which encompassed the 35 hours of training which they would later give the agent personnel in their cities, as well as an equal amount of background information and practice in teaching techniques.

Training in the field stations presented no real problem. A program was developed in the computer which allowed trainees to practice all possible inputs to the system without endangering the permanent records on disc or drum. Our personnel policy guaranteed that no permanent employee would lose his job as a result of SABRE. Thus morale was good and conversion to the new system easy. The checking features in the SABRE programs actually add to the confidence of the reservations agents.

6. Close to a half million lines of code were written to convert the program specifications into machine language. We tapped almost all types of sources of programming manpower. The control (executive) program was written by IBM in accordance with our contract with them. We used some contract programmers from service organizations; we used our own experienced data processing people; we tested,

trained and developed programmers from within American Airlines, and hired experienced programmers on the open market. Line-for-line programming was used in the real-time system for computer efficiency.

7. Testing of our real-time programs involved several steps. The first program checkout work was done without a control program or special equipment on a standard 7090 at the Time-Life Data Center. The method of testing employed a special hardware/software simulation routine called the SABRE Debugging Package (SDP). This package allowed program testing on a 7090 without the use of the special SABRE hardware, such as discs, drums, or the real-time channel. It simulates the existence of all the special hardware of the SABRE system as well as all control program functions previously noted.

TESTING THE SOFTWARE

With the arrival of the system at Briarcliff, individual programs could be combined into functional packages and, for the first time, run in conjunction with the actual control program. The method of testing these packages involved the programmer employing actual agent sets, constructing test cases, and testing the logic of his programs and the validity of the results utilizing the real system.

While this was an excellent way to test the logic of a single path through the system, this method of testing proved lacking for a number of reasons:

a. Only one programmer could adequately test his work at one time.

b. It was very time-consuming to construct the cases and get the system to test the desired paths.

c. It was difficult to tell what caused discrepancies when they did occur.

In order to solve these problems and maintain an adequate testing schedule, another simulation package was evolved. This package (as opposed to SDP) used all the special SABRE hardware, the control program and debugged operational programs. It simulated only the remote agent sets. Input messages were punched into cards and read by the simulator just as though they came from agent sets. They were then turned over to the actual program to operate on in a real-time environment.

In conjunction with the development of the

agent set simulator, we developed a set of preset system records called the pilot system. These records constituted all the records for a very small airline. They included several flights for a number of days, with different configurations of inventory pre-sold. The use of this system obviated the need for each programmer having to put in his test input deck the necessary inputs to get the system to a desired point, thus speeding up the running time of each test.

The agent set simulation package has since gone through many modifications and refinements; however, the basic logic of the package has remained unchanged. Today it is our main test tool and debugging aid prior to actually introducing any change into the system for live test.

The final thing to be done before the first city was cutover to SABRE was to run all individual packages together, operating on common data. The phase was called laboratory system testing. In it, 40,000 typical SABRE inputs on selected flights for a 36-day period encompassing two schedule changes were acted upon in a real life environment. Inventory and availability on these flights were compared to predetermined results. Many new discoveries were made running under this system. Several programming and operating problems were uncovered and corrections made to the system. Upon the successful completion of lab system, AA and IBM management felt that we had a working system, and in early 1963 we began processing reservations with the SABRE system. The last city was mechanized in December 1964.

Implementation of the checked-out system was performed on a location by location basis rather than function by function. This shortened the learning period in each city and enabled us to operate the airline with only a small percentage of our reservation function undergoing a major change at any one time.

No matter how careful you try to be in the planning, programming and testing phases, errors slip into a system, particularly when the system is as involved as SABRE. By using location by location implementation, we were able to work most of the major "bugs" out of our system during the cutover of our first few cities. By the time we had a large portion of our revenue dependent on SABRE, we had a rather smooth-running operation.

The chronology of SABRE ran as follows:

Preliminary study	1954–1958
Precontractual analysis	1958–1959
Contract	1959
Functional requirements	1960–1962
Program specifications	1960–1962
Coding	1961–1964
Single path testing	1961 on
Equipment arrival	January 1962
Package testing	1961–1962
Final checkout	Oct.–Dec. 1962
Test city parallel operation	Dec. 1962–Mar. 1963
First firm cutover	April 1963
Several more cities cutover	May 1963
Further cutover delayed pending addition of memory to 7090	June–Nov. 1963
Remainder of American cities added to system	Nov. 1963–Dec. 1964

THE VALUE OF HINDSIGHT

In retrospect there are some things which we would do a little differently if we were going to start over.

In the first place, we would start concentrating earlier on how to operate and control the implemented system. The control of the operation of the computer room has to be far more rigid in a real-time system than in a batch processing shop. Minor operating errors can cost major dollars. We are still working on programs to reduce our exposure to human error, and, of course, the best way to reduce this exposure is to eliminate operator intervention.

The second area we would now emphasize earlier is that of utility routines. Among the types of utilities required in a real-time system are those which analyze error conditions upon a stop of the real-time system and which permit a quick restart of the system with a minimum risk of violation of the vital records in storage. We have such utilities now but had we anticipated less than ideal operating conditions earlier in the game, we could have shortened our total implementation period.

Another type of utility required in a real-time system is real-time file fallback. A duplex system becomes simplex in a hurry when a file fails because of hardware problems. It is desirable in order to minimize risk when one file of a pair fails to copy the contents of the surviving file onto a spare and thus to re-establish the protection of a duplex mode. Our fallback utility was not ready when we went on the air and we, therefore, lost some operating time until it was completed.

Another factor which must be emphasized during our development phase is system measurement. It is extremely important to know how much computer time is being expended by each type of transaction in order to establish the capacity and useful life span of a given system. It is also desirable to develop means to measure the quality of input being performed in the field. Inefficient use of remote input devices can overload a real-time system and, in effect, shorten its life span. Thus the software must monitor the user and isolate those individuals or locations where improved supervision or training is required.

The introduction of communication into a data processing system results in a new management problem. There are new interfaces established within the user company and among the vendors of computer and communications equipment. Procedures must be established which quickly trace a source of trouble, whether the difficulty lies with the user, the computer vendor or the communication carriers. What is of prime importance is the development of an attitude among all concerned to expend effort to fight a problem to solution first and worry about jurisdictional or company loyalties after the line has been restored to service. We have been able to solve most of our "interface" problems due to excellent joint participation among American Airlines, IBM, AT&T and the local telephone companies. Without the establishment of collectively agreed-upon procedures and reporting techniques, the solution for each problem would, I am sure, be much longer.

47. MYTH OF REAL-TIME
MANAGEMENT INFORMATION

The latest vogue in computer information systems is the so-called real-time management information system. The general idea is to have in each executive's office a remote computer terminal which is connected to a large-scale computer with a data bank containing all of the relevant information in the company. The data bank updated continuously can be "interrogated" by the manager at any time. Answers to questions are immediately flashed on a screen in his office. Allegedly, a real-time management information system enables the manager to obtain complete and up-to-the-minute information about everything that is happening within the company.

The purpose of this article—aimed at a time span of the next five to seven years—is to raise some serious questions concerning the utility of a real-time information system for top management. I will try to show that it would not be practicable to operate a real-time *management control* system and, moreover, that such a system would not help to solve any of the critical problems even if it could be implemented. I will also try to show that in other areas of top management concern a real-time system is, at best, of marginal value. It is my personal opinion that, of all the ridiculous things that have been foisted on the long-suffering executive in the name of science and progress, the real-time management information system is the silliest.

MEANING OF REAL-TIME

One of the problems in any new field of endeavor is that there is frequently no universally

accepted definition for many of the terms. It therefore becomes nearly impossible to question the validity of the concepts underlying the terms because their meanings are different to different people. The term "real-time" is no exception. In fact, in a single issue of one computer magazine, back-to-back articles defined real-time differently; and one example, cited in the first article as an illustration of what real-time is *not*, appeared in the second article as an illustration of what a real-time system *is*.

Semantic Confusion

One concept of real-time is demonstrated by these two quotations:

• "A real-time management information system—i.e., one that delivers information in time to do something about it." [1]

• "A real-time computer system may be defined as one that controls an environment by receiving data, processing them and returning results sufficiently quickly to affect the functioning of the environment at that time." [2]

The problem with both of these definitions is that they are too broad. *All* management control systems must be real-time systems under this concept. It would be a little silly to plan to provide management with budget performance reports, for instance, if they were received too late for management to take any action.

The following is a description of real-time that comes closer to the concept of real-time as it is used by most systems and computer people:

SOURCE: *Harvard Business Review* (May–June, 1966), pp. 123–132. Reprinted by permission of *Harvard Business Review*.

[*] Professor of Business Administration, Harvard University.

[1] Gilbert Burck and the Editors of *Fortune, The Computer Age* (New York, Harper & Row, Publishers, 1965), p. 106.

[2] James Martin, *Programming Real-Time Computer Systems* (Englewood Cliffs, New Jersey, Prentice-Hall, Inc., 1965), p. 378.

The delays involved in batch processing are often natural delays, and little advantage can be obtained by reducing them. But elimination of the *necessity* for such delays opens new and relatively unexplored possibilities for changing the entire nature of the data processing system —from a passive recorder of history (which, of course, is valuable for many decisions) to an active participant in the minute-to-minute operations of the organization. It becomes possible to process data in *real-time*—so that the output may be fed back immediately to control current operations. Thus the computer can interact with people on a dynamic basis, obtaining and providing information, recording the decisions of humans, or even making some of these decisions.[3]

System Characteristics

To expand somewhat on this description, the term "real-time system" as used in this article will mean a computer system with the following characteristics.

1. *Data will be maintained "on-line."* In other words, all data used in the system will be directly available to the computer—that is, they will be stored in the computer memory or in random access files attached to the computer. (This is in contrast to data maintained on magnetic tapes, which must be mounted and searched before information is available to the computer.)

2. *Data will be updated as events occur.* (In contrast to the "batch" process, where changes are accumulated and periodically updated.)

3. *The computer can be interrogated from remote terminals.* This means that the information stored in the computer can be obtained on request from a number of locations at a distance from the place where the data are processed and stored.

Perhaps the most widely known example of a real-time system currently in operation is the American Airlines SABRE system for making plane reservations.

POTENTIAL APPLICATIONS

With the new generation of computers, random access memories have become much less

[3] E. Wainright Martin, Jr., *Electronic Data Processing* (Homewood, Illinois, Richard D. Irwin, Inc., 1965), p. 381.

expensive than has been true until now. This fact, coupled with the advances made in data transmission equipment and techniques, will make many real-time applications economically feasible.

Real-time methods will improve those systems where the lack of up-to-the-minute information has in the past resulted in increased costs or loss of revenue. I believe that many companies will employ real-time methods to control all or part of their logistics (the flow of goods through the company) systems. For example:

A manufacturer of major household appliances might have raw material and work-in-process inventories in his manufacturing plants, and finished goods inventories both in company and distributor warehouses and in dealer showrooms. There is a more or less continuous logistics flow all along the route from raw material to retail customer. If all of the data on inventory levels and flows could be maintained centrally and updated and analyzed continuously, this would not only solve many of the problems now faced by such a manufacturer, but would make it possible to provide better all-around service with lower inventory levels and lower costs (particularly in transportation and obsolescence).

There are, of course, many other potential applications for real-time management information systems, and I believe that they will be used extensively in the next few years. However, these applications will take place almost exclusively in logistics, and, as I shall explain later on, techniques that may improve a logistics system will not necessarily improve a management control system. I want to make it clear at this point that I am not opposed to real-time systems per se. I believe they have valuable applications in operating situations. I am only opposed to using real-time information systems where they do not apply. The balance of this article will consider top management's use of real-time systems.

MANAGEMENT FUNCTIONS

As used here, the term "top management" will apply to the president and executive vice president in centralized companies, plus divisional managers in decentralized companies. In other words, I am considering as top management those people responsible for the full range of a business activity—marketing, production, research, and so forth. I am also assuming that the company or division is sufficiently large and complex so that the executive makes only a limited number of operating decisions, if any. I believe that this is a reasonable assumption in considering real-time management information systems. A company where the president makes most of the operating decisions could scarcely be considering a sophisticated and expensive computer installation.

Six Categories

This part of the discussion considers, in general terms, the functions of top management. The purpose here is to establish how a typical executive might spend his time so that we may later evaluate the extent to which his decision making can or cannot be helped by real-time computer systems. I have divided top management's functions into six general categories —management control, strategic planning, personnel planning, coordination, operating control, and personal appearances. Each is discussed below.

1. *Management Control*. One of the principal tasks of a manager is to exercise control over the people to whom he has delegated responsibility. Ideally, this control consists of coordinating, directing, and motivating subordinates by reviewing and approving an operating plan; by comparing periodically the actual performance against this plan; by evaluating the performance of subordinates; and by taking action with respect to subordinates where and when it becomes necessary.

The formal management control system will, of course, vary with the type and size of business as well as with the type and amount of responsibility delegated to the subordinate. Nevertheless, all effective formal management control systems need three things:

(a) A good plan, objective, or standard. The manager and the subordinate must agree as to what will constitute satisfactory performance.

(b) A system for evaluating actual performance periodically against the plan. This would include both a clear explanation of why variances have occurred and a forecast of future performance.

(c) An "early warning" system to notify management in the event that conditions warrant attention between reporting periods.

2. *Strategic Planning*. This consists of determining long-range objectives and making the necessary decisions to implement these objectives. Much of top management's strategic planning activity involves reviewing studies made by staff groups. Capital expenditure programs, acquisition proposals, and new product programs are examples of studies that fall into this area.

Another phase of strategic planning consists of developing ideas for subordinates to study— that is, instead of waiting for staff or line groups to recommend courses of action, the executive develops ideas of his own as to what the company should be doing.

3. *Personnel Planning*. This important function of management deals with making decisions on hiring, discharging, promoting, demoting, compensating, or changing key personnel. In the broadest sense, this consists of organizational planning. Personnel planning is, of course, related both to management control and strategic planning. Nevertheless, there are so many unique problems associated with personnel planning that I believe it is reasonable to consider it as a separate function.

4. *Coordination*. Here management's function is to harmonize the activities of subordinates, especially where it is necessary to solve a problem that cuts across organizational lines. For example, a quality control problem might affect several operating executives, and the solution to this problem might require top management's active participation. In general, this activity tends to be more important at the lower organization levels. The president of a large, decentralized company would perform less of this coordination function than his divisional managers because interdepartmental problems are more common at the divisional level.

5. *Operating Control*. Almost all top executives perform some operating functions. For example, I know a company president who buys certain major raw materials used by his company. Usually, the operating decisions made by top management are those which are so important to the welfare of the company that the executive believes the responsibility for making them cannot be properly delegated.

6. *Personal Appearances*. Many top executives spend much time in performing functions that require their making a personal appearance. This can vary from entertaining visiting

dignitaries to giving out 25-year watches. (I shall assume the activities involving such personal appearances will not be affected by a real-time management information system.)

REAL-TIME PRACTICALITY?

The purpose of this part of the article is to examine, in turn, each of the management functions described above (except No. 6) to see whether or not it can be improved by a real-time information system.

Management Control

I do not see how a real-time system can be *used* in management control. In fact, I believe that any attempt to use real-time will considerably weaken even a good management control system. (In setting objectives or budgets, it may be useful to have a computer available at the time of the budget review to calculate the effects of various alternatives suggested by management. This, however, is not a real-time system, since a computer console need be installed only for the review sessions.)

Calculating Performance. In the area of performance evaluation, real-time management information systems are particularly ridiculous. When a division manager agrees to earn, say, $360,000 in 1966, he does not agree to earn $1,000 a day or $1,000/24 per hour. The only way actual performance can be compared with a budget is to break down the budget into the time periods against which performance is to be measured. If the smallest period is a month (as it usually is), nothing short of a month's actual performance is significant (with the exception of the events picked up by the early warning system to be described below). Why, then, have a computer system that allows the manager to interrogate a memory bank to show him the hour-to-hour or even day-to-day status of performance against plan?

Even assuming objectives could logically be calendarized by day or hour, we run into worse problems in calculating actual performance, and worse still in making the comparison of actual to standard meaningful. If the performance measures involve accounting data (and they most frequently do), the data will never be up-to-date until they are normalized (adjusted) at the end of the accounting period. I will not bore you with the details. Suffice it to

say only that a real-time accounting system which yields meaningful results on even a daily basis would be a horrendous and expensive undertaking.

Let us go one step further. Performance reports, to be meaningful, must include an explanation of the variances. This frequently involves considerable effort and often requires the analyst to spend time at the source of the variance in order to determine the cause. Would this be done every day or oftener? Ridiculous! There is one more thing about performance reports. The important message in many reports is the action being taken and the estimated effect of this action. In other words, the projection of future events is the important top management consideration. Will this be built into the real-time system? Since this involves the considered judgment of the subordinate and his staff, I do not see how this could possibly be done even on a daily basis.

Early Warning. How about real-time for providing an early warning? Here, also, I do not see how it could be of help. Early warning has not been a problem in any top management control system with which I have been acquainted. In most instances, when situations deteriorate to the point where immediate action is required, top management knows about it. As the manager of a division ($100 million a year in sales) said to me, when I asked him how he knew when things might be out of hand in one of his plants, "That's what the telephone is for."

In any case, it is possible to prescribe the situations which management should be apprised of immediately, without even relying on a computer. Furthermore, the important thing is to bring the situation to top management's attention *before* something happens. For example, it is important to inform management of a threatened strike. Yet a real-time management information system would pick it up only *after* the strike had occurred.

In summary, then, early warning systems have been put into operation and have worked satisfactorily without a real-time system. I see nothing in a real-time management information system that would improve the means of early warning, and such a system would certainly be more expensive. (Note that here I am talking about management control systems. The early warning techniques of many logistical control systems, in contrast, could be greatly improved by real-time systems.)

My conclusion on management control is that real-time information cannot be made meaningful—even at an extremely high cost— and that any attempt to do so cannot help but result in a waste of money and management time. Improvements in most management control systems must come from sources other than real-time information systems.

Strategic Planning

Since strategic planning largely involves predicting the long-run future, I fail to see how a real-time management information system will be of appreciable use here. It *is* true that past data are required to forecast future events, but these need hardly be continuously updated and immediately available. Furthermore, much of the preparation of detailed strategic plans is done by staff groups. While these groups may on occasion work with computer models, the models would certainly be stored away, not maintained on line between uses.

Perhaps the most persistent concept of a real-time management information system is the picture of the manager sitting down at his console and interacting with the computer. For example, as a strategic planning idea comes to him, he calls in a simulation model to test it out, or a regression analysis to help him forecast some event; or, again, he asks for all of the information about a certain subject on which he is required to make a decision.

It seems to me that the typical manager would have neither the time nor the inclination to interact with the computer on a day-to-day basis about strategic planning. Problems requiring computer models are likely to be extremely complex. In most instances, the formulation of these problems can be turned over to staff specialists. Furthermore, I think it would be quite expensive to build a series of models to anticipate the manager's needs.

Under any conditions, strategic planning either by the manager alone or by staff groups does not appear to be improved by a real-time system. Models can be fed into the computer and coefficients can be updated as they are used. Between uses, it seems to me, these models would be most economically stored on magnetic tape.

Personnel Planning

A real-time management information system does not help the top manager to solve his problems of personnel planning, although the computer can be useful in certain types of personnel data analysis. About the only advantage to the manager is that information becomes available somewhat more quickly. Instead of calling for the history of a particular individual and waiting for personnel to deliver it, the manager can request this information directly from the computer. Therefore, while a remote console device with a visual display unit *could* be used for retrieving personnel information, the question of whether it *should* be used is one of simple economics. Is the additional cost of storing and maintaining the information, plus the cost of the retrieval devices, worth the convenience?

Coordination

The coordination function is very similar to the management control function with respect to potential real-time applicability. A manager wants to know right away when there is an interdepartmental problem that will require his attention. As is the case with early warning systems developed for management control, a real-time system is not necessary (or even useful, in most cases) to convey this information. Further, I cannot see how a real-time management information system could be used in the solution of these coordination problems, except in unusual cases.

Operating Control

There is no question that real-time methods are useful in certain types of operating systems, particularly in logistics systems.[4] To the extent that a top executive retains certain operating control functions, there is a possibility that he may be able to use a real-time information system. Because of the necessity of doing other things, however, most executives will be able to spend only a limited amount of time on operating functions. This means generally that they must work on the "exception" principle. Under most conditions, therefore, it would seem much more economi-

[4] See Robert E. McGarrah, "Logistics for the International Manufacturer," *HBR*, March–April 1966, p. 157.

cal for a subordinate to monitor the real-time information and inform the top executives when a decision has to be made.

It is very difficult to generalize about this situation. Here, again, it appears to be one of simple economics. How much is a real-time system worth to the manager in relation to what it is costing? I cannot believe that there would be many instances where a manager would be concerned with operating problems to the extent that a real-time information system operating from his office would be justified.

REPORTING BY COMPUTER

In recent months, there have been experiments to replace traditional published reports by utilizing consoles and display devices to report information directly to management. Although these techniques, strictly speaking, are not real-time, they bear such a close relationship to real-time systems that it will be useful to consider them here.

Modus Operandi

The general idea is that the information contained in the management reports would be stored in the computer memory so that the manager could ask for only the information he needed. This request would be made from the computer console, and the information would be flashed on a screen in his office. For example, a manager could ask for a report on how sales compared with quota. After looking at this, he could then ask for data on the sales of the particular regions that were below quota and, subsequently, for detail of the districts that were out of line.

The benefits claimed for this type of reporting are as follows:

• The manager will receive only the information he wants.
• Each manager can obtain the information in the format in which he wants it. In other words, each manager can design his own reports. One manager may use graphs almost exclusively, while another may use tabulation.
• The information can be assembled in whatever way the manager wants it—that is, one manager may want sales by areas, and another may want it by product line. Furthermore, the manager can have the data processed in any way that he wants.

• The information will be received more quickly.

Important Considerations

Before installing such a system, it seems to me, a number of things should be taken into account.

First, what advantage, if any, does this system have over a well-designed reporting system? Since the storage and retrieval of data in a computer do not add anything that could not be obtained in a traditional reporting system, the benefits must be related to convenience. Is there enough additional convenience to justify the additional cost?

Second, is it possible that for many executives such a system will be more of a nuisance than a convenience? It may be much easier for them to open a notebook and read the information needed, since in a well-designed system the information is reported in levels of details so that only data of interest need be examined.

Finally, will the saving in time be of any value?

It seems to me that the two main considerations in installing such a system are the economics and the desires of the particular executive. There is one further possibility, however, that should be carefully considered. What will be the impact on the lower level executives? If these people do not know the kind of information their superiors are using to measure their performance, will this not create human relations problems?

Without going into the details, I can see many problems being created if this is not handled correctly. With a regular reporting system, the subordinate knows exactly what information his superior is receiving—and when he receives it—concerning his performance. Furthermore, the subordinate receives the information *first*. Any deviations in this relationship can cause problems, and the use of a computer to retrieve varying kinds of information from a data base is a deviation from this relationship.

THREE FALLACIES

If management information on a real-time basis is so impractical and uneconomic, why are so many people evidently enamored with this concept? I believe that the alleged benefits of real-time management information systems are based on three major fallacies.

Improved Control

Just about every manager feels, at some time, that he does not really have control of his company. Many managers feel this way frequently. This is natural, since complete control is just about impossible even with the best management control system. Since most companies have management control systems that are far from optimum, there is little wonder that a feeling of insecurity exists. In the face of this feeling of insecurity, the promise of "knowing everything that is happening as soon as it happens" has an overpowering appeal.

As explained previously, real-time will not improve management control and, consequently, will not help to eliminate the insecurity that exists. What is usually needed is a combination of improved management control systems and better selection and training of personnel. Even at best, however, the executive will have to accept responsibility for what other people do, without having full control over their actions.

"Scientific Management"

There appears to be considerable sentiment to the effect that the scientific way to manage is to use a computer. This fallacy implies that the executive with a computer console in his office is a scientific manager who uses man-machine communication to extend his ability into new, heretofore unavailable, realms of decision making.

I believe that it is nonsense to expect most managers to communicate directly with a computer. Every manager and every business is different. If a manager has the necessary training and wishes to do so, it may be helpful for him to use a computer to test out some of his ideas. To say, however, that *all* managers should do this, or that this is "scientific management," is ridiculous. A manager has to allocate his time so that he spends it on those areas where his contribution is greatest. If a computer is useful for testing out his ideas in a given situation, there is no reason why he should have to do it personally. The assignment can just as easily be turned over to a staff group. In other words, where a computer

is helpful in solving some management problems, there is no reason for the manager to have any direct contact with the machine.

In most instances, the computer is of best use where there are complex problems to be solved. The formulation of a solution to these complex problems can generally be done best by a staff group. Not only are staff personnel better qualified (they are selected for these qualifications), but they have the uninterrupted time to do it. It seems to me that there is nothing wrong with a manager spending his time managing and letting others play "Liberace at the console."

Logistics Similarity

This fallacy is the belief that management control systems are merely higher manifestations of logistics systems.

The fact is that the typical real-time system, either in operation or being planned, is a *logistics* system. In such a system, for example, a production plan is developed and the degree of allowable variances established in a centralized computer installation. The actual production is constantly compared to plan; and when a deviation exceeds the established norm, this fact is communicated to the appropriate source. On receiving this information, action is always taken. Either the schedules are changed or the deficiency is somehow made up.

Notice that speed in handling and transmitting vast amounts of information is essential. This is the critical problem that limits many manual logistics systems; and the computer, particularly with real-time applications, goes a long way toward solving the speed problem.

In contrast, speed in processing and transmitting large amounts of data is *not* a critical problem in *management control* systems. Consequently, the improvements that real-time techniques may effect in logistics systems cannot be extrapolated into management control systems.

The critical problems in management control are (a) determining the level of objectives, (b) determining when a deviation from the objective requires action, and (c) deciding what particular action should be taken. The higher in the organizational hierarchy the manager is positioned, the more critical these three problems tend to become. For example, they are usually much more difficult in planning divisional profit budgets than plant expense budgets. In some instances the computer can help the manager with these problems, but I do not see how it can solve them for him. Furthermore, the use of computers in solving these problems has nothing to do with real-time.

SHORT-TERM VIEW

While real-time management information systems may be very useful in improving certain kinds of operating systems, particularly complex logistics systems, they will be of little use in improving management control. This is particularly true in the short-range time span of the next five to seven years.

The following is a checklist of questions that I believe the manager should have answers to before letting anyone install a remote computer terminal and a visual display screen in his office:

1. What will the total incremental cost of the equipment and programming be? (Be sure to consider the cost of continuing systems and programming work that the real-time systems will involve.)

2. Exactly how will this equipment be used? (Be sure to obtain a complete description of the proposed uses and the date when each application will become operational.)

3. Exactly how will each of these uses improve the ability to make decisions? In particular, how will the management control system be improved?

With precise answers to these three questions, it seems to me that a manager can decide whether or not a remote terminal and visual display device should be installed. Do not be surprised, however, if the answer is negative.

LONG-RANGE OUTLOOK

What are the prospects of real-time systems, say, 15 or 20 years from now? Some experts believe that, by that time, staff assistance to top management will have largely disappeared. Not only will the staff have disappeared, but so will most of the paper that flows through present organizations. A manager in the year 1985 or so will sit in his paperless, peopleless office with his computer terminal and make decisions based on information and analyses displayed on a screen in his office.

Caution Urged

It seems to me that, at the present time, the long-term potential of real-time management information systems is completely unknown. No one can say with any degree of certainty that the prediction cited above is incorrect. After all, 15 or 20 years is a long time away, and the concept of a manager using a computer to replace his staff is not beyond the realm of theoretical possibility. On the other hand, this concept could be a complete pipedream.

Under any circumstances, many significant changes in technology, organization, and managerial personnel will be required before this prediction could be a reality for business in general. As a result, if such changes do occur, they will come slowly, and there will be ample opportunity for business executives to adjust to them. For example, I believe there is little danger of a company president waking up some morning to find his chief competitor has installed a computer-based, decision-making system so effective that it will run him out of business.

I believe all executives should be open-minded to suggestions for any improvements in management information systems, but they should require evidence that any proposed real-time management information system will actually increase their effectiveness. Above all, no one should rush into this now because of its future potential.

The present state of real-time management information systems has been compared to that of the transportation field at the beginning of the Model-T era. At that time, only visionaries had any idea of how transportation would be revolutionized by the automobile. It would have been foolish, however, for a businessman to get rid of his horse-drawn vehicles just because some visionaries said that trucks would take over completely in 20 years.

It seems to me that this is the identical situation now. Even if the most revolutionary changes will eventually take place in management information systems 20 years hence, it would be silly for business executives to scrap present methods until they are positive the new methods are better.

BIBLIOGRAPHY

1. Barrett, E. F., *Memory Considerations for an On-Line Processor,* Proceedings On-Line Data Processing Applications Conference, January, 1963.
2. Blumenthal, S. C., "Management in Real-Time," *Data Processing Magazine,* August, 1965.
3. Coyle, R. J., and J. K. Stewart, "Design of a Real-Time Programming System," *Computers and Automation,* September, 1963.
4. "Data Transmission and the Real-Time System," *Dun's Review,* September, 1965.
5. Desmonde, W. H., *Real-Time Data Processing Systems: Introductory Concepts,* Prentice-Hall, Inc., 1964.
6. Douglas, R. M., "Digital Computer Achieves Real-Time Flight Simulation," *Data Processing Magazine,* April, 1965.
7. Dowse, R. G., "The Systems Approach to Data Transmission," *Computer Journal,* October, 1963.
8. Hartmann, H. C., "Management Control in Real Time Is the Objective," *Systems,* September, 1965.
9. Hawk, R. H., and G. A. Bassett, "EDP: A Management Recruiting Tool," *Administrative Management,* August, 1965.
10. Head, R. V., *Real-Time Business Systems,* Holt, Rinehart and Winston, 1964.
11. Head, R. V., "The Programming Gap in Real-Time Systems," *Datamation,* February, 1963.
12. Head, R. V., "Real-Time Systems Configurations," IBM Systems Research Institute Paper, April, 1963.
13. Head, R. V., "Real-Time Programming Specifications," *Communications ACM,* July, 1963.
14. Holdiman, T. A., "Management Techniques for Real-Time Computer Programming," *Journal of the ACM,* July, 1962.
15. Hosier, W. A., "Pitfalls and Safeguards in Real-Time Digital Systems with Emphasis on Programming," *IRE Transactions on Engineering Management,* June, 1961.
16. Johnson, G. W., "The Growing Case for Data Display," *Business Automation,* May, 1963.
17. "Keeping Ahead on Real-Time," *Business Week,* March, 1965.
18. Mapletoft, J. T., "Satisfying the Need to Know in Real-Time," *Systems and Procedures Journal,* March–April, 1965.
19. Margartis, P., "A Real-Time Management Information Retrieval System," *Data Processing,* July, 1965.
20. "Medium to Large Computer Systems Summary—Estimating Time Requirements," Staff of Cresap, McCormick and Paget, *Control Engineering,* January, 1963.
21. Parker, R. W., "The Sabre System," *Datamation,* September, 1965.
22. Ream, N. J., "On-Line Management Information," *Datamation,* March, 1964.
23. Shays, E. M., "The Feasibility of Real-Time Data Processing," *Management Services,* July–August, 1965.
24. Spitler, R. H., and B. K. Kersey, "A Research Laboratory for Processing and Displaying Satellite Data in Real-Time," *Data Processing,* January, 1965.
25. "Time-Shared Programming," *Business Management,* January, 1965.
26. "Western Electric's Milestone Line: A Computer Polices Parts Flow," *Modern Materials Handling,* **16**, September, 1961.

Part XIV.   Information Retrieval

One of the unique properties of man distinguishing him from the other primates is the possession of culture. Though anthropologists and sociologists have defined culture in many and various ways,[1] one constant feature noted by all is that it is not inherited genetically but is acquired through learning. Culture is thus an accumulated storehouse of knowledge, knowledge of the ways of behaving, believing, and of doing things which the members of a social group acquire through learning.

From the beginning of time, man in his struggle for survival must have been concerned with the acquisition of knowledge. But only since the dawn of civilization, when he learned how to transmit his learning to others by means of a recorded language (on stone, wax, papyrus, etc.), could he have been faced with a problem that only now has reached an explosive stage. Until the recent exponential growth of published information man has been satisfied with the relatively simple mechanical processes available for retrieving such information. The worldwide flood of technical literature, however, has made increased mechanization of the retrieval process almost inevitable and to this task much thought has been devoted of late.

Data is being disseminated today in such a volume and at such a rate that untold human energy is dissipated by wasteful duplication of effort simply because of the lack of knowledge of what others have al-

ready done. Of more concern to us though is the realization that data is being increasingly categorized by its field of specialization and thus easy access to the fund of useful information from allied fields is rendered more and more difficult for one outside the specialty. Also to be considered is the fact that the very terminology so appropriate to distinct fields of specialization tends to create new barriers discouraging, and at times nearly preventing such knowledge from transcending the close bounds of its own domain. We saw this idea expressed in the very first selection of this book. There Boulding pointed up the unfortunate situation where physicists discourse only with physicists and economists only with economists, and, what is worse, nuclear physicists with nuclear physicists, etc., each mumbling to himself words in an esoteric language that only the elect can understand. Hence Boulding's concern for a more interdisciplinary approach. A similar line of thought was followed by Churchman when treating the decision problems inherent in measurement. The more specific the language, the less widely can it be communicated.

Information retrieval presupposes an information system. Such a system, broadly speaking, "consists of a file structure to index and hold information, an input language for entering new information into the system or changing the information currently in the system, an interrogating language for couching retrieval requests, a body of programs for performing the various processing tasks, a program language for specifying new information processing algorithms, and finally a lan-

[1] Alfred Kroeber and Clyde Kluckhohn, *Culture: A Critical Review of Concepts and Definitions* (Cambridge: Peabody Museum of Harvard University, 1952).

guage to control the operations of the system." [2]

In view of the fact that vast amounts of information are still retrievable through present albeit costly and time-consuming methods, the improvements to be made are not expected to be of an earthshaking nature. However, even within the present decade the achievements made have been tremendous, some born out of necessity, others of visionary thinking. To be sure, information retrieval has not yet come of age but with increased financial support coming from the government, which has high stakes in its development, it will mature rapidly enough.

Many government projects already call for a state-of-the-arts report as a prerequisite for the granting of contracts. Such reports will become routine since no one company has internally the library of total knowledge relevant to a specific problem; a central functional "knowledge" pool will not only be desirable but absolutely necessary. Then the task of job retrieval will become considerably easier for many industries, now overwhelmed by floods of data.

The amount of data being disseminated is truly phenomenal. "Consider only the press: 1,719 newspapers [are] published daily, each with at least ten pages of text; 9,300 weeklies with a minimum of four pages of text; and at least 3,000 magazines averaging a minimum of twenty pages of text each; a grand total of three-quarters of a million pages each month." [3]

As time goes on more and more areas of application of information retrieval will become available as a result of the extensive and intensive research going on in the field. In the not too distant future, inventory systems, financial data, personnel records, and logistic information will be

susceptible to immediate recall. Many private law firms as well as corporation attorneys will be utilizing information retrieval in search of precedents.

In the first selection, John T. Jackson reviews briefly the progress made in information storage and retrieval in non-management fields and sees great prospects ahead for business management. Though the concept is relatively easy to grasp and explain, its actual implementation is anything but easy. The Armed Forces Technical Information Agency has come up with an information storage and retrieval system that has proved invaluable over the past years. Business management too needs something comparable. However, there are special difficulties that first have to be overcome before such a dream becomes a reality. These difficulties are: (1) the creation of a proper thesaurus of key words to be used for indexing the kind of information needed by management, (2) better communication between the executives burdened with the responsibility for decision making but often lacking the information upon which to base their decisions and the information retrieval systems men with their computer interests and jargon of their own, (3) the nature of the information being sought by business managers. Once these problems are solved managers will be able to steer the ship of business unerringly in the turbulent sea of chaotic information.

The selection by Walter Williams gives the reader an idea of the various milestones that have been reached in the field of information retrieval since the days of the pioneer, Vannevar Bush. Sundry approaches to information retrieval that have been employed so far (classification schemes, dictionary heading, coordinate indexing) are outlined, but more attention is devoted to General Electric's "enriched coordinate indexing" and to the contributions of du Pont de Nemours.

Williams admits that much progress has already been made but much still remains to be made, especially with regard to pe-

[2] Robert A. Colilla and Burnett H. Sams, "Information Structures for Processing and Retrieving," *Communications of the ACM,* 1962, p. 11.

[3] Paul M. Lewis, "Mass Communications Retrieval," *Associated Management,* April 1965, p. 11.

ripheral page reading devices. Progress, he believes, will come not by a crash program but by a steady search for cost-saving methods of information retrieval. Smaller companies will increasingly be in a position to take advantage of the breakthroughs made by government and the giants in industry without having to pay the heavy penalties of research and development costs. In short, the fuse has been lit. We may soon see the actual "explosion."

One should note that the article by Benjamin Cheydleur entitled "Information Retrieval—1966" was written in 1961 and hence is a projection in time. In this article Cheydleur surveyed the five-year (1961–1966) prospects of progress in adapting data processing systems to the everyday needs of the user of information retrieval services. He carefully probed the cost picture, the input-display and rapport facility, the problem of automatic text transcription, the techniques of automatic indexing and abstracting, the means of iterated high-speed cross-referencing (avoiding serial search) in the form of associative memory, microfilm memory for texts and display, and communication devices online between man and computer and between computer and computer. At the time of writing, Cheydleur believed that there was every prospect that progress in each of these individual areas would be enough to make information retrieval self-sufficient by 1966. He even outlined two courses of action that industry and government could follow to speed up and to guarantee this progress. One was the encouragement of new electronic data processing product forms and the other the encouragement of the development of human techniques of index-assignment, interest-profiling, text manipulation, and relevancy and citation analysis. It is difficult to assess to what

degree failure in either of the two courses has been responsible for the non-fulfillment of his predictions. But there is every reason to hope that the vision that he perceived so clearly was not illusory, only perhaps a bit premature.

The personal observations on information retrieval by Gary Martins are quite lively and down-to-earth. Underneath the light but prodding touch of this talented writer is a truly sensitive contact with reality. Though seeming to treat lightly the banalities and trivialities of the trade, he still manages to reveal what for a better word could be called "the state of the art" as he sees it.

For Martins, information retrieval has for its objective "to make available unusually attractive library services dealing with recent publications (or other data), usually employing modern EDP hardware." Among the "unusually attractive" library services he would include (1) convenience of access, (2) high-speed results, (3) suggestive indexing and reference services, (4) unusually broad and/or deep stockpiles of available information, (5) abstracting services, and (6) creative retrieval. The term, "relatively recent," is, of course, dependent upon the application intended. It would mean one thing for the librarian of the physical sciences and an entirely different thing for one responsible for a strategic command and control system.

Each of the above advantages is explained in a way that gets to the fundamentals and unearths the problems and inconsistencies not often touched upon. After perusing his article one is more than convinced that the long-promised Golden Age of information retrieval has not just yet arrived.

48. INFORMATION SYSTEMS FOR

MANAGEMENT PLANNING

JOHN T. JACKSON *

In the decade that has elapsed since installation at the U.S. Census Bureau of the first electronic computer for data processing, much progress has been made in converting these scientific prodigies into effective tools of business management.

Despite the many advances in the art, one important area of computer potential remains virtually untapped by management—information storage and retrieval. Yet it's likely that use of the electronic computer for this purpose could work profound changes in the dynamics of the executive decision-making process.

We may not be too far away from such a development. For some years a painstaking progress towards making IS&R a practical reality has been negotiated in scientific and technical literatures. This work is now starting to return dividends.

An information retrieval system's utility in science is obvious. There is a tremendous volume of papers and documents in the scientific literature already, and thousands more are added each year. With the laborious indexing and filing procedures used by most libraries, it has become an impossibly formidable task for the student to become aware of all the literature dealing with any particular scientific subject, and to avoid duplication in his research.

The underlying theory behind information storage and retrieval is simple. Papers and documents are abstracted and indexed according to a preselected list of key words. The index code also includes the document's location in the archives. This information is then placed in the memory of a computer. To

SOURCE: *Data Processing* (March, 1962), pp. 25–27. Reprinted by permission of *Data Processing Magazine*, The Publication of Computers and Information Technology.

* Vice President, Remington Rand Univac.

discover all works dealing with any particular topic, it is necessary only to note the appropriate index words in the computer.

The computer then riffles through its memory units and prints out the abstract of every pertinent document and its location in the files. By scanning through the abstracts, the researcher can easily cull out the superfluous documents. He is left with just those works that suit his purpose.

As in so many other instances, the process is easier to describe than to implement. Creation of a practical indexing system, flexible enough to describe adequately all current and anticipated works and yet restricted enough to permit speedy isolation of desired documents by a researcher, has absorbed the talents of a great many programmers over the past few years.

But results have been forthcoming. Remington Rand Univac, for example, has recently completed an IS&R system for the Defense Department's Armed Services Technical Information Agency (ASTIA), which with the aid of a Univac Solid-State 90 computer will greatly expedite research through a mass of technical material. ASTIA receives on the average some 2,000 requests for information each day, 50 of which may ask all documentation on some particular subject. Filling these requests is no mean task since there are over 250,000 documents currently on file, and more are added daily.

The computer-based retrieval system makes it easy. For example, to aid in assessing the merits of a proposed budget request, the Air Force might wish to know how much money has been spent on a certain phase of projects doing work on keeping a man alive in space. This research may have been carried on for many years at many institutions under a number of auspices. ASTIA's information retrieval system will make it possible to come up with the right answer in a small fraction of the time it previously took.

RELATION TO BUSINESS

But how does this relate to business management? The answer is, as a solution to the Informational Crisis. Top executives in many corporations have been painfully aware of this crisis for many years. The rapid growth of most corporations, and that of the economy at large, has taxed the business executive's ability to maintain access to the kind of information he needs to do his job properly.

Electronic computers have earned their keep over the past ten years primarily by supplying management with statistical reports about the internal operations of a company. But an information retrieval system can pick up where routine data processing leaves off. It gives the overburdened executive rapid access to non-statistical and/or non-financial information essential to rational decision making. This sort of material crops up in many forms—newspaper clippings, trade journals, government reports, special subscription services, investigations by a company's own employees, etc. But its very bulk has kept management from fully mastering it.

If the executive is to know what he needs to know to make the right decisions—the *sine qua non* of the top level manager—it is imperative that he have a more efficient method of grasping the realities of the world. In the past the executive's decision-making ability has been in many important areas largely, though not wholly, intuitive. In resolving his mind on many matters he had to rely heavily on hunches, guesses and suppositions. Wrapped up in his own company, the executive may have little time to keep tabs on the doings of competitors, the workings of the economy, political and sociological trends, and the situation in foreign countries. These factors may figure most importantly in many manufacturing and marketing decisions.

The value of an information retrieval system to an executive varies with his organizational level and with the nature of his work. It has obvious benefits for the higher ranking executive as an aid to decision making. A collateral but less obvious benefit is that with such a system, lower level managers will find it far easier to put their decisions and actions into an overall corporate context if their superiors allow them access to the requisite channels of information that will become available. The superiors thus may be relieved of the necessity of making relatively minor decisions which need reach their levels only because of information deficiencies at lower levels.

It is obvious that information retrieval can be of tremendous use to business management, a relation not always apparent in the past. One reason for the change is that computer people are beginning to cease emphasizing hardware to the neglect of what it is this machinery is supposed to produce. The *Harvard Business Review* recently put it this way:

Computer manufacturers and communications companies are learning the worth of their own products. They show signs of recognizing that it is not hardware but an information system which is valuable in helping to solve management's problems.

This revelation with which the manufacturers of computers have been smitten should be gratifying to business management. It's nice to know that at last someone understands your problems. The attitude should be particularly beneficial when the time comes to work out the form and function of specific business information retrieval systems. As has proven to be the case in our work for the Defense Department, it's a job requiring the utmost in cooperation from both sides—user and manufacturer. Neither can afford to hold back.

BUSINESS IR COMPLICATED

The problem of concocting a proper thesaurus—a list of key words coded to the substance of filed documents—for a business management is likely to prove many times more difficult than in the case of scientific or technical literatures. This technical material is relatively compact and homogeneous, whereas the documentation upon which the executive will wish to draw will often be of a general nature, wide as the world in scope, chaotic and diffuse in nature.

But I do not doubt that it can be accomplished. The principles of such an information retrieval system are sound. So far as computers themselves are concerned, there are no substantial engineering difficulties to be overcome. Equipment already in existence can meet the requirements likely to be placed upon it by any IS&R system.

There exist other stumbling blocks, and these do not necessarily concern the mechanical workings of a system. One of the most imposing involves communication—communication between the executive with the decision-making responsibility and the management researchers who understand the computer and who propose to create an IS&R system.

Management has encountered some difficulty with computer usage in the past because of this communications block. It is mostly a matter of not fully comprehending one another's language. Executives often have difficulty in describing the requirements of their positions and what kinds of information they could best employ.

The management research man on the other hand is not always able to explain the computer in terms understandable to the businessman. Too often the average executive feels himself becoming submerged in jargon and throws up his hands in exasperation when trying to comprehend the technicalities involved. The confusion is not rare in our times when there have been wide chasms developing between highly specialized and rapidly advancing fields of knowledge.

True, there have been some efforts to break down or reduce the barrier in communication between the computer-oriented and the management-oriented. The development of COBOL (Common Business Oriented Language) for computer programming is a step in this direction. But much more needs to be done.

My personal observation has been that top management men are usually eager for guidance in technical matters, and willing to listen to those people who can provide it. The technical men likewise operate for the most part in good faith, but there are a few in this group who take a patronizing attitude towards the business executives they are presumably attempting to educate. This is most unfortunate because it leads to inefficient use of computing equipment; it restricts the advancement and leads to the frustration of the technical men, and thus it detracts from the optimum development of the U.S. competitive position in the world economy. Stuffed with knowledge that can't be gotten at, it's no wonder that many management researchers and planners have been described as "solutions looking for a problem."

Given the requisite executive acceptance, it is not inconceivable that some day we may see "critical path" scheduling by a computer of the information flow in a corporation. This would mean the distribution of information at times, in places and to persons in a manner that would permit the most efficient rendering and implementation of management decisions. Much work is being done presently in this regard on production processes, but it's a relatively unexplored area so far as management processes are concerned.

To keep our perspective, however, we should remember that there is little, if any, "pure" information in business. Unlike the scientist in his laboratory who often enjoys the luxury of data measured down to very close specifications, the material with which the businessman must most often deal has inevitably been subjected to conscious or unconscious human distortions.

In other words, management in the true sense of the word can never become an automatic function. The executive will at least in the foreseeable future have to supplement the output of information systems with the evaluation of human factors and other intangibles in making his decisions. Common sense, the intuitive weighing of tangibles and intangibles, will not yet go out of style.

Information storage and retrieval has its limitations, but it also has great value for business management. In a world grown as complex as ours, electronic techniques of this kind are perhaps our best hope to maintain our sense of proportion as we struggle in a sea of what is often chaotic information.

49. THE GROWING DATA VOLUME—
CAN IT BE MASTERED?

WALTER F. WILLIAMS *

Development of information retrieval techniques today commands the vital interest of America's business community. As the volume of technical knowledge increases, methods of profitably utilizing this information pose a very real problem. More sophisticated and more practically applied techniques and equipment are becoming available as a result of the growing demand which is outlined in this examination of the "State of the Art."

One of the most important causes of growth in this area is the need to obtain accurate information in a rapid manner. Without this material, critical management decisions are too often hampered by limited knowledge. For example, research expenditures, both inside and outside the government, are increasing. If properly developed, the ideas and inventions which are multiplying constantly can lead the way to dynamic businesses.

Another impetus for more efficient information retrieval systems is the uncontrollable costs in acquiring needed data. These costs are expressed in duplication of effort or duplication of errors.

In addition, the great volume of abstracts and purely scientific and technical journals creates a flood which is literally swamping researchers and practitioners in almost every field. As specialization increases, the possibility of bridging the gaps between disciplines becomes ever more difficult.

MILESTONES WITHOUT MEANING

Another reason for growth in information retrieval is the realization of a growing short-

SOURCE: *Business Automation* (November, 1963), pp. 20–27. Reprinted by permission of *Business Automation*, Copyright Business Publications International, Division of OA Business Publications, Inc.

* Consulting Engineer for General Electric Co.

age in the number of engineers. Industry will require about 80 thousand engineering graduates annually over the next several years. The current annual supply approaches 40 thousand. This situation will result in a shortage of 300 thousand engineers in this country by 1970. Advanced techniques in the handling of information used by the engineers could go a long way toward minimizing the shortage of men.

A great deal has been written in many different places concerning the state of the art of information retrieval. But today—almost 18 years after the stage was set for progress in an *Atlantic Monthly* article by Vannevar Bush—the state of the art needs explanation in terms of areas of progress. During these years, milestones have been established and passed, with implementation of the most well known and publicized of these stages still existing. However, very few of these stages represent key concepts which are likely to be remembered as fundamental and valuable in terms of lasting progress.

Documentalists will undoubtedly point to several areas of progress in government and the military. Examples would be the Air Force Minicard System, the 1958 International Symposium on Scientific Information, and the efforts of Congressional Committees on Scientific Information.

A firmer measure of progress during the past 18 years is the establishment of standards and approaches for information retrieval by American business. These accomplishments will be useful for years to come and will have a lasting impact.

The private enterprise segment of the American economy has probably contributed far more towards practical information retrieval systems than other institutions. The following events are considered to be the contributions which will provide the most definite, lasting and measurable milestones: Dr. Mortimer Taube's Uniterm System; inexpensive microfilm systems, Eastman Kodak Co.; large computers and serial data processing systems; concept coordination, E. I. du Pont de Nemours and Co., Inc.; permuted indexes, H. P. Luhn, IBM; structure tables and systems languages, General Electric Co.; inexpensive data storage and retrieval devices, Jonker Business Machines; copying equipment, Xerox Corp.; large-scale, high density random access devices, analog digital systems, still being developed; and page reading, reentry printing, and remote communications devices, also in development.

A look at development prior to 1945 might place in perspective the Batten Card; the Hollerith Card; tabulating equipment after invention of the codex to replace the scroll; movable type; Aristotle's classification systems; and others, such as the Dewey Decimal System.

Current events of information retrieval are becoming more critical, applicable and extendable as primary resources to fill manpower gaps, and to reduce costs of implementing scientific achievement and technical advances. Notice that the last two items on the above list of milestones are currently taking place. These typify state of the art.

The uninitiated may gasp at omission of another important event to come, that of solving semantic problems of information retrieval. However, none of the problems existing today are without practical solutions. And solutions are at hand. Combinations of concept-coordination and system languages can be adapted to take care of common semantic problems adequately.

Information retrieval problem areas of business (Figure 1), if arranged by endeavor and interest, can indicate the ranges and application of the foregoing events.

Throughout business, there are various organizations of information. Some are so-called centralized files, such as technical engineering

Problem Areas and Small Equipment Types

FIG. 1. Problem Areas of Business	FIG. 2. Functional Business Areas	FIG. 3. Small General Types of Equipment
Special Libraries—Scientific and Research Organization (Cataloguing, searching, ordering, bibliography, dissemination)	*Research*—Technical Reports, Abstracts, Patents	*Indexing Preparation Equipment*—Typewriters with Paper Tape Punching units, Keysort Punching Apparatus, Hollerith Card Punching Equipment
Technical Information—Advanced Engineering, Planning and Development (Indexing, analysis, storing, retrieving, dissemination)	*Engineering*—Standards, Vendors, Specifications	*Index Storage Media and Equipment*—Index Cards and Files, Hollerith Cards, Punch Paper Tape, Written Listings and Tabulations, Microfilm Cameras
Technical Data—Advanced Development Areas (Indexing, storing, retrieving, manipulating, reporting)	*Finance*—Personnel Accounting, Expense Accounting, Purchasing	
Standard Data—Product Engineering Systems (Updating, storing, retrieving, dissemination)	*Management*—Business Planning, Product Planning	*Document Storage Media and Equipment*—Manual File Cabinets, Motor-Operated Filing Cabinets, Aperture Cards, Microfilm Cabinets
Business Operating Data—Business Management (storing, updating, reporting)	*Manufacturing*—Processes, Standards, Shop Planning, Scheduling, Maintenance	*Index Retrieval and Display Equipment*—Paper Tape Readers, Microfilm Readers, Hollerith Card Sorters
Business Planning Data—Business Development (Modeling, storing, re-analyzing, reporting)	*Employe and Community Relations*—Personnel Record Files, Recruiting	*Document Retrieval and Reproduction on Equipment*—Microfilm Readers, Copiers

libraries or personnel files. Others are decentralized or functional files set up to assist small subgroups. In preparing a checklist, one can utilize a breakdown (Figure 2) which emphasizes that the greatest costs may be the result of poor information management.

SPECIALIZED PROBLEM SOLVING

There are also several broader categories of current problems concerning information retrieval systems. From the viewpoint of business organizational interest, these categories may be described as follows:

Scientific literature—the handling of loosely disseminated literature, concerned with the dissemination of information to appropriate receivers, and the critical time problem;

Project communication—the inter-project and intra-project communication necessary for the control of technical information as a project commodity;

Data retrieval and manipulation—those aspects of data recording which are technical information oriented;

Technical document storage and retrieval—the documentation of evaluation information, its transmission, storage and use;

Special files—drawings, flow sheets and other graphics, their routine recording and duplication;

Special reference libraries—the handling of relatively long life books, reports and periodicals.

Each one of these problems requires a specialized solution. However, each solution depends on a methodology and a language. As methods of coping with these problems multiply, the few language solutions are adequate.

The most difficult problem in communication of ideas has been lack of a common language development between originators and users of information. Unfortunately, words have different meanings to everyone.

Systems have been devised to bridge the gap between originator and user of information. These systems attempt in different ways to assure that, in response to a question, a potential user receives all information in the system pertinent to his problem.

One of the principal systems devised to overcome lack of communication between originator and user is the classification scheme, which attempts to create order out of chaos

by hierarchical arrangements of generic classes. This categorical system is not new, being used even in ancient times, for instance by Aristotle to express his 10 classes of being.

Classification systems such as Universal Decimal, and Dewey Decimal have few practical applications in a computer system. In fact, very little use is made of classification schemes by conventional librarians, except to organize library shelves. Virtually no one goes to the library and thumbs through Dewey Decimal System listings or the Library of Congress Classification to retrieve a desired reference book. Instead, information in a conventional library is retrieved by utilizing a unified catalog, which combines subject headings, authors' names, and publishers.

WATCH YOUR LANGUAGE

Another approach to organizing information for easy retrieval is the direct or dictionary type of subject heading, arranged alphabetically. This system is not a hierarchical plan, but in a sense, is the logical continuation of subdividing information into convenient, small units. Headings are based upon subject matter of the material to be catalogued. They are also used generically rather than specifically, since it would be uneconomical to assign a new subject heading for each item. Consequently, the subject heading technique is susceptible to some shortcomings of the classification system.

During the last few years, a different approach has been made to overcome lack of a common language between originators and users. This approach is referred to as coordinate indexing. Representative examples of this type are the Uniterm System and Concept Coordination.

In 1952 the Armed Services Technical Information Agency (ASTIA) retained Dr. Mortimer Taube, Documentation, Inc., Washington, D.C., to study indexing systems and classification schemes. This research by Dr. Taube and associates resulted in development of the Uniterm System, a form of coordinate indexing. It has proven successful in many applications, both commercial and governmental.

Coordinate indexing offers many advantages over other known systems. It is flexible and adjustable to particular needs, conditions, and requirements. In contrast to conventional systems mentioned above, which at best give only superficial coverage of subject matter, co-ordinate indexing assures complete and specific coverage. Lack of communication between originator and user is eliminated, since terms used to index items are selected from the information itself. Sole judgment exercised by indexers is in selecting key words to enable retrieval.

Many conventional library systems rely upon titles to contain adequate information, along with the author's name, to retrieve an item. A variation of this old concept permits computing machinery to be used to make multiple entry indexes from a simple title.

Through data processing techniques, every significant title word is advanced and placed with its context (remaining portion of title) in an alphabetical listing. Thus every important word in the title can be used as a subject obtainable through an alphabetic dictionary listing. Once a word is found, its remaining context can be read. If judged pertinent, reference to item location can be used to retrieve the entire document. This system is readily adaptable to a technique known as "browsing." A selected word may link a network of words involved in many documents thus relating combinations of ideas not necessarily known before the searcher began "browsing."

The foregoing "software" techniques and advances have led to various equipments now being manufactured and applied in business.

Although "data processing" and "computers" are well-known words, it may surprise many readers to learn the majority of equipment for information retrieval is still "small automation" hardware. Principal hardware associated with information retrieval are copying and reproduction equipment, index cards and cabinets, and microfilm equipment. While equipment in this category has had a steadily rising market and may soon soar over $1 billion annually, the market for forms and hardcopy is in itself approaching $500 thousand.

THIS CLEAVAGE OF TECHNIQUES

The small hardware associated with information retrieval can be classified as indexing, storing, or retrieval equipment. Much is general equipment used for other routine functions of the business. However, there are also specialized devices available on the market. Figure 3 shows this information retrieval equipment.

Large-scale equipment for information re-trieval can be roughly classified as analog and digital. Analog refers to photographic or image recording, storage and reproduction devices; digital to information transformed from printed to coded and electronic signals, and back to printed form after storage.

General-purpose digital computers have been applied to information retrieval, and are well suited for many tasks, especially those concerned with long listings and files of information which must be screened, compared and updated. Practically all file processing done on today's digital computers is a form of informational retrieval. Dependent on highly-structured records on file, the sorting and correlation of information to update these files, or selection of various records from these files, is accomplished by comparing tags or terms. Most common digital file-processing lacks the logical capability involving three or four levels for processing semantic questions.

Thus simple formats, long files, many records, batch processing, and simple logic describe conventional digital data processing and separate it from requirements of true information retrieval. However, the goal of data processing is relief from conventional restrictions. In the future, data processing can well utilize sophistication of multiple logic levels and involved questions so typical in retrieval of technical information. This cleavage of techniques which separates data processing from information retrieval will gradually close. Systems areas of network scheduling and information networks are quickening.

INNOVATION FOR PROFIT

Perhaps the beginning of this trend was development of a tabular systems-oriented language (TABSOL) by the General Electric Co. From 1955 to 1957, when other major companies were initiating systems efforts to bring industrial organizations up to date (one such other effort to be described later was du Pont's), General Electric was initiating a company-wide program to develop uses for decision structure tables, both in manual form and on digital computers. The company's manufacturing service engineers, and others concerned with this development, were initiating many innovations. Foremost were two: common digital machine languages, and information retrieval.

Information retrieval aspects of this development were outstanding. For the first time, fundamental communications throughout a manufacturing organization were being implemented by applying logic to standards. Assumption was made and subsequently proved that a typical manufacturing business was a "beehive" of decision activity, and that these repetitive decisions could be understood and codified. Facts pertaining to decisions could be stored in a computer memory. When a routine inquiry came through order-processing (for example, "could an armature coil be delivered according to the following specifications on the 23rd?"), up-to-date data could be scanned by the computer and an automatic decision made to answer, "yes" or "no." Since product description data changes more slowly than, for example, manufacturing process information, the rate of information change dictated that various feedback loops continuously feed production status to the information system. Thus, the evolution of on-line factory feedback information systems began.

When computer parts-explosion was introduced to determine production quantities (basic factory information describing which part numbers are identical among various products), list processing was developed. Rather than serial processing, a disc file could be used with a list structure which could be disconnected and reconnected logically using the more complex logic of technical information retrieval. This is the point at which the manufacturing industry is today.

On the other hand, process or chemical industry extension and use of information retrieval is typified by E. I. du Pont de Nemours and Co. During this same period, circa 1957, through massive expenditures and risk of advance development money for administrative and engineering systems, du Pont produced such impact on internal systems that apparently proprietary techniques such as Critical Path Scheduling, Concept Coordination, and Integrated Engineering Control have become by-words throughout the chemical process and construction industries.

Integration of control systems with logistic and technical information systems is primarily a du Pont contribution to technical advancement. The integration of decision points based on organization of decision information is a longer term goal. However, with advent of RAMPS (a CEIR-du Pont development), a multiple-project resource-loading and scheduling system, complete integration of engineering resource-capital placement optimization is practical.

For pure technical information systems, General Electric has made furthest advancement into complete structuring of information. With the concept of "enriched coordinate indexing," multiple dimension list processible disc files, and high speed computer technology, together with thermoplastic recording, the analog medium for information storage, techniques and equipment concepts are available and can be combined.

The combination permits design not only of complete manufacturing business systems for the electrical industry, but could also be applied to completely solve equipment and language aspects of the du Pont system. Needless to say, these same combinations of equipment and concepts could be applied to practically all industrial systems problems and to many others in insurance, banking, and governmental information problem areas.

Besides these heavily logic oriented "information computers" with associative list memories, two more aspects must be emphasized. They are:

Communications ability: with users and originators usually at geographically dispersed locations, information retrieval will utilize telephone and teletype communications.

Remote devices and peripheral page reading devices: advances beyond Magnetic Ink Character Recognition and Optical Character Recognition must be made to provide universal character reading with as wide font differentiation as possible. Remote inquiry stations must be provided, accessible as the telephone, and dependable for printing and reproducing information.

BREAKTHROUGHS WITHOUT PENALTY

Independently, there have been developments of large microfilm processing systems which are to be considered in the same class as digital computers in performance and cost. They are marketed to large businesses and exist mostly for special applications. Among these are the Command Retrieval system, by Information Retrieval Corp.; the Miracode System, by Recordak Corp.; and Media, by the Magnavox Co. These are usually designated million-page systems.

Timing has been set, not by technological

slowness, but through steady progress required by competitive enterprise. No complete and stupendous breakthroughs are needed. Rather than happening via a 5-year expenditure of several billions of dollars on a crash basis, the steady, proof-seeking, cost-saving progress of information retrieval science will take place along with progress in the sciences, businesses and institutions.

It has to be pointed out, however, that despite giants of industry moving technological walls aside, smaller businesses can and are able to take advantage of breakthroughs without tremendous penalties of research and development costs of their own in the field of information retrieval. For example, less than 8 years ago the Government, General Electric, du Pont, and others were initiating large expenditures for research in information retrieval. Their findings are available in technical journals and engineering societies.

Smaller, less costly versions of large systems required by big companies are available. Manually selected aperture cards of the small company compete favorably with burdensome sorting requirements of its large competitor.

Termatrex, with its million or more bits of information readily manipulated by human fingers, is as powerful as the same sized file in a computer.

Total business operations must necessarily include information retrieval systems. Figure 4 shows the relationship of such systems to a total multi-product, multi-project organization.

The basic integration force is a complete information and data retrieval function which serves to store, retrieve, and manipulate information and data throughout the complete cycle, from basic research to sales. Another basic function is scheduling and planning, which concerns logistics and capital placement strategy.

Major problems in multiple product operations, having high turnover of products, are effective placement of capital and determination of probable timing. In the chemical industry, a process plant constructed six months ahead of competition may help gain complete product control of the market. Marketing of other products, on the other hand, may not be so critically affected by the time cycle.

MISMANAGING INFORMATION

Cycle determination, from basic research through sales and production, is repeated for every new product. In applied research on a product, early generation of information can help all succeeding major operating functions. It is important to maintain information generated early in research, so it may be made easily available for all subsequent needs. It is likewise important that information between

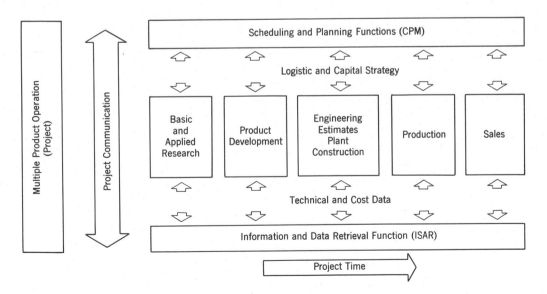

FIG. 4. Integration of an information retrieval system.

product lines be exchanged through a communication system, such as an information and data retrieval function.

As early in the cycle as possible, it becomes important to estimate return on investment for a particular product. To determine this, estimates for manufacturing facilities, construction and production costs must be made. At this time, for example, it is important to be able to retrieve past construction estimates for similar plants or processes. With proper techniques, then, it is possible to continuously improve estimates until decisions on placement of capital can be made.

Currently, fundamentals, techniques, and services of information retrieval are available for application to business problems. These tools have been enumerated and briefly described to illustrate the vast capability awaiting potential users.

Unfortunately, business has not used these tools. Apparently, management has failed to isolate real total costs of poor information-management. A basic need, therefore, is executive awareness of economics involved. Furthermore, executives must know where and what to look for in information-management.

THE TROUBLE WITH RETRIEVAL

While state of the art of information retrieval has advanced spectacularly in the past decade, general application in business is not widespread and has remained essentially static—confined to trials in the shopworn area of library searching. This is why total state of the art must include applications as well as fundamental knowledge.

Greatest need is in the former area, where problems must be established in a general way by systems workers. Meanwhile, your business can: survey, to become aware of, and to define your problems through isolation of actual costs attributable to inferior information management; obtain knowledge of fundamentals, techniques, and services for application to the problems revealed by the survey, and proceed to implement information retrieval systems.

Surveys of businesses, to isolate costs of information storage and retrieval, or lack of it, should include all functions, especially technically oriented research and engineering activities; finance; expense accounting and purchasing; business planning and management; manufacturing, especially standards, mainte-

nance, planning and scheduling; and employer-community relations.

A checklist of functions involving information retrieval, and costs, must be prepared to guide you in an initial cost survey. Ultimate pinpointing can be accomplished through data studies so that resultant definitions of distinct problems can be provided. These problems often can be assimilated for an integrated solution.

The second task, after isolating costs and defining problems, is to find and estimate costs of applying available tools. This is where the state of the art of information retrieval becomes important to solutions to your problems. To summarize, we will broaden our look into the current art.

The state of the art of information retrieval may be described in terms of two tasks: preparing and using indexes, and storing and retrieving documents.

Fundamental operations of information storage and retrieval are indexing (methods of recognition to facilitate organized storage and searching), storage (methods of maintaining indexes to facilitate searches), and retrieval (methods of extracting required identification of documents and records from the index and ways to extract documents and records from storage).

The techniques for accomplishing these operations include the following: indexing—coordinate, classification, subject headings, permuted, title and authors; storage of indexes—card catalogs, punched and drilled hole cards, notched cards, printed lists, punched paper tape, magnetic tape, magnetic memory devices, photographic and other films; storage of documents and records—paper bound, master copies, microfilm strips and reels, microfilm chips, aperture cards, reduced image masters, electronic-magnetic; retrieval of record and document identifications—serial searching, selective searching, batch searching, logical searching, browsing; and retrieval of records and documents—serial, selective, duplicating.

THE FUSE IS LIT

Services available to aid in applying and using these techniques include consulting firms, equipment suppliers, abstract services, government agencies, and professional societies.

Each of the foregoing lists shows the field is advanced sufficiently to proceed from the initial check list and information-management cost survey directly through to implementation. Whether your business is small or large, in need of automation or manual solutions, there is a potential to reduce operating costs, to improve competitive advantage, or to seek technological advancements and their rewards.

The functional activities of your business need information help. Beginning with the individual contributor—requirements for the data and information he needs personally to do his job, to acquire knowledge, and his own retraining when necessary—the need for information-management increases. The project, the functional activity, the decision-making activity (management), and inter-project communication all depend on acquisition of timely and adequate information.

A maximum information effort now appears less than three years away. Fuses have been lighted for the "information explosion," and the technical "manpower implosion" expected in the middle or late 1960's. These events are apt to skyrocket costs of competitive technology, marketing and planning. If you are to employ information-management competitively, it is advised that you take the necessary steps now.

50. INFORMATION RETRIEVAL—1966 *

Benjamin F. Cheydleur †

In the last few years, the course of Information Retrieval has resembled the nurturing of an eighteen-year-old juvenile; during at least ten of his years parents and neighbors have been debating his genius versus his delinquency. On the one hand they nourish a hope that the young genius may solve some of the problems that have beleaguered the older generation; the problems, for example, of rigidity and obsolescence that are built into the hierarchical classification systems used in card catalogues. Yet on the other hand, they cannot believe that the fledgling of the library world, called Information Retrieval or "IR" for short, can be entrusted with these and other problems when he one-handedly drives a computing machine so wildly and expensively across the meandering highways of human communication.

The parents (traditional librarians) are not used to the budgets that these computing systems demand; they distrust machines and electronics; they look on the retrieval process as being naturally embedded in the total system of library operations, including acquisition, housing, item-retirement, and administration—as well as search services. For progress they still look to the kind of authority that was enthroned in the days of their collegiate training, in the representatives of which they have often perceived surpassing wit, insight, prudence, and unflagging commitment to the further subdividing and structuring of knowledge. They have watched the first failures of the radicals who have applied various mechanizations to the library processes, and since they own no developed sense of the systems-power and depth of data-processor programming, they cannot see clearly how IR can be successfully mechanized—least of all the "nonroutine phases" of it.[1]

Yet they know that the worldwide flood of technical documentation is issuing at such an increasing rate that further mechanization is inevitable and imminent; that centralized IR is to be followed and indeed accompanied by decentralized mechanization, at first for special libraries, and soon after, for all kinds of collections anywhere. Almost everyone concerned has heard that the market for all types of IR equipment will have moved from $2 or $3 million in 1960 to about $100 million in 1965.

Meanwhile the insurgent information scientist has been gaining experience and developing his theories. He has come to appreciate more fully the subtleties of programming and operating electronic data processors. His sense of proportion as to the practical use of magnetic tapes and microfilm has been growing slowly and steadily. On the theory side he has found ways to index, abstract, and summarize technical documents automatically.[2] Out of his direct contact with high-speed computer memories he is revising the art of list-structuring in terms of associative micro-sequencing of those memories so as to get out from under the slow serial scanning methods of earlier efforts.[3]

In short, he has developed a healthy faith through practice, but he has failed to produce standard systems and standard operating procedures. Because the computing machines that were available to the information scientist have not been designed as complete IR systems, not a few information scientists have had to build a faith through hardship. To some of them, computers have offered little facility beyond the function of printing machines.

The neighbors would like to know when IR is going to settle down. What is it going to take to do the job? The key to the matter is the proper design of equipment. It is said that there is really no equipment required for IR

SOURCE: *Datamation* (October, 1961), pp. 21–25. Reprinted by permission of *Datamation*.

* The author acknowledges the significant and helpful suggestions contributed for this paper by his colleague, Joseph D. Chapline, Jr., of Philco.

† Philco Corporation

that demands any fundamental technological breakthroughs. This does seem to be the case if we consider that equipment modifications, extensions and a few cases of new designs based on known techniques are all that are needed. There is a fundamental point of view required that commits the equipment designer to aim at the totality of library processing, on-line-with-the-user: designs which force the use of procedures of batching and piecemeal approaches, with segregated off-line mysteries in the computer room, are no longer tenable. In cooperation with the information scientist, who is the procedure specialist in the case, the equipment designer can provide the knowledge of engineering realizability and economic good sense. Eventually, all the major problems in equipment design and use will be resolved. How many of them bid fair to be resolved within *five years?* In what follows, we venture prognostications on the major stumbling blocks.

ECONOMIC PROSPECTS

First, the key to the economic problem of supporting IR development lies temporarily in the intensity of interest of the national government in IR as a means of avoiding duplication in billions of r and d expenditures. There is already established a federal apparatus for underwriting some of the development of electronic information retrieval. This financial support is being directed increasingly toward new facilities, procedures, and basic information retrieval research (such as finding how scientists use their information sources,[4] etc.). A number of federal and civilian institutions are directly benefitting from this support as their retrieval services undergo mechanization. In turn, the data processing equipment makers are now able to custom design some of their product-line equipment specifically for IR.

Beyond this temporary stimulus, there will be strong and sustaining support once IR comes of age. The government will then insist that project proposals and project reviews commit contractors to determine the true state-of-the-art by means of IR as a condition for granting of contracts for advancing the state-of-the-art. To meet this demand, contractors will have to survey all relevant material *quickly* and *thoroughly.*

With continued dynamic development of IR mechanization, the cost per inquiry of shared multi-programmed computer processing will be measured in pennies.[5] Multi-processing, now realized in many standard computers, makes possible the automatic interlacing of computer operations for a variety of problems, so that the prorated costs per IR inquiry can be very small indeed. It should be noted in this connection that the shared processor under executive program control can process many inquiries from different keyboard inputs, or a few inquiries plus several data processing or computing problems. The cost of the stand-by equipment to make this possible is the cost of on-line keyboards (ranging from teletype to flexowriter at about $5000 per instrument, at present-day, low-volume prices).

Coupled with this factor of economy are others which taken together are unusually significant. One of these is the general increase in the computer capability per dollar which has been shown to be not less than 300% every three years! Another factor is the achievement of low-cost, general-purpose computers such as the Philco 2400, the Honeywell 400, the IBM 1401, in which the cost of the buffering-hardware that connected the central processor to peripheral equipment has been almost completely absorbed. Still another factor is the enormous increase in speeds of memory which is being incorporated in the very latest designs for moderate-size processors, leading to still cheaper control and buffering logics. Finally the development of chained list-structure strategies for managing high-speed memories, discussed below, promises that each IR inquiry will entail only 2 or 3 memory cycles per item retrieved. Thus pre-sorting and batching processes are soon to be obsolete, and certainly uneconomical. Hence the older notion that inquiries need be batched for economy, which was true for the decade in which there were no techniques and equipment for multi-processing (and multi-input), can be laid to rest in this five-year stretch.

Based on these many factors, there is every prospect of sufficient economic support for, and payoff from, IR systems during the next five years.

QUERY AND RAPPORT FACILITIES

The *second* major stumbling block in the IR future during the next five years has to do with inputs and displays for the user. With respect to these, it should be noted that many military systems have incorporated multi-on-line inquiry and typeout instruments. Realizability is so advanced that a prominent eastern technical school is now considering the acquisition of a set of instruments for a large classroom, one for each desk.[6] Furthermore, along with on-line type-out devices, military technology has brought to fruition several forms of multiple station closed-circuit TV systems; also techniques are now known for coupling closed-circuit TV directly to the data processor through standard radar-repeater tubes at economic rates ($5000 to $10,000 per instrument).

Why have we made the assumption that the scholar and technical worker need a "rapport facility" for their IR activity? The answer is that no one person, in almost any intellectual pursuit of today, can comprehend and contain within his own personal memory the total conceptual "vocabulary" that is relevant to his field. Therefore, he is always in need of probing the larger vocabulary—the library—of his own and allied fields. The trouble begins in attempting to match the specific inquiry to the vast resources of today's libraries. The complexity of today's technologies is so great that the libraries must be animated if they are to match the animation and needs of the workers in each field.

This concept of the animated library is new. It has been brought about by the development of high-capacity-storage devices, by the rapid processing ability of the modern electronic computing system, and finally, by the maturation of multiple input devices and multiprocessing which permit simultaneous inquiries and multiple access to a single computer and file system.

Thus in the upcoming stretch of five years, the economic availability of on-line query and display instruments, leasable for about $100/month will soon constitute the necessary means of maintaining rapport between user and IR file. By this means the user may key-in an inquiry and subsequently receive from the processor, a typewritten or displayed list of relevant items. If such a list is too long, the processor will transmit its statistics and a list of descriptors suggested to specify more precisely and less voluminously, the subject field. After the inquirer receives a series of such approximations, a final appropriate list is developed for him automatically, in much the same way as he could be served

by a well-trained librarian and bibliographer,—all in a matter of moments.

In the ultimate system, abstracts and summaries can be displayed, and finally texts, in the form of TV projections of microfilm. If the inquirer wishes hard copy, a xerograph reproduction could be formed *in situ*. Because the achievement of such services requires no new technology, but only system organization, it is clear that within the coming five years, such facilities can be so coordinated as to enable the user to remain *en rapport* with mechanized files, until by recursive questions he retrieves exactly what he wants. Other things being feasible, the widespread use of these query and rapport facilities will mark the transformation of mechanized IR facilities from a state of subsidization to a state of self-sustainment and resource.

AUTOMATIC TEXT TRANSCRIPTION

Of course there are two kinds of input to an IR system. The one we have been discussing so far is concerned with the input and shaping of an inquiry from the user. The other input is the huge mass of text which must be incorporated into the "electronic files." The *third* bottleneck for the immediate future of IR is concerned with this kind of input.

It is known that the U.S. government will shortly be completely transcribing on a continuing basis, the bulk of significant foreign technical articles for purposes of automatic translation to English. In other words, these texts are to be available on magnetic tape that can be reproduced for any library or company. There is a serious need to reduce the cost of manual transcription (key-punching) of these masses of text material. Fortunately, for the objective of automatic input of printed material into computers, there has been recent heavy encouragement and progress in the development of character-recognition equipment. Capability for full-font text-reading is very likely to come through in another two years, and certainly in the next five. Digital fonts for bank checks and cash register tapes are handled fairly well at present. Special alphanumeric fonts for credit cards are also quite operational and widely used. Thus there is no doubt that in this five-year period continuous automatic input of raw text is and will be more accepted as standard procedure.

AUTOMATIC INDEXING AND ABSTRACTING

Why is it important that texts be transcribed into computer-readable form, when ultimately these materials are to be stored and retrieved for the user in the microfilm mode? The answer, fundamental for the successful mechanization of the total library process, is that the texts must be analyzed at high speed and with the programmed versatility of adaptive computer algorithms in order to be automatically indexed, abstracted, and summarized. In other words, the subject-headings that are relevant to each item that has been newly acquired for a document collection must be assigned *quickly, cheaply,* and in a way which corresponds to the *current* as well as *past* modes-of-inquiry in each field of knowledge. The user interest and the national interest are most critically concerned with *current* documents that can be retrieved from a collection, not with those that are available months or a year or so after authorship.

(Of course, the retrieval of older materials also has inestimable scholarship and tutorial values.) This is the *fourth* area of critical need in the IR field.

The cost of manual classification and abstracting of all the articles in the world's hundred thousand technical periodicals would be fantastic. The practicality of carrying it out in a coordinated and timely way by manual methods is unrealizable. There is also a pressing need to extend the coverage to a myriad of unpublished working papers. Hence, there is an utter necessity for automatic indexing, abstracting, and summarization by electronic data processors. Only as raw text is available on some form of computer media, such as magnetic tape or computer-readable microfilm does the mechanization of the indexing process become feasible—and in as many forms as there are programmed systems to suit particular requirements.

How are these processes for mechanization of indexing to be made so feasible? The preliminary forms of the procedures that will be used have already been tried with amazing success and sophisticated improvements have been brought forth and carefully analyzed. Some of the concepts which they use are: (a) The formation of abstracts by retention of clauses having significant key words in con-

text; [7] (b) The use of computer programs to form concatenations of other descriptors relevant to those descriptors which a user names in a particular query-action; [8] (c) The formation of interest-profiles by questionnaires having suggested descriptors, plus places for nomination of new descriptors; [9] and, (d) Automatic table search by use of a chain of secondary keys.[10]

Because each of these important concepts has been well-supported by several easily available papers apiece, we will add underscoring only to the last two.

Of these two, the technique of forming interest-profiles is one of describing the long-term and/or short-term IR needs of a user by the same descriptorizing techniques as are used to index and descriptorize a document. The maintenance in a local computer file of on-line profiles of user-interests and subject heading thesauri can be exploited through the application of auto-indexing and auto-relevancy programming, to assist in or to directly provide the codification of items in the collection. Such interest-profiles also make possible the selective dissemination of copies of new items to appropriate users—just as is possible in the ASTIA system.[11] Similarly, through glossaries and relevancy chains of descriptors, these profiles-of-interest can be used, via a duality technique, to assist the worker in any search-for-novelty.

Part of the promise of success of these techniques lies in their flexibility and universality, while remaining relatively free from any doctrine of classificatory structurization. Part of their promise inheres in their dependence on human intervention. That is, the descriptorization of user-interests must come from the user himself; the mediation of the user is permitted at every moment during the on-line interrogation of the files. The abstracting experts, whose skills are so necessary in specialized fields, are provided full scope in mediating directly in the files of a system. Thus the future IR system never will exclude the product of human activity in the field of classification but will feed on it and augment it with automated abstracting when such is desired. It will be enabled to do this because concordances and interest-profiles can be programmed and maintained automatically with modern processors.

The ordinary library of today is a passive thing in which the operation is largely dependent upon how much time and ingenuity a given inquirer is willing to give to supply the necessary dynamism from himself coupled with the well-intentioned, helpful, but limited services of a librarian. The fault is not at all the librarian's, but is attributable mostly to the inability to be an expert with fine evaluating capacities in every field represented in the library. Cleverness, quick-wittedness and a prodigious memory are all valuable qualities in a librarian, but they merely cover up the basic problem that there is no substitute for the direct and specific knowledge of the inquirer himself. Therefore, the first requirement of the animated library is the help and cooperation of the inquirers even before the inquiries are ever made. The recent concept-developments in IR recognize the need for help from the user in the descriptorizing process. The universality of descriptorization is applied alike to documents and to user interests; the more a given person uses the IR-type library, the better will be the results for both user and the library.

ASSOCIATIVE MEMORY

The control of computer memory to effect iterated cross-reference in a high-speed electronic processor is the domain of the *fifth* bottleneck in the IR future. Among the techniques we have mentioned above, is that of referencing the contents of a memory by a method called "table look-up," with secondary keys (e.g., that discussed by L. R. Johnson). There are several other methods worth mentioning and having unique merits: the list structures of Simon, Newell, and Shaw have led to such specializations for IR as the Gray and Prywes "Associative List Structures" (*op. cit.*). Independently Robert Ledley has developed the somewhat less redundant Table-dex method (*op. cit.*). All these methods incorporate some variety of *chaining*, i.e., of coupling a data-name with computer addresses of associated data. In E. Fredkin's TRIE memory, some micro-chaining (of word-parts rather than words) has been ingeniously formed. The author is interested in a general schema for chaining called SHIEF memory. All these constructs are useful in organizing normal computer memory into an effective instrument for "addressing-by-content," i.e., for recall of data when no knowledge is available as to the physical address or location of

that data in the computer memory. Another phrase that refers to these modes of memory organization is "Associative Memory." None of these structures-concepts for attaining associative memory relies on special memory hardware such as cryogenic, multi-apertured or multi-coincident-circuitry arrangements. All of them operate on the assumption that search or "scanning" of any region of memory is to be minimized or eliminated. All of them assume that memory behavior is governed by small sequences of macro- or micro-programming. Any or all of them are realizable in physical hardware which has already been developed and tested in a wide range of computers; only the novel control circuitry (made of already available standard modules) is required for the proper sequencing. Thus there is every reason to expect that the IR processors, to be available during the next five years, will incorporate the basic facility of associative memory. With this facility, automatic associative cross-referencing, without the need for serial scanning, will have reached a critical stage of practicality.

MEMORY CAPACITY

The *sixth* bottleneck is the physical capacity of processor memories. Univac and others have already announced small workable magnetic film memories. There is every prospect that the total capacity of high-speed computer memory will markedly increase while cost decreases during the next five years. Thus all the required high-speed capacity for index cross-referencing and associativity is to be available. For retrieval of materials more extensive than indicia, namely abstracts and summaries, the newer disc memory devices should be expected to attain easily the necessary 300,000,000-character capacity levels in the coming half-decade.

But within the relatively short period of five years, it is too much to expect that film memory can be made so cheaply that it can be substituted for microfilm when storage of millions of pages of text are necessary even in small libraries. Furthermore, because whole pages must be quickly displayed during the browsing and rapport activities of the user, the slow, serial nature of locating an item on magnetic tape precludes the use of this medium for storing and displaying principal file items. Thus the techniques of microfilm reduction and non-serial locating, such as is used in an AVCO prototype [12] or in equivalent systems, seem most optimum. Here is indeed an area where present-day equipment is not adequate, and in which equipment manufacturers should endeavor to cooperate. Film companies should eschew the temptation to produce "integrated electronic systems"; electronic system companies should avoid producing high-cost, special film-handling systems. Here again is an area where no new technology is needed, only new systems aggregates of existing devices. With the right stimulation, five years should be sufficient to resolve the configurations that would have the somewhat obvious working requirements discussed above.

COMMUNICATION LINKAGES

The *seventh* bottleneck is due to fade away fairly steadily. It is concerned with the need for the IR user to work with the computer over the telephone (on the one hand) and directly with the computer while it works with files and computers in other libraries and plant locations (on the other hand). Already communication facilities such as Bell System's Dataphone equipment make this possible. Military message centers under the monitorship of digital data processors such as Philco's DCA surveillance system also are examples of the workability of existing technology in satisfying this basic IR need. Pacing the use of telephone lines within metropolitan areas is the onrush of economic microwave devices available to any customer with optically-uncomplicated paths between plants.

SPECIFIC IMPLICATIONS FOR EQUIPMENT

In the foregoing we have surveyed the five-year prospects of progress in adapting data processing systems to the work-a-day needs of the user of information retrieval services. We have probed the cost picture, the input-display-rapport facility, the problem of mass-text-transcription, the techniques of automatic indexing and abstracting, the means of high-speed cross-referencing (avoiding serial search) in the form of associative memory, microfilm memory for texts and display, communication devices on-line between man and computer, and between computer and computer.

In every case a step-up in capability in one

of these areas adds to the overall effectiveness of devices in the other areas. We have seen that there is every prospect that progress in each individual area in five years will be sufficient to go over the top, i.e., to bring mechanized IR into a state of self-sufficiency and of resource from which benefits will pour into business and science.

There are two courses which industry and government can follow which will ensure and expedite this progress. The first is the encouragement of new EDP product forms, which, serving the established EDP market, can be simply accommodated to IR devices, without high-cost custom engineering. This encouragement should pay off doubly because in almost every instance coupling of so-called IR devices, such as inquiry keyboards and displays and on-line communication linkage, is needed everywhere for normal EDP process functions. The key to this first course is that the EDP manufacturer must simplify and standardize his buffer-linkages between control processor and special devices. The second course is the intensive encouragement of human techniques of index-assignment, interest-profiling, text manipulation, and relevancy and citation analysis—working with the full scope of programming and process-simulation techniques afforded by the modern electronic computers. Automatic programming should be developed for these IR simulation activities. The human beings to be encouraged here above all should include the many seasoned work-a-day librarians who are willing and able to learn and practice computer programming for at least a year of internship.

Without these approaches, the course of mechanized IR may be a muddling bumble for many years. With these approaches, equipment manufacturers and users can cooperatively develop effective, flexible, standard operating procedures and devices in five years. Then in truth we can hope to add to the twentieth century's many laurels the achievement of on-demand retrieval of human knowledge and recorded activity, any time and anywhere.

NOTES

1. For an information scientist's "go-slow" point of view, see Bar Hillel, "Some Theoretical Aspects of Machine-Literature Searching," TR #3, April 1960, Hebrew University, Jerusalem, sponsored by United States ONR and NSF.

2. For theory, see, for example, C. N. Mooers, "The Application of Simple Pattern Inclusion Selection to Large-Scale Information Retrieval Systems," *Tech. Bull. 131*, April 1959, AD-215,434. Zator Co., Cambridge, Mass.; "A Mathematical Theory of Language Symbols in Retrieval," *Proc. International Conf. on Scientific Information*, 1958; R. A. Fairthorne, "The Problems of Retrieval," *Amer. Doc. 7, #2* (April 1956), 65–75.

For evaluation, see, for example, C. N. Mooers, "The Intensive Sample Test for the Objective Evaluation of the Performance of IR Systems," *Tech. Bull. 132*, Aug. 1959, Zator Co.; M. E. Maron, "Automatic Indexing: An Experimental Inquiry," *J. ACM* 8 (1961) 404–417.

For automatic abstracting, see, for example, H. P. Luhn, "The Automatic Creation of Literature Abstracts," *IBM J. Res. and Dev. 2, #2* (April 1958), 159–165; "Keyword-In-Context Index for Technical Literature," *Am. Doc.* 11, 4 (Oct. 1960), 288–295.

3. See, for example, J. C. Shaw, A Newell, and H. A. Simon, "A Command Structure for Complex Information-Processing," *Proc. WJCC* (May 1958), 119–128: H. J. Gray and N. S. Prywes, "Outline for a Multi-List Organized System," *14th Natl. Mtg., ACM* (Sept. 1959); R. S. Ledley, "A New Coordinate Indexing Method for Bound Book Form Bibliographies," *Proc. of International Conference on Scientific Information*, 1958.

4. A similar study of this kind is reported by Saul Herner, "The Information-Gathering Habits of American Medical Scientists," *Proc. International Conference on Scientific Information*, 1958, p. 277.

5. See, for example, the costs cited three years ago by Opler and Baird in "Developing Retrieval Systems on Large Computers," *Proc. International Conference on Scientific Information*, Wash., D.C., 1958, National Academy of Sciences, page 701; costs cited here should be reduced further, as they were based on batching methods.

6. Increasing awareness of the natural role of on-line IR facilities for educational purposes is bound to accelerate the demand for automatic IR equipment.

7. M. E. Maron and J. L. Kuhns, "On Relevance and Probabilistic Indexing and Information Retrieval," *J. ACM* 7 (1960), 216–244; H. P. Luhn, *op. cit.*

8. H. Edmund Stiles, "The Association Factor in Information Retrieval," *J. ACM* (April 1961), 271–279.

9. C. K. Schultz and C. A. Shepherd, "The 1960 Federation Meeting—," *Federation Proceedings* (July 1960), 682–699; H. P. Luhn, "Business Intelligence Systems," *IBM J. of Res. and Dev.* (Oct. 1958).

10. H. J. Gray and N. S. Prywes, *op. cit.;* R. S. Ledley, *op. cit.;* L. R. Johnson, "An Indirect Chaining Method for Addressing on Secondary Keys," *Comm. ACM*, 4, 5 (May 1961), 218–222.

11. The pertinence of interest-profiles can be augmented by the automatic accumulation of requestedness statistics. Also with such statistics, the continual up-to-date maintenance of the most actively demanded materials in the higher-speed areas of processor memory and the orderly retirement of inactive materials to discs and tapes can be carried out.

12. Holding 100 x 100 pages on one square foot of film and a set of 100 such pages in approximately a cubic foot; incorporating direct mechanical and optical selection for projection.

51. SOME COMMENTS ON
INFORMATION RETRIEVAL

GARY R. MARTINS *

One of the most evil of all effects of the Information Explosion is the mild hysteria occasioned within the text-processing community upon the publication of new and ever more alarming evidence of the Information Explosion's progress and implications. It is my experience that even mild emotions within the professional data processing community are sufficient cause for alarm. Another more insidious, evil effect of the Information Explosion is the accumulation of incalculable megatons of high-quality paper rendered useless by marring its surfaces with meaningless patterns of printer's ink; a generous percentage of these patterns represents "state-of-the-art" reporting, a lot of it dealing with Information Retrieval.

And a new menace looms before us—the proliferation of "state-of-the-'state-of-the-art'" surveys and reviews. The larval state of this novel parasite's development resembles the somewhat more acceptable bibliographic survey and "overview" report, both long familiar to workers in the more baroque sciences such as Aristotelian metaphysics and astronautics. Contemplating the full-grown beast is a delight (like the study of fallout-mutants) that must be left to future generations of scientists. Rather than indulge in more of this type of nonsense, let me simply review here, for the nonspecialist, some aspects of the things Information Retrieval workers worry about. At the heart of it all, one can discern a single, complex purpose: *to make available unusually attractive library services dealing with relatively recent publications (or other data), usually employing modern EDP hardware.*

There are two parts worthy of separate consideration in the foregoing statement of

purposes; both of these contrast modern IR goals with those of the traditional library systems. The phrase "unusually attractive" library services merits some consideration. I assume that, fearful of Mooers' Law,[1] IR workers aim to develop systems that will be used—systems that offer advantages not available from the neighborhood library and its academic and corporate counterparts. Such advantages might include any of the following: 1) convenience of access, 2) high-speed results, 3) suggestive indexing and reference services, 4) unusually broad and/or deep stockpiles of available information, 5) abstracting services, 6) "creative" retrieval, and so on.

The statement of purposes also mentions "relatively recent" source materials. This point might well have been subsumed under the "unusually attractive" services were it not such an important issue all by itself. "Relatively recent" takes on different degrees of significance for different potential IR user groups; to many geologists, for instance, it may be almost meaningless. To the command and control and telemetry communities, on the other hand, it may well constitute the single most important criterion for a useful IR system. Let's consider in somewhat greater detail these two complementary goals of modern IR activity.

A PLETHORA OF PAPERS

The short-range aims of the various IR projects now in existence are so multifarious that it is almost impossible to write anything worthwhile about the subject of Information Retrieval as such. Strangely enough, this is a healthy symptom of the field. The overall

SOURCE: *Datamation* (December, 1964), pp. 24–27. Reprinted by permission of *Datamation*.
* System Analyst, Bunker-Ramo Corporation.

[1] *Information Retrieval Selection Study, Part II: Seven Retrieval Systems Models,* by Calvin N. Mooers, Zator Company, Report No. RADC-TR-59-173, Contract AF 30(602)-1900.

problem of Information Retrieval is one of those many problems which can be called "unstructured"; i.e., so little is known about it, *as a single, unified problem area,* that words are not available to formalize, or clarify, its situation and general topography. This may explain the avalanche of "state-of-the-art" papers —there's very little else that can be said.

Since there is so little which can reasonably be said about the problem *as a whole,* it is encouraging that so many different kinds of activity, devoted to such a broad range of immediate goals, are in progress at one time (in spite of the difficulties this poses in trying to talk about them all at once).

One of the six possible "unusually attractive" library services is "convenience of access." This is illustrated by the location of at least one of Project MAC's I/O typewriters in a key project worker's bedroom.[2] The whole idea here is to put the library at the user's fingertips through numerous and widespread remote-access "consoles." The problems involved in providing such consoles to information users are entirely dependent upon the kind of library services the console has to mediate; mainly, the problem is one of cost—the more worthwhile the underlying library services, the more expensive the remote console setup (which can range from a simple I/O typewriter to an impressive array of CRT, keyboard, lineprinter, and facsimile gear, not to mention the centrally-located buffering and query-stacking devices that service the remote consoles).

"High-speed results" as a novel library service was a key motivation for most early work in IR. Overawed with the speed and power of modern computational systems, some early workers in the field promised truly astounding results in time for 1984. The all-important question regarding just what sort of library services were to be provided (much less, perish the thought!, how) was often neglected.[3] The weakness of this early wishful thinking was summarized, in 1961, as follows:[4] "Speed itself may be of some relevance but, . . . (we cannot justify) the unfortunately prevalent belief that mechanization of a process that doesn't work to begin with will improve matters." The speed can be bought, like the remote consoles, but only when the customer can be persuaded that the rapid and convenient stuff he gets is worth more than its cost.

Turning to the availability, through IR work, of "unusually broad and/or deep stockpiles of available information," we encounter again cost/effectiveness ratios. Engineers will provide, on demand, whatever is needed in the way of ultra-large, very-fast-random-access storage media (even at reasonable costs) as soon as the demand is backed up with cash. Also available will be useful multifont page readers, to load these memories, as soon as the requirement is justified, if not before. The key questions are: what will we load these mammoth memory systems with? And also: how do we find what we want, once it's there? Unusually attractive data bases are not yet of very great concern within the IR community as a whole; this will become a pressing issue (by virtue of certain correlaries to Parkinson's Law, if for no other reasons) only when the ways and means of providing unusually attractive access to quite ordinary repositories of data are solved.[5]

The question of getting at particular fragments of data, even in more humble storage systems, is however already a most important one. And here we have a moral obligation to note that in contrast to size there is another means of achieving attractiveness in a library data base. How attractive it would be to enter a library that had just those documents that really meant something—nothing but high quality sources! However few.

Unfortunately, there has been no enlightening work done yet on the problems of *direct*

---

[2] F. J. Corbató, Massachusetts Institute of Technology; from a lecture given in April 1964 before the Western Los Angeles chapter of the A.C.M.

[3] One is reminded of early talk about tele-reproduction in people's homes of such nonsense as the morning newspaper!

[4] *Information Retrieval: State of the Art,* by Don R. Swanson, Thompson Ramo Wooldridge, Inc., presented at the Western Joint Computer Conference, May 1961.

[5] Studies have been made, for instance, of the problems of automating some functions of the Library of Congress (a most attractive data base); but no one really expects anything serious to be done about these problems until the Library's contents overflow into the reserved Congressional parking spaces outside the building itself.

quality identification in library materials. Several schemes for complicating the judgment of ordinary librarians on incoming materials have been proposed, but none of these offers any real advantages over traditional screening methods. Frequently, the discretion of committees, rendered through a maze of "rating forms," is substituted for that of a single reviewer. There is no hope of automating any of these schemes.

One more democratic direct quality identification scheme that has been proposed would require library *users*, as part of their "payment" for services, to score documents on a simple machine-readable data card; it would be no problem then to automate the tallying of such scores.

There are two *indirect* quality identification techniques which may also be of some help in reducing the trash problem that threatens, at times, to strangle existing library systems. Both these techniques can easily be automated, and neither depends upon the whim of evaluation committees. The first such technique may be called "citation-scoring." This technique determines the "value" of a document or other data group by the frequency with which it is cited in other documents. The basic notion underlying this technique is at once simple and convincing; numerous methods for implementing it have been studied, involving more or less elaborate linear rating functions.

THE REQUEST-SCORING TECHNIQUE

A second, indirect quality identification technique which has been widely studied is not much different from the first. Here a document's popularity with library users, rather than with authors, is used as the basis for determining its "value." We may call this the "request-scoring" technique. The most heavily used documents are considered to be the most valuable. One or the other of these schemes, and quite possibly both, will almost certainly be incorporated in most future IR systems. They both share an important shortcoming, however, which should be mentioned here. In order for any of these quality identification schemes to be effective, we need to have "experience" on the document. That is, it must have been around long enough, in our library or elsewhere, to build up some kind of score. Which simply means that both techniques will

be more useful for library *purging* than for input control.

On returning to the question of getting at already stored materials we can consider the unusually attractive "suggestive indexing and reference" services which a useful IR system should provide. The goal here is to provide, as a minimum, an automated version of the ordinary three-way library card catalog (which ordinary libraries can't afford), and, at a foreseeable cost, an associative indexing method which would respond pleasingly to intricate, direct natural-language requests. There are two related sub-goals in this problem: to avoid the burdening of the system's user with unwanted information, and to make sure that he is not "cheated" out of documents (or parts of documents) implicitly addressed by his request. Unfortunately, it is probable that both these sub-goals cannot ever be fully satisfied even in theory; but we ought to be able to come as close as anyone wants to pay for.

Several complex issues involved in automatic indexing and reference techniques have been isolated for concentrated study by IR workers, and the volume of reports devoted to these studies is considerable. Some of these are worth reading. In the broadest terms, two highly refractory sub-problems occupy the IR specialist's attention in this area:

1. effective indexing of the library's contents:
2. development of powerful request processing methods.

The indexing problem is, briefly, one of finding a workable set of categories that describe the libraries' contents, defining the network of relationships with this set, and producing a procedure for properly labelling the contents of the library with appropriate categories. Most proposals for the solution of this exasperating problem involve the use of a rather large number of categories/descriptors/index-terms, and a thesaurus to define their relationships. The procedures that have been used for labelling the contents of libraries range from straightforward manual indexing, in the traditional manner (i.e., arbitrarily), to elaborate key-word and title-manipulation schemes designed for automation. Many presumably programmable schemes have been considered for this purpose, none of them completely satisfactory. Generally, these involve the identification of key terms in a text by means of weighted frequency counting, the weights being assigned on the basis of "physical" location in text (e.g., heavy weighting for words in a document's title), syntactic function (e.g., heavier weighting for the subjects of sentences than for objects of prepositions), critical-term lists, and so forth.

THE NEED FOR TESTS

It has never been easy to estimate the worth of the many indexing and reference schemes proposed simply because, in most cases, it has been impossible to gather convincing evidence and agree on how to evaluate it. The sheer labor and expense involved in the compilation of a broad thesaurus, suitable for Information Retrieval tasks, have combined to make such work unpopular. For this and similar reasons very little automatic indexing is actually done. The complexity of the difficulties involved makes it impossible to determine the relative merits of the various proposals solely on the basis of their authors' claims. The possibility of automatic thesaurus compilation, using reciprocal dictionaries (e.g., Russian-English and English-Russian), may help to reduce the magnitude of this one obstacle, at least, to the large-scale testing of automatic indexing and reference methods. Without such testing, it appears unlikely that any outstanding progress in this area will be made or, if made, be recognized.

Very closely related to the indexing problem is the problem of processing data requests. The ideal IR system might accept such requests in the form of ordinary voice telephone calls with the same professional patience as today's librarians. But that won't happen soon. A large-scale step in that direction will have been taken, however, when IR system users are allowed to type information requests in ordinary English. Something very near this could certainly be implemented within the bounds of present technological competence; again the problem is an economic one. There are many challenging syntactic, semantic, and stylistic subtleties that must be dealt with whenever we want to automate the "understanding" of natural language; most of these difficulties have been discussed at great length in machine-translation circles for some time. In spite of all this discussion, there is today

only one full-time production-oriented machine-translation facility in this country, and its operations are justified on other than purely economic grounds.[6]

INDEXING AND REQUEST PROCESSING

For the foreseeable future, it is highly likely that IR system users will have to learn some kind of so-called "query language" in which to express their information requirements. In general, of course, the more restricted and complex is the query language, the simpler will be the IR program which "understands" requests formulated in it—and thus one portion of the initial cost will be less. On the other hand, highly artificial and/or cumbersome languages (like Esperanto or English, for example) tend not to be learned unless we're too young to know better—and consequently don't get used. But the most formidable obstacle to the development of useful request-processing procedures is the lack of indexing systems into whose terms data requests must be translated. Neither the indexing problem nor the request processing problem can really be solved by itself; a great deal more of real work is needed in both areas before many of the early dreams of IR forecasters can be realized.

Similar to the problem of indexing the library's contents though much simpler, is that of indexing its (most frequent) users. By building up a file of so-called "user profiles," derived from past data requests, automatic dissemination of appropriate new materials to interested parties can be achieved. All in all this doesn't seem to be so difficult to set in motion just as soon as somebody decides they can afford it.

Yet another unusually attractive library service that IR research has promised is that of automated abstracting of documents. If this could be done economically it would be of great benefit to library users since manual abstracts are both costly and slow, and are ordinarily available only by subscription to specialized user communities (e.g., lawyers and chemists). That genuine auto-abstracting is still a long way off is guaranteed by the singu-

[6] This system is operated by the Foreign Technology Division at Wright-Patterson AFB near Dayton, Ohio.

lar banality of much of the literature dealing with it. On the other hand auto-extracting, in which key sentences are automatically selected to characterize the source document, is now being done routinely on a small scale and with reasonable, if not earthshaking, results. The programs which perform this service are not terribly sophisticated; it's quite likely that as progress in auto-indexing is made a resultant increase in the sophistication of auto-extracting programs will considerably enhance the product.

Probably the most fascinating of all the unusually attractive services that some future IR system might offer are those that can be collectively called "creative retrieval." This would include all processes which produce *responsive data* directly rather than *references to responsive data* as output. Let me bury this crude distinction under an example: Suppose you wish to know which is the most widely used plastic. You can request from an automated IR system "all works on plastic," and be drowned in an avalanche of references (or full texts, depending on the kind of output the system produces). Perhaps the query language will allow you to specify "use of plastics" or some other more restricted expression of your needs. You will still have to hunt through a large number of documents to find the answer to the question. If, however, the IR system has a creative retrieval capability, the query language might allow the question, "Which is the most widely used plastic?" After a suitable delay you would be given the output: POLYETHYLENE. Or perhaps: POLYETHYLENE IS THE MOST EXTENSIVELY USED PLASTIC, which the system could have picked up from the top of page 81 of November's *Scientific American*.

CREATIVE RETRIEVAL METHOD

But that's still fairly elementary compared to some other creative retrieval functions since it only involves lifting a responsive phrase or sentence from a stored data base. Suppose, for another example, the system has the sentences, "Socrates is a man" and "All men are mortal." And not another word about Socrates. Now, ask the obvious, "Is Socrates mortal?" The system having failed to find a stored answer must deduce the correct response.

Many forward-looking IR workers have studied different kinds of creative retrieval

problems, including automatic essay writing, fact correlation, question answering, and inferential response. The implementation of any or all of these capabilities, when finally achieved, will usher in a whole new generation of automated systems.[7]

The ideal IR system's ability to deal with "relatively recent" data deserves separate consideration. Just what is meant by "recent," of course, depends upon the application. For the librarian of the physical sciences, it probably means something like "less than 2 years old," particularly with reference to journal articles. On the other hand, in a strategic command and control system the term "relatively recent" might mean something like "within the last eight hours." In telemetry applications it could come down to a matter of seconds, or less. Where the capability to deal with "relatively recent" data is of primary importance, and where the term takes on a meaning that demands performance approaching that expected of "real time" systems, the singular power of modern EDP techniques is most clearly appreciated. There is, after all, a complete, running, long-established model that embodies *all* the capabilities we have discussed earlier: the special Congressional services groups in the Library of Congress! A member of Congress has only to pick up his phone to avail himself of a wide range of unusually attractive library services. The one type of service he *can't* get is precisely what we're talking about here—access at very high speed to a rapidly changing data base.

Prestigious users of information, such as the military and NASA, have placed a premium on systems involving highly dynamic data bases and have been willing to pay for their development. Generally, however, very little if any genuine text-processing is involved in such systems; their performance depends mainly on the engineering and numerical methods talents of their creators. We cannot, therefore, look to such systems for guidelines toward the solution of the more ordinary library system's problems in dealing with "relatively recent" documents. This problem will have to await the slow and painful develop-

---

[7] In a very real sense machine translation can be considered a "creative retrieval" problem of a very complex kind; the history of machine translation illustrates the difficulty such problems involve.

ment of useful indexing methods as well as very-high capacity input and storage devices before it will be solved—that will take both time *and* money and in large quantities.

Perhaps a word on the many ingenious mathematical models for IR systems may be said here. These formulations, based upon analogies with linear and nonlinear electrical circuits, the percolation process, genetics, and a variety of other structures, seek to portray the behavior of different parts of a general IR system. Much of this literature has only intrinsic interest, however, due to our inability to map the elements of the model meaningfully onto corresponding elements of an observable (and often even thinkable) operating system. A more immediately useful subset of this literature is that which deals with file organization and search strategies and with related hardware design. And, of course, there is an inevitable residue of more or less clumsily disguised trivia.

ON-LINE RETRIEVAL

Recently it has become fashionable to talk about the application of so-called "on-line" data processing techniques to problems whose structural density defies a direct analytic approach. The "on-line" approach in this dialect simply refers to a division of tasks between men and machines,[8] assigning to each what they can do best. This can be a useful approach only if we don't ever become too happy

[8] This same term ("on-line") is often used in other, and equally legitimate, ways (in process control applications, for instance).

with it—so long as we keep working at assigning more and more of the total system's labor to the machines.

It is not difficult to envision an evolving IR system which involved a good deal of man-machine interaction, and which also incorporated a heuristic subsystem which would gradually "learn" how the human element behaved. Consider the indexing problem in this light. Begin with a very "permissive" thesaurus, which would associate each index term with a rather large number of other terms ranging from the obvious to the absurd. After a set of associations has been made, the system's user is then called upon to "cross out" irrelevant associations and to add relevant ones which the system overlooked. The user's intervention could be requested again when the system produced a group of presumably responsive references—nonresponsive references would be "crossed out" and possibly additional relevant references would be added by the user. A suitable heuristic subsystem, acting on the results of many such man-machine encounters might eventually be able so to modify the thesaurus and the assignment of index terms as to make further man-machine interactions unnecessary.

Similar remarks can be made about fact retrieval, abstracting, and so on. Several contracts have already been let for research in this particularly promising area; it is possible that, once the magic of the words "on-line" and "man-machine" has tarnished somewhat, the dutiful exploration of this approach will bring us several steps closer to the long-promised Golden Age of truly useful and economical Information Retrieval.

BIBLIOGRAPHY

1. American Management Association, *Information Retrieval Seminar*, Special Library, March, 1963.
2. Becker, J., and R. M. Hayes, *Information Storage and Retrieval: Tools, Elements, Theories*, John Wiley and Sons, 1963.
3. Blumberg, D. F., "Information Systems and the Planning Process," *Data Processing*, May, 1965.
4. Fairthorne, R., *Toward Information Retrieval*, Butterworth and Co., 1961.
5. Hattery, L., and E. M. McCormick (eds.), *Information Retrieval Management*, American Data Processing, Inc., 1962.
6. Herman, Saul, "Methods of Organizing Information for Storage and Searching," *American Doc.*, January, 1962.
7. Kent, Allen, *Textbook on Mechanized Information Retrieval*, Interscience Division of John Wiley and Sons, 1962.
8. Nicolaus, J. J., "The Automated Approach to Technical Information Retrieval," *Naval Engineers Journal*, December, 1964.
9. Perry, James, *Documentation and Information Retrieval*, Cleveland Press of Western Reserve University, 1957.
10. Sharp, H. S., *Readings in Information Retrieval*, Scarecrow Press, 1964.
11. Sharp, John, *Some Fundamentals of Information Retrieval*, International Publication Service, 1965.
12. Shaw, Ralph, "Information Retrieval," *Science*, July, 1963.
13. Simonton, W. C., *Information Retrieval Today*, University of Minnesota, 1963.
14. Spangler, M., *General Bibliography on Information Storage and Retrieval*, General Electric Computer Dept., Technical Information Series, R62CD2.
15. Swets, J. A., "Information Retrieval Systems," *Science*, July, 1963.
16. Vickery, B. C., *On Retrieval System Theory*, Butterworth and Co., 1961.

Part XV. Prologue to the Future

The Roman seers read the entrails of animals, the Greeks consulted oracles, while the American? Well, the common man looks up his horoscope in the daily paper while the sophisticate will program a computer to predict the future course of events.

Since this book has dealt with management systems as currently used in the business world, it seems appropriate to survey here the future applications of systems and to depict the future state of the arts. It is an easy enough task to formulate sweeping generalizations that are sufficiently ambiguous to encompass all possible contingencies and then to proclaim one's personal infallibility when all events fall neatly under the blanket statement. No one would be unduly aroused by the pronouncement that it is anticipated that business organizations will in the future utilize the systems approach even more than at present. Such an encyclopedic prediction is reminiscent of the thinking evidenced by J. P. Morgan who, when asked to predict the future course of the stock market, blandly replied, "I predict that it will continue to fluctuate."

While it is indeed difficult to make precise, exact, and unambiguous predictions, nevertheless, projection of present trends can serve as a starting point. It is, no doubt, a truism to assert that the systems concept will be integrated to a much greater extent in the near future both because of the availability of the new tools facilitating this approach and because of the obvious need to ensure corporate survival in a dynamic, competitive economy. The current need for continually improving

upon the managerial processes has been amply demonstrated by both educators and businessmen. Forrester, in discussing the managerial process, enjoins the business organization to view itself as a system of interrelated and interfunctioning parts. He states:

Management has been practiced, so far, as a skilled "art," lacking a foundation on a "science" of *integrated* underlying principles. The science of industrial systems is now rapidly evolving and should provide to management of the future a basis similar to that which physics provides to engineering. This does not imply "automatic management" but the reverse—a new managerial opportunity and challenge. The demands on the manager will become greater rather than less. In addition to experience, judgment and intuition, the manager will need a professional understanding of the dynamics of business growth and fluctuation. Adequate theory and technical methods now exist for "designing" more successful organizations. Lacking is the counterpart of an "applied science" and "practical engineering" for interpreting theory into results. As theory and methods are extended and the gap between them and practicing management is closed, we can expect management education to take on the characteristics of a profession wherein skilled art is superimposed on a foundation structure of basic principles of economic growth and corporate evolution.[1]

[1] Jay W. Forrester, *Management and Management Science*, M.I.T., School of Industrial Management, Memorandum D-48, June 1, 1959, p. 1.

Much of what the future holds in store is simply more of what we have today, with perhaps an overlay of more sophistication. In fact, many of the forces that will shape the future have already been at work for a number of years. Recent developments in the area of information technology (discussed in Parts II and III) are beginning to make inroads in the organizational structure. Several companies have already reorganized around information centers. With the widespread adoption of digital computers which store, transmit, and report data, the information available to managers has increased to such a degree that decisions are typically being made more efficiently. The ability to immediately retrieve information from memory files has already proven to be a valuable asset in decision making. The very near large-scale adoption of on-line computers will further facilitate management control. While the use of automated management control devices has, it is true, been largely confined to the military, the potential for the business firm remains highly promising. Within the next five years real-time systems will no longer command the awe that now envelopes the onlooker; the mystique will have disappeared and it will be regarded as another matter-of-fact piece of hardware in the computer complex. Remote computing and time-shared systems will also have become commonplace.

The use of simulation, characteristically embedded in the industrial dynamics model, will be the subject of ever more costly research. More routinizable managerial functions will be assigned to computer decision making. The whole texture of managerial decision making will be so altered that the manager of the future would regard today's decision-making apparel as one belonging to the equivalent of management's Stone Age.

Operations research will come of age as business firms become better acquainted with this scientific technique. The various tools generally associated with operations research, such as queuing theory, inventory theory, linear programming, and search theory will daily find more practical applications to the problems of the business world. The successful applications, well-publicized, will contribute much to breaking down the skepticism and overcoming the resistance of businessmen reluctant to try the new approach. The potential areas of application are indeed numerous, and while current efforts have been largely expended in the sphere of production, possible extensions to marketing and finance will soon become common. Attempts have already been made to relate operations research to sales effort, to promotional effort, etc.; the use of game theory in capital budgeting and the application of scientific techniques to mergers and acquisitions have already taken place. While operations research is basically quantitative, it nevertheless neither avoids nor overlooks the behavioral aspects of management problems.

Within the past few years there have been dramatic changes regarding the traditional functions of planning, organizing, and controlling. An earlier selection by Emery foretold the centralization of the planning function and the routinization of many day-to-day operations. The organizing function has already seen many changes and the success achieved by the military in establishing project control managers with authority cutting across traditional organizational lines presages future industrial acceptance.

The control function will also assume new dimensions with the rapid response made possible by on-line computers. The cybernetic approach to control discussed earlier is only now beginning to make a dent in the business world. The development of new planning and control techniques and the refinement of presently existing ones, such as PERT and PERT/ COST, will continue to assist the busy and harassed manager in making timely and responsible decisions wherever and whenever necessary.

The systems manager of the future may

be a new breed, distinctly different from the one on the contemporary scene. One of the prime requirements of the new breed of manager will be that he understand the entire business, not as so many isolated elements but as a "going concern," as a *system*. He must be capable, above all, of bringing together the many individual segments, frequently diverse and sometimes strongly self-oriented, into an integrated dynamic system, thus blending individual objectives into a common organizational goal.

Unlike the traditional specialist, the new systems manager will be a super-generalist. As a systems man he will be concerned with the optimization of overall organizational objectives. He will be a problem-solver instead of a technically oriented machine-man or specialist. Whether or not the systems manager of the future will be an updated experienced manager of today or a distinctly new breed is immaterial; in any case an almost radical orientation toward the job will be required, for the successful manager of the future must utilize the systems approach to the management problems that will face him in an ever growing complex business world. The systems approach is not something like a suit of clothes that can be donned at will; it is rather a way of life itself, a way of thinking, a conceptual frame of reference that must permeate one's every decision and outlook.